REPRODUCTION
IN
FARM ANIMALS

Monozygotic (identical) twins originate from one fertilized ovum and are always of the same sex. Such twins are invaluable for experimental work because of their identical genetic constitution.

Reproduction in Farm Animals

Edited by

E. S. E. HAFEZ

Washington State University,
Pullman, Washington

85 Illustrations and 38 Plates

Lea & Febiger

Philadelphia

1962

Library of Congress Catalog Card Number 62:17820

Printed in the United States of America

To our teachers . . .

Foreword

MUCH effort has been expended on the improvement of farm animals for milk, meat, wool, eggs and other purposes; this, however, will be of no avail unless a high degree of fertility also is maintained. This book dealing with all aspects of reproduction supplies the basic knowledge necessary for the maintenance and for the increase in fertility of farm animals.

The negative aspect of fertility, that is the prevention of both male and female sterility, is considered from the points of view of anatomy, physiology, genetics and pathology. The positive aspects dealt with are the factors that increase the fertility of both males and females. This subject is of great importance now that artificial insemination can increase the availability of fertile males of high genetic worth, and steps to increase female reproductive performance are necessary since meat animals are now being slaughtered at an earlier age than heretofore.

The study of reproduction does not end with fertility only, however, for the changes taking place during pregnancy have an important bearing on the production of strong and vigorous young, so necessary for a high survival rate and the prevention of economic losses due to the death of the young shortly after birth. The inclusion, too, of facts concerning the structure of the mammary gland, lactation and the hormones concerned, are of importance not only for the dairy but also for the meat industry for the rapidity of growth of the young after birth in both beef cattle and sheep depends to a great extent on the milk supply of the dam.

Differences described in the pattern of reproduction between the various species, both avian and mammalian, have not been sufficiently appreciated in the past. These are no doubt due not only to anatomical differences but also to differences in hormone balance which dictate variations in the estrous cycle and are the major physiological cause of infertility.

The book should prove most useful to Agricultural and Veterinary students and everyone interested in an up to date account emphasizing the physiological viewpoint on the reproduction in farm animals.

University of Cambridge   JOHN HAMMOND

Preface

THIS volume is a concise textbook for the beginning student of comparative reproduction in the fields of agriculture, veterinary medicine, zoology and related sciences. It is not intended to displace the revised edition of Marshall's classical publication nor the excellent reference works in various languages which appeared recently.

Our basic knowledge of animal reproduction is derived from research in the biological sciences, such as embryology, anatomy, genetics, physiology, endocrinology, biochemistry, bioclimatology, nutrition, behavior, husbandry and pathology. In planning the present book, it was obvious that our knowledge of the anatomy and histology of reproduction is more complete than the physiology, biochemistry and pathology. More is known about the physiology and biochemistry of sperm than is the case with mammalian ova. This work attempts to bring a general balance to the discussion of the various aspects of reproduction with particular emphasis on physiology.

Understanding of the reproductive processes in farm animals is yet far from complete. Therefore, the material in a number of chapters includes information derived from studies on laboratory animals and man. An effort is made to confine comments to established facts and to omit aspects about which uncertainty exists.

The material in the book is arranged in four parts. Part I is a brief discussion of reproductive endocrinology. Part II discusses the anatomy and physiology of the male and the female. Part III includes the species-specific characteristics of fertility and infertility in the five major species of farm animals including poultry. Part IV deals with the effects of stress and pathogens on reproduction.

Eminent research workers from different disciplines have contributed chapters to the volume. Their contributions have been integrated by the editor to ensure continuity, uniformity, conciseness, and to avoid duplication of unduly controversial material. Authors of related chapters have critically reviewed each other's contributions. Several other people have also generously given their time in reading manuscripts and commenting on the text.

In many instances data on comparative anatomy and physiology have been compiled and shown in simple tabular form. Also various structures and concepts under discussion have been illustrated by line drawings and plates. Technical terms have been explained in their simplest form to help students with little previous formal instruction in life sciences. No attempt is made to provide a detailed bibliography, but a selected number of classical papers and review articles are listed at the end of each chapter. For students and lecturers who wish to seek additional information, a list of general references including books, journals, symposia and proceedings of national and international conferences, is given at the end of the book. Pertinent questions are posed after each chapter so that the reader can test his comprehension of the subject. A glossary of technical terms has been compiled.

The sincere thanks of the editor are extended to all contributors and to the staff of Lea and Febiger for their excellent cooperation during the preparation and production of the book.

Pullman, Washington   E. S. E. HAFEZ

Contributors

BLOM, E.; *State Veterinary Serum Laboratory, Bulowsvej 27, Copenhagen V, Denmark*

DAY, B. N.; *Department of Animal Husbandry, University of Missouri, Columbia, Missouri*

FRANK, A. H.; *Animal Disease and Parasite Research Division, Agricultural Research Service, U.S.D.A., Ames, Iowa*

GIBBONS, W. J.; *Department of Surgery and Medicine, School of Veterinary Medicine, Auburn University, Auburn, Alabama*

GORDON, I.; *Department of Animal Science, Washington State University, Pullman, Washington*

HAFEZ, E. S. E.; *Department of Animal Science, Washington State University, Pullman, Washington*

HARVEY, E. B.; *The Worcester Foundation for Experimental Biology, Shrewsbury, Massachusetts*

HAMMOND, SIR JOHN; *School of Agriculture, University of Cambridge, Cambridge, England*

KOSIN, I. L.; *Department of Poultry Science, Washington State University, Pullman, Washington*

LASLEY, J. F.; *Department of Animal Husbandry, University of Missouri, Columbia, Missouri*

McLAREN, ANNE; *Institute of Animal Genetics, West Mains Road, Edinburgh, Scotland*

NISHIKAWA, Y.; *Department of Animal Husbandry, Kyoto University, Kitashirakawa, Kyoto-Shi, Japan*

O'BERRY, P. A.; *Animal Disease and Parasite Research Division, Agricultural Research Service, U.S.D.A., Ames, Iowa*

PARER, J. T.; *Department of Livestock Husbandry, The University of New England, Armidale, N.S.W., Australia*

PARKER, J. E.; *Department of Poultry Science, Oregon State University, Corvallis, Oregon*

REECE, R. P.; *Department of Dairy Science, Rutgers University, New Brunswick, New Jersey*

TERRILL, C. E.; *Sheep, Goat and Fur Animal Research Branch, Agricultural Research Service, U.S.D.A., Beltsville, Maryland*

TRIMBERGER, G. W.; *Department of Animal Husbandry, Cornell University, Ithaca, New York*

ULBERG, L. C.; *Department of Animal Industry, North Carolina State College, Raleigh, North Carolina*

WHITE, I. G.; *Department of Veterinary Physiology, University of Sydney, Sydney, Australia*

YEATES, N. T. M.; *Department of Livestock Husbandry, The University of New England, Armidale, N. S. W., Australia*

ZARROW, M. X.; *Department of Biological Sciences, Purdue University, Lafayette, Indiana*

Acknowledgements

THE contributors wish to express their best thanks to editors and publishers who gave permission to reproduce illustrations or tables from original articles, monographs and books. The source of such illustrations and tables is indicated in each case: Academic Press, Inc., New York, N. Y.; Acta Endocrinologica, Stockholm, Sweden; Acta Agriculturæ, Scandinavica, Sweden; American Breeders Service, Madison, Wis; American Journal of Anatomy; American Poultry and Hatchery Federation, Kansas City, Mo.; Annals of Agricultural College of Sweden; A. R. C. Unit of Reproductive Physiology and Biochemistry, Cambridge, England; Arti Grafiche Riamondi, Milan, Italy; Bailliere, Tindall & Cox, London, England; Beacon Feeds, Beacon Division of Textron Inc., Cayuga, N. Y.; Biological Review, England; Blackwell Scientific Publications, Oxford, England; British Veterinary Association; Cambridge University Press, England; Canada Department of Agriculture, Alberta, Canada; Carnegie Institution of Washington, Washington, D. C.; Comstock Publishing Association, Ithaca, N. Y.; Cornell University Agriculture Experiment Station, Ithaca, N. Y.; Cornell University Press; Cornell Veterinarian; Dairy Breeding Research Center, Pennsylvania State University, University Park, Pa.; Endocrinology; Faculty of Agriculture of Okyama University, Japan; Freeman & Co., San Francisco, Calif.; International Journal of Fertility; Japan Racing Association, Tokyo, Japan; John Wiley, New York, N. Y.; Journal of Agricultural Science, England; Journal of American Veterinary Medical Association; Journal of Animal Science; Journal of Biophysical and Biochemical Cytology; Journal of Dairy Science; Journal of Experimental Biology, England; Journal of Morphology; Journal of Reproduction and Fertility, England; Journal of Royal Microscopical Society, England; Kyoto University, College of Agriculture, Kyoto, Japan; Lea & Febiger, Philadelphia, Pa.; Longmans Green & Co., London, England; Lucas Brothers, Columbia, Mo.; Minnesota Agriculture Experiment Station, St. Paul, Minn.; Missouri Agriculture Experiment Station, Columbia, Mo.; Nebraska Agriculture Experiment Station, Lincoln, Nebr.; Nordisk Veterinaemedicin, Denmark; North Carolina State College, Raleigh, N. C.; Onderstepoort Laboratories, South Africa; Oregon Agriculture Experiment Station, Corvallis, Ore.; Oxford University Press, New York, N. Y.; Parey Publishing Co., Berlin, Germany; Poultry Science; Proceedings of Society of Experimental Biology and Medicine, N. Y.; Panstwowe Wydawnictwo Rolnicze i Lesne Publishing Co., Warsaw, Poland; Royal Veterinary Agricultural College, Copenhagen, Denmark; W. B. Saunders Co., Philadelphia, Pa.; Skand. Vet. Tidskr.; Society for Study of Fertility, England; Society of Experimental Biology, England; Tennessee Agriculture Experiment Station, Knoxville; The Iowa State University Press, Ames, Iowa; The Wistar Institute of Anatomy and Biology, Philadelphia, Pa.; University of Missouri Cooperative Store, Columbia, Mo.; University of Natal, Pietermaritzburg, Natal, South Africa; University of Phillipines, College of Agriculture, Laguna, Phillipines; U. S. Department of Agriculture; Veterinary Record, England; Washington Agriculture Experiment Station, Pullman; The Williams & Wilkins Co., Baltimore, Md.

Acknowledgements are also due to the following who assisted the contributors in reviewing the manuscripts or providing original photographs: C. E. Adams, F. D. Allan, C. W. Alliston, J. O. Almquist, H. Andersen, L. L. Anderson, M. Y. Andres, F. N. Andrews, Virginia Apgar, L. Arey, V. S. Asmundson, C. R. Austin, A. Bane, J. Barfield, C. A. V. Barker, W. Bielanski, M. W. H. Bishop, R. Bogart, T. Bonadonna, G. Bowman, H. Boyd, D. L. Black, C. A. Brandly, M. C. Chang, L. Clamahoy, Y. Clermont, H. H. Cole, E. O. Conrad, J. J. M. L. Crombach, L. Dauzier, O. S. Davis, B. N. Day, F. T. Day, G. T. Dimopoullos, Mrs. Julia Dow, R. H. Dutt, P. Eckstein, C. W. Emmens, N. L. First, R. H. Foote, J. L. German, III, R. Getty, R. W. Goy, R. G. Greeley, A. M. Guhl, J. Hammond, Jr., J. L. Hancock, A. Hansen, A. E. Harrop, D. E. Hughes, C. V. Hulet, C. A. H. Hultnäs, Miss Dorothy Hunt, G. Hunter, D. Jakovljevic, T. W. Jenkins, J. W. Kendrick, J. M. Kling, O. Krölling, E. P. Lindley, R. G. Loy, J. L. Lush, C. A. Manthei, H. Marsh, D. Mayer, T. J. McClure, G. L. McClymont, J. A. McCracken, K. McEntee, F. F. McKenzie, R. M. Melampy, W. R. M. Morton, H. W. Mossman, A. V. Nalbandov, J. E. Neal, Y. Nishikawa, W. R. Nunn, R. Ortavant, F. Paredis, M. Parez, A. S. Parkes, W. Plewinski, G. Porter, K. R. Porter, J. I. Raeside, E. Rajakoski, J. T. Reid, F. J. Rice, E. D. Roberts, S. J. Roberts, A. L. Romanoff, K. Rottensten, A. H. Safanie, J. R. Sotelo, M. W. Schein, E. Schilling, R. N. P. Shoffner, A. W. Stinson, M. Stob, T. Sugie, L. J. Sumption, A. V. Taylor, L. W. Taylor, G. W. Trimberger, C. D. Turner, C. W. Turner, M. Vanderplassche, J. H. Venable, J. C. Wallace, A. C. Warnick, C. Westerfield, S. Wierzbowski, P. H. Winther, M. H. Wykoff and J. Yochim.

Contributors wish to make personal acknowledgements to the following:

Chapter 1: The chapter was written while the author was conducting a research program on endocrine physiology supported by grants RG-6263 from the National Institute for Mental Health and RG-7831 from the Division of Research Grants, National Institutes of Health.

Chapter 6: The chapter was written while the author was conducting a research program on physiology of mammalian ova supported by research grants from the National Science Foundation (G 9938), and the Population Council, Inc., New York, N. Y.

Chapter 10: The author wishes to thank Dr. M. C. Chang for aid in organizing the chapter; Miss Dorothy Hunt for the line drawings and The Worcester Foundation for Experimental Biology, Shrewsbury, Mass. for assistance during the preparation of the chapter.

Contents

(15)

Part I

REPRODUCTIVE ENDOCRINOLOGY

Chapter 1

The Hormones of Reproduction

By M. X. ZARROW

I. CLASSIFICATION AND PROPERTIES OF THE HORMONES

A. Classification

ESSENTIALLY all the hormones of the mammal are involved in some aspect of mammalian reproduction. This involvement may be through a direct action of the hormone on a specific aspect of reproduction or through an indirect action in that the presence of the hormone is necessary for the proper maintenance of the internal environment to insure successful reproduction. Examples of the former may be seen in the direct action of follicle stimulating hormone (FSH) on the testis leading to spermatogenesis or the luteinizing hormone (LH) on the Graafian follicle of the ovary leading to ovulation. Examples of the latter may be seen in the specific need for the presence of such hormones as thyroxine, adrenal corticoids and insulin in order to obtain a successful pregnancy. Thus, on the basis of type of action we can divide the hormones of reproduction into two groups, (a) the primary hormones of reproduction (Table 1–1) and (b) the secondary hormones of reproduction (Table 1–2). The former are directly involved in the various aspects of reproduction such as spermatogenesis, ovulation, sexual behavior, implantation, maintenance of gestation, parturition, lactation and maternal behavior. The latter are necessary for the general well being and metabolic state of the organism and permit reproduction to occur. In general the latter group of hormones influence growth, development and metabolism and may be considered as permissive in their action on reproduction, *i.e.*, these hormones maintain the metabolic state of the individual and thereby permit the full effect of the primary hormones of pregnancy. Successful reproduction is, therefore, the resultant of the interplay of many endocrine secretions on specific target organs and reactions in the body.

The various hormones involved in reproduction may be divided into two types according to their chemical structure, *i.e.*, proteins (or polypeptides) and steroids. The former range in size from a molecular weight of 1000 up to 50,000; the latter group have a molecular weight of approximately 300 to 400 and are characterized by the presence of a cyclopentano-perhydro-phenanthrene nucleus (see page 33). The exception to this is the thyroid hormone which is an iodinated amino acid.

Table 1–1. The Primary Hormones of Reproduction

Gland	Hormone	Some Functions
Anterior pituitary	Follicle stimulating hormone (FSH)	spermatogenesis; ovarian follicular growth
	Luteinizing hormone (LH) (ICSH)	androgen release; ovulation
	FSH & LH	estrogen release
	Prolactin (luteotropic hormone) (LTH)	progesterone release; lactation; crop sac stimulation
Posterior pituitary	Oxytocin	parturition; uterine contractions; milk let-down
Testis	Testosterone	maintenance of male reproductive duct system and secondary sexual characteristics; male sexual behavior; spermatogenesis
Ovary	Estradiol	maintenance of female reproductive duct system and secondary sexual characteristics; female sexual behavior; mammary gland stimulation; calcium & fat mobilization in birds
	Progesterone	implantation; pregnancy maintenance; mammary gland stimulation
	Relaxin	relaxation of uterine cervix and pubic symphysis; inhibition of uterine contractions
Placenta	Human chorionic gonadotropin (HCG) (primate)	LH-like
	Pregnant mare's serum (PMS) (horse)	FSH-like
	LTH (rodent)	luteotropic action
	Estradiol	see ovary
	Progesterone	see ovary
	Relaxin	see ovary

Table 1–2. The Secondary Hormones of Reproduction

Gland	Hormone	Some Functions
Anterior pituitary	STH	body growth; protein synthesis
	TSH	stimulation of thyroid gland; thyroxine release & iodine uptake by thyroid
	ACTH	stimulation of adrenal cortex; release of adrenal corticoids
Posterior pituitary	Vasopressin (antidiuretic hormone) (ADH)	water balance
Thyroid	Thyroxine	body growth; development & maturation; oxidation of feeds
	Tri-iodothyronine	
Adrenal cortex	Aldosterone	electrolyte & water metabolism
	17-OH corticoids (cortisone) (cortisol) (corticosterone)	carbohydrate, protein & fat metabolism
Pancreas	Insulin	carbohydrate, fat & protein metabolism
Parathyroid	Parathormone	calcium & phosphorus metabolism

B. Definition and Mode of Action

We may now ask the question what is a hormone and how does it act? Originally hormones were defined as specific agents secreted in the blood stream by a well defined organ and acting at a point distant from the site origin. This definition was found to be inadequate as new discoveries were reported, so that today a hormone is defined as a *physiologic, organic substance liberated by living cells of a restricted area of the organism which diffuses or is transported to a site in the same organism where it brings about an adjustment that tends to integrate the component parts and actions of the organism.* Indeed the recent discoveries that hormones of the posterior pituitary originate in the hypothalamus are stored and released from the posterior pituitary gland and that the hypothalamus is also the site of release of specific substances (hypothalamic hormones?) which activate the anterior pituitary indicate the need of making the definition of a hormone broad enough to encompass these substances. It is now apparent that not only in the mammal but in other species including insects, cells of the nervous system possess the capacity of producing hormones. Finally hormones may be distinguished from vitamins on the basis that vitamins are supplied in the diet or synthesized from essential dietary or metabolic precursors.

The second part of the question concerning the mechanisms of action of hormones is still unanswerable. Certain facts have been reported which indicate that hormones may act on cell membranes and on enzyme systems. It should also be kept in mind that a single hormone may act through several different mechanisms; hence no single mechanism can explain all the actions of a hormone.

Some of the biochemical characteristics of hormone action may be summarized as follows:

(a) Hormones do not supply energy to a reaction.

(b) Hormones act in minute amounts, *e.g.*, estradiol applied directly to the vaginal mucosa or uterine endometrium is active in the order of 10^{-6} μg.

(c) Hormones are rapidly removed from the blood stream, *e.g.*, 90 per cent of the steroid hormones like progesterone will disappear from the blood stream within 10 to 20 minutes yet the action of the hormone may not be apparent in hours and even days.

(d) Hormones regulate rates of reaction but do not initiate new reactions, *e.g.*, thyroxine stimulates increased utilization of oxygen by the organism, but the organism still utilizes oxygen in the absence of the hormone even though at a reduced rate.

The general effects produced by the action of hormones in the living organism may be classified as follows: (a) morphogenesis, (b) maintenance of the internal environment, and (c) integration of physiologic events. The somatotropic hormone (STH) is an outstanding hormone with regard to morphogenetic action where the over-all growth of the organism reflects the action of this hormone. The morphogenetic action of the steroid hormones on the reproductive tract is seen in the growth of the uterus following treatment with estradiol and of the prostate following treatment with testosterone. The maintenance or constancy of the internal environment is the state of the organism in which the internal environment is kept constant, *e.g.*, although the sugar in the blood stream is being constantly utilized by the tissue, the concentration is maintained at a constant level of approximately 100 mg. per cent. This is true not only for blood sugar but for other substances present in the blood such as electrolytes, calcium, non-protein nitrogen, urea, *etc.* The maintenance of this constancy of the internal environment is due in part to the endocrine system, wherein such hormones as insulin, parathormone, epinephrine, and adrenal corticoids play a major role. Finally the integration of physiologic events is important in many aspects of the bodily economy of the organism and especially in reproduction. Reproductive events are so regulated by the endocrine system that sexual receptivity in the female occurs shortly before or after ovulation and permits copulation to occur with the resultant fertilization of the ovum. The fertilized ovum then moves down the Fallopian tube and remains unattached in the uterus until it is ready to implant in the uterine wall. Simultaneously with the above events the uterus is being changed by the action of the ovarian hormones so as to permit the uterus to receive the embryo. If these two chains of events are not properly synchronized, implantation and pregnancy will fail to occur. In events such as these the endocrine system acts in conjunction with the nervous system. The major function of the nervous system is integrative in back on the pituitary to regulate the release of FSH. When an excessive amount of FSH is released, the circulating level of estradiol increases and acts on the anterior pituitary to shut off the release of FSH until the level of estradiol has fallen (Fig. 1–1). This type of system has been likened to the thermostat-furnace relationship in maintaining a constant temperature in the home.

Control of hormone release by specific metabolites is also *humoral* in nature but

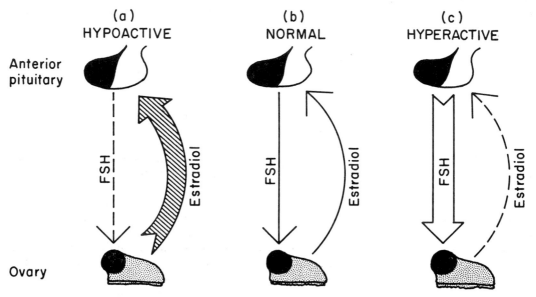

Fig. 1–1.—Illustration of the servo-mechanism type of control over the release of FSH in the female. In the hypoactive state (*a*), the high level of circulating estrogen blocks the release of FSH from the pituitary. As the high level of estrogen falls, due to the decreased release of FSH, the block on the pituitary is removed, more FSH is released (*c*) and the estrogen secretion rate is increased again. The circulating level of estrogen is the result of the difference between the rate of secretion and the rate of utilization, degradation, etc.

nature and this function is shared by the endocrine system which has other functions as well. It must be kept in mind that both systems frequently work together to integrate physiologic events in the organism.

C. Regulation of Hormone Secretion

Regulation of the secretion of hormones is quite varied and several mechanisms may be involved. The *servo-mechanism* or *negative feedback* involves primarily the tropic (stimulating) hormones of the pituitary gland and the hormones released by the target glands. Thus, estradiol released from the ovary acts involves a control over the gland by the substance on which the hormone acts. Thus, a high level of blood calcium inhibits the release of the parathormone and a low level permits release of the hormone, thereby insuring a constant level of serum calcium.

A third method of control is via the nervous system: the release of LH in the rabbit following copulation or stimulation of the uterine cervix is a good example. In this instance, excitation of the central nervous system causes the release of LH by the anterior pituitary gland.

The amount of hormone to which a tissue is exposed not only depends on the secretion rate, excretion and degradation rates, but also on the capacity of blood proteins to bind certain hormones. A good example of this is thyroxine which is found in the blood bound to albumin and α-globulin. In this form the hormone is not available to the target cells but must be freed from its protein carrier before it can act at the cellular level. Hence a regulatory mechanism also exists at the cellular level to split off the hormone and make it available to the cell. Similarly many steroid hormones form specific complexes with the blood proteins which is of major importance in the transport and activity of these hormones. The protein bound estrogens are called estroproteins and the protein binding occurs in the liver. This binding appears to be necessary for the activity of the estrogen since estrogens are inactive following subtotal hepatectomy (partial removal of the liver from the animal) which interferes with the binding of the hormone.

D. Methods of Study

Over the years endocrinology has expanded through investigations that have used similar approaches in defining and identifying a hormone. In general the steps used are as follows:

Ablation (surgical removal of the endocrine gland): This should lead to a deficiency syndrome ascribable to the removal of the gland.

Replacement therapy (prevention of deficiency syndrome by the implantation of gland in an animal following surgical removal or by injection of crude extract): Hypersecretory effects may also be produced.

Isolation of the hormone (isolation, purification, and identification of the hormone): A good biological assay is needed during this procedure. Chemical techniques for assay may be developed after the hormone is identified.

Regulation of the endocrine gland (determination of changes in rate of secretion of the hormone under normal and abnormal conditions): The use of isotopes, such as I^{131} for studies on thyroid activity, are of great value here.

In vivo synthesis and intermediate metabolism of the hormones (determination of the steps in the biogenesis of the hormone and routes of degradation and excretion): This includes an understanding of the specific enzymes involved both in biosynthesis and degradation of the hormone.

Nature of action (the mechanism whereby the action of the hormone is manifested): This area is least understood.

Physiology of endocrine system (relationship of the gland to target organ, structure, nervous system, bodily function, *etc.*): This involves the interrelationships of hormones, homeostasis, nervous system, activity and external environment.

II. PRIMARY HORMONES OF REPRODUCTION

A. Pituitary Gland (Hypophysis)

1. ANATOMY AND HISTOLOGY

The pituitary gland lies in a bony depression at the base of the brain known as the *sella turcica* and secretes a wide variety of hormones, some of which are directly concerned with reproduction (Table 1–1) and others indirectly (Table 1–2). In addition, other hormones such as MSH (melanophore stimulating hormone) are also secreted by the pituitary gland. The gland develops embryologically from the gut ectoderm of the roof of the mouth and the neural ectoderm of the developing hypothalamus. This double origin is partly carried over into the adult organism wherein the two major divisions are retained as distinct entities, the *anterior pituitary* and the *posterior pituitary* gland (Fig. 1–2).

The anterior pituitary (anterior lobe) consists of the pars distalis and the pars tuberalis. The posterior pituitary (posterior lobe) consists of the pars intermedia and the pars nervosa (infundibular process). The hypophyseal stalk consists primarily of the neural stalk which connects the posterior pituitary with the hypothalamus.

The pars distalis forms the major portion of the anterior lobe, and contains the hormone producing cells which secrete STH, ACTH, TSH, FSH, LH and LTH. The pars tuberalis is a thin epithelial outgrowth from the pars distalis and surrounds the neural stalk. The pars tuberalis is highly vascular, receives many nerve fibers, contains few glandular cells and is not known to have any endocrine function. The pars intermedia is a narrow strip of tissue between the pars distalis and the pars nervosa, and is absent in certain birds and mammals. The major portion of the posterior lobe is made up of the pars nervosa which contains many nerve endings. The posterior lobe

hypothalamo-hypophyseal portal vessels to the pars distalis where the vessels break up and distribute the blood into the sinusoids of the pars distalis (Harris, 1955).

The nerve supply of the pituitary gland consists of sympathetic fibers from the perivascular plexuses, parasympathetic fibers and the hypothalamo-hypophyseal tract. The pars distalis appears to be devoid of any nerve endings. The majority of reports

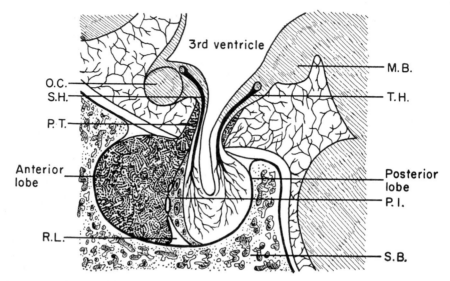

Fig. 1-2.—Diagrammatic saggital section of the pituitary gland *in situ*. M.B.—mammillary body; O.C.—optic chiasma; P.I.—pars intermedia; P.T.—pars tuberalis; R.L.—residual lumen; S.B.—spenoid bone; S.H.—supraoptic hypophyseal tract; T.H.—tubero-hypophyseal tract. (*Adapted from Turner, 1960, General Endocrinology, courtesy of W. B. Saunders Co.*)

secretes the two hormones vasopressin (ADH) and oxytocin.

Blood and Nerve Supply. The vascular supply to the pituitary gland is comparable to that seen in the liver. Both organs have a systemic arterial supply, a portal blood supply and a systemic venous drainage. The posterior hypophyseal arteries originate from the internal carotids and supply the posterior lobe. The anterior hypophyseal arteries originate from the internal carotids and the circle of Willis. Some of these vessels supply the pars distalis directly, whereas others pass into the pars tuberalis and break up into a primary plexus of capillary loops or tufts which penetrate into the tissue of the median eminence (see Fig. 1-4). The blood is then drained by the

indicate nerve endings are present only in the pars tuberalis and especially the posterior lobe where the nerve tracts from the hypothalamus end.

Types of Cells. Over the past two decades, a number of cell types have been described in the anterior pituitary gland with evidence adduced for the sites of formation of the various hormones. Two major types of cells have been described based on the presence or absence of staining granules which are believed to be the precursors of the hormones. These cells are the *chromophobes* and *chromophils*. The former lack granules which take a stain, while the latter show specific staining affinities. The chromophils may be classified as *basophils* or *acidophils* depending on the tinctorial properties of the granules present.

Plate I

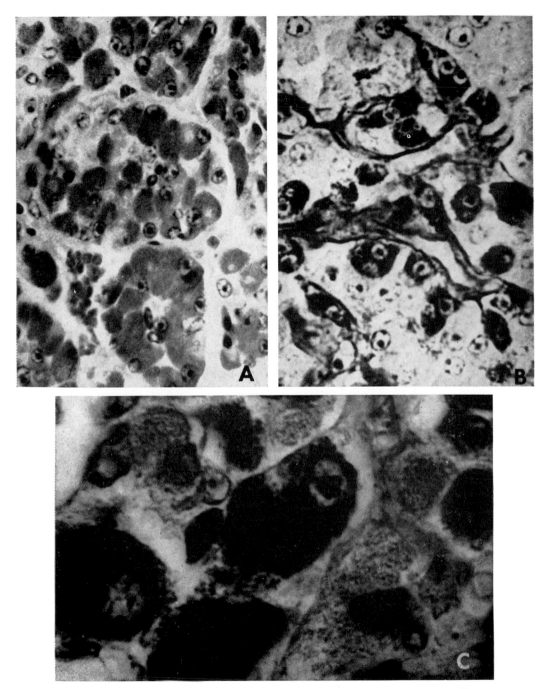

Sections through the anterior pituitary of the cow to show the cytology of the pars distalis.

a. Normal active acidophil cells (H & E stain) ($\times$ 450).

b. The gonadotrophs. These cells produce the gonadotropins (LH & FSH), are basophils, and are typically opposed to sinusoid reticulum. (PAS-celestine blue stain) ($\times$ 650).

c. The large thyrotrophs (TSH producing basophil cells). The small dark cells are gonadotrophs and the gray cells are acidophils. (Aldehyde-fuchsin stain). ($\times$ 1400).

(From Jubb & McEntee, 1955, Cornell Vet. 45:593.)

This division into two types of secretory cells poses the question of whether one cell secretes more than one hormone since six hormones have been ascribed to these two cell types. Evidence is now available to indicate that distinct cell types are present for each of the six hormones of the anterior pituitary. The evidence is based on staining reactions, chemical properties of the hormones and changes in the cytological constituents of specific cells and cell populations following experimental manipulation.

The chromophobic cells of the anterior lobe are believed to be the reserve cells of the gland. As the basophils or acidophils discharge their specific granules, these cells acidophils and the various types of basophils. The latter type of cell may be separated into the thyrotrophs and gonadotrophs (Jubb & McEntee, 1955). The thyrotrophs secrete thyroxine, are polyhedral in shape and located centrally in the gland. The gonadotrophs are oval to round in shape, and are located primarily in the cortical portion of the gland. The peripherally located gonadotrophs are distinguished by coarse granules and secrete FSH; the centrally located gonadotrophs contain fine granules and secrete LH. As yet there is no complete agreement on the origin of ACTH, although the consensus of opinion favors the basophils.

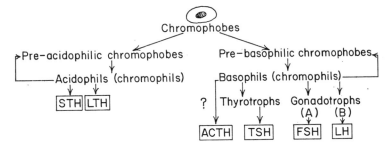

Fig. 1–3.—Diagrammatic scheme of the cell types in the anterior pituitary gland, the discharge cycle and the hormones released by specific cells.

become chromophobic; as the granules accumulate the cells revert to the chromophil state. Hence a release and accumulation cycle is present and the cell may be in either the chromophobic or chromophilic state depending on the presence of the secretory granules (Severinghaus, 1939). Such a cycle is visualized in Figure 1–3 and assumes that the chromophobes are also specific for whichever chromophil they revert to and can only give rise to a specific basophilic or acidophilic cell.

The secretion of both STH and prolactin has been ascribed to the acidophils of the anterior pituitary. Data have been presented to show that the STH producing acidophils are arranged radially around blood vessels or along connective tissue septa whereas a second type of acidophil is found located in the interior of the cords and is thought to secrete prolactin. Plate I illustrates both the cord arrangement of the

2. Hypothalamus

The hypothalamus may be described as that portion of the diencephalon which forms the floor and part of the lateral wall of the third ventricle of the brain. It includes the optic chiasm, mammillary bodies; tuber cinereum, infundibulum and pars nervosa. However, the term hypothalamus, as commonly used, excludes the pituitary gland although the pars nervosa is derived from the diencephalon and is anatomically an extension of the hypothalamus (Hansel, 1961). The anterior lobe of the pituitary is linked to the hypothalamus by a portal blood supply. The portal vessels arise from the internal carotid or branches from the Circle of Willis, form a plexus in the hypothalamus consisting of capillary loops or tufts and come in close contact with the tissue of the median eminence and nerve tracts. The blood from the capillary plexus is then drained into the portal trunks which lie on the surface of the pituitary stalk and eventually break up again into the sinusoids of the pars distalis (Fig. 1–4). Two large nerve tracts, the tubero-hypophyseal and supraoptico-hypophyseal, traverse the hypophyseal stalk and connect the nuclei in the hypothalamus to the posterior lobe of the pituitary.

Specific experiments on ovulation indicate that the action of the sex steroids is by way of the hypothalamus. Ovulation in the rat following estrogen is prevented by cholinergic and adrenergic blocking agents. The ability of progesterone to hasten ovulation in the cow at the beginning of estrus is blocked by atropine. Finally the injection of pro-

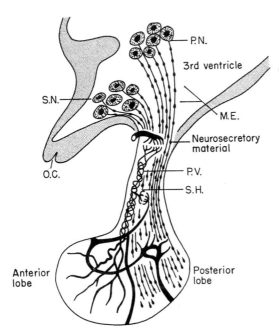

Fig. 1–4.—A diagrammatic section illustrating the relationship of the hypothalamus to the pituitary gland. M.E.—median eminence; O.C.—optic chiasma; P.N.—paraventricular nucleus; P.V.—portal vessels; S.H.—supraoptic hypophyseal tract; S.N.—supraoptic nucleus. (*Adapted from Hansel, 1961, Inter. J. Fertil., 6:241*).

Hypothalamus and Anterior Pituitary. Evidence for the control of gonadotropin release by the hypothalamus may be summarized as follows:

(a) Copulation induces ovulation in the non-spontaneous ovulator (*e.g.* the rabbit) and this can be prevented by cholinergic and adrenergic blocking agents.

(b) Ovulation in the spontaneous ovulator (*e.g.,* cattle, sheep) can be prevented by cholinergic and adrenergic blocking agents.

(c) Transection of the portal blood supply interferes with the maturation and function of the gonads (testes and ovaries).

(d) Stimulation of certain areas of the hypothalamus leads to ovulation and behavioral estrus (sexual heat).

(e) Lesions to the hypothalamus induce changes in gonadotropin release depending on site of lesion, extent of lesion and species involved (Chapter 9).

gesterone into the hypothalamus in dosages inadequate to give any effect systemically induces ovulation in the bird.

These investigations indicate that a neurohumoral substance is involved in the gonadal changes during reproduction. The current concept of neurohumoral transmission proposes the synthesis and release of a chemical mediator or mediators from the hypothalamus which are carried directly to the anterior pituitary, via the portal circulation, where they induce the release of the pituitary gonadotropins. The release of the hypothalamic neurohumors may then be due to stimuli such as copulation in the rabbit or certain unknown stimuli in other species and may also involve the higher cortical centers of the central nervous system. The role of the steroid hormones in this system could be that of changing the threshold of centers in the central nervous system.

Hypothalamus and Posterior Pituitary.
The cells of the supraoptic and paraventricular nuclei appear to be modified neurons that have developed a secretory function and are called neurosecretory cells. These cells contain secretory droplets that are believed to be the precursors of oxytocin and vasopressin. Histochemical studies indicate that the two hormones of the posterior pituitary are formed in the hypothalamic nuclei, flow along the axons of the hypothalamic-hypophyseal nerve tracts and are released from the posterior pituitary. Direct electrical stimulation of the hypothalamus, copulation or suckling are among the stimuli which will induce release of the posterior pituitary hormones. Indeed it is interesting to note that a stimulus for the release of one hormone invariably causes the release of the other hormone also. Suckling will not only induce reflexly the release of oxytocin but also vasopressin as indicated by antidiuresis.

Hypothalamus and Other Pituitary Hormones. Hypothalamic control over the release of ACTH, TSH and STH has also been postulated. Hypothalamic lesions or stalk section lead to atrophy of the adrenal and thyroid gland and to a disturbance in the release of ACTH, TSH and STH.

3. PITUITARY GONADOTROPINS

The anterior pituitary gland secretes the 3 gonadotropic hormones, FSH, LH and LTH. These hormones are of major significance in regulating the ovaries and testes both with regard to production of sperm and ova and the release of the specific gonadal hormones, testosterone, estradiol and progesterone. In addition, LTH has a direct effect on peripheral tissues such as the mammary gland and the crop sac. The interrelationship of these hormones with each other and with the events of reproduc-

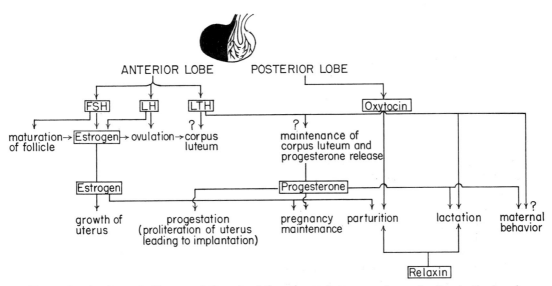

FIG. 1–5.—A schematic diagram of the role of the primary hormones of reproduction in the female.

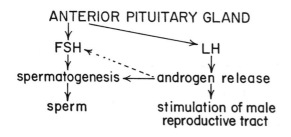

FIG. 1–6.—A schematic diagram of the role of the primary hormones of reproduction in the male. Note that androgens can stimulate spermatogenesis directly. The broken line indicates inhibition of FSH release.

tion are schematized for both the female and the male in Figures 1–5 and 1–6.

FSH. FSH is a glycoprotein with a molecular weight of approximately 67,000. Although it has not been isolated in pure form a number of its chemical and biological properties have been determined (Table 1–3). The hormone is water soluble and comparatively stable at pH 4 to 11. It has an isoelectric point of pH 4.5 and contains hexoseamine, hexose, nitrogen and sulfur. Incubation of FSH with carbohydrate-splitting enzymes such as amylase inactivates the hormone. Since these enzymes act on the carbohydrate portion of the molecule, this would indicate that the carbohydrate portion is essential for the biological activity of the hormone.

A molecular weight of 40,000 has been reported for LH from sheep pituitaries and 100,000 for the hormone from swine pituitaries. LH is a glycoprotein but the carbohydrate moiety is not necessary for its biological activity since destruction or removal of the carbohydrate portion of the molecule does not lead to a loss in LH activity.

LH stimulates the Leydig (interstitial) cells of the testis in the male with a subsequent release of testosterone (male sex hormone). The observable effects of LH are therefore secondary to testosterone release and include stimulation of the secondary and accessory reproductive tissues. In addition, LH causes spermatogenesis in the hypophysectomized animal but this is probably the result of androgen release.

Table 1–3.—Physico-chemical Properties of the Gonadotropins

Hormone	Molecular wt.	Iso-electric point	Hexosamine	Hexose
FSH (ovine)	67,000	4.5	1.5	1.23
LH (swine)	100,000	7.45	2.8	2.8
LH (ovine)	40,000	4.6	5.8	4.5
LTH (ovine)	22–27,000	5.5	–	–
LTH (bovine)	32–35,000	5.65	–	–
HCG	100,000	3.2	6.3	10.0
PMS	30,000		8.4	17.6

The main functions of FSH are stimulation of growth and maturation of the Graafian follicle in the ovary and spermatogenesis in the seminiferous tubules of the testis. Pure FSH stimulates growth of the ovarian follicle in the hypophysectomized animal but does not cause ovulation, luteinization or stimulation of the interstitial tissue of the ovary. In the hypophysectomized male animal, pure FSH leads to testicular enlargement due to stimulation of the seminiferous tubules but again no indication of androgen release is apparent as would have been indicated by hypertrophy of the Leydig cells of the testes or by stimulation of the accessory sex glands (Greep *et al.*, 1942).

LH. Both Li and co-workers and Shedlowsky and co-workers reported the isolation of LH in pure form in 1940. The LH molecule varies with regard to both chemical and physical properties in different species.

LH acts in conjunction with FSH to promote maturation of the ovarian follicle and estrogen release. Following maturation of the follicle, LH causes ovulation by inducing a rupture of the follicle wall and release of the ovum (Chapter 5). It may also be involved in the subsequent formation of the corpus luteum which is derived from the ruptured follicle but has no effect on maintaining the secretory activity of this structure, *i.e.*, the secretion of progesterone. We shall see later that this is a function of prolactin.

FSH:LH ratio. Variations in the ratio of FSH to LH are found in the pituitary gland under different conditions and in different species. These variations in ratio also affect the response of the target tissue. The pituitary gland of the cow is lowest in FSH; and the pituitary of the mare is about 10 times richer in the FSH than in either the ewe or the sow. The relative potency of

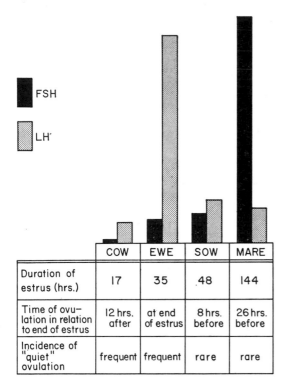

	COW	EWE	SOW	MARE
Duration of estrus (hrs.)	17	35	48	144
Time of ovulation in relation to end of estrus	12 hrs. after	at end of estrus	8 hrs. before	26 hrs. before
Incidence of "quiet" ovulation	frequent	frequent	rare	rare

FIG. 1–7.—Species differences in duration of behavioral estrus, time of ovulation, incidence of quiet ovulation and the FSH & LH content of the anterior pituitary gland. (*Adapted from Salisbury & Van Demark, 1961, Physiology of Reproduction and Artificial Insemination of Cattle, San Francisco, Courtesy of Freeman & Co.*)

FSH and LH in farm mammals may be responsible for species differences in the duration of estrus, the time of ovulation and the incidence of quiet ovulation (commonly called silent heat) (Fig. 1–7).

Bioassay. The classical assay for pituitary gonadotropins found in normal urine is a measure of the increase in uterine weight of the immature or hypophysectomized animal treated with urinary extracts. Since FSH alone will not induce estrogen release it is obvious that the urine must contain a mixture of FSH and LH. This type of assay has been modified for use with pure FSH by the addition of LH or HCG (which has LH-like activity) as a synergist. This is called the augmentation assay and an example of the type of regression lines obtained may be seen in Figure 1–8. It may be noted that the slope of the regression line for FSH increases with increasing amounts of HCG (Steelman & Pohley, 1953). This is a characteristic of the augmentation phenomenon (also referred to as synergism) in which the response obtained with the two

hormones is greater than the sum of the effects obtained with the hormones given singly.

The standard assay for LH utilizes the increase in weight of the prostate or vesicular glands (commonly called seminal vesicles) of the immature or hypophysectomized rats as endpoints. Both methods suffer from interference with synergists and may actually measure ratios of gonadotropins. In addition, several new tests for LH have been suggested. These include: (a) the induction of nuptial plumage in the Weaver Finch; (b) superovulation in the immature rat or mouse; (c) ovarian hyperemia, and (d) ascorbic acid depletion in the ovary. In the superovulation test, immature or hypophysectomized rats are pretreated with PMS and followed 56 hours later with LH. Approximately 20 hours after injection of the LH, the oviduct is removed and the number of ova counted (Zarrow *et al.*, 1958). The ovarian hyperemia test is somewhat subjective but the response of hyperemia in the ovary may be obtained in 2 hours. The ascorbic acid depletion test involves the use of immature,

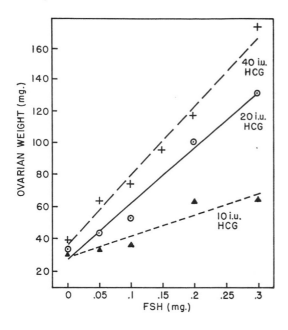

Fig. 1–8.—Regression lines for the augmentation assay of FSH. The synergist used in this assay is HCG. The end-point is the weight of the ovary of the immature rat. (*From Steelman & Pohley, 1953, Endocrinology, 53:604*).

pseudopregnant rats. These animals are injected with LH and the amount of decrease in ovarian ascorbic acid used as an index of LH activity.

LTH (Prolactin). LTH is a protein hormone of the anterior pituitary with a molecular weight of 22,000 to 35,000. It is inactivated by pepsin, trypsin and other agents which react with free amino groups but is not a glycoprotein like the other gonadotropins. Prolactin from sheep and cows seems to be composed of a single peptide chain with a cyclic configuration and contains disulfide bridges.

Prolactin must be considered a hormone of reproduction by virtue of its ability to stimulate lactation in the mammal and growth of the crop sac in pigeons and doves. Thus it is essential for the feeding of the newborn in these species. The hormone also maintains the functional activity of the corpus luteum. This is referred to as the *luteotropic activity* of the hormone and has been demonstrated by its ability to stimulate growth of a deciduoma in the uterus of hypophysectomized rat or mouse (*see* Chapter 7). Since the maintenance of a deciduoma is dependent on progesterone it may be concluded that prolactin stimulates the

release of progesterone. This activity has been demonstrated in sheep also but has not been demonstrated in cows or swine (Duncan *et al.*, 1961). The hormone has also been shown to stimulate maternal behavior such as broodiness in birds, the regurgitation-feeding behavior in birds, feathering molt and the drive to a water habitat in the newt. Prolactin also possesses metabolic activity especially in birds where it increases food consumption, body weight and size of the viscera.

Bioassay. The classical assay for prolactin involves the stimulation of the crop sac of pigeons. Immature birds are injected daily for 4 days via the intramuscular route. The animals are killed on the 5th day and the crop sac removed and weighed. A dose-response curve is obtained over a dosage of 0.5 to 32 *i.u.* of prolactin. Increased sensitivity can be obtained by the intradermal injection of the prolactin. Again the hormone is injected daily for a 4-day period intradermally over the crop sac. The animal is killed on the 5th day and the crop sac removed and the extent of the reaction graded from 1 to 4 +. In order to obtain more objective data, the area of stimulation may be measured with a planimeter and the

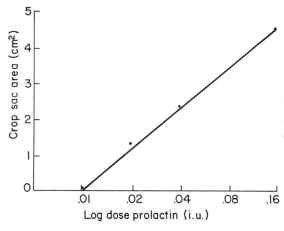

FIG. 1–9.—A dose-response curve for the assay of prolactin based on the area of the crop sac stimulated followed by treatment with prolactin. The prolactin is injected intradermally just over the crop sac in this assay.

results plotted against the dose of prolactin (Fig. 1–9).

4. OXYTOCIN

Oxytocin is still considered a hormone of the posterior pituitary gland although the evidence now indicates that the hormone is synthesized in the supra-optic and para-ventricular nuclei of the hypothalamus and released from the posterior pituitary gland. The isolation, description of its physical properties and synthesis of this hormone was achieved by du Vigneaud and his collaborators. du Vigneaud was awarded the Nobel prize in 1955 for this brilliant work. Oxytocin is an octapeptide containing the following 8 amino acids: tyrosine, leucine, isoleucine, proline, glutamic acid, aspartic acid, glycine and cystine. It has a molecular weight of 1,000 and is relatively basic with an iso-electric point in the alkaline pH range.

Experimentation with various mammals has elicited the following major physiologic activities for this hormone: (a) contractions of the uterus and (b) let-down of milk. In both instances the hormone is associated with events that occur at copulation, parturition and the post-partum feeding of the young. The increased uterine contractions induced by oxytocin are thought to facilitate the transport of sperm in the female duct system after copulation. This would account for the speed with which sperm reach the Fallopian tube and which cannot be accounted for solely by the motility of the sperm themselves.

Oxytocin has been used clinically for many years to aid in the induction of parturition by stimulating uterine contractions. It is now generally accepted that oxytocin is the hormone that induces delivery of the young at the end of pregnancy. Evidence in favor of such a concept may be listed as follows: (a) oxytocin induces premature delivery; (b) oxytocin induces uterine contractions in an estrogenized uterus (and the uterus is estrogen dominated toward the end of pregnancy), and (c) oxytocin is liberated during normal delivery.

Unequivocal evidence for the release of oxytocin at the time of parturition is still wanting but the following may be cited in support for such a view: (a) the drop in oxytocin content of the posterior lobe of the dog at parturition indicating the hormone has been expended; (b) the similarity between spontaneous labor and that induced by oxytocin or electrical stimulation of the supra-optic nucleus; (c) increase in uterine contractions after mechanical dilation of the uterine cervix presumably via a nervous reflex release of oxytocin. These observations tend to indicate that the release of oxytocin occurs reflexly at the time of parturition possibly due to pressure on the uterine cervix leading to a reflex stimulation of the hypothalamus and the subsequent release of oxytocin which can then induce uterine contractions (Fitzpatrick, 1957). The fact that parturition may occur in the hypophysectomized animal does not disprove the need of oxytocin for normal delivery nor the possible release of the hormone from the hypothalamus.

The milk let-down effect of oxytocin is due to the action of oxytocin on the myo-epithelial cells of the mammary gland (*see* Chapter 11). These cells contain contractile elements and contract when stimulated by oxytocin with a rise in milk pressure in the gland. The reflex arc responsible for oxytocin release and milk let-down is also a neurohumoral one (Cross & Harris, 1952). The suckling or milking stimulus activates the sensory nerves which conduct the impulse to the hypothalamus with a subsequent release of oxytocin from the posterior pituitary. Thus the afferent part of the reflex arc is composed of the sensory nerves and the motor part consists of the hormone, oxytocin.

Bioassay. The classical assay for oxytocin is a measure of the increase in uterine contractions either *in vivo* or *in vitro*. In general, young guinea pigs are used and the uterus suspended in a physiological salt solution and oxytocin is added to the suspending fluid. The finding that oxytocin causes a marked depression in the blood pressure of the bird led to the utilization of this phenomenon for the assay of the hormone. In both instances the unknown sample is compared to a standard preparation. It has also been suggested that oxytocin can be assayed at very dilute concentrations by measuring its action on the contraction of the mammary gland.

B. Gonads

The primary sex organs are the gonads, *i.e.*, the testes in the male and ovaries in the female. These organs are the site of formation of the male and female gametes (germ cells) and also the male and female sex hormones. In addition, specific accessory sexual organs and secondary sexual characters are present in each sex. The former refer to the various ducts, exocrine glands and structures needed for the passage of the germ cells and maintenance of the fetus. The latter consist of such external manifestations of sexuality as mammary glands, pelvic modifications, body configuration, hair dis-

tribution, voice, horns when present and such characteristics as plumage in the bird.

In general, the maintenance of the accessory sexual organs and secondary sexual characteristics is due to the action of the gonadal hormones. In addition the female sex hormones are necessary for the maintenance of pregnancy. Ovariectomy in most species such as the rabbit, rat, mouse, goat and except for terminal stage of pregnancy in cow and sow, leads to a termination of pregnancy. However, in a few species such as man, ewe, guinea pig and mare, the placenta releases an adequate amount of gonadal hormones for the maintenance of gestation so that ovariectomy does not interfere with pregnancy in these species.

Finally it should be pointed out that the hormones of both sexes are present in both sexes. That is to say, the male has a small amount of estrogen and the female a small amount of androgen. Masculinization of the female or feminization of the male is not seen, however, except under abnormal conditions.

1. ANDROGENS

As indicated above, the testis is the site of production of the male sex hormone, testosterone. This hormone belongs to the class known as androgens and possesses the property of stimulating the male sexual characteristics. A limited amount of androgen is also secreted by the adrenal cortex. However, since marked atrophy of the sex accessories occurs following castration it is obvious that the amount of physiologically significant androgen released to the organism from the adrenal cortex is indeed slight. In addition to the secretion of androgens, the testes secrete small amounts of estrogen except for the stallion whose testis secretes large amounts of estrogen. Under abnormal conditions, especially testicular tumors of the dog, extremely high levels of estrogen have been found in the urine.

The androgens belong to the steroid group of hormones which are characterized by a cyclopentano-perhydro-phenanthrene nucleus (Fig. 1–10). This consists of the phenanthrene structure and a 5 carbon cyclopentane ring, which is found not only in the steroid hormones such as estrogens, pro-

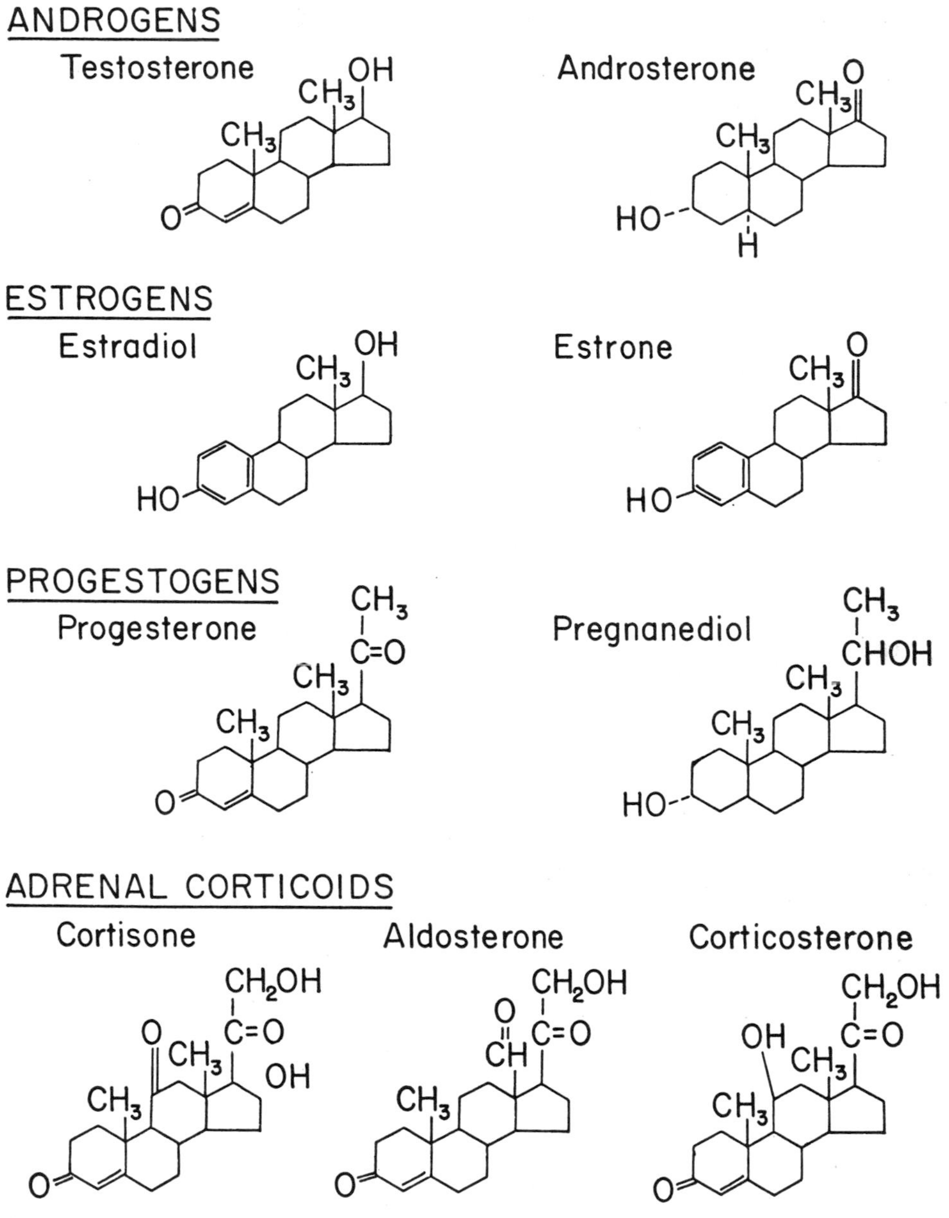

ANDROGENS

Testosterone

Androsterone

ESTROGENS

Estradiol

Estrone

PROGESTOGENS

Progesterone

Pregnanediol

ADRENAL CORTICOIDS

Cortisone

Aldosterone

Corticosterone

FIG. 1–10.—Some of the major steroid hormones of the mammal. Androsterone, estrone (and estradiol) and pregnanediol represent the degradation products of testosterone, estradiol 17β and progesterone respectively

3

gestogens, androgens and adrenal corticoids but also includes such substances as cholesterol, bile acids and vitamin D. In view of the structural similarity of these hormones it is not too surprising that both an overlapping of activities occurs such as is seen with progesterone and desoxycorticosterone and that one hormone can be converted to another, such as the conversion of testosterone to estradiol.

The specific androgen released by the testis is testosterone which is probably present in the form of its ester, testosterone propionate, and circulates bound to the blood proteins. The hormone is not stored but is rapidly utilized or degraded and excreted through the urine or bile and feces. The principle urinary products are androsterone, epiandrosterone and etiocholanolone. These are all 17-ketosteroids and appear in the urine as water soluble sulfates or glucuronides. In general, the degradation products show a decreased activity or no activity. Both the liver and to a lesser extent the kidney are the sites of steroid hormone degradation.

The following pathway has been described for the biogenesis of testosterone:

acetate or cholesterol → pregnenolone → progesterone → 17 α-hydroxyprogesterone → $\triangle^4$ androstene-3, 17-dione → testosterone.

Regulation of testosterone release is controlled by LH as indicated previously. This still leaves open the question of how LH release is controlled. However, data has been presented to show that testosterone acts directly on the pituitary to inhibit FSH release and by way of a center in the hypothalamus to inhibit LH release and hence androgen synthesis (Davidson & Sawyer, 1961). Implantation of small amounts of testosterone into the region of the hypothalamus leads to aspermia and both testicular and prostatic atrophy. It must also be assumed that seasonal factors such as light, temperature, etc. are responsible in seasonal breeders for both LH and FSH release.

Functions. The action of androgens is particularly evident on the accessory and sexual characteristics of the male. Androgens possess the following biological activities in the male:

(a) Androgens stimulate spermatogenesis in the hypophysectomized animal and hasten the onset of spermatogenesis in the seasonal breeder.

(b) Androgens prolong the life span of epididymal sperm. Sperm motility lasts for approximately 30 days in the guinea pig following castration, whereas androgen treatment will increase sperm viability to the normal period of 70 days.

(c) Androgens promote growth, development and secretory activity of the accessory sexual organs such as the prostate, vesicular glands, bulbo-urethral gland, vas deferens, Cowper's gland, penis and scrotum.

(d) Androgens stimulate growth of the secondary sexual characteristics which are specific for the male such as body configuration, cock's comb, distribution of pubic hair in man, pitch of the voice, etc.

(e) Androgens stimulate sexual behavior and libido in the male.

(f) Androgens induce nitrogen retention distinct from its action on the reproductive tract. In other words, testosterone possesses protein anabolic activity which involves the total organism.

Bioassay. A number of bioassays for testosterone are available. These assays include the increase in comb weight of the cockerel or castrated cock. In this assay the hormone may be applied systemicly or placed directly on the comb in which case the sensitivity of the assay is increased many fold. Other assays for androgenic activity include measures of increase in weight of the prostate or vesicular glands in the immature or castrated rat and the 17-ketosteroid content of the urine.

2. Estrogens

The ovary, like the testis, possesses two functions: the production of ova and the release of three types of hormones. These hormones are the estrogens, progestogens and relaxin. The first two are commonly referred to as the female sex hormones and are steroids with the typical cyclopentanoperhydro-phenanthrene nucleus. Relaxin is a polypeptide with a molecular weight of approximately 10,000 and is active during the latter part of gestation.

The estrogenic hormone is probably secreted by the theca interna of the Graafian follicle (*see* Chapter 4). This tissue is rich in estrogen and exhibits maximum activity during the estrogenic phase of the cycle. The follicular fluid is also rich in estrogen, probably due to diffusion from the thecal tissue. Substances with estrogenic activity have been found in both the animal and plant kingdom, *e.g.*, subterranean clover, and have also been synthesized. At least eight estrogens, estradiol 17β, estrone, estriol, 16-epiestriol, 16-hydroxyestrone, equilin, equilenin and hippulin, have been found in mammals. All of these estrogens contain the typical steroid structure, whereas the naturally occurring plant estrogens such as genistin, genistein, and coumestrol are non-steroidal. In addition, a group of synthetic, non-steroidal estrogens such as stilbestrol and hexestrol are now available.

The two estrogenic steroids secreted by the ovary are estradiol and estrone. Estriol is a conversion product of estradiol and estrone and is found in the urine. In the case of the mare, equilin and equilenin are the primary degradation products. Little is known of the synthesis of estrogens but it is thought that cholesterol is the basic precursor of these hormones as is probably true for all steroids. The pathway of biogenesis, *i.e.*, the intermediate products have not been isolated although an interconversion with androgens has been shown, and it has been suggested that androgens may act as estrogen precursors. Specific proestrogens have been demonstrated and shown to possess no activity but are converted systemicly into biologically active estrogens (Emmens, 1942). Approximately two-thirds of the estrogens present in the blood is bound to protein and is in equilibrium with the free estrogen. Both the protein binding and the conversion take place in the liver.

Like the androgens, estrogens are not stored in the body but are removed through inactivation and elimination in both the urine and feces. Approximately 10 per cent of the blood estrogens are eliminated and the remainder inactivated. The liver appears to be the critical organ involved in these processes. Elimination via the urine involves prior inactivation of the estrogen by conjugation to form water soluble glucuronides and sulfates and subsequent elimination. The liver excretes free estrogens in the bile which pass to the small intestine and are subsequently eliminated or reabsorbed and returned via the enterohepatic system. Inactivation may occur via the following methods: (*a*) transformation to inactive degradation products, (*b*) conjugation with formation of less active products and (*c*) transformation to inactive isomers.

Stimulation of estrogen release from the ovary is under the control of the gonadotropins from the anterior pituitary gland. Hypophysectomy of the female is followed by atrophy of the reproductive tract and all structures dependent on the presence of estrogens. According to current concepts, two systems may be involved in the regulation of pituitary and ovarian hormone release. It is believed that a feed-back mechanism operates whereby the level of FSH and LH is controlled by the concentration of estradiol and progesterone in the blood. Very low levels of estradiol appear to stimulate FSH release which in conjunction with LH causes marked increase in estradiol release. When the estradiol level in the blood gets high enough it acts back on the pituitary inhibiting further release of FSH and hence a drop in estradiol occurs (Fig. 1–1). Increased LH release is then induced by the estrogen and progesterone. Experiments indicating the presence of excessive quantities of FSH following castration and decrease in FSH following injection of estradiol are further evidence for a feedback mechanism in the regulation of the secretion of estrogen.

In addition to the above experiments there is good evidence that the hypothalamus is involved. This may be both by way of an estrogen feed-back on the hypothalamus and by external factors such as light acting on the hypothalamus. The ability of adrenergic and cholinergic blocking agents to inhibit ovulation and the induction of ovulation after electrical stimulation of the hypothalamus all indicate the involvement of the nervous system in LH release. The action of light in hastening the onset of gonadal activity in both birds and mammals would appear to indicate a route involving the eyes → optic nerve → hypothalamus → release of substance into the hypothalamic portal system→the pituitary→FSH release.

Functions. The action of estradiol is primarily on the female reproductive duct system. The hormone stimulates growth and secretory activity of structures receptive to the hormone and in addition produces characteristic behavioral patterns. It should also be borne in mind that estrogens act not only alone but in concert with other hormones especially progesterone and relaxin. Some of the manifold action of estradiol is listed below.

(*a*) Uterus: Estrogens stimulate marked growth of the uterus resulting in increase in the mass of both the endometrium and myometrium. The increased mitoses indicate hyperplasia in addition to hypertrophy.

(*b*) Uterine contractility: Estrogens stimulate uterine contractility by increasing both amplitude and rate of contraction.

(*c*) Vagina: Estrogens stimulate increased growth of the vaginal epithelium leading to cornification.

(*d*) Fallopian tubes: Estrogens stimulate growth and muscular activity.

(*e*) Mammary gland: Estrogens stimulate growth and development of the duct system in all species and both the duct and alveolar systems in some species (*see* Chapter 11).

(*f*) Pelvis: Estrogens stimulate loosening of the pubic symphysis and increase in size of the interpubic ligament.

(*g*) Skeleton: Estrogens stimulate development of female contours, cause maturation of epiphyseal cartilage and inhibit growth of long bone.

(*h*) Mineral metabolism: Estrogens stimulate retention of water, sodium, calcium, nitrogen and phosphorus.

(*i*) Estrus: Estrogens induce behavioral estrus (sexual heat).

Bioassay. The assay of estrogen utilizes a number of the activities stimulated by the hormone in either the immature or castrated animal. Some of these are (*a*) induction of vaginal estrus as indicated by a vaginal smear showing cornified cells in the rat or mouse, (*b*) increase in weight of the uterus, (*c*) increase in weight of the oviduct

in chicks, and (*d*) chemical assays for estrogens involving colorimetric or fluorimetric changes.

3. PROGESTOGENS

Progesterone is the most prevalent, natural occurring progestogen and is secreted by the lutein cells of the *corpus luteum*. In addition this hormone is also secreted by the placenta. Small amounts of progesterone have been isolated from both the testis and the adrenal gland which is not too surprising since progesterone is probably an intermediate in the biosynthesis of adrenal corticoids and testicular androgens. A wide variety of progestogens have been synthesized such as 17-α-ethyl-19-nortestosterone, 17-α-ethinyl-19-nortestosterone, 17-α-OH-progesterone caproate and 6-α-methyl-17-α-acetoxyprogesterone. These derivatives of 19-nortestosterone and other synthetic progestogens have been shown to be highly potent and effective orally.

Like the other steroids, progesterone is not stored in the body; it is either rapidly utilized or excreted and is present in low concentrations in the body tissues. The biosynthesis of progesterone is believed to start with acetate or cholesterol. Experiments involving the use of isotopes revealed that injection of deuterium-tagged cholesterol led to the finding of pregnanediol with a deuterium tag in the urine. Since pregnanediol is the urinary end-product of progesterone one may conclude that the cholesterol was the precursor in the biosynthesis of progesterone which was then degraded to pregnanediol. Progesterone does not appear in the urine as such but is excreted as pregnanediol glucuronide which is inactive. Both the degradation and the conjugation of progesterone occurs in the liver.

The regulation of the secretion of progesterone is not too clearly understood. The classical concept indicates that following ovulation induced by LH a *corpus hemorrhagicum* is formed in the ovary which develops into a corpus luteum and that this structure is stimulated by prolactin to release progesterone. That prolactin is truly luteotropic and stimulates release of progesterone can be readily demonstrated in the hypophysectomized rat or mouse wherein prolactin acts to maintain a deciduoma by way of the release of progesterone from the corpus luteum. As indicated previously, however, prolactin has no effect on the rate of progesterone synthesis by the corpus luteum of the sow either *in vitro* or *in vivo*. It would appear that the luteotropic action of prolactin is species specific since prolactin is without effect on the corpus luteum of the sow or cow, but does stimulate progesterone secretion by the corpus luteum of the rat, mouse and ewe.

Functions. The action of progesterone is difficult to separate from that of other hormones such as the estrogens. This is due to the fact that progesterone normally acts in conjunction with estrogens and other steroids and produces few specific effects when acting alone. In general, it may be said that estrogens primarily promote growth processes whereas progestogens encourage tissue differentiation. Some of the specific effects of progesterone are listed below.

(*a*) Uterine endometrium: Progesterone induces the formation of a secretory endometrium in a uterus previously sensitized by estrogens. The endometrium is characterized by increase in mucosal thickness, increased coiling of the glands, edema of the stroma, and presence of glycogen droplets in the glandular cells. This secretory type of endometrium is necessary for implantation of the blastocyst.

(*b*) Uterine myometrium: Progesterone inhibits spontaneous uterine motility and the response of the myometrium to oxytocin.

(*c*) Deciduoma: Progesterone promotes the growth of a deciduoma in the uterus.

(*d*) Vagina: Progesterone induces mucification of the vaginal epithelium.

(*e*) Mammary gland: Progesterone in conjunction with estrogen induces growth and development of the lobule alveolar system.

(*f*) Pregnancy: Progesterone is necessary for the maintenance of gestation.

(*g*) Sexual heat: Progesterone acts synergistically with estrogen to induce behavioral estrus in the female.

(*h*) Maternal behavior: Progesterone is necessary for the induction of maternal behavior in the rabbit. Prior treatment with estrogen is necessary (Zarrow *et al.*, 1961).

(*i*) Ovulation: Progesterone will induce ovulation in the cow, bird, rat, and rabbit and will also inhibit ovulation when given chronically.

Bioassay. The assays for progesterone include such procedures that involve (*a*) the decidual reaction (formation of deciduoma) (*b*) progestational proliferation of the endometrium in the rabbit, (*c*) carbonic anhydrase levels in the rabbit uterus, (*d*) pregnancy maintenance, and (*e*) pregnanediol levels in the urine. The decidual reaction which may be likened to the differentiation of the maternal portion of the placenta was first described by Loeb and is dependent on progesterone. Hence a rat may be made pseudopregnant, the uterus scratched on days 3 to 5 after the onset of pseudopregnancy and the ovaries removed. The increase in the size of the uterus will be an index of the developing deciduoma and will depend on the amount of progesterone given over a 3 to 4 day period. The progestational reaction in the uterus was first reported by Corner & Allen in their classical work on the isolation of progesterone and utilizes the castrated or immature rabbit. The degree of progestational proliferation induced by progesterone is an index of the amount of the hormone. The discovery by Lutwak-Mann that the concentration of carbonic anhydrase in the uterus of the rabbit varies with the level of progesterone has led to the use of this finding for the assay of progestogens.

None of these assays is sensitive enough to measure plasma levels of progesterone except the Hooker-Forbes test. This assay involves the direct application of progesterone to the uterine endometrium of the mouse and depends on cytological changes in the nuclei. Most of the work on progesterone levels in the body has involved studies on pregnanediol excretion patterns. Recently chemical procedures have been devised that can determine circulating progestogen levels if adequate amount of blood is available for the assay.

4. RELAXIN

The initial discovery by Hisaw in 1926 of

the presence of an active substance in the blood of the guinea pig that induced relaxation of the pubic symphysis has led to the characterization of this substance as a true hormone of reproduction and specifically parturition (Hisaw & Zarrow, 1951; Zarrow *et al.*, 1956). Relaxin is a water soluble polypeptide with a molecular weight of approximately 10,000. As yet the hormone has not been isolated in the pure form so that its physico-chemical properties are not fully defined. Indeed it is possible that the relaxin preparation now available is a complex of several substances with relaxin-like activity.

Relaxin is secreted primarily by the corpus luteum of the ovary during pregnancy. In addition, the placenta and possibly the uterus secrete relaxin in some species. The concentration of relaxin in the ovary of the sow increases markedly in early pregnancy and reaches a plateau of approximately 10,000 GPU per gm. fresh weight of ovary and which is maintained until parturition. A GPU (guinea pig unit) represents the amount of relaxin necessary to produce pubic relaxation in 66 per cent of a group of 15 guinea pigs. In the cow, rabbit, woman and guinea pig, the concentration of relaxin has been shown to increase as pregnancy progresses until a plateau is reached. In general, the shape of the curve is the same for all species.

No information is available on the biosynthesis of relaxin or the regulation of its release. While minute amounts may be present at different phases of the estrous cycle, significant amounts appear only during gestation and usually towards the last third of gestation. The hormone disappears from the blood following parturition.

Functions. The physiologic action of relaxin is concerned primarily with parturition. Again it must be indicated that the action of this hormone is intimately tied up with the estrogens. Under physiologic conditions, many of its effects are obtained only after pre-sensitization with estrogens occurs. The action of relaxin is listed below and it may be noted that its major activity revolves about parturition and the delivery of young.

(*a*) Pubic symphysis: Relaxin induces a separation of the pubic symphysis of the guinea pig and mouse following pre-treatment with estrogen. This allows for passage of the fetus.

(*b*) Uterine cervix: Relaxin induces a dilation of the uterine cervix of the sow, cow, rat, mouse and possibly human being following estrogen and progestogen. Again this allows for passage of the fetus.

(*c*) Uterine myometrium: Relaxin inhibits myometrial activity, *i.e.*, uterine contractions.

(*d*) Uterus: Relaxin increases water content of the uterus; in conjunction with estrogen also causes increased growth of uterus.

(*e*) Mammary gland: Relaxin causes increased growth of mammary gland if given in conjunction with estradiol and progesterone.

Bioassay. Three bioassays have been utilized for studies on relaxin. These are separation of the pubic symphysis in the guinea pig, separation of the pubic symphysis in the mouse and inhibition of uterine contractions in the rat or mouse. In the first assay immature or castrated guinea pigs are primed with estradiol and then injected with relaxin. Pubic relaxation is determined by palpation and the data expressed as the percentage of animals showing relaxation per dose level. The second assay utilizes the immature female mouse which is also primed with estrogen for one week. This is followed by relaxin and the degree of pubic separation determined under the microscope with an ocular micrometer. The third assay involves the ability of relaxin to inhibit uterine contractions in the estrous mouse or rat. This test is usually carried out *in vitro*, although it may be done *in vivo*. The endpoint is the minimum amount of relaxin that will inhibit both the amplitude and rate of contractions.

C. Placenta

1. Gonadotropins

Placental gonadotropins have been found in the mare, monkey, chimpanzee, human being, and rat. The physiological properties of these placental hormones differ markedly and may represent divergent evolutionary steps in the adoption of pituitary-like activity by the placenta. The placental hormones of the mare (pregnant mare's serum or PMS) and the human being (human chorionic gonadotropin or HCG) have been studied in much detail. These hormones differ markedly in both chemical and physiological properties. The presence of HCG in the urine and the absence of PMS in the urine indicates that PMS is a very large molecule and is unable to pass through the kidney filtration system. Physiologically, PMS is highly active in producing follicular growth and some luteinization, whereas HCG has no effect on follicular growth but will induce ovulation. It is of some interest to note that the appearance of the placental gonadotropins in the blood of horse and man occurs at approximately the same relative time in pregnancy, *i.e.*, during the first third of pregnancy. The role played by these two hormones in gestation is still not clear, but it is significant that their disappearance corresponds roughly with the time when ovariectomy no longer interferes with the maintenance of the pregnancy.

PMS. The presence of a gonadotropin in the blood of the pregnant mare was first described by Cole & Hart in 1930. The hormone appears in the blood about the 40th day of pregnancy and increases rapidly to a concentration of 50 to 100 r.u. per ml. by the 60th day of pregnancy (Cole & Saunders, 1935). This concentration is maintained for approximately 40 to 65 days (*see* Chapter 16). By day 170 it falls to a non-detectable level.

Cole & Goss have suggested that the endometrial cups are the source of the hormone (*see* Chapter 10). These structures form in the endometrium opposite the chorion in the area where the allantoic blood vessels fan out. The cups develop precisely at the time when the hormone is first obtained in the serum of the pregnant mare and destruction of the endometrial cups is complete at the time of the disappearance of the hormone from the maternal blood. Analyses of the cups for gonadotropin content reveal a correlation between the concentration of the hormone

in the maternal blood and the concentration in the endometrial cups. Histochemical stains for glycoprotein indicate the presence of this substance only in the epithelial cells lining the uterine lumen and the uterine glands in the cup area.

HCG. The concentration of chorionic gonadotropin (HCG) in the blood of pregnant women correlates with the concentration in the urine. A peak value of 120 I.U. per ml. of serum is obtained on the 62nd day after the last menses and a rapid decline is noted to a low of approximately 10 I.U. per ml. of serum on day 154. A subsequent rise to 20 I.U. is obtained by day 200 and this is maintained until the end of pregnancy.

An analysis of the distribution of chorionic gonadotropin in the mother and fetus led to the finding that the ratio of maternal blood to urinary gonadotropin is not constant, although the ratio of gonadotropin in the chorion (*i.e.* placental membrane) to maternal blood is constant. Consequently, it was concluded that the concentration of gonadotropin in the urine does not depend entirely on the rate of production of the hormone and that the method of gonadotropin elimination changes during pregnancy. It was shown that a significant amount of chorionic gonadotropin is found in the fetus due to the fact that the chorion releases the hormone into the maternal blood, and some of it evidently passes the placental barrier and enters the fetal system.

2. NON-GONADOTROPIC HORMONES

The placenta has long been recognized as a gland of internal secretion. This was first realized beyond question of a doubt following the discovery of the placental gonadotropins. It is clear that the placenta has become specialized as an endocrine organ during the evolution of viviparity in mammals and gradually assumed certain functions of the pituitary gland, the ovary and possibly other endocrine glands. The endocrine activity of the placenta varies with different species. We have already seen that the placental gonadotropins in the mare differ markedly from those in the woman. It is as yet unknown whether such species as the cow or ewe even possess placental gonadotropins. In the case of the non-gonadotropic hormones, it is also probable that species differences exist with regard to the endocrine activity of the placenta.

It is rather clear now that the placenta of a large number of species secretes both estradiol and progesterone. This has been demonstrated in women (Diczfalusy, 1960) and probably holds true for many farm animals. Castration of such species as the ewe, mare, and human being does not interfere with pregnancy indicating that the placenta has taken over the secretion of these hormones. The placenta may produce relaxin, adrenal corticoids, STH and ACTH. Although the evidence is far from complete, relaxin has been extracted from the placentas of rats and rabbits. Perfusion experiments on human and bovine placentas have indicated the release of adrenal corticoids. In the case of STH and ACTH, the evidence is less direct and conclusive. Growth promoting activity as demonstrated in hypophysectomized rats was found in the blood of pregnant hypophysectomized rats; and ACTH-like activity has been reported in placental extracts.

III. SECONDARY HORMONES OF REPRODUCTION

It should be recognized at the outset that the hormones listed as secondary hormones of reproduction are endocrine substances with a metabolic action and as such maintain the organism in a state that permits reproduction to occur. These hormones may also have an additional role during reproduction although in the final analysis the role may be an extension of their metabolic activity to a new condition, i.e., pregnancy.

A. Pituitary Hormones STH, TSH & ACTH

It has already been stated that the STH is concerned with general growth and as such is needed throughout the reproductive period of the animal. There is also some indication of increased release of STH during pregnancy, possibly by the placenta. Finally, purified STH has been shown to act directly

on the reproductive duct system of the female rat. STH stimulates growth of the uterus directly and indirectly by stimulating the ovary to release estrogen. In both of these effects it also synergizes with estradiol and with LH in its action on the ovary. Since the main action of thyrotropin (TSH) and adrenocorticotropic hormone (ACTH) is mediated through the release of the target gland hormones, i.e., thyroxine and adrenal corticoids, their action will be discussed under the section on thyroxine and adrenal corticoids.

B. Thyroxine

It is quite apparent that normal functioning of the thyroid gland and proper secretion of its hormones, thyroxine and tri-iodothyronine are a prerequisite for good reproduction. The thyroid hormone influences reproduction and fertility not only by helping to maintain the pituitary hypophyseal-gonadal relationship (Maqsood, 1952), but indirectly by affecting the metabolic pool of nitrogen and available energy, thus regulating the fulfillment of demands on this pool by the tissues of the reproductive system and the growing embryo.

Hypothyroidism leads to cretinism with marked delay in onset of puberty and failure of development of the gonads and reproductive duct system. Treatment with thyroxine leads to stimulating or toxic effects so that it is necessary to consider both the dosage and the species involved. High or toxic levels of the hormone lead to an impairment of testicular function although in the absence of thyroxine, gonadal damage will also be present. Reports of increased testicular activity following thyroxine treatment in ram, mouse and rabbit must be accepted and not regarded as contradictory but as indicative of the stimulating action of this hormone. It is highly probable that all species will show gonadal impairment if high or toxic doses are used.

In many species reproduction occurs despite thyroidectomy but the fertility level and parturition may be subnormal. In the pig, hypothyroidism leads to an increase in length of pregnancy of 14.5 days and reduction in litter size from 8.7 to 3.3. Hypothyroidism in the rat results in a resorption of the fetuses or reduction in litter size. Thyroidectomy in the rabbit may cause a resorption of young, abortion or prolongation of pregnancy and death of the young.

In some species the thyroid hormone is involved directly in pregnancy. In the absence of the hormone, the fetus is resorbed or aborted; or if gestation is maintained, the duration is lengthened. This is probably due to an interference with the mechanism of parturition. In certain species such as the guinea pig only a parturitional problem has been demonstrated; in others an entire galaxy of symptoms may be present. Reduction in the size, number and viability of the young give evidence to an essential role for thyroxine in pregnancy.

Thyroid activity varies with estrous cycle or breeding season of the ewe (Robertson & Falconer, 1961). Increased protein bound iodine levels which mirror the level of circulating thyroid hormone indicate that an increase in thyroid activity occurs at or 48 hours before the onset of estrus. No change in thyroid activity was noted during conception and early pregnancy but increased I^{131} uptake occurs during the last month of pregnancy. In the ram, summer infertility has been shown to be due to low thyroid activity and can be easily corrected by treatment with thyroxine. In the rabbit low thyroid activity leads to delay in onset of sexual maturity, testis size and spermatogenesis. Proper treatment with thyroxine results in precocious sexual maturity.

C. Adrenal Corticoids

The involvement of the adrenal cortex in reproduction is due to (a) the ability of the gland to secrete sex steroids, (b) the basic need of the adrenal corticoids for the maintenance of life, and (c) the specific need for adequate amounts of adrenal corticoids to maintain reproduction. The first two items need not be considered further here since it is apparent that both play a role. Hence we shall now consider whether the adrenal cortex is specifically necessary for reproduction.

Cyclic variations in size and weight of the adrenal gland occurs coincidental with the reproductive stages. Adrenalectomy causes a loss of sex drive and some disorganization of the testis in the male rat and a suppression of the estrous cycle with frequent occurrence of pseudopregnancy in the female. With regard to the ovary follicular atresia has been reported in the human being and ovarian atrophy due to a loss of sensitivity to FSH in the rat. Extensive studies in the human being during pregnancy have revealed a marked increase in the secretion of both the glucocorticoids (adrenal steroids with a major action on carbohydrate metabolism) and the mineralocorticoids (adrenal steroids with a major action on salt and water metabolism).

Injection of the adrenocortical hormones will correct all the disturbances of adrenalectomy and restore normal reproductive activity; treatment with excessive amounts of cortisone leads to regressive changes in the reproductive tract probably secondary to the general catabolic action of the hormones.

D. Pancreas

In general, pancreatectomy or damage to the islet cells of the pancreas with a resulting diabetes leads to a dysfunction of reproductive activities. Among the defects reported are prolongation or cessation of estrous cycle and a delay in the onset of puberty. Ovaries from diabetic rats at 50 days of age weighed half of that noted for normal rats of the same age and contained no mature follicles. Treatment with insulin restored normal estrous cycles in the diabetic rat and permitted breeding to occur. In the majority of depancreatized animals fetal resorption and death occurs if insulin is withdrawn at the time of breeding.

E. Parathyroids

Increased parathyroid activity is seen during pregnancy as indicated by hypertrophy of the gland, presence of parathormone-like activity in serum and the relative sensitivity of the pregnant animal to parathyroidectomy. Parathyroidectomy during pregnancy in the cow failed to interfere with gestation although milk production was decreased. In the goat, however, parathyroidectomy led to tetany and failure of lactation.

CONCLUSIONS

It is obvious that the endocrine glands play a major role in reproduction. In this role certain hormones are of paramount importance while others play a subsidiary, but nevertheless necessary part. However, the hormones are not the only factors involved; the germ cells must be considered in addition to environment, nutrition, and heredity. It is the purpose of the following chapters to examine all these factors in detail.

REFERENCES

COLE, H. H. & SAUNDERS, F. J. (1935). The concentration of gonad-stimulating hormone in blood serum and of estrin in urine throughout pregnancy in the mare. *Endocrinology*, **19**, 199–208.

CROSS, B. A. & HARRIS, G. W. (1952). The role of the neurohypophysis in the milk-ejection reflex. *J. Endocrin.*, **8**, 148–161.

DAVIDSON, J. M. & SAWYER, C. H. (1961). Evidence for an hypothalamic locus of inhibition of gonadotropin by androgen in the male. *Proc. Soc. Exp. Biol. & Med. N.Y.*, **107**,, 4–7.

DICZFALUSY, E. (1960). Endocrine functions of the human placenta. *First Inter. Congr. Endocrinol. Symposium*, **7**, 129–134. Copenhagen.

DUNCAN, G. W.; BOWERMAN, A. M.; ANDERSON, L. L.; HEARN, W. R. & MELAMPY, R. M. (1961). Factors influencing *in vitro* synthesis of progesterone. *Endocrinology*, **68**, 199–207.

EMMENS, C. W. (1942). The differentiation of oestrogens from proestrogens by the use of spayed mice possessing two separate vaginal sacs. *J. Endocrin.*, **3**, 174–177.

FITZPATRICK, R. J. (1957). On Oxytocin and Uterine Function. In: *The Neurohypophysis*. H. Heller, (edit.), p. 203, New York, Academic Press.

GREEP, R. O.; VAN DYKE, H. B. & CHOW, B. F. (1942). Gonadotropins of the swine pituitary. 1. Various biological effects of purified Thylakentrin (FSH) and pure Metakentrin (ICSH). *Endocrinology*, **30**, 635–649.

HANSEL, W. (1961). The hypothalamus and pituitary function in mammals, *Internat. J. Fertil*, **6**, 241–259.

HARRIS, G. W. (1955). *Neural Control of the Pituitary Gland*. Chapter 2, pp. 7–41, London, Edward Arnold, Ltd.

HISAW, F. L. & ZARROW, M. X. (1951). The physiology of relaxin. *Vitamins & Hormones* **8**, 151–178.

JUBB, K. V. & MCENTEE, K. (1955). Observations on the bovine pituitary gland. II. Architecture and cytology with special reference to basophil cell function. *Cornell Vet.*, **45**, 593–641.

MAQSOOD, M. (1952). Thyroid functions in relation to reproduction of mammals and birds. *Biol. Rev.*, **27**, 281–319.

ROBERTSON, H. A. & FALCONER, I. R. (1961). Reproduction and thyroid activity. *J. Endocrin.*, **22**, 133–142.

SEVERINGHAUS, A. E. (1939). Anterior hypophyseal cytology in relation to the reproductive hormones. Ch. 19, pp. 1045–1087. In: *Sex & Internal Secretions*. 2nd Ed., Baltimore, The Williams & Wilkins Co.

STEELMAN, S. L. & POHLEY, F. M. (1953). Assay of the follicle stimulating hormone based on the augmentation with human chorionic gonadotropin. *Endocrinology*, **53**, 604–616.

ZARROW, M. X., CALDWELL, A. L., HAFEZ, E. S. E. & PINCUS, G. (1958). Superovulation in the immature rat as a possible assay for LH and HCG. *Endocrinology*, **63**, 748–758.

ZARROW, M. X.; NEHER, G. M.; SIKES, D.; BRENNAN, D. M. & BULLARD, J. (1956). Dilation of the uterine cervix of the sow following treatment with relaxin. *Am. J. Obstet. & Gynecol.*, **72**, 260–264.

ZARROW, M. X.; SAWIN, P. B.; ROSS, S.; DENENBERG, V. H.; CRARY, D.; WILSON, E. D. & FAROOQ, A. (1961). Maternal behavior in the rabbit: Evidence for an endocrine basis of maternal nest-building and additional data on maternal-nest building in the Dutch-belted race. *J. Reprod. & Fertil.*, **2**, 152–162.

QUESTIONS

1. Discuss the structural and functional relationship of the hypothalamus and the pituitary gland.
2. List the names and major functions of the primary hormones of reproduction.
3. Describe the role of the thyroid gland in pregnancy.
4. Discuss the differences between pituitary and placental gonadotropins.
5. What is the source or sources of the following hormones: FSH, PMS, LTH, HCG, STH, estrogens, progesterone, relaxin and androgens?
6. Define a hormone. Distinguish between hormone and vitamin.
7. What is meant by the servo-mechanism in hormone regulation? Give an example.
8. If you suspected a certain structure of being an endocrine gland, how would you establish this as a fact?
9. What will happen if progesterone is injected just prior to parturition?
10. What is the essential action of estradiol during gestation?

Part II

REPRODUCTIVE PHYSIOLOGY

Chapter 2

Male Reproductive Organs of Farm Mammals

By ERIK BLOM

THE male reproductive system can be divided into three components: (*a*) the primary sex organs, *i.e.* the gonads, testes or testicles, (*b*) a group of accessory sexual glands and ducts, *i.e.* the epididymis, vesicular glands and prostate, and (*c*) the external genital or copulatory organ, *i.e.* the penis. In this chapter we will discuss the ontogenesis (embryonic development) of the male reproductive organs and the anatomy, histology and function of these organs in the *adult bull*. Species differences will be also tabulated and illustrated diagrammatically.

I. EMBRYOLOGY OF THE REPRODUCTIVE ORGANS

The undifferentiated gonads of the early embryo differentiate in the female into ovaries and in the male into testes. In all species the testes descend from the abdomen and in the bull, ram, boar and stallion are located permanently in the scrotum. From the temporary kidney of the embryo, the mesonephros, 12 to 15 tubules are maintained. These tubules are called efferent ducts (*ductuli efferentes testis*) and form the final connection between the testis and the excretory canal, *i.e.* the Wolffian duct (Fig. 2–1). From the Wolffian duct are developed the epididymis, the deferent duct with its ampulla and the vesicular gland close to the outlet of the duct into the urogenital sinus.

Only very small parts of the Müllerian duct, which in the female develops into the main duct system, persist in the adult male. A rudimentary *uterus masculinus*, covered by the prostate and pea-sized Müllerian cysts may be found in the urogenital fold of some bulls (Blom & Christensen, 1958).

II. THE TESTES

The two testes are the primary sex organs; they produce the sperm and secrete the male sex hormones, *i.e.* they are glands with both "external" and "internal" secretions. In the bull, testes are elongated ovoid organs placed with their long axis vertical in the scrotum; in the mature animal they are 12 to 16 cm. in length and 6 to 8 cm. in diameter (Plate II). Each weighs (including the epididymis) 300 to 500 gm. depending on the age and breed of the bull. Normally the testes in the bull are equal in size, have a firm but not hard consistency and can be freely moved up and down within the scrotum.

When the serous coat of the testis, the *tunica vaginalis propria*, and the dense white

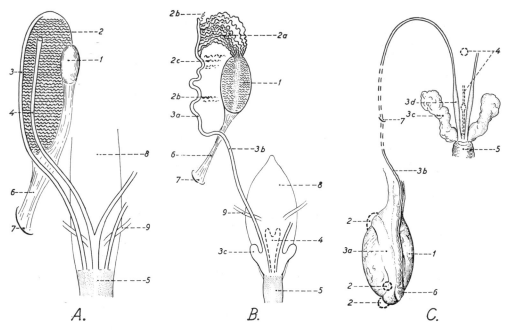

FIG. 2–1.—Diagram of the ontogenesis of the male reproductive organs.

A. The indifferent stage. *1)* Indifferent sexual gland. *2) mesonephros. 3)* Wolffian duct. *4)* Müllerian duct. *5) sinus urogenitalis. 6) gubernaculum. 7) ostium vaginale. 8) urachus. 9)* ureter.

B. The reproductive organs differentiated in the male direction. *1)* testis. *2a)* efferent ducts. *2b)* aberrant ducts. *2c) paradidymis. 3a)* epididymal duct. *3b)* deferent duct. *3c)* anlage of vesicular gland. *4) uterus masculinus. 5)* urogenital sinus. *6) gubernaculum. 7) ostium vaginale. 8) vesica. 9)* ureter.

C. The fully developed organs of the bull. *2)* Possible cystic growths emanating from aberrant ducts or paradidymis. *4)* possible cystic rudiments from the Müllerian duct. (*For further legends see B.*)

(*Blom & Christensen, 1951, Yearbook, Royal Vet. Agric. Coll. p. 1, Copenhagen.*)

capsule, the *tunica albuginea*, are cut the yellowish parenchyma bulges through owing to considerable turgor of the tissue. In median sagittal section, the cut surface shows a cord of connective tissue called the *mediastinum testis*, extending from the proximal pole towards the distal pole, and measuring 0.5 to 1 cm. in width. From this cord extend small streaks of connective tissue, the *septula testis*, between the seminiferous tubules, so that the testicular tissue appears slightly lobulated. In cross sections of the testis, the *mediastinum* appears as a central stellate figure enclosing the *rete testis* which serves as collecting tubes for the seminiferous tubules (Fig. 2–2).

A. Histology

The *septula testis* radiate from the *mediastinum* to the *tunica albuginea* dividing the testis parenchyma into cone-shaped lobules with their apex at the center and their base at the surface (Fig. 2–2). These lobules, the functional units of the gland, are only partly separated in the normal bull because the septula are rather thin and incomplete. Within each lobule the glandular parenchyma consists of one or more convoluted seminiferous tubules. These tubules have a diameter of 0.1 to 0.3 mm., are 50 to 100 cm. long and sometimes anastomose (connect) with each other. It has been estimated that the total tubule length in a pair of bull testes is as high as 15,000 feet.

The wall of a seminiferous tubule consists of a basement membrane and a multi-layered sperm producing epithelium. This epithelium consists of two types of cells; (*a*) germ cells, differing in age and morphology, generally arranged in concentric layers (see Chapter 3); (*b*) *Sertoli cells,* which

PLATE II

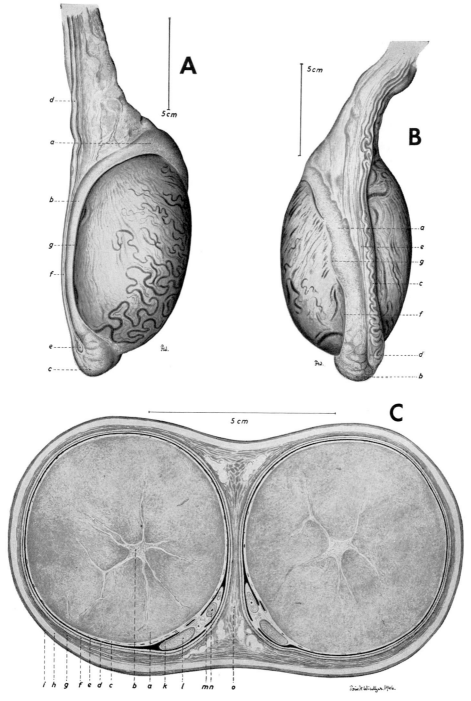

A. Right testis-epididymis from a 3 year old bull (right-side view). *a*) head of epididymis. *b*) body of epididymis. *c*) tail of epididymis. *d*) deferent duct. *e*) *ligamentum testis* (cut). *f*) peritoneal fold (cut). *g*) space between testis and epididymis.

B. Left testis-epididymis from a 2 year old bull (right-caudal view). *a*) body of epididymis. *b*) tail of epididymis. *c*) deferent duct. *d*) *ligamentum testis* (cut). *e*) peritoneal fold (cut). *f*) *saccus epididymidis*. *g*) area where *saccus epididymidis* is missing.

C. Horizontal section through the scrotum of the bull. *a*) testis. *b*) mediastinum. *c*) *tunica albuginea* with vessels. *d*) peritoneal cavity. *e*) *tunica vaginalis communis*. *f*) loose connective tissue. *g*) *tunica dartos*. *h*) *corium*. *i*) epidermis. *k*) *saccus epididymidis*. *l*) body of epididymis. *m*) peritoneal fold. *n*) deferent duct in its fold. *o*) *septum scroti*.

(*Blom & Christensen, 1947. Skand. Vet. tidskr. 37, 1.*)

PLATE III

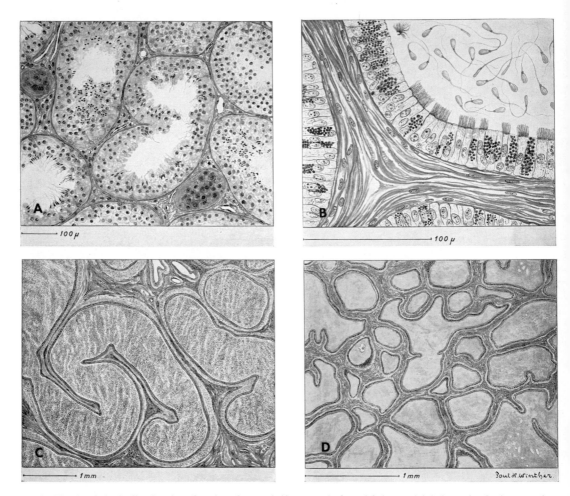

A. Testis of the bull.   Section showing the seminiferous tubules with interstitial tissue in the intervening spaces.   Two dark groups of interstitial cells are seen between the tubules (van Gieson-Hansen stain). ($\times$ 90 approx.)

B. Epithelium of *ductuli efferentes* in the bull.   Ciliated epithelial cells alternate with non-ciliated cells having large granules.   Note the detached ciliated border and the low sperm concentration in the lumen (Azan stain; slide prepared by Anker Hansen) ($\times$ 325 approx.)

C. *Cauda epididymidis* of the bull.   The coiled wide tubules are cut at different directions and the lumina are densely packed with stored sperm.   The light layer surrounding the tubules consists of smooth muscular fibers.   (van Gieson-Hansen stain) ($\times$ 13 approx.)

D. Vesicular gland of the bull.   Section showing an irregular system of wide tubules and ducts lined with a columnar secretory epithelium (van Gieson-Hansen stain).   ($\times$ 24 approx.)
(Original camera lucida drawings by Poul H. Winther.)

are slender pillar like structures perpendicular to the basement membrane, to which they are attached by a flat base. They are situated among the densely crowded germ cells to support and nourish them (Plate III).

The seminiferous tubules pass into the body of the *mediastinum* and unite with a network of ducts, the rete testis, which is lined with a cubic epithelium. At the proximal pole of the testis, the network of rete passes through a 4 to 5 mm. wide opening in the *tunica albuginea* (*porta mediastini*) and connects with the epididymis by the 12 to 15 tubules constituting the *ductuli efferentes testis*.

Between the seminiferous tubules there is loose connective tissue containing blood and lymph vessels, nerves and isolated groups of polygonal interstitial cells (Leydig cells) with large spherical nuclei (Plate III). The Leydig cells are the main source of the androgen, testosterone (see Chapter 1).

B. Functions

Testicular tissue has prolific activity: in the bull 1 gm. of testicular tissue manufactures on the average 9×10^6 sperm per day (Willett & Ohms, 1957), *i.e.* about 6,000 per minute. In some mammals the testes and the accessory sexual organs only function fully during the breeding season. In farm mammals, sperm production is maintained throughout the year with some seasonal variations (see Chapters 14 to 16).

The newly formed, non-motile sperm are transported from the lumina of the seminiferous tubules and through the *rete testis* by a current of fluid which originates in the tubules. This "testicular fluid" in which the sperm are suspended is secreted under considerable pressure and gives the testicles their characteristic tense consistency. A few drops of a cloudy fluid with a sperm concentration from 25,000 to 350,000 per mm³., may be collected on puncturing the *rete testis* shortly post-mortem. In cases of segmental aplasia of the Wolffian duct (epididymis partly or completely missing) the testicular fluid may accumulate in the *rete testis* or in the efferent ducts causing

well-marked cystic formations (Blom & Christensen, 1951).

III. THE EPIDIDYMIS

Epi-didymis (greek: on testis) is an elongated body closely adherent to the testis. It contains the intricately convoluted *ductus epididymidis*, more than 120 feet long in the adult bull. It is divided into head, body and tail (Plate II). The head (*caput epididymidis*) forms a flattened, somewhat cup-shaped protrusion starting at the proximal pole of the testis. It is usually U-shaped and varies in outline and size covering as much as one third of the front of the testis. Through the serosa, the ducts are arranged into lobules some of which are greyish-green and contain the efferent ducts (*ductuli efferentes testis*). These tubes forming the connection between rete testis and the epididymal duct are 12 to 15 in number and their arrangement is shown schematically in Figure 2–2. Near the proximal pole of the testis, the caput epididymidis tapers and is continued in the slender body (*corpus epididymidis*) which runs distally along the posterior border of the testis (Plate II). At the distal pole of the testis the body turns into the well defined tail or *cauda epididymidis*, which in the adult bull is about the size of the distal phalanx of the thumb, and is more or less pendulous. Near the *ligamentum testis* (Fig. 2–2) the epididymal duct becomes coarser and on looping around the ligament continues proximally as the deferent duct (*ductus deferens*).

On examining the living adult bull, the *cauda* can be usually felt as a well defined projection, lying lowest in the scrotum, but firmly connected to the lower pole of the testis. The *caput* can be palpated at the upper pole of the testis because the consistency of this part of the epididymis is firmer than the testis. Normally the body of the epididymis is more difficult to locate as this cord-like structure lies close to the septum of the scrotum (Plate II).

A. Histology

The 12 to 15 efferent ducts occupy about one-third of the caput of the epididymidis

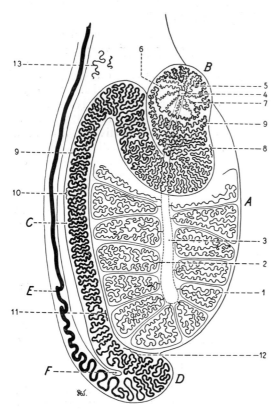

Fig. 2–2.—Schematic drawing of the tubular system of testis-epididymis in the bull (for clarity the duct system of *rete testis* is omitted).

A, testis. B, head of epididymis. C, body of epididymis. D, tail of epididymis. E, deferent duct. F, site of *ligamentum testis*.

1) lobule with seminiferous tubules. 2) *tubulus rectus. 3–4) rete testis.* 5) efferent duct. 9) epididymal duct. *6,7,8,10,11,12,13)* blind ducts and duct rudiments from where cyst formation may eventually occur (*Blom & Christensen 1960. Nord. Vet. Med. 12,* 453).

(Fig. 2–2). They have a diameter of 100 to 300 μ, contain only a few sperm in the lumen and have a very characteristic epithelium (Plate III). Two types of cylindrical epithelial cells are found attached to the thin basement membrane of the ducts: (*a*) *secretory* cells with large cytoplasmic granules and (*b*) *ciliated cells* with kinocilia (motile cilia) all beating outwards. In the bull, Blom (1944) has found that these ciliated cells normally detach their ciliated borders and excrete them into the semen at the rate of one per 10,000 sperm (*i.e.* about 500,000 in an average ejaculate). It is possible that both secretory and ciliated cells are two different functional phases of one cell type.

Near the center of the caput of the epididymis, the epididymal duct (*ductus epididymidis*) starts its long and tortuous course through the rest of the epididymis (Fig. 2–2). The *ductus epididymidis* can be differentiated into six histologically and cytochemically distinct regions (Nicander, 1958). The diameter of the duct increases while the height of the epithelium decreases from about 140 μ in the caput to about 60 μ in the cauda. All the way through the duct, the cylindrical epithelial cells have stereocilia (non-motile cilia) about 15 μ long except in the cauda where they are about 5 μ. The basement membrane of the duct is surrounded by a circular layer of smooth muscular fibers which increase in thickness towards the cauda (Maneely, 1959). The lumen of the duct is here about 1 mm. in diameter (Plate III).

B. Functions

The epididymis has four major functions; transport, concentration, maturation and storage of the sperm.

(*a*) *Transport.* The sperm are transported from the *rete testis* to the efferent ducts by the fluid pressure in the testis. Their passage through the efferent ducts is aided by the active outward beating cilia of the ciliated cells and in the epididymal duct by the peristaltic movements of musculature in the wall. The transport of sperm from the germinal epithelium to the cauda of the epididymis takes 7 to 9 days in the bull depending on the frequency of ejaculation (Knudsen, 1954).

(b) *Concentration.* From the dilute sperm suspension originating in the testis, water is resorbed into the epithelial cells, during the passage through the epididymis, and a highly concentrated sperm suspension (4,000,000 or more/mm.^{3}) is left in the tail of the epididymis.

(c) *Maturation.* The sperm mature in the epididymis and the cytoplasmic droplet of the sperm migrates along the middle-piece from the base of the head (proximal droplet) to the end of the middle-piece (distal droplet). This maturation is achieved as a result of secretions from the epithelial cells. In the bull the migration of the cytoplasmic droplet occurs only in the caput epididymis.

(d) *Storage.* The tail of the epididymis is the sperm depot. The concentration of sperm is very high and the lumen of the duct wide. It is not surprising, therefore, to find that about half of the total number of sperm are stored in this part (Bialy & Smith, 1958) which constitutes only about a quarter of the length of the epididymal duct. Conditions in the tail are optimal for preserving the viability of sperm which are immotile and in a quiescent state of metabolism. If the epididymis in the bull is ligated, the sperm will remain alive and fertile in the epididymis for about 60 days. On the other hand, after extremely long periods of sexual rest the first few ejaculates contain non-fertile sperm. Detachment of the *galea capitis* is one of the first changes visible in sperm after a long period of sexual rest (Blom, 1945). The depot of sperm may be discharged during masturbation or, in sexually inexperienced males, during urination.

4

IV. THE SCROTUM

The scrotum is the pouch containing the testes. In the relaxed state the scrotum of the bull is bottle-shaped. The thin packing of the scrotum usually has only a light coat of hair. Beneath the skin is the *tunica dartos* which is a coat composed of smooth muscle fibers with collagenous and elastic connective tissue. It surrounds both testes and forms a partition between the two halves of the scrotum, the *septum scroti* (Plate II). The next layer of white, dense scrotal fascia, the *tunica vaginalis communis*, surrounds the two halves of the scrotum separately, and is covered centrally by the parietal layer of the *processus vaginalis*, an evagination of the peritoneum.

Functions. The scrotum serves a necessary regulatory function in maintaining the temperature of the testis and epididymis 4 to 7° C. lower than that of the body. It accomplishes this by a double muscle system that draws the testes close to the abdominal wall for warmth and lets them down from the abdominal wall for cooling. The two muscles involved are the external cremaster muscle and the *tunica dartos*. Exposure to cold makes the *dartos* contract, thus causing the scrotal skin to pucker and wrinkle, shortening the scrotum and so forcing the testes closer to the body wall. In cold weather bulls should be left in a warm stable for clinical examination; the thermo-regulatory muscles will be relaxed and examination much easier.

The thermo-regulatory mechanism of the scrotum is important for normal sperm production in almost all mammals. In very hot weather, particularly if there is no shade, the mechanism may break down and cause degenerative changes in the germinal epithelium. Similar degenerative conditions can be induced artificially by insulating the scrotum. Temporary sterility can even be produced in rams by tying the testes close to the abdominal wall and thus preventing them cooling when the environmental temperature rises. Bilateral cryptorchids (animals with two undescended testes) are completely sterile. However production of testosterone by the interstitial cells does not seem to decline in undescended testes. On the contrary, cryptorchid stallions (commonly called ridglings) are known to be sexually more vigorous and aggressive than normal males.

V. VAS DEFERENS & THE ACCESSORY SEX GLANDS

A. Vas Deferens & Ampulla

The vas deferens (*ductus deferens*) transport the sperm from the tail of the epididymis to the *urethra* (Plate II & Fig. 2–4). The duct is about 2 mm. in diameter and the thick muscular wall makes it feel firm and cord-like. Near the tail of the epididymis, the vas deferens is convoluted and runs parallel to the body of the epididymis. Near the head of the epididymis, the vas deferens is straight and forms, with blood and lymph vessels and nerves, the spermatic cord (*funiculus spermaticus*) which passes through the inguinal canal to the abdominal cavity. The two deferent ducts, lying side by side above the bladder, gradually become thicker thus forming the ampullae (*ampullae ductus deferentis*) (Plate IV). This thickening of the duct, which does not particularly involve the lumen, is due to an abundant occurrence of glands in the wall. The ampullar glands are tubular and histologically very similar to the structure of the vesicular glands. The two ampullae pass under the body of the prostate and open together with the excretory ducts of the vesicular glands into the *urethra* with a slit-like orifice on each side of the *colliculus seminalis*. During courtship and precoital stimulation (teasing), the sperm are transported from the tail of epididymis to the ampulla, aided by the peristaltic movements of the vas deferens.

B. Vesicular Glands

The vesicular glands (*glandulae vesiculares*) were once erroneously regarded as reservoirs for semen, as indicated by their old name in human anatomy *i.e.* seminal vesicles. In the bull they are paired markedly lobulated glands, situated in the urogenital fold lateral to the ampullae (Plate IV). The vesicular glands may vary quite considerably in size and lobulation between individuals. On

sectioning, the yellowish glandular tissue usually oozes from the cut-surface. The secretory ducts from the individual lobules form one main excretory duct which is located in the center of the gland and extends posteriorly under the body of the prostate. Each excretory duct unites with a deferent duct at its outlet into the *urethra* forming the two *ostia ejaculatoria*. The anatomical relation of the ampullae and vesicular glands varies from individual to individual within the same breed.

Histology and Secretion. The vesicular gland in the bull is lobulated with strong muscular septa between the lobules. The secretory tubules measure about 0.3 mm. in diameter and are winding and bifurcating. They are lined by a double layer of cells, centrally tall columnar cells about 25 to 30 μ high, and peripherally cells filled with large droplets of lipid.

The secretion of the vesicular glands can be easily obtained *post-mortem* and is a faintly opalescent, sticky fluid. Mann and associates have found that it contains a high concentration of potassium, citric acid, fructose and several enzymes; it is often distinctly yellow in color, because of a high flavin content. The pH varies from 5.7 to 6.2. The secretions of the vesicular glands constitute about 50 per cent of the volume of a normal ejaculate in the bull.

C. Prostate and Cowper's Glands

The prostate gland which surrounds the urethra is composed of two parts: body of prostate (*corpus prostatae*) and the disseminate or cryptic prostate (*pars disseminata prostatae*). The secretions of these two parts pass through numerous small ducts which open in the urethra in rows (Plate IV).

The paired Cowper's glands (*glandulae bulbourethrales*) are round compact bodies with a dense capsule and are about the size of a walnut in the bull. They are located above the urethra near its exit from the pelvic cavity. The secretory ducts from each gland unite in one excretory duct which is 2 to 3 cm. in length. The two excretory ducts of the glands have small separate

PLATE IV

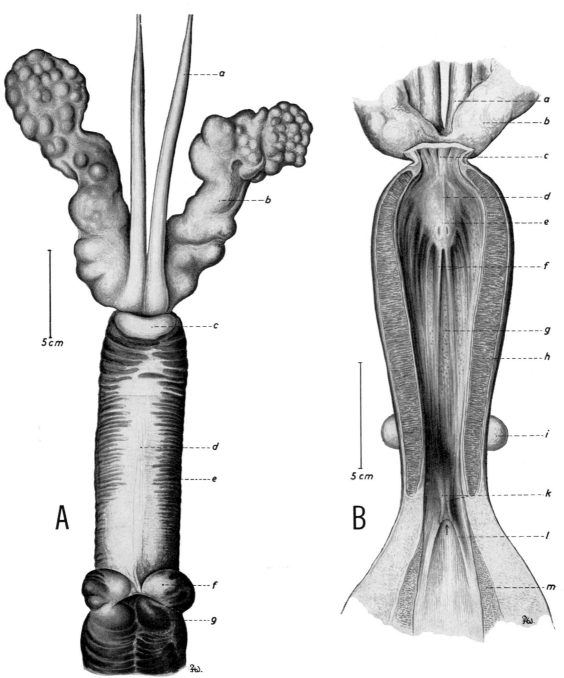

A. The pelvic genital organs of a $3\frac{1}{2}$ year old bull (dorsal view). Superficial muscular streaks have been removed to show the Cowper's glands. *a)* ampulla of deferent duct. *b)* vesicular gland. *c)* body of prostate. *d)* pelvic part of the urethra. *e)* urethral muscle. *f)* right Cowper's gland. *g)* deep streaks of bulbocavernosus muscle.

B. The proximal part of the urethra of the bull (opened ventrally). *a)* ampulla of deferent duct. *b)* vesicular gland. *c)* *vesica* (cut). *d)* *crista urethralis*. *e)* *colliculus seminalis* with *ostia ejaculatoria*. *f)* *frenula colliculi seminalis*. *g)* duct openings from prostate gland. *h)* urethral muscle. *i)* left Cowper's gland. *k)* excretory ducts from Cowper's glands. *l)* mucosal fold of *recessus urogenitalis* (see arrow). *m)* *corpus cavernosum urethrae*.

(*Blom & Christensen, 1947. Skand. Vet. tidskr. 37, 1.*)

openings in the margin of a mucosal fold of the urethra.

Histology and Secretion. The greyish-yellow parenchyma of the prostate and Cowper's glands—in contrast to the vesicular glands—is compact and always looks "dry" on the cut surface. The prostate and Cowper's glands are lobulated, tubular glands and the thick septa between the lobules contain unstriated muscle as in the vesicular glands. These muscles enable the glands to discharge their secretion suddenly (not gradually as in most other glands). The secretory cells are columnar to cubical in shape and often show granules and secretion droplets; the lumina are narrower than in the vesicular glands.

The secretions of all the accessory sex glands are *apocrine, i.e.* the central part of the cytoplasm of cells is transformed to secretion. The "dribblings" from the prepuce of the bull before mounting are secretions from the Cowper's glands (and prostate?). These clear, watery, sperm-free drops are similar to the secretion collected by "incomplete ejaculation" which occurs when a bull is allowed to mount an artificial vagina too quickly without proper preparation. The pH of both fluids is 7.5 to 8.2 (Blom, 1950).

D. Palpation of Accessory Sex Glands in the Bull

The vesicular glands can easily be palpated *per rectum.* A lubricated gloved hand is inserted into the rectum and the cylindrical pelvic part of the urethra located ventrally just within the anus. This cylindrical structure is followed forward for about 10 to 15 cm. (according to size of bull) and the vesicular glands are found diverging at each side above the bladder (Plate IV). They are more or less lobulated and of almost equal size and their consistency depends on the age of the bull and whether or not their secretion is recently discharged. Between the vesicular glands, the two ampullae can be felt as parallel smooth cords about 1 cm. in diameter; they can be moved slightly from side to side on the neck of the bladder. Where the ampullae enter the urethra

posteriorly, the body of the prostate can be felt as a hard smooth prominence lying across the pelvic urethra. The Cowper's glands are usually covered by strong muscle streaks and are therefore not palpable.

VI. URETHRA

The masculine urethra (*canalis urogenitalis*) is the joint excretory canal for urine and semen. Three parts may be distinguished: (*a*) the pelvic part, a 15 to 20 cm. long cylindrical tube enclosed by the powerful urethral muscle and situated on the pelvic floor; (*b*) the bulb of the urethra which designates the part bending around the ischiadic arch; and (*c*) the penile part, belonging to the penis proper.

Prior to ejaculation the sperm concentrate from the ampullae is mixed with the accessory fluids in the pelvic part. Posterior to the neck of the bladder there is a hazelnut-sized prominence (*colliculus seminalis*). On top are the joint orifices of the ampullae and the excretory canals from the vesicular glands (Plate IV). The *colliculus seminalis* consists chiefly of cavernous tissue (tissue filled with wide blood vessels) which closes up the neck of the bladder during ejaculation and so prevents a simultaneous entrance of semen to the bladder. The outlets for the prostate glands are numerous small openings arranged in rows along the walls of the urethra. The two openings of the excretory ducts from the Cowper's glands are situated so that their jets of secretion will flush the distal parts of the urethra free of urine before ejaculation (dribblings).

VII. PENIS AND PREPUCE

A. The Penis

The copulatory organ, the penis, has a twofold function *viz.* the expulsion of urine and the deposition of semen in the reproductive duct system of the female. Before the latter process can occur the organ must become erect. The long cylindrical penis of the bull is of the fibro-elastic type; it is rather rigid even in the non-erect condition. The organ is encircled by a white, dense fibrous tunic, the *tunica albuginea.*

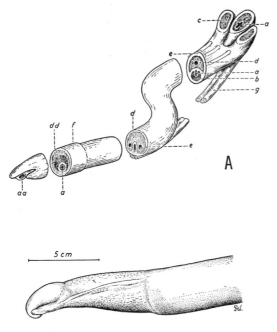

A

5 cm

B

Fig. 2–3.—Penis of the bull.

A, Schematic drawing in four sections. *a)* urethra. *aa)* orifice of urethra. *b) corpus cavernosum urethrae.* *c)* right *crus penis. d) corpus cavernosum penis. dd) corpus fibrosum. e) tunica albuginea. f)* epithelium lining the free part of penis. *g)* retractor penis muscle. (*Adapted from Krölling & Grau, 1960: Lehrbuch der Histologie und vergleichenden mikroskopischen Anatomie der Haustiere,* 10th ed., *Berlin, courtesy Parey.*)

B, Anterior extremity of penis, left view. Note the external urethral orifice. (Original drawing by *Poul H. Winther.*)

The penis consists of a root, a body and a free extremity terminating in the glans penis. The root of the penis is attached to the pelvis by two lateral branches, the right and left *crus penis* (Fig. 2–3). The body contains three elongated erectile "rods" or cavernous bodies which lie parallel to each other. The two dorsally situated rods (*corpora cavernosa penis*) originate within the lateral branches of the penis, they unite to form one cavernous body which, towards the free anterior part of the penis, changes to a central fibrous body (*corpus fibrosum*). The lower structure (the *corpus cavernosum urethrae*) encloses and follows the penile part of the urethra. These erectile structures contain cavernous tissue, which becomes distended with blood during sexual excitement and stiffens the fibro-elastic penis without much enlargement. The erection is to some extent due to the temporary inablity of blood to drain from the cavernous rods of the penis. The greater part of the body of the penis is arranged in an *S*-shaped curve or sigmoid flexure, so that the length of the non-erect penis is "reduced" by about one-third. During erection the penis of the

bull protrudes when the sigmoid flexure is completely straightened out. The free terminal part of the penis, ending in the *glans penis*, is pointed and is slightly twisted along the longitudinal axis and on the left side of the tip forms a groove in which lies the external urethral orifice. The two narrow bands of the penis retractor muscle originate from each side above the anus and run down and forward along the lower curve of the body of the penis. They are inserted on the surface of the organ near its free extremity, serving to retract the penis into the sheath after ejaculation (Hafez, 1960) and keep it fixed in this position in the non-erect state.

B. The Prepuce

The prepuce or sheath (*praeputium*) in the bull is long and narrow. It is developed as an invagination of the skin and completely incloses the free extremity of the retracted penis. The orifice of the prepuce is surrounded by the long and tough preputial hairs which form a characteristic tuft. The opening is placed about 5 cm. behind the

Table 2-1.—Comparative Anatomy of Male Reproductive Organs in Adult Farm Mammals

Organs		Bull	Ram	Boar	Stallion
Testis + Epididymis	measurements (cm.)	14 × 7 × 7	10 × 6 × 6	13 × 7 × 7	11 × 6 × 4
	weight-single (gm.)	300–500	250–300	250–300	200–300
	location	vertical	vertical	nearly horizontal	horizontal
	epididymal duct length (meter)	40–50	45–55	55–65	70–85
Accessory Sexual Glands	Ampullae[1] length × thickness (cm.)	14 × 1.2	7 × 0.6	missing (only a few glands scattered in the wall)	24 × 2
	Vesicular glands[2] structure	compact	compact	compact	elongated piriform sacs
	Vesicular glands[2] measurements (cm.)	14 × 4 × 3	4 × 2 × 1	13 × 7 × 4	13 × 5 × 5
	Prostate body[3] measurements (cm.)	3 × 1 × 1	missing	3 × 3 × 1	center: 3 × 1.5 × 0.5
	Prostate disseminate[4]	12–14 cm. long layer dorsal 1–1.5 cm. thick ventral 0.2–0.3 cm. thick	formed as in the bull	0.4 cm. thick layer	two lobes: 8 × 5 × 1
	Cowper's glands[5] size	walnut-size	hazelnut-size	highly developed: 17 × 3 × 3 cm.	walnut-size
Penis	Type	fibro-elastic	fibro-elastic	fibro-elastic (spiral)	vascular-muscular
	Total length (post mortem) (cm.)	100	35	55	90
	Diameter-erected (cm.)	3	2	2	10
	Sigmoid flexure	post-scrotal	post-scrotal	pre-scrotal	missing

[1] ampullae ductus deferentis [2] glandulae vesiculares [3] corpus prostatae [4] pars disseminata prostatae [5] glandulae bulbourethrales

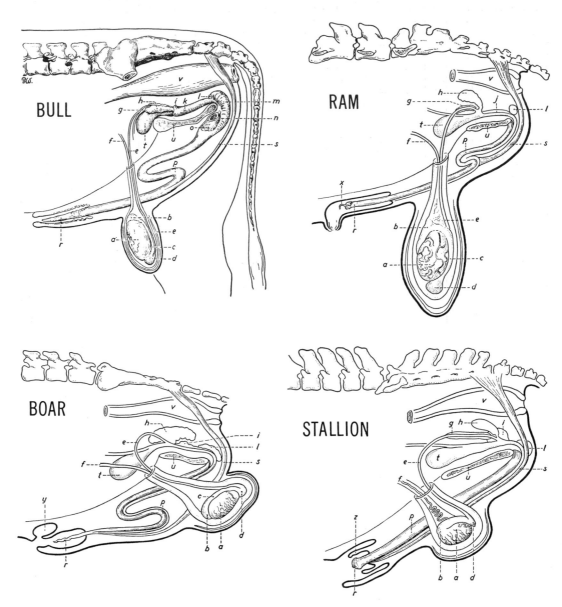

Fig. 2–4.—Comparative anatomy of the male reproductive organs of farm mammals.

a) left testis. *b*) head of epididymis. *c*) body of epididymis. *d*) tail of epididymis. *e*) deferent duct *f*) spermatic vessels and nerves. *g*) ampulla of deferent duct. *h*) vesicular gland. *i*) body of prostate. *j*) prostate disseminate (body is missing in the ram). *k*) pelvic part of the urogenital canal. *l*) Cowper's gland. *m*) bulbocavernosus muscle. *n*) left crus of the penis (cut). *o*) ischiocavernosus muscle (cut). *p*) penis. *r*) free part of the penis. *s*) retractor penis muscle. *t*) bladder. *u*) symphysis of pelvis. *v*) rectum. *x*) the urethral process (in ram). *y*) preputial pouch (in boar). *z*) fold of the internal prepuce (in stallion).

(Bull, adapted from Blom & Christensen, 1947. Skand. Vet. tidskr. 37, 1. Ram, boar & stallion, adapted from Bielanski, 1962, Rozrod zwie rzat gospodarskich–Reproduction of Farm Animals, Warsaw, courtesy of P.W.R.i.L.)

navel and is usually only large enough to admit one finger. The preputial cavity is 35 to 40 cm. long and 3 to 4 cm. in diameter. The lining mucous membrane is greatly folded and contains numerous coiled tubular glands producing a fatty secretion. This secretion, mixed with cast epithelial cells and bacteria, forms a thick and often ill-smelling product called *smegma praeputii.*

VIII. REPRODUCTIVE ORGANS OF THE RAM, BOAR AND STALLION

The comparative anatomy of the male reproductive organs are shown for the four species of farm mammals (Table 2–1, Fig. 2–4).

A. The Ram

The reproductive organs of the ram resemble those of the bull but the testes weight in relation to body weight is much larger. The scrotum is shorter than in the bull, and has no proper neck. The skin of the scrotum is usually well covered with wool. The prostate is entirely disseminate. The glans penis has a 3 to 4 cm. long twisted filiform appendage, the *processus urethrae,* containing the terminal part of the urethra. This filiform body rotates rapidly during ejaculation and sprays the semen around the external uterine opening.

B. The Boar

The scrotum is just below the anus and is not so well defined as in the other mammals. The testes are very large but comparatively soft, and are nearly horizontal in the scrotum. The deferent duct lacks a distinct ampulla. The vesicular and Cowper's glands are very large and dense. The latter are nearly cylindrical and lie astride the pelvic part of the urethra (Nickel, 1954). The penis is fibro-elastic and its distal free part is corkscrew-shaped. The sigmoid flexure is placed anterior to the scrotum. The prepuce has a narrow orifice with stiff hairs and in the upper wall of the preputial cavity is an opening into an ovoid pouch, the preputial diverticulum. The preputial pouch contains a mixture of decomposing

urine and macerated epithelial cells which has a characteristic and very unpleasant odor. This is responsible for the strong sex odor of boars which permeates their meat and gives it a disagreeable taste.

C. The Stallion

The scrotum is somewhat asymmetrical and less pendulous than in the bull. In the relaxed state the testes lie horizontally, but when the cremester muscles are retracted the testes are almost vertical. The ampullae of the deferent ducts are highly developed (Mann *et al.*, 1956). The vesicular glands are elongated piriform sacs; their mucous membrane is thin and folded in the form of a network. The prostate consists of two lateral lobes and a connecting center (*isthmus*). The penis is of the vascular type containing plenty of muscular tissue but without a sigmoid flexure; it can readily be palpated as a smooth cylinder with the urethra as a compressible tube on its lower surface. In the non-erect condition the penis is flaccid and is withdrawn into the prepuce. On erection it increases 50 per cent or more in length and diameter. The prepuce has a secondary fold within the praeputial cavity constituting the "internal prepuce" in which the anterior part of the penis lies (Fig. 2–4). The glans penis is surrounded by a prominent denticulated margin, and the mushroom-like formation can be readily seen when a stallion withdraws his penis after service. The urethra protrudes as a 2.5 cm. long tube, the urethral process, in a depression (*fossa glandis*) on the front surface of the glans penis.

REFERENCES

Bialy, G. & Smith, V. R. (1958). Number of spermatozoa in the different parts of the reproductive tract of the bull. *J. Dairy Sci.,* **41,** 1781–1786.

Blom, E. (1944). On the occurrence in bull sperm of certain "medusa-formations" derived from the epithelium of the efferent ducts of the testis. *Acta Path. Microbiol. Scand.,* **21,** 713–720.

——— (1945). Spontaneous detachment of the galea capitis in spermia of bull and stallion. *Skand Vet. Tidsskr.,* **35,** 779–789.

——— (1950). *On the Evaluation of Bull Semen with Special Reference to its Employment for Artificial Insemination.* Diss., Copenhagen, Mortensen, pp. 223.

BLOM, E. & CHRISTENSEN, N. O. (1958). Cysts and cyst-like formations (inter alia spermiostasis) in the genitals of the bull. *Yearbook Royal Vet. Agricult. Coll.*, 101–133.

HAFEZ, E. S. E. (1960). Analysis of ejaculatory reflexes and sex drive in the bull. *Cornell Vet.*, **50**, 384–411.

KNUDSEN, O. (1954). Cytomorphological investigations into the spermiocytogenesis of bulls with normal fertility and bulls with acquired disturbances in spermiogenesis. *Diss., Acta. Path. Microbiol. Scand. Suppl. 101*, pp. 79.

MANEELY, R. B. (1959). Epididymal structure and function: a historical and critical review. *Acta Zool.* **40**, 1–21.

MANN, T., LEONE, E. & POLGE, C. (1956). The composition of the stallion's semen. *J. Endocrin.* **13**, 279–290.

NICANDER, L. (1958). Studies on the regional histology and cytochemistry of the ductus epididymidis in stallions, rams and bulls. *Acta Morph. Neerlando-scand.*, **1**, 337–362.

NICKEL, R. (1954). Zur Topographie der akzessorischen Geschlechtsdrüsen bei Schwein, Rind und Pferd. (On the topography of the accessory sex glands in the boar, bull and stallion). *Tierärztl. Umschau*, **9**, 386–387.

WILLETT, E. L. & OHMS, J. I. (1957). Measurements of testicular size and its relation to production of spermatozoa by bulls. *J. Dairy Sci.*, **40**, 1559–1569.

QUESTIONS

1. Draw a diagram of the male reproductive organs of one species of farm mammals.
2. Identify the following anatomical structures: Cowper's gland; *tunica dartos*; Wolffian duct; *crus penis*; urethral process; *fossa glandis*; retractor penis muscle; efferent ducts; vesicular gland; *colliculus seminalis*.
3. Give a full account of the urethra.
4. Discuss the functions of each of the accessory sex glands.
5. What are the major anatomical differences between the accessory sex glands of the bull and the boar?
6. Describe the anatomical and histological characteristics of the epididymis. Give illustrations.
7. Explain the anatomical and physiological mechanisms involved in (a) transport of sperm from the seminiferous tubules to the penis, (b) mixing of sperm with seminal plasma, (c) preventing the discharge of urine during ejaculation of semen.
8. Explain why the term vesicular gland is preferable to the old name: seminal vesicle.
9. Discuss which parts of the reproductive system can easily be palpated in the living bull.
10. (a) Discuss the functions of the scrotum. (b) Give a full account of the preputial pouch in the boar.

Chapter 3

Physiology of Mammalian Semen

By I. G. WHITE

SEMEN is the male secretion, containing the sperm or reproductive cells. It is normally ejaculated into the female reproductive tract during copulation, but can be readily collected and has been intensively studied in recent years because of its importance in artificial insemination and in problems of infertility.

Semen is composed of two parts, the *sperm* suspended in a liquid or semi-gelatinous medium, known as the *seminal plasma*, in much the same way as blood consists of a cellular and plasma fraction. The sperm are produced in the testes but the seminal plasma is the mixed secretion of the accessory sex glands *e.g.* the epididymis, vesicular glands and prostate; the epididymis also stores the sperm prior to ejaculation. Both sperm production by the testes and the secretory activity of the male accessory glands are controlled by hormones carried to them in the blood stream (see Chapter 1). The testes are regulated by pituitary FSH and LH and, in turn, produce testosterone which controls the development and secretion of the accessory glands.

This chapter will be concerned primarily with the semen of the bull, ram, boar and stallion. The anatomy (see Chapter 2), and hence the relative contribution of the accessory glands to the seminal plasma, varies greatly with the species and it is not surprising, therefore, to find considerable differences in both the volume and composition of the semen. Bull and ram semen have a small volume and a high sperm density which gives it a creamy appearance; stallion and boar semen is a much more voluminous whitish fluid with a lower sperm density (Table 8–3). Another major difference is that ram and bull semen is normally ejaculated instantaneously, but stallion and boar semen is emitted over a period of several minutes. Boar and stallion semen can be readily collected in *pre-sperm*, *sperm-rich* and *post-sperm* fractions. The post-sperm fraction is usually gelatinous, however, gelatinous material may also be sometimes present in the pre-sperm fraction. The watery *post-coital penis drip* or tail end sample discharged by the stallion on dismounting from the mare is part of the post-sperm fraction.

I. PROPERTIES AND CONSTITUENTS OF SEMINAL PLASMA

The chemical and physical properties of semen (Mann 1954, 1959, 1960, White, 1958) are largely determined by the seminal

(57)

Table 3–1.—Chemical Composition of Whole Semen.† Average Values (mg./100 cm.³ of Semen Unless Otherwise Indicated) Are Given with the Range in Brackets

(*Adapted from White, 1958. Anim. Breed. Abstr., 26, 109.*)

Constituent or Property	Bull		Ram		Boar		Stallion	
pH	6.9	(6.4–7.8)	6.9	(5.9–7.3)	7.5	(7.3–7.8)	7.4	(7.2–7.8)
Water, g./100 cm.³	90	(87–95)	85		95	(94–98)	98	
Sodium	260	(150–370)*	100		650	(290–850)	70	
Potassium	170	(50–390)*	70		240	(80–380)	60	
Calcium	37	(24–60)	9		5	(2–6)	20	
Magnesium	8	(0–18)	3		11	(5–14)	3	
Chloride	180	(110–290)*	86		330	(260–430)	270	(90–450)
Fructose	530	(150–900)	250		13	(3–50)	2	(0–6)
Sorbitol		(10–140)	72	(26–120)	12	(6–18)	40	(20–60)
Citric acid	720	(340–1150)	140	(110–260)	130	(30–330)	26	(8–53)
Inositol	35	(25–46)*	12	(7–14)	530	(380–630)	30	(20–47)
Glycerylphosphoryl choline (GPC)	350	(100–500)*	1650	(1100–2100)		(110–240)		(40–100)
Ergothioneine	Nil		Nil			(6–23)		(40–110)
Protein g./100 cm.³	6.8		5.0		3.7		1.0	
Plasmalogen		(30–90)	380					

*Analysis of seminal plasma rather than whole semen
†Volume and sperm concentration are given in Table 8–3

plasma which constitutes its bulk, particularly in the boar and stallion (Table 3–1).

A. pH, Osmotic Pressure and Inorganic Ions

Seminal plasma has a pH of about 7.0 and an osmotic pressure similar to blood (*i.e.* equivalent to 0.9 per cent sodium chloride).

The inorganic ions, *e.g.* Na, K, Mg, Ca, Cl, common to other body fluids also occur in semen and some, particularly potassium, can influence the viability of the sperm. Semen also contains phosphate and bicarbonate buffers but they may not maintain a neutral pH in face of the large amount of lactic acid which can be formed by ram and bull sperm from the fructose present in the seminal plasma (see Section IV).

B. Organic Substances

Seminal plasma is of great biochemical interest as it contains some unusual organic compounds (Fig. 3–1) (*e.g. fructose, citric acid, sorbitol, inositol, glycerylphosphoryl-*

choline, and *ergothioneine*) which are not found elsewhere in the body in such high concentrations. These substances are produced by the various accessory glands in response to testosterone from the testes and their estimation in ejaculated semen, or directly in the glands, can be used as an index of accessory gland function. Thus after castration, each constituent disappears from the seminal plasma but reappears after injecting testosterone into the animal.

Fructose, Sorbitol, Citric Acid and Inositol. In the bull, ram, boar and stallion, all four substances are produced by the vesicular glands, although to a different degree.

Fructose is the sugar found in bull, ram and boar semen and is derived from blood glucose. Stallion semen contains only traces of fructose and none is found in the semen of some species, *e.g.* the dog. Mammalian semen does not contain glucose. The fructose concentration of ram and bull semen is particularly high and in these species it is an important nutrient for the sperm which break it down (see Section IV). The occur-

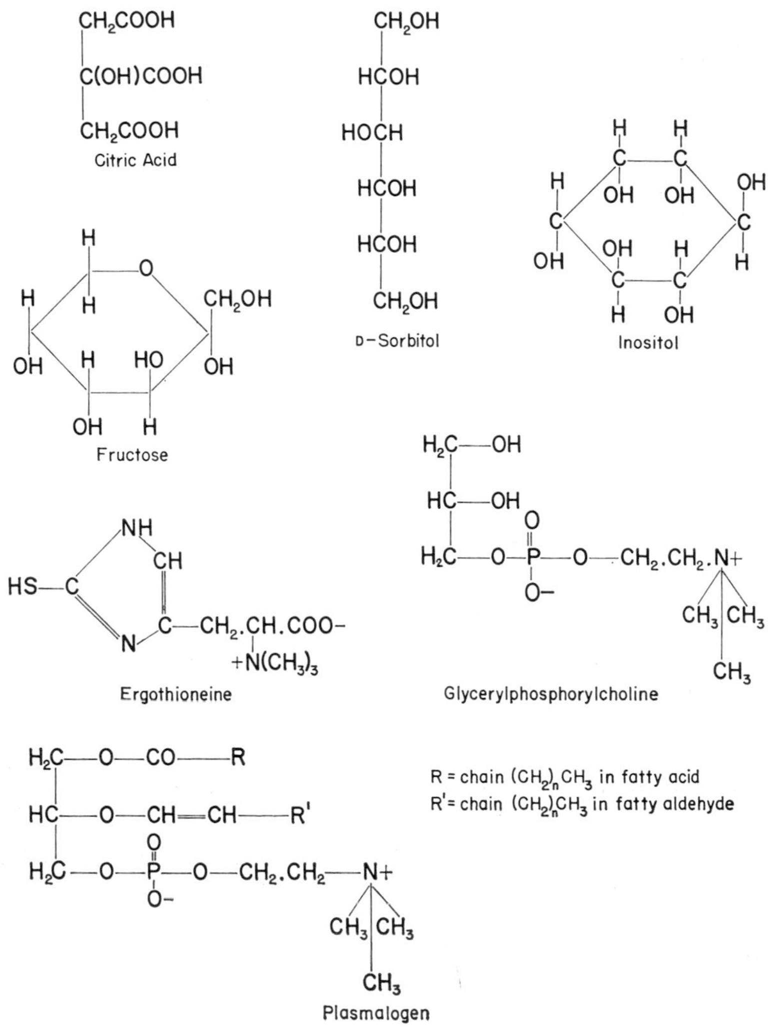

FIG. 3–1.—Formulae of some semen constituents.

rence of fructose, rather than glucose, in semen is puzzling since glucose is quite as well utilized by sperm. Sorbitol, a sugar alcohol related to fructose, is also present in semen and can be oxidized to fructose by the sperm and thus also serves as a nutrient.

Bull semen contains the highest concentration of citric acid; however, it is not utilized by sperm and is of no importance to them as an energy source. Inositol is one of the major constituents of boar semen, but like citric acid, is not metabolized by sperm.

Glycerylphosphorylcholine (GPC) and Ergo-

thioneine. The nitrogenous base, GPC, occurs in high concentrations in the seminal plasma of all the larger farm animals and is produced chiefly by the epididymis. Sperm are incapable of attacking GPC as such, but an enzyme in the secretions of the female genital tract can break it down into simpler units that sperm can utilize. GPC may, therefore, act as a source of energy for sperm in the female tract (White & Wallace, 1961).

Ergothioneine, a sulfur-containing nitrogenous base, occurs in appreciable quantities only in stallion and boar semen. It is

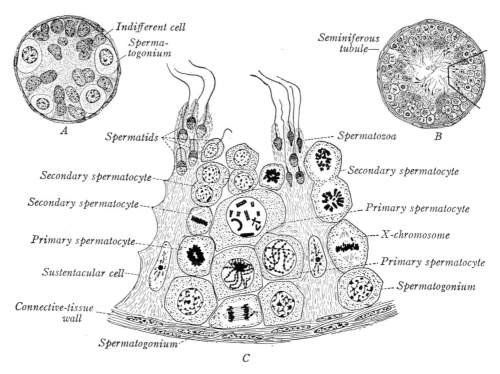

Fig. 3-2.—Drawing of a tranverse section through a seminiferous tubule of a mammal. A, Newborn (× 400); B, Adult (× 115); C, detail of area outlined in B, (× 900). Note that the spermatogonia lie against the basement membrane of the connective-tissue wall and that the primary and secondary spermatocytes, spermatids and sperm—in that order—form layers extending to the lumen of the tubule. The cytoplasm of the large sustenacular or Stertoli cells is in intimate contact with all the other cells. (From Arey, 1954. Developmental Anatomy, Philadelphia, courtesy of W. B. Saunders Co.)

formed chiefly in the ampullae of the stallion, which are particularly well developed, and the vesicular glands of the boar.

The Function of Seminal Plasma. The primary function of the seminal plasma is to act as a vehicle for conveying sperm from the male to the female reproductive duct system. It is well adapted for this role as in most species it constitutes a buffered medium containing either a source of energy directly available to sperm (*i.e.* fructose and sorbitol) or one that can be unlocked on mixing with the female secretions (*i.e.* GPC). The function of the other unusual constituents of seminal plasma and the significance of the great variation in the volume of semen produced by different species is not known.

Sperm taken from the epididymis are fertile on artificial insemination and some workers question whether the secretions of the accessory glands, or at least those beyond the epididymis, have any importance in reproduction other than flushing the sperm into the female genital tract. The importance of the seminal plasma as a medium for the sperm after ejaculation into the female genital tract will, of course, depend upon the extent to which they remain in contact.

II. FORMATION AND DEVELOPMENT OF SPERM

Sperm are formed in the testes, a process known as *spermatogenesis*, but undergo further maturation in the epididymis where they are stored until ejaculation takes place.

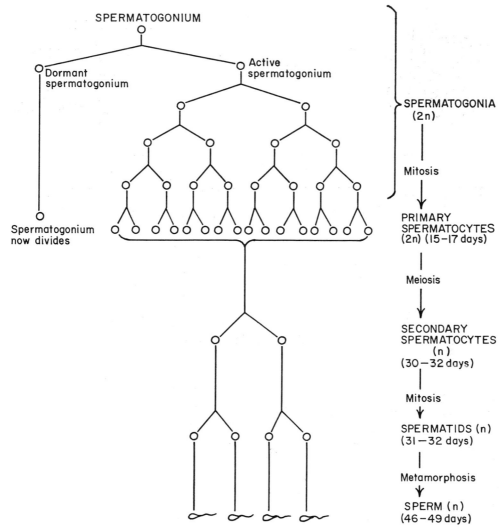

SPERMATOGONIUM

Dormant spermatogonium

Active spermatogonium

SPERMATOGONIA (2n)

Mitosis

Spermatogonium now divides

PRIMARY SPERMATOCYTES (2n) (15–17 days)

Meiosis

SECONDARY SPERMATOCYTES (n) (30–32 days)

Mitosis

SPERMATIDS (n) (31–32 days)

Metamorphosis

SPERM (n) (46–49 days)

FIG. 3–3.—Diagram of spermatogenesis in the ram. The sequence of events is probably similar in the bull but may differ slightly in other mammals including the boar and stallion. The chromosome number and the time from the start of the division of the original spermatogonium are given in brackets. (*Adapted from Ortavant, 1959. In Reproduction in Domestic Animals, H. H. Cole & P. T. Cupps, eds., Vol. 2, New York, courtesy of Academic Press.*)

A. Spermatogenesis

Sperm are formed within the seminiferous tubules from spermatogonia or sperm mother cells which lie on the basement membrane (Fig. 3–2). The process is complex and involves cell division and differentiation, during which the number of chromosomes is halved and both nuclear and cytoplasmic components of the cell are extensively reorganized (Ortavant, 1959; Bishop & Walton, 1960*a*, Knudsen & Bryne, 1960).

1. FORMATION OF SPERM FROM SPERMATOGONIA IN THE TESTES

Spermatogenesis in the ram is summarized in Figure 3–3; the process, which can be divided into four phases, is probably similar in the bull but may differ slightly in the boar and some mammals. The developing sperm cells progressively migrate from the basement membrane to the lumen of the seminiferous tubule. During this time, however, they remain in contact with the Sertoli

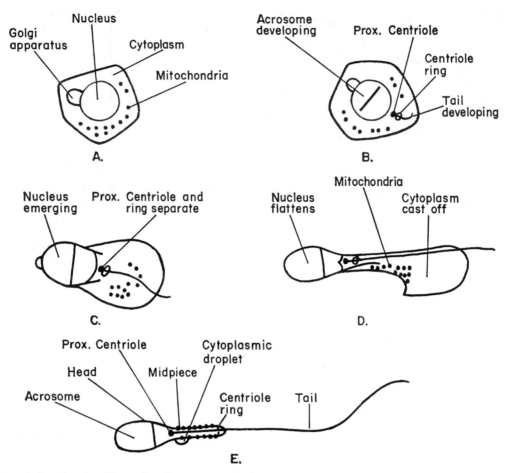

FIG. 3–4.—Drawing illustrating the metamorphosis of a spermatid into a sperm (spermiogenesis) in the ram. The process is similar in other mammals including the bull, boar and stallion. (*A*) the acrosome arising from the Golgi apparatus; (*B*) the tail developing from the centriole which separates into a proximal and distal (ring) structure; (*C*) the nucleus emerging from the cytoplasm and flattening to form the head; (*D*) the casting off of the cytoplasm leaving only a droplet and the mitochondria that migrate to the midpiece; (*E*) final stage. (*Adapted from Clermont, original and Ortavant, 1959. In Reproduction in Domestic Animals, H. H. Cole & P. T. Cupps, eds., Vol. 2, New York, courtesy of Academic Press.*)

or sustentacular (supporting) cell cytoplasm which probably nourishes them.

Phase I. (15 to 17 days) *Mitotic division* of spermatogonia, each into a dormant spermatogonium, to ensure continuity of spermatogenesis, and an active one which divides four times giving more spermatogonia and finally 16 primary spermatocytes.

Phase II. (about 15 days) *Meiotic division* of the primary spermatocytes during which the number of chromosomes is halved.

Phase III. (a few hours) Mitotic division of the secondary spermatocytes into spermatids.

Phase IV. (about 15 days) Metamorphosis of the spermatids into sperm without further division. This involves radical alteration in cellular form during which most of the cytoplasm—including ribonucleic acid, water and glycogen—is lost. The spermatid is a fairly large rounded cell whereas the sperm is a compact elongated motile cell consisting essentially of a head and tail (see Section III). The *Golgi apparatus* of the spermatid gives rise to the anterior cap or *acrosome* of the sperm and the *mitochondria* of the cytoplasm congregate in the tail which grows out from the *centriole* of the spermatid

(Fig. 3–4). The sperm, 64 from one original spermatogonium, are finally released from the Sertoli cytoplasm and pass into the lumen of the seminiferous tubule.

After about 15 days the dormant spermatogonia commences to divide in a similar manner so that the process repeats itself indefinitely. Phases I, II and III are often grouped together under the name of *spermatocytogenesis* and Phase IV is called *spermiogenesis*.

Production of X and Y Chromosome-Bearing Sperm. The genes determining sex are carried on a pair of chromosomes which in the male mammal are not alike. In the Phase I mitotic division, each chromosome divides longitudinally. However, in the Phase II meiotic division involved in the formation of secondary spermatocytes from primary ones, the chromosomes become paired and one chromosome from each pair goes to each of the newly formed cells. Thus the secondary spermatocytes and subsequent cells only have half the number of chromosomes characteristic of the species and the sperm are of two types, one carries an X chromosome and the other a Y chromosome.

2. THE CYCLE AND WAVE OF THE SEMINIFEROUS EPITHELIUM

Examination of transverse sections of seminiferous tubules shows that the cells are arranged in concentric layers. The cells of any particular layer being at the same stage of development. Thus one finds, proceeding from the basement membrane to the lumen layers of spermatogonia, spermatocytes and spermatids (Fig. 3–2). Up to five types of spermatogonia may be found, corresponding to the five generations of spermatogonia in Figure 3–3. Four successive types of primary spermatocytes can be seen during their long meiotic division into secondary spermatocytes and several types of developing spermatids are also easily distinguishable (Fig. 3–4).

If any one area of the seminiferous epithelium is considered, it is seen to consist of synchronously developing cells and their parallel evolution into sperm proceeds according to an ever repeating pattern. Thus spermatids at a given stage in their develop-

ment are always found associated with the same types of spermatocytes and spermatogonia. As a consequence a certain number of *cellular associations* arise which keep repeating themselves indefinitely in an orderly and regular manner. This succession of cellular associations would be seen by an observer if he could watch one section of the living tubule over a long period.

The number of cellular associations or stages identified by different workers is variable. Ortavant (1959) has defined 8 in the ram, bull and boar based on the meiotic division, variations in shape of the spermatid nucleus and the release of sperm into the lumen of the seminiferous tubules. Clemont & Leblond recognize 12 stages using the development of the acrosome as a criterion.

A complete series of these cellular associations, which follow one another in any given area of the seminiferous epithelium, is known as the *cycle of the seminiferous epithelium*. The duration of the cycle is the time required for the appearance of a complete series of cellular associations (*i.e.* the time between two successive appearances of the same cellular association) in one given area of the tubule. It is the same throughout the testis and is about 10 days; approximately 5 cycles are required for the complete evolution of a spermatogonium into a free sperm in the ram. The cycle of the seminiferous epithelium is a time concept and should not be confused with the distribution of the various cellular associations along the tubules which also follow in regular succession. The wave of the seminiferous epithelium does not, however, rigidly reproduce in space the constantly repeating cyclic changes occurring in time in any area of the seminiferous epithelium.

Estimation of Duration of Spermatogenesis. Radioactive phosphorus (P^{32}) like the naturally occurring element, is taken up from the bloodstream by the testis and becomes incorporated into the deoxyribonucleic acid (DNA) of the young primary spermatocyte, but after this no further exchange of phosphorus occurs. It is possible, therefore, to estimate the duration of spermatogenesis by injecting P^{32} into animals and determining the time required for the labelled sperm to appear in the lumen of the seminiferous tubules. This takes about 30 days in the ram and it can be calculated that the total time for spermatogenesis is about 49 days. In the bull, labelled sperm apparently take longer (*i.e.* about 40 days) to be liberated into the lumen of the tubules. The technique known as radio-autography is used for detecting labelled phosphorus in the seminiferous tubules. When thin slices are fixed and placed in contact with a photographic emulsion the presence of the radioactive phosphorus is indicated by dark tracks on developing the films.

B. Passage of Sperm Through the Epididymis

Sperm pass quickly from the lumen of the seminiferous tubules into the rete testis and via the *vasa efferentia* into the head of the epididymis. Studies using sperm labelled by injecting P³² indicate that they take 2 to 3 weeks to pass through the epididymis to the tail where they are stored.

Maturation of Sperm in the Epididymis. During their passage through the epididymis sperm are believed to mature or ripen. The *cytoplasmic droplet* which is attached to the proximal region of the sperm mid-piece at the head of the epididymis moves distally so that in the tail of the epididymis the droplet is attached to the distal end of the midpiece. Normally in ejaculated semen the cytoplasmic droplet is completely detached from the sperm and the presence of attached droplets is taken as a sign of their immaturity, particularly when placed proximally.

As sperm pass through the epididymis a shrinkage and dehydration of the protoplasm occurs. There is apparently also an increase in their fertilizing capacity and, in some species at least, the sperm acquire the potential to move.

Storage of Sperm and Their Ejaculation. Sperm are able to survive for long periods in the epididymis. Rabbit sperm, for example, are still fertile after being maintained in the ligated epididymis, at near body tempera-

ture, for 38 days. This is usually attributed to the belief that sperm are immotile, or nearly so, in the epididymis and that their metabolism is in a quiescent stage (Salisbury, 1956). There is little or no fructose or other reducing sugar in the epididymal fluid and the most quantitatively important constituent is GPC. Sperm are not, however, able to utilize GPC as an energy source, unless it first comes in contact with the secretions of the female tract, and the nature of the substrate for any basal metabolism of sperm stored in the epididymis is unknown.

Although the tail of the epididymis constitutes only 30 per cent of its total length, the volume available for storing sperm is much greater in this part, since the diameter of the lumen is greater than elsewhere. If an animal does not ejaculate regularly, sperm will eventually degenerate in the tail of the epididymis and at any one time the sperm population will represent a balance between the newly formed sperm arriving from the testes and those degenerating. This should be borne in mind when evaluating semen. If an animal has not ejaculated for some time before taking the test sample, one may well come to the false conclusion that the animal produces poor quality semen. A second sample taken a little later is a more accurate guide.

At ejaculation sperm suspended in epididymal secretion are passed forward from the tail of the epididymis down the *vasa deferentia* into the urethra, probably as a result of successive contractions of the *vasa deferentia*, epididymis and *vasa efferentia*. The secretion of the accessory glands is emptied into the urethra and the mixture, forming semen, emitted via the penile urethra. In the ram and bull there is a complete mixing of the seminal components at ejaculation, in the stallion and boar, the semen is emitted in fractions corresponding to the secretions of the different parts of the reproductive system.

III. STRUCTURE AND MOTILITY OF SPERM

Sperm were first studied nearly 300 years ago by the famous Dutch microscopist,

PLATE V

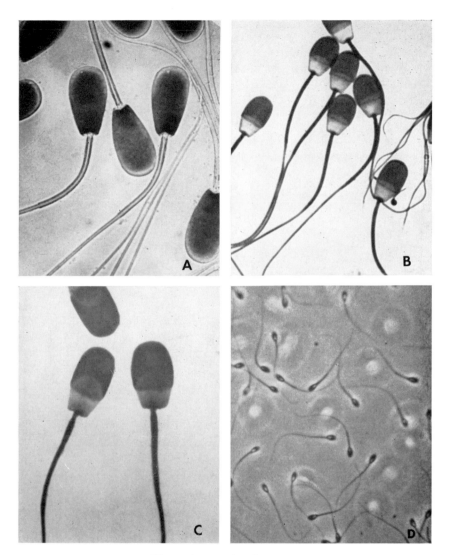

Photomicrographs of sperm.

A, Bull sperm in ultraviolet light showing the strong adsorpton of radiation by the nuclei and in the nucleus ($\times$ 2,000 approx.). (*From Hancock 1952. J. Exp. Biol., 29, 445.*)

B, Ram sperm ($\times$ 1,000 approx.). (*Onderstepoort Laboratories, original.*)

C, Boar sperm (Giemsa stain; $\times$ 2,500). (*From Hancock, 1947. J. Roy. Microscop. Soc., 76, 84.*)

D. Stallion sperm ($\times$ 300 approx.). (*Nishikawa, original.*)

PLATE VI

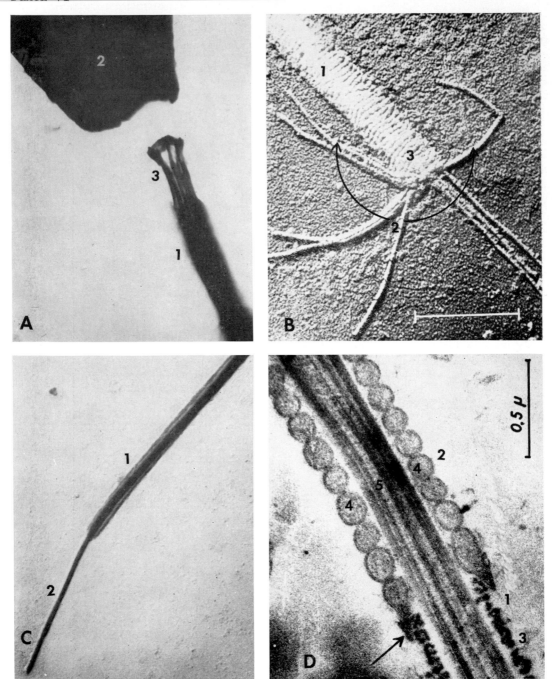

Electronmicrographs of sperm

A, A dead boar sperm showing the mid-piece (*1*) detached from the head (*2*). The fibers (*3*) running through the mid-piece are visible in the region where the mid-piece is normally implanted into the head. (× approx. 12,000). (*From Hancock, 1957. J. Roy. Microscop. Soc. LXXVI, 84.*)

B, The broken main-piece (*1*) of a bull sperm showing some of the fibers (*2*) protruding out from the end (*3*); |—| indicates 1μ. (*From Bretschneider & Iterson, 1947. Proc. Koninkl. Nederland, Akad. Wetenschap. 50, 88.*)

C, The terminal region of the main-piece (*1*) of a boar sperm tapering into the very thin end-piece (*2*). The end-piece, unlike the main-piece, is not surrounded by a protein sheath. (× approx. 12,000). (*From Hancock 1957. J. Roy. Microscop. Soc. LXXVI, 84.*)

D, A longitudinal section through the junction (*1*) of the mid-piece (*2*) and the main-piece (*3*) of a bull sperm. Note the mitochondrial sheath (*4*) surrounding the fibers (*5*) of the axial filament in the mid-piece. The distal centriole or ring is indicated by the arrow. (*From Blom, 1960. Nord. Vet. Med. 12, 261.*)

Antoni Van Leeuwenhoek. The microscopes available in his time were very crude and early pictures of sperm were fanciful and included alimentary tracts, other organs, and even complete little embryos. In recent years our knowledge of the fine structure of sperm has increased enormously due chiefly to the development of the electron microscope (Hancock, 1957; Bishop & Austin, 1957; Fawcett, 1958; Bishop & Walton, 1960a), but needless to say, many of the bizarre notions of the pioneers have not been confirmed!

The sperm is a highly specialized and condensed cell, which does not grow or divide. It consists essentially of a head, containing the paternal hereditary material, and a tail which provides a means of locomotion. It plays no part in the physiology of the animal that produces it and is solely concerned with fertilizing an ovum and thus producing new individuals of the kind from which it arose. Sperm lack the large cytoplasm characteristic of most cells, the volume of a bull sperm, for instance, is only about one twenty-thousandth of an ovum to which it is equivalent in hereditary significance (see Chapter 6). On the other hand, sperm are produced in much greater numbers and a good bull ejaculate contains about 10,000 million sperm which is sufficient to inseminate 1000 cows.

The normal sperm of farm mammals are 50 to 60 μ (micron) long and are similar in appearance and size (Fig. 3–5, Plates V & VI). Some abnormally shaped sperm are, however, frequently encountered in all species (see Chapter 12).

A. The Head

In the farm mammals the head is a flattened ovoid structure (approx. $8 \times 4 \times 1\mu$) made up chiefly of a nucleus covered anteriorly by the *acrosome* or *galea-capitis* and posteriorly by the *post-nuclear cap*. The head of the sperm of some mammals has quite an exotic shape; the rat, for instance, has a hook-shaped head and a well defined pronged structure—the *perforatorium*—lies at the apex beneath the acrosome.

The nucleus is composed of deoxyribonucleic acid (DNA) conjugated with protein.

The genetic information carried by the sperm is in some way "coded" and stored in the DNA molecule, which is made up basically of many *nucleotides* (Fig. 3–6). Each consists of 1 molecule of phosphoric acid, 1 molecule of the sugar, *deoxyribose*, and 1 molecule of a purine or pyrimidine base; *adenine, guanine, cytosine*, or *thymine*. In mammals the hereditary properties of the sperm nucleus include the determination of the sex of the embryo. As a result of the reduction division which occurs during spermatogenesis (see Section II), sperm contain only half the amount of DNA present in the somatic cells of the same species, and two kinds of sperm are formed; those that carry the X chromosome produce female embryos and those that carry the Y chromosome produce males (see Chapter 7). The two kinds of sperm cannot be distinguished morphologically, but attempts have been made to separate them by electrophoresis and countercurrent centrifuging with the aim of controlling the *sex ratio*. The production of either female or male offspring at will, on artificially inseminating the appropriate sperm, would be a tremendous advantage, in for instance the dairying industry, but so far little success has been achieved.

The acrosome forms a cap-like structure over the anterior of the nucleus and is probably composed of an inner and outer layer: it arises from the Golgi apparatus of the spermatid as it differentiates into a sperm and apparently has some vital role in fertilization, since bull sperm with a hereditary deformity of the acrosome are sterile. The acrosome consists of protein-bound polysaccharide, composed of fucose, mannose, galactose and hexosamine it is responsible for the periodic acid—Schiff (PAS) staining reaction of sperm.

B. The Tail

The long (40 to 50 μ) thin tail is differentiated into three parts, *mid-piece, main-piece* and *end-piece*, and arises from the spermatid centriole during spermatogenesis. It propels the sperm by two-dimensional waves which pass distally along it like a whip-lash.

5

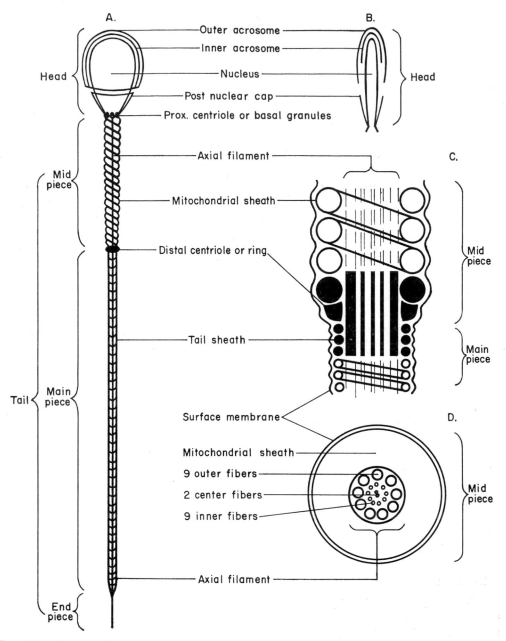

Fig. 3–5.—Diagram illustrating the tentative structure of a typical ungulate sperm. (*A*) General view, (× 2,700 approx.).

(*B*) Longitudinal section through the head in a plane at right angles to the paper (× 2,700 approx.).

(*C*) Longitudinal section at junction of mid-piece and main-piece, (× 30,000 approx.).

(*D*) Transverse section through the mid-piece (× 30,000 approx.). For clarity, the surface membrane which envelops the sperm completely is not shown in *A* or *B* and the number of turns in the mitochondrial and tail sheaths has been very much reduced in *A*.

((*B*) *adapted from Hancock, 1957, Vet. Rec. 69,996*; (*C*) *adapted from Challice, 1952. Studies on Fert. 4,21*; (*D*) *adapted from Bradfield, 1955. Symp. Exp. Biol. 9, 306.*)

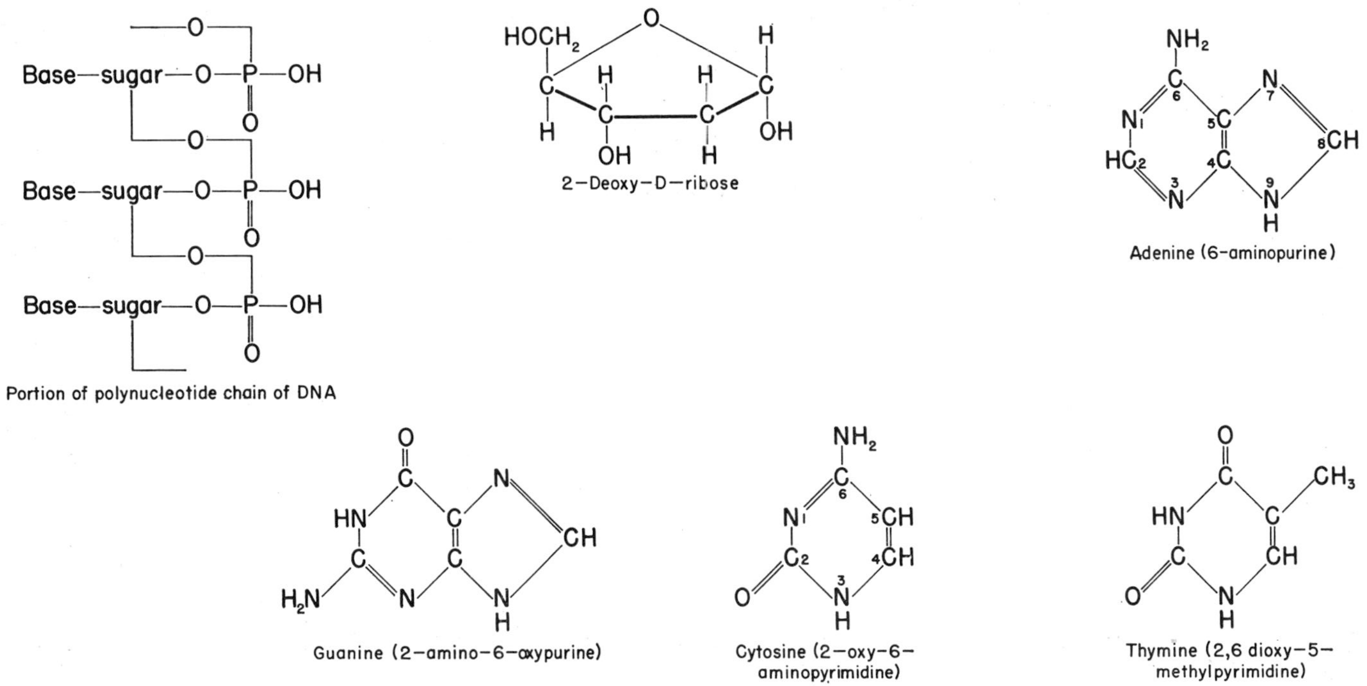

Fig. 3-6.—Formulae of the components of deoxyribonucleic acid.

The anterior end of the mid-piece connecting with the head is known as the implantation region (Blom & Birch-Anderson, 1960). Separation of the head and tail may occur here, *e.g.* in bulls with a specific hereditary defect, when heat is applied to the testes, or in animals with fever. The electron microscope shows that the implantation region has a complex structure and contains the *proximal centriole* which shows up as two or three *basal granules* by staining techniques.

An *axial filament* consisting of 20 *fibers* runs from the region of implantation through to the end of the tail. The fibers are arranged in the form of a central pair surrounded by two concentric rings each of nine fibers $(2 + 9 + 9)$, a pattern common to the flagella of ciliated cells and many micro-organisms.

The mid-piece (10 to 15 μ) is the thickened region of the tail between the head and main-piece and may be regarded as an important power house for supplying energy to the sperm. Here the sperm is surrounded by a so-called *helix or spiral of mitochondria* which contains the enzymes (*e.g.* cytochrome system) concerned in the oxidative metabolism of the sperm (Blom & Birch-Anderson, 1960). The mid-piece is rich in the phospholipid, plasmalogen, which contains a fatty aldehyde and a fatty acid linked to glycerol as well as phosphoric acid and choline (see Fig. 3–1). The fatty acid can be oxidized and represents an endogenous store of energy for sperm activity (see Section IV). The enzymes breaking down fructose to lactic acid are probably located between the fibers of the tail.

The main-piece (about 30 μ) is the longest part of the tail and provides most of the propellant machinery. The axial filament in this region is surrounded by a tough protein *tail sheath*, which according to several investigators is wound spirally around it.

In the short terminal portion of the tail (3 μ) or end-piece, the filament is not surrounded by a sheath.

C. The Surface or Cell Membrane

The surface of the sperm is covered by a membrane of phospholipid. When the cell dies the permeability of the membrane increases, particularly in the region of the post-nuclear cap, and this provides the basis for staining techniques which distinguish living from dead sperm. The stain most commonly used is eosin or Congo red against a background of nigrosin. During senescence or aging there is also a passage of material out of sperm and their heads show a tendency to stick to each other (*head agglutination*) or to a glass surface. Living sperm can, in fact, be separated from dead ones by filtration through a bed of glass beads. It may be noted that when sperm are administered parentally they evoke the formation of antibodies in the blood, and such serum will agglutinate sperm *in vitro*. In this case, however, the sperm usually adhere together by the tail (*tail agglutination*).

D. Motility of Sperm

The most striking feature of sperm is their motility which makes them admirably suited for physiological studies and also provides a simple means of evaluating semen for artificial insemination. Such microscopic observations are, however, subjective and much effort has been directed towards obtaining more critical methods for measuring sperm movements (Rothschild, 1953; Bishop, 1962). The best known device is the *impedance bridge* which measures the rate of change of the electrical resistance of a sperm suspension. The impedance change frequency (I.C.F.), as it is called, is correlated with the activity of dense sperm suspensions.

The sperm-tail contains all the apparatus necessary for motility and tails that have become separated from heads, can be fully motile. The nine larger outer fibers of the tail are thought to be the main contractile elements and to be capable of propagating localized contractions along their length. The smaller inner fibers may be specialized for the rapid conduction of impulses, arising rhythmically at the neck and co-ordinating the localized contractions in the outer fibers.

Waves of sperm swimming in the same direction are a characteristic feature of undiluted ram and bull semen when viewed under the microscope. The speed of the sperm varies with the medium and tempera-

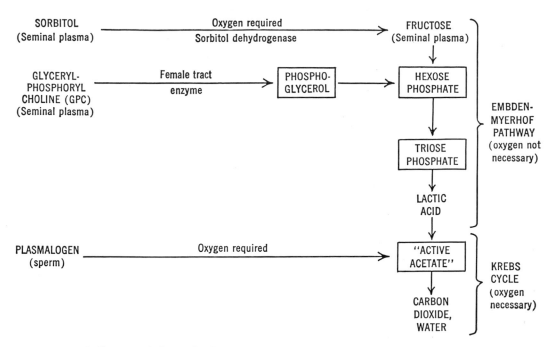

FIG. 3–7.—A diagram of the probable routes by which sperm metabolize substances in semen. The origin of the four substrates—fructose, sorbitol, glycerylphosphorylcholine and plasmalogen—is shown in brackets. The end products are lactic acid, carbon dioxide and water. Intermediates which do not accumulate are enclosed by boxes.

The concentration of the seminal plasma substrates (see Table 3–1) and hence their relative importance in sperm metabolism varies from one species to another.

ture but is of the order of $100 \, \mu$ per second at $37°C$. The motility of sperm probably plays an important part in the final encounter of the gametes and, in general, there is a fairly good correlation between motility and fertilizing capacity.

IV. METABOLISM OF SPERM

The energy yielding reactions that take place in semen (Mann, 1954, 1959; White, 1958; Bishop & Walton, 1960b) are confined to the sperm (Figure 3–7). Seminal plasma and *azoospermic semen* (*i.e.* ejaculates with no sperm) are devoid of such metabolic activity, although boar seminal plasma shows some oxygen uptake. There are at least four substances in semen which can be utilized either directly or indirectly by the sperm as energy sources for the maintenance of motility. These are fructose, sorbitol, GPC and plasmalogen; (see Section I & Table 3–1) the first three are constituents

of the seminal plasma, but plasmalogen is present in the sperm itself. All four can be utilized by sperm in the presence of oxygen, which would normally be available in most parts of the female tract, provided in the case of GPC it has first come into contact with an enzyme in the female tract secretions; none are broken down by the seminal plasma.

The *oxygen uptake or respiration* of most semen, will reflect the overall oxidation of these substances and is between 5 and $20 \, \mu l.$ per hundred million sperm/hr. at $37°C$. Lactic acid which accumulates in semen as the result of the metabolism of the sperm is derived from the plasma constitutents, but not from plasmalogen. In addition to these four physiological substrates sperm can metabolize a large number of related substances that do not occur in semen. The respiration of semen can be measured by the Warburg technique. The diluted sample is shaken in a flask connected to a manometer;

the carbon dioxide evolved is usually absorbed in alkali so that the pressure change gives a direct estimate of the oxygen consumed.

A. Metabolism of Fructose and Sorbitol

The metabolism of fructose by sperm proceeds via the *Embden-Meyerhof pathway* which is common to most animal tissues. Hexose phosphates, triose phosphates and pyruvic acid are involved as transient intermediates leading to lactic acid, which tends to accumulate, although in the presence of oxygen it is further oxidized to carbon dioxide and water. The oxidative phase of metabolism takes place over *the Krebs tricarboxylic acid cycle* as in other tissues.

If the sperm are deprived of oxygen, for instance by letting semen stand in long narrow tubes, oxidation of the lactic acid cannot take place and the fructose is quantitatively converted into the acid. It is convenient to measure the fructose breakdown (or *fructolysis*) under these essentially anaerobic conditions and at 37°C. the rate for bull and ram sperm is 1.5 to 2 mg./thousand million motile cells/hour, but is much lower for the boar (*e.g.* 0.2 to 1.0). Fructose solutions turn red when heated with the keto reagent, resorcinol, and this provides the basis for the colorimetric estimation of fructose in semen. The sample must, however, be first deproteinized with zinc sulfate and alkali or with ethanol. In the absence of oxygen sperm depend solely upon the breakdown of fructose to lactic acid as a source of energy. Ram and bull sperm survive quite well under such conditions provided fructose is present. Boar sperm, on the other hand, become immotile even when adequate fructose is available, presumably because of their reduced ability to metabolize it to lactic acid, which cannot be further utilized without oxygen (Aalbers *et al*, 1961).

Although fructose is the sugar normally found in semen, two other hexoses, glucose and mannose, are similarly metabolized by sperm when added to semen. The sugar-alcohol, sorbitol, which occurs in seminal plasma is oxidized to fructose by ram and bull sperm, but not by the boar. The enzyme sorbitol dehydrogenase is responsible for the oxidation which only takes place in the presence of oxygen. The fructose so formed, will be metabolized in the same way as the fructose initially present in the seminal plasma, and the sorbitol can, therefore, act as a nutrient for the sperm.

B. Metabolism of Glycerol and Glycerylphosphorylcholine (GPC)

In view of the widespread use of glycerol in diluents for the deep freezing of semen (see Chapter 8), it is of interest that ram and bull sperm can utilize it under aerobic conditions. Glycerol presumably enters the glycolytic cycle at the triose phosphate stage, a step which requires oxygen, and is converted into lactic acid which can be further oxidized.

Sperm are incapable of attacking GPC, as such, but there is an enzyme in the secretions of the female duct system that splits off choline thus liberating phosphoglycerol which, like glycerol, is utilized by sperm (White & Wallace, 1961). GPC may therefore constitute an additional source of energy for sperm after semen has been ejaculated into the female duct system.

C. Metabolism of Plasmalogen

In addition to fructose, sorbitol and GPC, which are available from the seminal plasma, the sperm themselves carry a reserve nutrient. This endogenous source of energy, which is probably brought into play when others are exhausted, is plasmalogen (Fig. 3-1). One fatty acid residue can be detached from the plasmalogen molecule and oxidized as two carbon atom fragments (*i.e.* "active acetate") via the Krebs tricarboxylic acid cycle giving carbon dioxide and water. The substance remaining is called *lyso-plasmalogen* and oddly enough depresses the viability of sperm; the physiological significance of this auto-intoxication is unknown.

D. Metabolism of Amino Acids

Ram and bull sperm are able to oxidize the aromatic amino acids phenylalanine and tryptophane when added to semen, by means of an enzyme, *L-amino acid oxidase*.

Hydrogen peroxide is formed in the process and is spermicidal, as catalase—the peroxide-destroying enzyme found in most tissue—is absent from ram and bull semen. Egg yolk, which is a common constituent of artificial insemination diluents, contains the aromatic amino acids, but any detrimental effect on the sperm is apparently outweighed by the beneficial qualities of the non-dializable fraction which protects sperm from the harmful effects of cold shock and dilution (see Section V).

E. Relation Between Metabolism, Motility and Fertility

Both the rate of fructolysis and respiration are correlated with the motility of sperm and *necrospermic semen* (*i.e.* ejaculates containing only immotile cells) has little metabolic activity.

The co-enzyme, *adenosine triphosphate* (ATP), which plays an important part in muscle contraction, is present in sperm and provides a link between the energy yielding reactions and motility. The breakdown of ATP probably furnishes the energy necessary for the contraction of the sperm fibers in much the same way as it does in muscle fibers; the loss of ATP being made good in sperm, by the energy yielding reactions of fructolysis and respiration. A close correlation has been found between the ATP content of sperm and their motility, thus for instance, the ATP content and motility of ram sperm, fall off under anaerobic conditions unless fructose is present.

In addition to the estimation of fructolysis and the manometric determination of oxygen consumption, at least one other metabolic test, *viz.* methylene blue reduction, has been used for evaluating semen. This depends on the dehydrogenase activity of sperm and is measured by the time required for a semen sample to decolorize a standard amount of methylene blue. In general, however, the correlation between metabolic rate and fertility is not sufficiently high to give such tests an advantage over the much simpler microscopic examination of semen (see Chapter 8). Chemical studies have, of course, greatly added to our knowledge of the properties of semen and such investiga-

tions are clearly relevant to increasing the efficiency of storing and handling semen for artificial insemination.

V. FACTORS AFFECTING THE SURVIVAL OF SPERM IN VITRO

The physical and chemical properties of the diluent, the degree of dilution, and factors such as temperature and light are important in handling and storing semen for artificial insemination (White, 1956; Emmens, 1959; Parkes, 1960; Bishop & Walton, 1960b).

A. Effects of pH, Osmotic Pressure, Electrolytes and Non-Electrolytes

In general, sperm are most active and survive for the longest period at a pH of about 7.0. There is a fairly rapid fall off in motility on either side of the optimal pH, but at least partial motility is observed between 5 and 10. Although sperm are fairly rapidly immobilized by acid conditions, motility can be restored in some species, if the pH is brought back to neutral within say, an hour. Bull and ram sperm produce large amounts of lactic acid from seminal fructose, and it is necessary to have a buffer such as phosphate, citrate, or bicarbonate in the medium.

Sperm remain motile for the longest period in media having about the same tonicity as semen or blood. In general, they are less readily affected by hypertonic than by hypotonic conditions in the range of 50 to 150 per cent of normal tonicity.

Potassium is necessary for the normal functioning of the sperm and it would seem advisable to include some potassium and possibly also magnesium in semen diluents. On the other hand, calcium and high concentration of phosphate and potassium depress motility and should be avoided. Copper and iron are toxic to sperm, but the danger of contaminating semen with heavy metals in artificial insemination practice is not great if glass vessels and distilled water are used.

The presence of a certain amount of non-electrolyte in the form of a sugar, such as fructose or glucose which would nourish the sperm, might be expected to be beneficial in a diluent. Over and above this, however, the replacement of electrolyte (*e.g.* sodium chloride) by osmotically equivalent amounts of non-electrolyte (*e.g.* glucose) does not improve the survival of ram and bull sperm except where the medium is very alkaline.

B. Effect of Dilution

Moderate dilution of semen, particularly in a buffered, isotonic medium containing a sugar such as fructose is not harmful to sperm motility and may stimulate activity and increase their life span. It is even possible to revive the activity of senescent samples in this way.

Excessive dilution (greater than 1 in 1000) even in an optimal medium, however, depresses motility. The harmful effect of diluting ram and bull semen can largely be prevented by including a proportion of seminal plasma in the medium, but the effectiveness of such plasma is usually increased if it has been left in contact with sperm for some time. The depression of motility at low cell concentrations would seem, therefore, to be due to both dilution of seminal plasma and loss of substances from the sperm. The nature of the beneficial substances in the seminal plasma and also those lost from the sperm cell is not known, but a variety of high molecular substances (*e.g.* proteins and starch) have a protective action on diluted ram and bull sperm and presumably act by preventing the escape of intracellular constituents. In storing semen it would seem advisable to avoid excessive dilution and to add a protective agent to the diluent. The protective agent widely used in artificial insemination practice is egg yolk; the active constituent is probably a lipo-protein.

The fertility of bull semen falls off when it is diluted to less than 8 million sperm per ml. and inseminated in 1 ml. doses. It is not yet known, if this is a true dilution effect, as described above, or is due to the reduced number of sperm inseminated. In the rabbit, however, the fertility of a given number of sperm has been shown to vary inversely with the volume of fluid inseminated. Although the motility of ram sperm is less affected than the bull by high dilution, fertility may fall off much more strikingly and some investigators report that a dilution of only 1 in 4 in egg yolk-citrate can cause a 50 per cent decrease in conception rate.

The seminal plasma of the boar and stallion is much less favorable for survival of the sperm, which in fact, live longer if they are centrifuged down and concentrated in an artificial medium.

C. Effect of Temperature

The rate of sperm metabolism and motility both vary with temperature. A 10° C. increase above ambient temperature will more than double the metabolic rate and there is a corresponding decrease in life span. Above 50° C. sperm suffer an irreversible loss of motility within 5 minutes and most cells then stain with Congo red. The difference between motility at room temperature (20° C.) and body temperature (37°C.) can be quite striking. It is clearly important, therefore, to evaluate semen quality at a constant temperature and 37°C. is usually chosen. At body temperature the life of the sperm *in vitro* is only a few hours, because of the exhaustion of substrate, the fall in pH of semen due to accumulation of lactic acid, senescent changes in the sperm, and the growth of bacteria.

Cooling semen decreases the activity of the sperm and increases their life span, but it is important to avoid *cold shock* if the sperm are to survive. The sperm of farm animals suffer severe damage if they are cooled much below 0°C. unless glycerol is included in the medium.

Cold Shock. When ejaculated ram, bull, boar and stallion sperm are *quickly* cooled to about freezing point they suffer an irreversible loss of viability called *cold shock*. Sperm with attached cytoplasmic droplets taken directly from the epididymis are more resistant than ejaculated sperm, and sperm from a second ejaculation tend to be more resistant than those from the first; resistance to cold shock is mainly a property of the cell and is not due to the seminal plasma.

The most obvious sign of cold shock is loss of motility which is not regained on warming the semen. There is also an increase in the proportion of cells staining with dyes like eosin or Congo red (see Section III). The surface of the sperm disintegrates and gross changes in cell permeability occur with leakage of potassium and proteins (*e.g.* cytochrome). There is also a decrease in the rate of fructose breakdown by the sperm, and a decrease in oxygen uptake and a fall in ATP, which can no longer be resynthesized and used to supply energy for motility.

Cold shock can be avoided by cooling bull, ram and stallion semen slowly in the critical region from 15 to 0°C. When the sperm are cooled in this way there is a reduction in motility and metabolism, but on rewarming full activity is restored. Cold shock can also be prevented in these species by adding egg-yolk to semen; the active principle is the phospholipid, lecithin. Ejaculated boar sperm are particularly susceptible to cold shock and should not be cooled below 15°C.

Low Temperature Storage. At temperatures near freezing point, it is possible to keep sperm for several hours or days, particularly if antibiotics, which are innocuous to mammalian sperm in bacteriostatic quantities, are added to the diluent. A slow cooling technique, to 2 to 5°C. for the bull, ram and stallion and to 15°C. for the boar, usually using an egg-yolk or milk diluent, provides the basis for routine artificial insemination (see Chapter 8).

The successful deep freezing of sperm to very low temperatures (*i.e.* −80°C. or lower), at which they might be preserved more or less indefinitely has opened a new era in the breeding of livestock. It was not until the discovery of the protective action of glycerol about a decade ago that the deep freezing of the sperm of farm animals, became possible (Polge & Parkes, 1952; Emmens & Blackshaw, 1956; Polge, 1957). Since then many modifications of the technique have been tried and a combination of glycerol and a sugar seems to give better revival than glycerol alone, particularly when freezing ram sperm. Leaving the sperm in contact with glycerol for a few hours (*i.e.* equilibration prior to freezing) also improves results. Although glycerol can be utilized by bull and ram sperm, it seems unlikely that the life-preserving action of the glycerol at low temperature is dependent on its metabolism by sperm. The concentration that must be used for freezing purposes is very high and the physical properties of glycerol are probably more important in this regard.

The fertility of bull semen frozen to −80°C. (*i.e.* the temperature of an alcohol dry ice mixture) and thawed, approaches that of ordinary cooled liquid semen, however, the fertility of deep-frozen ram semen has proved poor despite satisfactory recovery of motility. Surprisingly enough when bull semen is stored for very long periods (*e.g.* 16 months) at −80°C., there does seem to be a fall off in motility on revival and liquid air or liquid nitrogen is now being used as a refrigerant so that semen can be stored at −190°C. (see Chapter 8).

D. Effect of Light

Exposure of sperm to sunlight might be expected to decrease their life span because of an increase in temperature. Recently, however, it has been found that light is, in itself, harmful to sperm and motility, metabolism and fertility can apparently be depressed by light intensities which normally prevail in the laboratory (Norman & Goldberg, 1961). Light of wave length 440 mμ produces the maximum effect and long wave lengths (*i.e.* red light) are not harmful. The harmful effect only occurs in the presence of oxygen or air and the enzyme catalase prevents it; this suggests that light causes a photochemical reaction in the sperm during which toxic amounts of hydrogen peroxide are produced.

E. The Basis for Artificial Insemination Diluents

The survival of sperm might be expected to be best in a balanced, buffered, medium of about a neutral pH containing a source of energy such as glucose or fructose along with protective agents to prevent cold shock and the harmful effect of dilution. It should, however, be remembered in any discussion of the requirements of an ideal diluent that simplicity, cheapness and ready availability of its constituents are important practical considerations. In most parts of the world these are fairly well met, for bull semen at least, by milk or egg citrate diluents, and it rema'ns to be seen whether any economically important increase in fertility would result from the use of more complex, physiological medium in artificial insemination practice. Great interest has recently been aroused by the observation that the motility and metabolism of bull sperm can be reversibly suppressed by carbon dioxide (Salisbury *et al.*, 1960). Bull semen can apparently be preserved in this way for several days at room temperature without great loss in fertility (see Chapter 8).

VI. SPERM IN THE FEMALE REPRODUCTIVE TRACT

The site at which the penis deposits semen in the female reproductive tract during copulation varies with the species. In sheep and cattle and many other species the small volume of semen is passed into the cranial end of the vagina and on to the cervix; the boar and stallion on the other hand project their voluminous ejaculate through the relaxed cervical canal into the uterus (reviewed by VanDemark, 1958; Austin, 1959; Chang, 1959.)

A. Transport of Sperm

In the cow and ewe some sperm reach the site of fertilization, *i.e.* the ampullae of the Fallopian tubes, in less than 15 minutes. This is too short a time to be accounted for solely by the motility of the sperm and must be largely accomplished by movements of the female duct system. Dead sperm and even inert particles *e.g.* India ink, are also quickly transported up the reproductive tract and demonstrate the small contribution made by swimming movements of the sperm. At the site of fertilization, however, motility would be expected to be of importance in increasing the chances of a sperm colliding with, and fertilizing an ovum. Contractions of the uterus increase during estrus and are greatly augmented in the cow on copulation, due most probably to reflex stimulation of the posterior pituitary gland and the

resultant release of oxytocin. Such contractions no doubt play an important part in sperm transport (VanDemark, 1953).

B. Capacitation and Time Relations

Normally, mating takes place early in heat and ovulation towards the end or after this period, depending on the species. In view of their rapid ascent of the female reproductive tract, therefore, sperm will usually reach the site of fertilization several hours before the ova. During this time the sperm of the domestic species probably undergo preparation for the task of fertilization, *i.e.* *capacitation*, as it is called in laboratory animals.

It is known that rat and rabbit sperm for instance, are not capable of participating in fertilization immediately upon entering the female reproductive tract and must spend at least 2 to 4 hours in the uterus or Fallopian tubes before they are capable of penetrating the zona pellucida of the ovum. Capacitation appears to involve a change in the properties of the acrosome which leads to its detachment when the sperm makes contact with the zona pellucida. Capacitation in the uterus, but not in the Fallopian tubes of the rabbit, is inhibited by the presence of the corpus luteum or by injecting progesterone.

As mating usually occurs before ovulation there is little chance of the ova having to wait for the sperm under natural conditions. In artificial insemination, however, unless due care is taken there is a risk that the natural time relations will be disturbed and fertility reduced.

C. Viability of Sperm and the Luminal Fluids

Sperm usually remain viable in the female reproductive tract for 1 or 2 days only. Living sperm have, however, been recovered from the mare after 6 days, which is significant in view of the long estrous period and the possibility that mating may occur several days before ovulation.

Little is known about the luminal fluid which bathes the mucous membranes of the female reproductive tract; in admixture with seminal plasma, it must, however, not only serve as a vehicle for sperm, but also as a medium for ova, early embryos, and the bacteria of the female reproductive tract. The secretion of mucus from the cervix increases, and becomes more watery at estrus and collects in the vagina. It is particularly abundant in the cow at this period and its discharge from the vagina is, in fact, taken as a sign of estrus. The volume of fluid in the uterus and Fallopian tubes is usually quite small and the total is less than 1 ml. in the cow and ewe.

Chemical analyses have been made on the cervico-vaginal, uterine, and Fallopian tube fluids of the cow, but information for other species is lacking. (Olds & VanDemark, 1957). The fluids are usually about neutral or slightly acid (pH 6.4 to 7.1), although the vaginal fluid may appear more alkaline when examined *in vitro* (pH 7.5 to 7.8). The major ions are sodium (170 to 300 mg. %), potassium (40 to 220 mg. %) and chloride (370 to 530 mg. %), with smaller concentrations of calcium (11 to 15 mg. %) and inorganic phosphate (2 to 10 mg. %). The most characteristic constituent of the cervico-vaginal fluid of the cow is a *mucoid* containing fucose, galactose, glucosamine, sialic acid and a number of amino acids (Gibbons, 1959). The sialic acid content, which decreases at estrus and increases during pregnancy, seems to be related to the physical properties of the mucus and may determine the ease with which sperm can penetrate it. This is easiest at estrus, when the cervico-vaginal fluid is watery and more difficult during pregnancy when the fluid is gelatinous.

The cervico-vaginal fluid of the cow contains little free reducing sugar (9 to 16 mg. %), but higher concentrations occur in the uterine (50 to 80 mg. %) and Fallopian tube (90 mg. %) fluids and might be available to the sperm as a source of energy. Practically nothing is known about the metabolism of sperm in the female reproductive tract, but a number of subtrates are potentially available in the seminal plasma, the uterine fluid and within the sperm themselves. Conditions in the uterus are essentially aerobic so that one might expect not only a breakdown of plasma fructose and luminal reducing sugar to lactic acid, but also further oxidation to carbon dioxide and water (Section IV & Fig. 3–7). GPC, another important plasma constituent, should also be made available to the sperm by the action of a disterase enzyme in the female tract secretions which converts GPC to phosphoglycerol. When all exogenous sources of energy are exhausted the sperm can also utilize its own plasmalogen reserves.

D. Numbers of Sperm and Fate

Although prodigious numbers of sperm are introduced into the vagina or uterus at copulation, only a few hundred get to the site of fertilization in the ampullae of the Fallopian tubes. Even so, the chances of a sperm colliding with an ovum are high and in the rabbit, for instance, it has been estimated that they occur every 2 minutes during the first four hours after ovulation, which in this species occurs 10 to 14 hours after mating.

Although sperm are actively transported up the female reproductive tract, it is not a mass movement since there are very effective barriers to prevent this. The barriers vary with the species, in the ewe and cow it is mainly the narrow cervical canal and in the sow, the utero-tubal junction. The cervix of the ewe is particularly well adapted for this function; it is about 4 cm. long and the lumen is practically closed by mucosal folds. The normal ram ejaculate contains about 3000 million sperm, but less than a million pass the cervix.

Despite this screening out process the number of sperm in each ejaculate is vastly in excess of the minimum required for optimal fertility. In the artificial insemination of cattle, high conception rates are obtained with 10 million sperm *i.e.* 1/500 to 1/1000th of the number in a normal bull ejaculate. When bull semen is diluted much beyond this point there is some fall off in fertility, but it is not clear if this is due to a reduction in the number of sperm or to the dilution of protective substances in the seminal plasma.

Before a sperm can penetrate an ovum, it must first pass through the surrounding cumulus or layer of *follicular cells* which are cemented together by *hyaluronic acid*. The sperm head contains an enzyme *hyaluronidase* which readily diffuses out and by breaking down the hyaluronic acid may enable the sperm to burrow through between the follicular cells. The actual mechanism of penetration into the egg and subsequent events in fertilization is discussed in Chapter 7. Residual sperm are removed within a few days as a result of phagocytosis in the female tract.

VII. FACTORS AFFECTING SPERM PRODUCTION

The sperm producing capacity of the testes is predetermined by heredity and, during the life of the animal, controlled by the anterior pituitary and other factors acting either indirectly via the gland or directly on the testes themselves (Clegg & Ganong, 1959; Emmens, 1959; Moustgaard, 1959; Perry, 1960). The testes have prolific activity and 4 to 9 thousand million sperm are produced by the ram and bull every day. There is a good correlation between sperm production and testis size; one gram of testes produces over 8000 sperm per minute!

Heredity. The importance of heredity in determining sperm production and other semen characteristics in normal animals has been demonstrated by studies on identical and fraternal twin bulls. Sperm production may also be grossly affected by genetic abnormalities *e.g.* testicular hypoplasia and congenital segmental aplasia of the Wolffian duct (see Chapter 2). Hereditory defects in sperm production or maturation causing abnormality of the acrosome and separation of the head and tail, are also sometimes encountered in sterile bulls.

Age. Spermatogenesis commences at *puberty, i.e.* when the animal is sexually mature. Puberty is not reached suddenly, but gradually; the testes fully descend from the abdomen and both the seminiferous tubules and the interstitial cells become active. At birth the tubules have no lumen and only two types of cell are present, spermatogonia and indifferent cells (Fig. 3–2). During puberty the tubules acquire lumina and the germinal epithelium changes from a simple to a complex state characteristic of the sexually mature male (see Section II and Fig. 3–2). Puberty is reached in the

ram and boar at about 6 months, in the bull about 9 months and in the stallion at 18 months. Although fertile matings are possible at puberty, the testes continue to develop and produce more sperm; it is customary to restrict the use of young male animals or not to allow mating until after puberty (see Chapters 8, 13, 14, 15 & 16). Spermatogenesis will normally continue throughout life until senility sets in when progressive atrophy of the tubules occurs and only a few are capable of producing sperm.

Effect of Hormones. FSH stimulates development of the seminiferous tubules whereas LH (ICSH) stimulates production of testosterone by the Leydig or interstitial cells. Testosterone, however, maintains not only the accessory organs, but also the seminiferous tubules of hypophysectomized animals and LH will therefore indirectly have a similar dual action (see Chapter 1). Most of the work has been done with small animals, but similar mechanisms probably operate in the domestic species and all three hormones no doubt have a physiological role in the control of spermatogenesis. There is no good evidence however, that any of these hormones increases sperm production when administered to normal males.

In a number of animals, including the boar and ram, prolonged treatment of males with estrogens will produce testicular atrophy and eventually sterility. In very hot climates thyroid deficiency may cause sterility in rams, but no other hormones have an important effect on the fertility of male farm animals.

Nutrition. As a rule diets that maintain body weight and general good health are sufficient for normal spermatogenesis in farm animals (see Chapter 8 & 18). In the bull and ram very severe inanition (*i.e.* underfeeding) is required to cause much decline in semen production. Even then the testes are less affected than the accessory organs, and a fall in the fructose and citric acid levels of the semen occurs before a drop in sperm numbers. In young animals gross underfeeding causes a delay in puberty, but again the effect on the testes and sperm production is not as great as on the accessory organs and their secretions. Inanition exerts its action via the gonatropins of the pituitary gland; the seminiferous tubules must, however, be less affected than the interstitial cells which produce testosterone and so control the accessory glands.

Lack of vitamin A is the only specific dietary deficiency that has been shown with any certainty to affect semen production in farm animals. Atrophy of the germinal and general epithelium throughout the body occurs when bulls and rams are kept for many months on a diet containing little or no vitamin A. Sperm production and libido are depressed, but by this time other more obvious clinical symptoms are well advanced; in calves and lambs the onset of puberty is also delayed. Pituitary cysts are found in vitamin A deficient rams and bulls and suggest that this gland may be involved, as in inanition.

In rats a deficiency of vitamin E or manganese in the diet causes testicular degeneration and presumably these substances have an important, but as yet unexplored role in spermatogenesis.

Season and Climate. Wild species breed only at certain seasons in the year and the cycle is usually dependant on changes in the duration of daylight. In such animals the testes regress completely during the nonbreeding season and the germinal epithelium returns to the state of the young, sexually immature male. In farm animals seasonal breeding is not as clearly defined, at least so far as the male is concerned. The testes usually remain in the scrotum after puberty and do not undergo marked cyclical changes.

The ram shows the most extreme example of seasonal breeding in the larger domestic species, but even here there are great breed differences (see Chapters 14 & 18). In European breeds there is a decline in sexual behavior during the summer months and a marked fall in sperm production which returns to normal in the fall. On the other hand, fat-tail breeds produce good quality semen all the year round in the tropics and subtropics and so does the Merino in temperate parts of Australia. The change in the duration of daylight, acting on the testes via pituitary FSH, is probably the most important factor in controlling seasonal variation in spermatogenesis in the ram of European breeds. High environmental temperatures, however, quite independently of light will also depress sperm production, but it is not known if this is a direct effect on the testes or caused indirectly by depressed secretion of the thyroid gland. In most mammals the testes are maintained in the scrotum at a temperature several degrees below that of the body by contraction or relaxation of the cremaster muscle (see Chapter 2). This lower temperature is essential for spermatogenesis in these species and degeneration of the seminiferous tubules occurs if the testes do not descend, a condition known as *cryptorchidism*, or if the descended testes are kept warm by insulation (see Chapter 18).

Seasonal variation in sperm production have also been recorded in the bull, including some deterioration during summer months, but it is even less clear how far these changes are conditioned by daylength, temperature and other factors (see Chapter 13).

Although our understanding of the production and the properties of semen has greatly increased during the past 30 years there are still many gaps in our knowledge. This is particularly so in the case of the boar and stallion; these two species have not been as intensely studied as the bull and ram, and provide a fertile field for future research.

REFERENCES

AALBERS, J. G., MANN, T. & POLGE, C. (1961). Metabolism of boar semen in relation to sperm motility and survival. *J. Reprod. Fertil.*, **2**, 42–53.

AUSTIN, C. R. (1959). Fertilization and development of the egg. In: *Reproduction in Domestic Animals.* H. H. Cole & P. T. Cupps (edits.) Vol. 1. New York, Academic Press.

BISHOP, D. W. (1962). Sperm motility, *Physiol. Rev*, **42**, 1–59.

BISHOP, M. W. H. & AUSTIN, C. R. (1957). Mammalian spermatozoa. *Endeavour.*, **16**, 137–150.

BISHOP, M. W. H. & WALTON, A. (1960a) Spermatogenesis and the structure of mammalian spermatozoa. In: *Marshall's Physiology of Reproduction.* A. S. Parkes (edit.) Vol. 1, Part 2, London, Longmans.

——— (1960b). Metabolism and motility of mammalian spermatozoa. In: *Marshall's Physiology of Reproduction.* A. S. Parkes (edit.) Vol. 1, Part 2, London, Longmans.

Blom, E. & Birch-Anderson, A. (1960). The ultrastructure of the bull sperm. 1. The middle-piece. *Nord. Vet-Med.*, **12**, 261–279.

Chang, M. C. (1959). Fertilizing capacity of spermatozoa. In: *Recent Progress in the Endocrinology of Reproduction.* C. W. Lloyd (edit.) New York, Academic Press.

Clegg, M. T. & Ganong, W. F. (1959). Environmental factors other than nutrition affecting reproduction. In: *Reproduction in Domestic Animals.* H. H. Cole & P. T. Cupps (edits.) Vol. 2, New York, Academic Press.

Emmens, C. W. (1959). Fertility in the male. In: *Progress in the Physiology of Farm Animals.* J. Hammond (edit.) Vol. 4, London, Butterworth.

Emmens, C. W. & Blackshaw, A. W. (1956). Artificial insemination. *Physiol. Rev.*, **36**, 277–306.

Fawcett, D. S. (1958). The structure of mammalian spermatozoon. *Intern. Rev. Cytol.*, **7**, 195–234.

Gibbons, R. A. (1959). Chemical properties of two mucoids from bovine cervical mucin. *Biochem. J.*, **73**, 209–217.

Hancock, J. L. (1957). The structure of spermatozoa. *Vet. Rec.*, **69**, 996–997.

Knudsen, V. & Bryne, N. (1960). The spermiocytogenesis of the bull. *Acta. Vet. Scand.*, **1**, 140–160.

Mann, T. (1954). *The Biochemistry of Semen.* London, Methuen.

———— (1959). Biochemistry of semen and secretions of male accessory organs. In: *Reproduction in Domestic Animals.* H. H. Cole & P. T. Cupps (edits.) Vol. 2, New York, Academic Press.

———— (1960). Evaluation of semen by chemical analysis. In: *The Artificial Insemination of Farm Animals.* E. J. Perry (edit.) New Brunswick, N.J., Rutgers University Press.

Moustgaard, J. (1959). Nutrition and reproduction in domestic animals. In: *Reproduction in Domestic Animals.* H. H. Cole & P. T. Cupps (edits.) Vol. 2 New York, Academic Press.

Norman, C. & Goldberg, E. (1961). The effect of visible light on spermatozoa. *J. Reprod. Fertil.*, **2**, 511–513.

Olds, D. & Vandemark, N. L. (1957). Physiological aspects of fluids in the female genitalia with special reference to cattle—A review. *Amer. J. Vet. Res.*, **18**, 587–602.

Ortavant, R. (1959). Spermatogenesis and morphology of the spermatozoon. In: *Reproduction in Domestic Animals.* H. H. Cole & P. T. Cupps (edits.) Vol. 2, New York, Academic Press.

Parkes, A. S. (1960). The biology of spermatozoa and artificial insemination. In: *Marshall's Physiology of Reproduction.* A. S. Parkes (edit.) Vol. 1, Part 2, London, Longmans.

Perry, E. J. (1960). Factors influencing the quantity and quality of semen. In: *The Artificial Insemination of Farm Animals.* E. J. Perry (edit.) New Brunswick, N.J., Rutgers University Press.

Polge, C. (1957). Low temperature storage of mammalian spermatozoa. *Proc. Roy. Soc. B.*, **147**, 498–508.

Polge, C. & Parkes, A. S. (1952). Possibilities of long term storage of spermatozoa at low temperatures. *Anim. Breed. Abst.*, **20**, 1–5.

Rothschild, Lord. (1953). The movement of spermatozoa. In: *Mammalian Germ Cells.* G.E. Wolstenholme (edit.) London, Churchill.

Salisbury, G. W. (1956). The function of the epididymis of the bull. 1. A theory for the activation of spermatozoan motility. *Tijdschrift voor Diergeneeskunde*, **81**, 616–623.

Salisbury, G. W., Vandemark, N. L., Lodge, J. R. & Cragle, R. G. (1960). Inhibition of spermatozoan metabolism by CO_2, pH, K ion and antibacterial compounds. *J. Physiol.*, **198**, 659–664.

Vandemark, N. L. (1953). Physiological processes involved in spermatozoa transport in the cow. In: *Mammalian Germ Cells.* C. E. Wolstenholme (edit.) London, Churchill.

———— (1958). Spermatozoa in the female genital tract. *Internat. J. Fertil.*, **3**, 220–230.

White, I. G. (1956). Studies relating to the storage of mammalian spermatozoa. In: *Studies in Fertility.* R. G. Harrison (edit.) Vol. 8, London, Blackwell.

———— (1958). Biochemical aspects of mammalian semen. *Anim. Breed. Abst.*, **26**, 109–123.

White, I. G. & Wallace, J. C. (1961). Breakdown of seminal glycerylphosphorylcholine by secretions of the female reproductive tract. *Nature* (Lond.), **189**, 843–844.

QUESTIONS

1. How does the composition of semen compare with blood and other body fluids? What factors affect its production and composition?

2. How many sperm might you expect to find in an average ejaculate of a bull, ram and boar? What percentage reach the site of fertilization? How do you account for the decrease?

3. What changes occur in the properties and composition of semen when it is left for several hours at room temperature after ejaculation?

4. What part do enzyme reactions play in the biology of sperm?

5. Why is the sperm considered an atypical and highly specialized cell?

6. What is the significance of the seminal plasma? Which accessory organs produce the organic constituents? Under what conditions would you expect variation in their concentration in the plasma?

7. What environments are harmful to sperm? What do you consider the properties of an ideal sperm diluent?

8. Outline the changes undergone by a sperm cell from its origin as a spermatogonium to the fertilization of an ovum?

9. How are sperm transported up the female reproductive tract and what nutrients are available for their survival? What is meant by capacitation?

10. How are the following properties of the sperm interrelated: structure, metabolism, motility and fertilizing capacity?

Chapter 4

Female Reproductive Organs of Farm Mammals

By E. S. E. Hafez and I. Gordon

THE female reproductive organs can be divided into three major components: (a) the primary sex organs (gonads), i.e. the ovaries; (b) the reproductive tract, consisting of the Fallopian tubes, uterus, and vagina; and (c) the external genitalia, consisting of the vestibule, clitoris, labia and certain glands which open into the posterior part of the vagina (Plate VII). In this chapter we are concerned with the embryology, basic morphology, comparative anatomy, basic histology, cyclical histological changes and functions of the female reproductive organs in farm mammals.

I. EMBRYOLOGY OF THE REPRODUCTIVE ORGANS

The reproductive organs are differentiated in the late stages of embryonic development; e.g. in the cow, sex differentiation is completed a little before the 45th day of gestation. Sex differentiation begins when the length of the embryo (crown/rump length) is 25 to 30 mm. in cattle and 20 to 25 mm. in swine (Thomson, 1942). The basic layout of the following three structures appears whether the embryo is to develop as a male or female (Fig. 4–1):

(a) A pair of sexually *undifferentiated*

gonads which arise from a germinal ridge on either side of the dorsal wall of the abdominal cavity and situated on the ventro-medial border of, and a little posterior to, the kidneys of the embryo.

(b) Two pairs of ducts, the *Wolffian* and *Müllerian* ducts stretch from the region of the undifferentiated gonad of the embryo. One of each of these ducts lies on either side of the embryo mid-line, the Müllerian ducts lying nearer to the center.

(c) The *urogenital sinus* is a cleft on the surface of the body wall, just below the anus. The sinus is flanked laterally by two lips between which is a small prominence, the *phallus*.

The gonads are differentiated following invasion of the germinal ridges by a group of large granulated cells which migrate from the yolk sac. There are two invasions of the ridges in the development of the female. The primary invasion is abortive. In the secondary invasion which follows, sex cords are formed which later break up to give rise to the *primordial germ cells* (oögonia). With the appearance of the secondary sex cords, those formed at the primary invasion cease to grow and eventually disappear into the connective tissue of the medulla of the ovary (Gruenwald, 1942).

In the sexually undifferentiated stage of the embryo, both the Wolffian and Müllerian ducts are present. In the female the Müllerian ducts grow and develop into the female tract, whereas the Wolffian ducts regress and remain rudimentary. Posterior to these structures, the ducts from either side come together and fuse to form the common body of the uterus, the cervix and the anterior portion of the vagina.

The urogenital sinus gives rise to the vestibule. Folds on either side of the sinus form the lips of the vulva. In the female, the phallus makes little growth in comparison with that observed in the male. The eventual organ is the clitoris, which has as its homologue the male penis.

II. THE OVARIES

The two ovaries, unlike the testes, remain in the abdominal cavity near the kidneys and do not undergo any elaborate descent. The ovaries perform both an exocrine and endocrine function. They are the source of the ovum, through the processes of oögenesis and ovulation; they are concerned in the production of ovarian hormones, estrogen and progesterone.

The shape of the ovary varies with the species (Fig. 4–2) and the stage of estrous cycle. In the *monotocous* (single bearing) animals, the ovary is ovoid in the cow and ewe and kidney-shaped in the mare. In the *polytocous* (litter-bearing) sow, the organ resembles a cluster of grapes, the markedly protruding follicles and corpora lutea obscuring the underlying ovarian tissue. Morphological changes in the sow ovary are dealt with in detail by Burger (1952). The part of the ovary which is not attached to the mesovarium (supporting ligament) is ex-

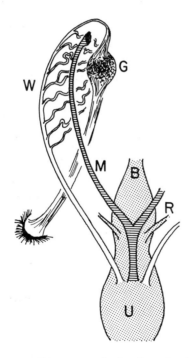
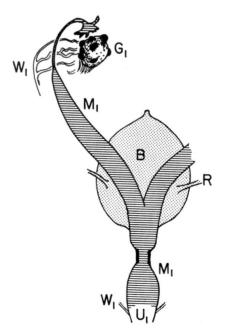

Fig. 4–1.—Diagrammatic drawings showing stages in the formation of the female reproductive organs. The undifferentiated stage and the female differentiated organs are drawn on different scales of magnification in this comparison.

Undifferentiated stage (left)	*Female* (right)
G = indifferent gonad	G_1 = ovary
W = Wolffian duct	W_1 = rudiments
M = Müllerian duct	M_1 = Fallopian tube, uterus and anterior vagina
U = urogenital sinus	U_1 = vestibule

B = urinary bladder
R = ureter

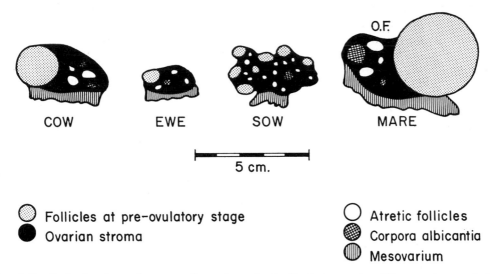

Fig. 4–2.—Scale drawings of cross sections of ovaries to illustrate species differences in morphology, number and size of Graafian follicles. Note the ovulation fossa (O.F.) in the mare's ovary and the fact that follicles in the other species are distributed over the surface of the ovary, except at the connection with the mesovarium.

Table 4–1.—Comparative Anatomy of the Ovary in the Adult Female of Farm Mammals

Organ	Animal			
	Cow	Ewe	Sow	Mare
Ovary				
shape	almond-shaped	almond-shaped	berry-shaped (cluster of grapes)	kidney-shaped; with ovulation fossa
wt. of one ovary (gm.)	10–20	3–4	3–7	40–80
Mature Graafian follicles				
number	1–2	1–4	10–25	1–2
diameter (mm.)	12–19	5–10	8–12	25–70
ovary which is the more active	right	right	left	left
Mature corpus luteum				
shape	spheroid or ovoid	spheroid or ovoid	spheroid or ovoid	pear-shaped
diameter (mm.)	20–25	9	10–15	10–25
maximum size attained (days from ovulation)	10	7–9	14	14
regression starts (days from ovulation)	14–15	12–14	13	17

The measurements included in this table vary with age, breed, parity, plane of nutrition and reproductive cycle.

6

posed and bulges into the peritoneal cavity. It is on this free surface that the ovarian follicles protrude (Plate VII). The ovary of the mature mare is peculiar: ovulation is restricted to a small area termed the *ovulation fossa* (Chapter 16).

The dimensions and weight of the ovary in the adult vary with the species (Table 4–1) and in general the weight of the ovary at birth increases 4 to 7 times by the onset of puberty. The mature ovary comprises the medulla (center portion) and the cortex (outer portion).

Medulla. The medulla has a rich blood and nerve supply which enters the ovary by way of the hilus (the attachment between the ovary and mesovarium). The arteries are derived from the ovarian branch of the utero-ovarian artery and also from the uterine artery. These pass into the medulla, where they give off the many branches which supply the entire tissue of the ovary and especially the *theca* (case) of the ovarian follicles. The ovarian arteries are remarkable for their spiral shape. The ovary is supplied by sympathetic nerve fibers.

Cortex. The cortical stroma, which consists of connective tissue and long fibroblastic cells, contains the ovarian follicles and corpora lutea in varying stages of development or regression. The total number of follicles in both ovaries varies with age: estimates of follicle number vary from 75,000 in the new born calf ovaries to as few as 2,500 in the organ of the aged cow (12 to 14 years old).

Near the surface of the cortex, the connective tissue is somewhat denser than that lying toward the medulla, and the cells are arranged roughly parallel to the ovarian surface. This rather dense fibrous layer is known as the *tunica albuginea*. On the surface of the ovary is a layer of flattened cells, known as the *germinal epithelium*. Although in the new-born foal the surface of the ovary is covered by germinal epithelium, the ventral border of the organ becomes concave shortly afterwards and the germinal tissue begins to sink below the surface to form the ovulation fossa.

A. Ovarian Follicle

In contrast to the male, where the germinal epithelium is located deep within the seminiferous tubules (see Chapter 2), this tissue lies on the surface of the ovary. For many years, germinal epithelium in the ovary has been a center of controversy which has not yet been adequately resolved. The generally held view is that, with a few exceptions, *primary follicles are not formed during adult life* (Brambell, 1960).

1. Development of Graafian Follicle

The successive stages through which follicles reach maturity are as follows— primary, secondary, growing (tertiary) and mature Graafian follicles (Fig. 4–3).

Primary Follicle. The primary follicle consists of a "potential ovum" and a single enveloping layer of much smaller follicular cells. Aggregations of these follicles form a thick layer under the *tunica albuginea*. The "potential ovum" is at this stage termed an *oögonium*.

Secondary Follicles. Groups of follicular cells proliferate to form a thick (multicellular) membrane around the vitelline (cytoplasmic) membrane of the oögonium. The homogenous area which develops between the oögonium and follicular cells is termed the *zona pellucida*. The secondary follicle moves away from the outer area of the cortex towards the center of the cortical stroma.

Graafian Follicles. The cells of the follicular layer separate to form clefts and gradually an *antrum* (cavity) is formed, into which the oögonium will eventually protrude. The cavity is lined by many layers of small follicular cells which are collectively known as the *membrana granulosa*, and is filled with a clear fluid, the *liquor folliculi*, which is rich in protein and contains estrogens (Plate VIII). This is the growing (*tertiary*) follicle.

The cells of the cortical stroma which surround the follicular cells form the tissue known as the *theca folliculi*; this consists of two layers of cells, the vascular *theca interna* and the fibrous *theca externa*. It is thought

PLATE VII

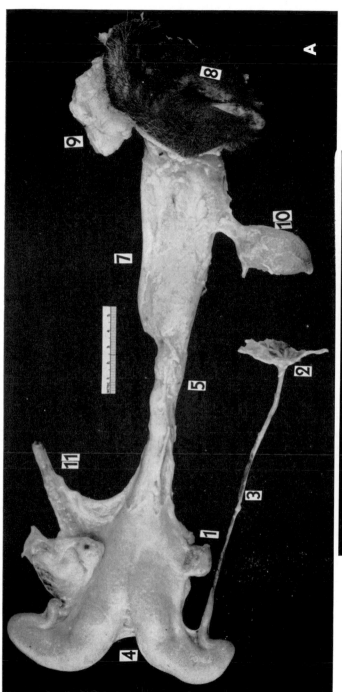

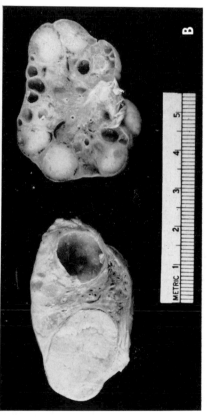

A, Genitalia of a ewe. *B,* Cross sections of ovaries in the luteal phase. Note size of corpora lutea in cow and sow (*left to right*).

PLATE VIII

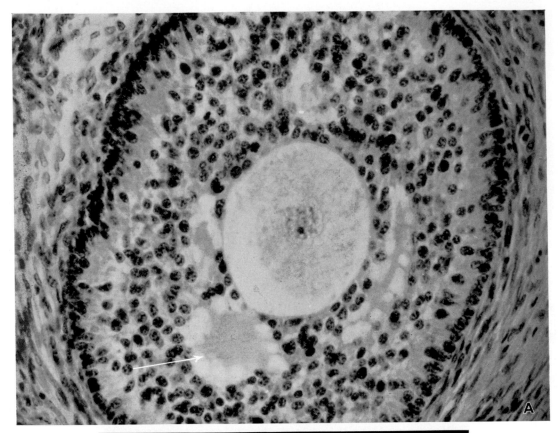

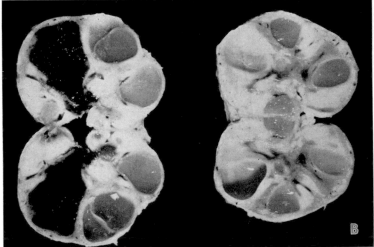

A. Cross section in ovary of a heifer to show tertiary follicle and the first formation of antrum (*arrow*). Note the granulosa cells around the oöcyte ($\times$ 350 approx.). (*From Rajakoski, 1960. Acta Endocrin. 34 (suppl.) No. 52, 20.*)

B. Cross section of mare ovaries in the luteal phase ($\times$ .6) (*Photograph by Y. Nishikawa*).

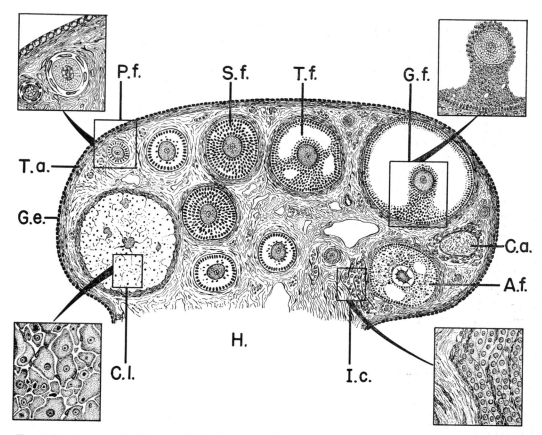

FIG. 4–3.—A composite diagram of the mammalian ovary. Progressive stages in the differentiation of a Graafian follicle are indicated (*upper left to upper right*). The mature follicle may become atretic (*lower right*) or ovulate and form a corpus luteum (*lower left*). *A.f.* = atretic follicle; *C.a.* − corpus albicans; *C.l.* ▪ corpus luteum; *G.e.* = germinal epithelium; *G.f.* = Graafian follicle; *H.* = hilus; *I.c.* = interstitial cells; *P.f.* = primary follicle; *S.f.* = secondary follicle; *T.a.* = tunica albuginea; *T.f.* = tertiary follicle. (*Partly adapted from Turner, 1948. General Endocrinology, Philadelphia, Courtesy of Saunders.*)

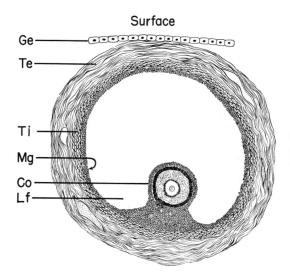

FIG. 4–4.—Microdrawing of a Graafian follicle. *Co* = cumulus oöphorus; *Ge* = germinal epithelium; *Lf* = liquor folliculi; *Mg* = membrana granulosa; *Te* = theca externa; *Ti* = theca interna.

that estrogen is formed in the cells of the theca interna and passes into the follicles through a basement membrane, the *membrana propria*, which separates the theca interna from the *membrana granulosa*. In the neighborhood of the growing follicle there is a progressive development of the cortical vascular system. With the formation of the two layers of the theca, a basket-like vascular meshwork develops around the follicle, particularly in the theca interna. Eventually, because of its great increase in size, the follicle extends through the whole thickness of the ovarian cortex, protruding above the ovarian surface like a "blister." This is the mature Graafian follicle (Fig. 4–4).

There is little evidence of changes in ovarian cells other than those associated with follicles, during the estrous cycle. In the mare, however, the ovary becomes very congested during estrus, and the cortical stroma becomes soft.

2. Number and Size of Follicles Ripened

In any one ovarian cycle, the number of follicles which ripen to maturity is fixed for each of the species. Monotocous animals (*e.g.* the cow and mare) ripen a single Graafian follicle in the majority of estrous cycles. Polytocous species (*e.g.* the sow) ripen 10 to 25 follicles. Others, such as the ewe, ripen 1 to 3 follicles according to breed, age and environmental conditions.

The diameter of the mature Graafian follicle varies with species (Table 4–1). The growth of the follicle in sows is slow at first but speeds up greatly during the last few days before ovulation. The growth of the follicles is more linear in other species of farm mammals. The follicles destined to produce the ovum reach their maximum size just before ovulation.

3. Hormonal Mechanisms

The growth and development of the ovarian follicles depends on the activity of the pituitary gonadotropins. In the adult female, only a limited amount of gonadotropin is available to the ovary. Consequently, only a few of the primary follicles can obtain the amount necessary for complete maturation. In animals injected with large doses of gonadotropins, as in superovulation, many follicles mature and ovulate.

It is well established that many more follicles grow during the first stages of the estrous cycle than are actually ovulated. Less hormone may be required to start follicular growth than to maintain larger follicles and bring them to ovulation size. Some investigators believe that the large number of follicles is necessary to allow the ovulation of the few, possibly because they supply substances (*e.g.* estrogen) which are essential for the ovulation of the smaller number.

4. Mechanics of Ovulation

In the period before ovulation, the follicle pushes through the cortical stroma of the ovary until the follicle projects beyond the surface of that organ. At this time the ovum is embedded in a solid mass of follicular cells, the *cumulus oöphorus*, which protrudes into the fluid filled antrum. The cumulus oöphorus is usually attached to the main body of granulosa cells on the surface which lies opposite that side which is to rupture at ovulation (Fig. 4–4). This attachment is eventually reduced to narrow cytoplasmic bridges, which finally break; the follicle is then ready for rupture. As the wall of the follicle ruptures the follicular fluid flows out, carrying the ovum.

Many views have been advanced to explain the rupture of the follicular wall, but the precise mechanism involved remains uncertain (see Hisaw, 1947). It is known that the follicle does not rupture because its ultimate size has been reached or because the internal pressure of the liquor folliculi is so great that it bursts the wall. In cattle, sheep and swine, the follicles destined for ovulation lose much of their turgidity and become pliable as the time of ovulation approaches (see Asdell, 1960). Observation of the ovulation process shows that the outermost layer of the follicle is the first to part, and that the inner layers protrude through the gap to form a papilla. In turn, these inner layers also rupture and the follicle collapses.

In the mare, follicles develop toward the ovulation fossa while ripening. Follicular rupture is followed by fairly extensive hemorrhage into the follicle cavity in the mare. Hemorrhage is also noted in the cow and sow, but is slight in the ewe.

The right and left ovaries function in differing degrees. Though the evidence for many polytocous species shows that ovulations are distributed at random between the ovaries, this is not true in farm mammals. In the cow and ewe, the right ovary functions more frequently than the left. In the mare and sow, the left ovary appears to be slightly more active than the right. In cattle, where follicular development is evident early in calf-hood, differences in favor of the right ovary in average weight and total follicular volume have been recorded. The cause of variation in ovarian function is not apparent, although it has been suggested that it may arise from differences in the vascularization of the two ovaries or location of the ovaries in relation to other abdominal organs *e.g.* the rumen.

5. ATRESIA OF FOLLICLES

At the onset of estrus, several follicles start to develop. Some reach the ovulatory stage, while others undergo atresia (degeneration) and fail to rupture. Atresia must be viewed as a normal process, and is only regarded as abnormal where large numbers of follicles become atretic. Atresia is associated with degeneration of the oöcyte and the follicular epithelium. The cells of the theca interna enlarge and invade the degenerating oöcyte and granulosa cells and resorption occurs. In due time the thecal cells also undergo gradual resorption.

6. FOLLICLE ABNORMALITIES

Abnormal follicles are occasionally found in the ovaries for one reason or another. *Hemorrhagic* follicles, the result of incomplete ovulation of the Graafian follicle, are sometimes encountered in cattle which have been induced to superovulate by PMS (pregnant mare serum) treatment. They are unruptured follicles containing blood clots.

Cystic follicles are rarely encountered in sheep, but are common in dairy cattle and swine. In the cow, such follicles may reach an enormous size (10 cm.). This condition may severely limit fertility in some proportion of animals. Cystic follicles in the dairy cow may be associated with malfunction of the adrenals (Garm, 1949).

Corpora lutea atretica may form from follicles whose walls become luteinized (ingrowth resembling corpus luteum) without ovulation. The hormonal factors concerned in follicle abnormalities in different species are not fully understood.

B. The Corpus Luteum

1. FORMATION

Immediately after ovulation, the walls of the follicle collapse in folds and the cavity is filled with clotted blood forming the *corpus haemorrhagicum*. Follicular cells increase in number and in size forming the *corpus luteum*. Occasionally the corpus luteum forms a central cavity filled with fluid; the cavity disappears eventually and is replaced by proliferated granulosa cells. The cells of the mature corpus luteum are called *lutein cells* and measure 25 to 30 microns. The lutein cells are organized by highly vascular connective tissue sprouts which derive from cells of the theca interna. As the organ develops, it is permeated by an extensive capillary network (Fig. 4–5).

Color. The color of the corpus luteum varies with the species and the stage of the reproductive cycle (Chapter 16). The enlarged granulosa cells contain yellow or colorless lipoid granules. The cells of the cow and mare contain a yellow pigment, lutein. This pigment gives rise to the yellow color of the organ (the yellow body) in those two species. In the ewe and sow, the corpus luteum is flesh colored because the proliferated granulosa cells have no lutein.

Shape and Size. The shape of the corpus luteum varies with the species. In the cow and ewe, the corpus luteum may protrude considerably above the surface of the ovary or a major part may be buried in the ovarian stroma; in the mare it is completely buried in the stroma (Plate VIII).

The initial increase in the size and weight of the corpus luteum is extremely rapid. In the ewe and cow, 50 to 60 per cent of the eventual size of the organ is reached 4 days after ovulation. The corpus luteum of the sow increases from 8 to 9 mm. diameter at 7 days to its maximum of 10 to 11 mm. about 14 days after ovulation. In general, the period of growth of the corpus luteum lasts a little longer than half the total length of the estrous cycle. The diameter of the fully mature corpus luteum is larger than that of a mature Graafian follicle except in the mare where it is smaller (Table 4–1).

2. REGRESSION

If fertilization and implantation occur, the

after estrus in those that have 21-day cycles. Regression proceeds rapidly, the size of the corpus luteum may be halved in a space of 36 hours. After the 14th day of the cycle, regression of the corpus luteum is rapid in the ewe. In the sow, an abrupt and rapid decrease in size of the corpus luteum occurs after the 13th day of the cycle, and this regression continues throughout the follicular phase. In the mare, the corpus luteum functions for 15 to 17 days before starting to regress.

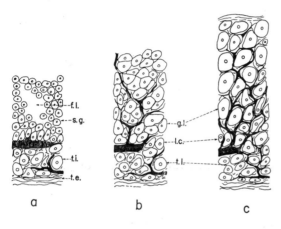

a   b   c

FIG. 4–5.—Diagram showing the organization of cells in the corpus luteum of the ewe. (*a*) corpus haemorrhagicum, (*b*) corpus luteum of the 2nd day following estrus and (*c*) corpus luteum of the 4th day following estrus. Blood vessels are shown with heavy black lines. *f.l.*, is a lake of follicular fluid; *g.l.*, lutein cells from the membrana granulosa; *l.c.*, lutein cells of uncertain origin; *t.l.*, lutein cells from the theca interna; *s.g.*, membrana granulosa; *t.i.*, theca interna and *t.e.*, theca externa. (*Adapted from Warbritton, 1934. J. Morphol., 56, 181*).

corpus luteum retains its size and functions throughout pregnancy in all farm mammals except the horse. The organ is known in this instance as the *corpus luteum verum* and is in general significantly larger than the *corpus luteum spurium* of the estrous cycle. Where fertilization does not occur, the corpus luteum regresses and allows other Graafian follicles to grow to maturity. As the lutein cells degenerate, the whole organ decreases in size and becomes white or pale brown and is known at this time as the *corpus albicans*. After 2 or 3 cycles, this becomes a barely visible scar of connective tissue. The remnants of the bovine corpus albicans of diestrus persist as progressively smaller red patches of lipochrome pigments during several successive estrous cycles. On the other hand, the corpus albicans representing a previous pregnancy is large (about 1 cm. in diameter), whitish, and has a very rough fibrous consistency.

Regression of the corpus luteum in the non-pregnant cow commences 14 or 15 days

III. FALLOPIAN TUBE
(Oviduct or Uterine Tube)

The paired Fallopian tubes are the means of conveying ova from the ovaries to the uterus. Each tube is suspended in a peritoneal fold (*mesosalpinx*) derived from the lateral layer of the broad ligament. The parts that comprise the duct are the isthmus, ampulla and infundibulum with its fimbriae. Length and degree of coiling of the tubes vary in the farm mammals (Table 4–2).

The *isthmus* is the constricted portion lying next to the uterus; this merges with the dilated section, known as the *ampulla*, which makes up about half the tube's length. The ampulla widens into a funnel shaped part of the tube, the *infundibulum*. The opening into the body cavity is the *ostium abdominale*, which lies in the center of a fringe of irregular processes, the *fimbriae*, which form the extremity of the tube.

There is an intimate anatomical relationship between the ovary and the tube. In

Table 4–2.—Comparative Anatomy of the Reproductive Tract in the Adult Non-pregnant Female of Farm Mammals

Organ	Animal			
	Cow	*Ewe*	*Sow*	*Mare*
Fallopian tube				
length (cm.)	25	15–19	15–30	20–30
Uterus				
type	bipartite	bipartite	bicornuate	bipartite
length of horn (cm.)	35–40	10–12	40–65	15–25
length of body (cm.)	2–4	1–2	5	15–20
surface lining of endometrium	70–120 caruncles	88–96 caruncles	slight longitudinal folds	conspicuous longitudinal folds
Cervix				
length (cm.)	8–10	4–10	10	7–8
outside diameter (cm.)	3–4	2–3	2–3	3.5–4
Cervical lumen				
shape	2–5 annular rings	annular rings	corkscrew-like	conspicuous folds
Os Uteri				
shape	small & protruding	small & protruding	ill-defined	clearly-defined
Anterior Vagina				
length (cm.)	25–30	10–14	10–15	20–35
Hymen	ill-defined	well-developed	ill-defined	well-developed
Vestibule				
length (cm.)	10–12	2.5–3	6–8	10–12

The measurements included in this table vary with age, breed, parity, and plane of nutrition.

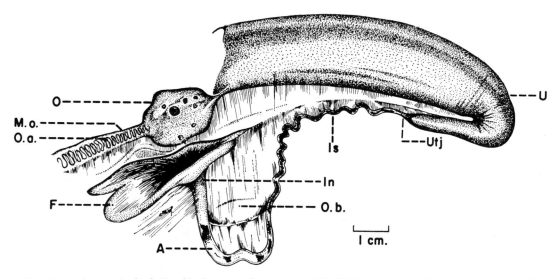

FIG. 4–6.—Anatomical relationship between the ovary and the Fallopian tube in the ewe. *A* = ampulla; *F* = fimbriae; *In* = infundibulum; *Is* = isthmus; *Mo* = mesovarium; *O* = ovary; *Oa* = ovarian artery; *Ob* = ovarian bursa; *U* = uterus; *UTJ* = utero-tubal junction. Note the suspended loop to which the ovarian bursa is attached. The tube in the ewe is pigmented.

the farm mammals, the ovary lies in an open *ovarian bursa*; in some species (*e.g.* rat, mouse) the ovarian bursa is a closed sac. The structure, in the farm species, is a pouch consisting of a thin peritoneal fold, of the mesosalpinx, attached to a suspended loop, the upper portion of the Fallopian tube (Fig. 4–6). In the cow and ewe, the ovarian bursa is wide and open; in the sow it is well developed and although open, the ovaries are largely hidden from view by the bursa. In the mare the ovarian bursa is narrow, cleft like, and does not enclose more than the area of the ovulation fossa.

The tube continues directly into the uterine horn, and there is no well defined sphincter muscle at this point, the *utero-tubal junction*. In the sow, however, the junction is guarded by long finger-like processes of the mucosa. The tube enters the uterine horn in the form of a small papilla in the mare.

A. Histology

The wall of the tube consists of the mucosa, the muscularis and the outer serous coat. Variations in the nature of the mucosa and muscularis are observed in different portions of the tube. Normally, the infundibulum and fimbriae, mainly composed of thin serous and mucous membranes, are collapsed. In this region, blood vessels are very numerous, with interspersed muscle bundles forming a structure similar to erectile tissue.

Mucosa. The mucosa of the tube forms large primary and small secondary folds. (Fig. 4–7) This folding is negligible in the isthmus but increases greatly in the ampulla, being more pronounced in the mare and sow than in the ewe and cow. In the mare, the ampulla may possess up to 60 secondary folds. In all species, the lumen of the tube gradually narrows as the uterus is approached. The mucosa consists of surface epithelial cells, an underlying connective tissue containing fine blood and lymph vessels, and some muscle fibers.

At the ovarian end of the tube the lumen is almost entirely lined with ciliated columnar epithelium. The number of such cells gradually decreases towards the uterus. In addition to the ciliated cells, at least two other types are found in the epithelium, columnar secretory (without cilia) and extremely thin columnar (rod-shaped) cells. Some investigators regard the rod cells as emptied secretory cells in the process of

Isthmus   Ampulla

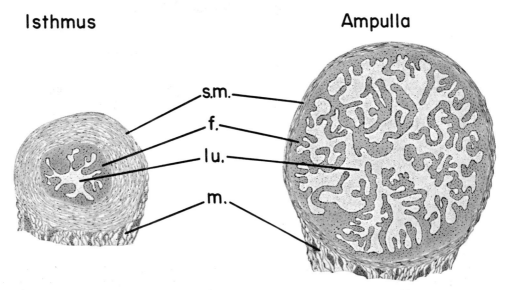

Fig. 4–7.—Schematic drawing of a cross section in the ampulla isthmus and ampulla of the Fallopian tube (× 20 approx.). *f* = folds of the mucosa; *lu* = lumen; *m* = mesosalpinx with its blood and lymph supply; *s.m.* = serous membrane. Note primary and secondary folds in the ampulla and primary folds in the isthmus.

expulsion. In ruminants, the epithelium of the ampulla contains more secretory cells than that of the isthmus At the start of diestrus, nucleated cytoplasmic projections appear and become detached from the cells where they lie freely in the lumen of the tube (Hadek, 1955).

Muscularis and Serosa. The muscularis is made up of outer longitudinal and inner circular unstriated muscle fibers. Fibers pass into the mucosa making the entire wall capable of coordinated contractions. The thickness of the musculature increases in the midportion of the tube and even more so towards the uterus. The serosa consists of connective tissue and an external coat formed from the peritoneum.

Cyclical Changes. During the estrous cycle, there are changes in the size of epithelial cells, activity of secretory cells, prominence and abundance of cilia and the size of sub-epithelial capillaries. In some species (*e.g.* ewe) these changes in the Fallopian tubes are more definite than in any other part of the reproductive tract. The ciliated columnar epithelium is highest in early diestrus and the cilia longest. These changes occur first at the ovarian end of the tube and shortly afterwards in the mid-tubal area. In the cow the height of the epithelium varies from 27 microns in diestrus to 45 in estrus (Lombard *et al.*, 1950). Secretions by the non-ciliated cells are more marked in estrus and leucocytes are found in the lumen in greater numbers. In the sow, the muscle fibers of the Fallopian tube undergo cyclical changes in length: the fibers are largest during estrus and smallest during implantation of the embryo (Anopolsky, 1928). These changes are correlated with cyclical changes in the degree of contraction of the tube, the large fibers corresponding to the period of rapid, the small fibers to the period of slow contractions.

B. Functions

At ovulation, the ovum is swept into the fimbriated end of the tube by ciliary action and by muscular contractions (Chapter 6). The tube is also the site of fertilization and the early cleavage of the ovum (Chapter 7).

The physiological significance of tubal secretions in fertilization and cleavage of the ovum is in question, for it is possible for these processes to proceed *in vitro* in the absence of tubal factors. The chemical composition of fluids found in the lumen of the Fallopian tube and uterus is given by Olds & Vandemark (1957).

IV. THE UTERUS

The uterus of domestic mammals consists of two horns, which unite to form the common body. The cervix, also an integral part of the uterus, is considered under a separate heading later in the chapter because morphologically and physiologically it can be regarded as a distinct organ.

The uterus of the sow is of the bicornuate type (*uterus bicornis*); the uterine horns are folded or convoluted and may be as much as 4 to 5 feet long, while the body of the uterus is very small (Fig. 4–8). The length of the horns is an anatomical adaptation for the multiple-fetation in swine. In the cow, ewe and mare, the uterus is of the bipartite type (*uterus bipartitus*). In this a septum separates the two horns and the uterine body is prominent, especially so in the mare, in which the uterus consists of a long slender uterine body joined by two comparatively short and straight uterine horns almost at right angles. In cattle and sheep, the uterine horns are curved rather like the horns of a ram, which explains their description. In the young cow, each uterine horn forms one complete spiral turn before joining the Fallopian tube; in cattle which have had a number of pregnancies, the spiral is often only half a turn.

In cattle, sheep and swine, the uterine horns are especially well developed for this is where the fetus or fetuses are located. In the mare, fetal development takes place in the body of the uterus and the uterine horns are poorly developed.

The uterus is attached, at both sides, to the pelvic and abdominal walls by the broad ligament (Fig. 4–9). Through this ligament the organ receives its blood and nerve supply. The uterus receives blood anteriorly from the region of the kidney as well as from the lateral walls of the pelvic cavity. The blood

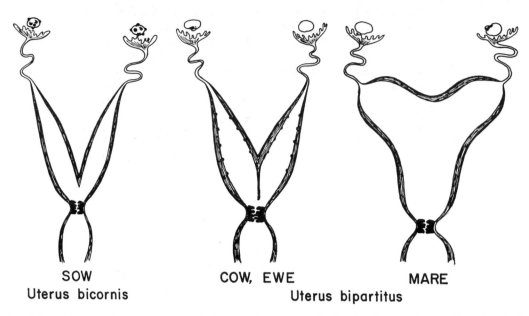

SOW
Uterus bicornis

COW, EWE
Uterus bipartitus

MARE

FIG. 4–8.—Diagram of different types of uterus in farm mammals showing the relative length of the uterine horns and uterine body after dissecting the broad ligament.

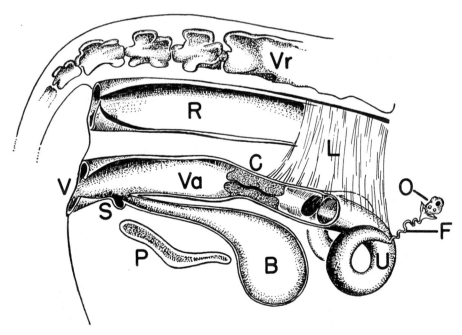

FIG. 4–9.—The reproductive organs of the cow (side view). *B* = urinary bladder; *C* = cervix; *F* = Fallopian tube; *L* = broad ligament; *O* = ovary; *R* = rectum; *P* = pelvic bone (*os coxae*); *S* = suburethral diverticulum; *U* = uterine horn; *Va* = vagina; *V* = vestibule; *Vr* = vertebral column.

PLATE IX

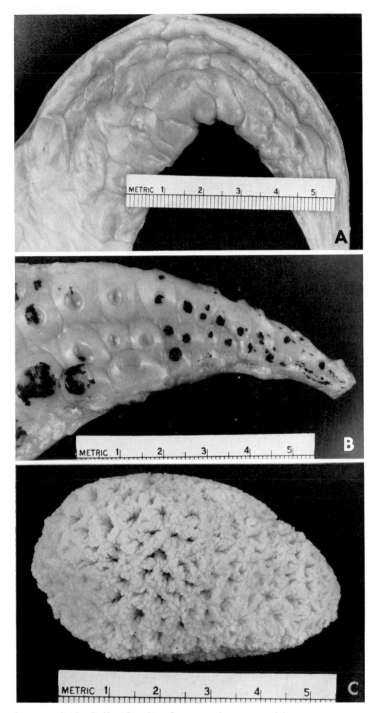

A, Uterine horn (cut open) of a heifer showing the caruncles arranged in rows.

B. Uterine horn in the non-pregnant ewe showing pigmentation of the endometrium and caruncles.

C. Caruncle dissected from a pregnant cow. Note the spongy-like crypts where the chorionic villi attach.

PLATE X

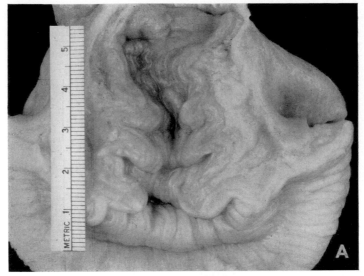

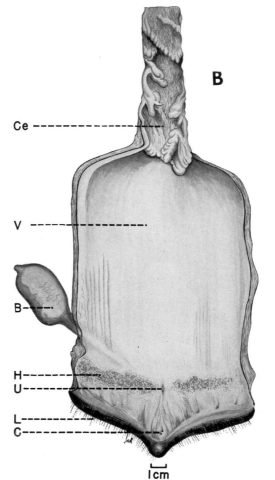

A. Cervix (cut open) of a heifer 4 days after estrus. Note the right annular folds around the cervical canal.

B. Cervix, vagina and external genitalia in a non-pregnant ewe. Note the annular folds in the cervix.
B = urinary bladder; Ce = cervix; C = clitoris; H = hymen; L = labia; U = external urethral opening; V = vagina.

vessels are very numerous, thick-walled and follow a tortuous course in the musculature of the uterus (see Reuber & Emmerson, 1959). The uterus receives its sympathetic nerve supply through the uterine and pelvic plexuses, the nerves terminating partly in the muscle fibers and partly in the mucosa.

In older animals which have bred several times, the uterine ligaments are stretched, with the result that the uterus is suspended at a lower level. This, in the mare, may hinder the removal of uterine luminal fluids and might even allow the backflow of small amounts of urine through the cervix, during estrus, with consequent mild catarrhal inflammation.

A. Histology

1. UTERINE WALL AND LINING

The uterus comprises the mucosa (endometrium), the muscularis and the serosa.

Endometrium. The endometrium consists of the *epithelial lining*, the *glandular layer* and the *connective tissue*. In the mare, the epithelial lining is built of simple columnar cells, which are temporarily ciliated (Hammond & Wodzicki, 1941).

The glandular layer contains many simple, branched tubular glands which are coiled, especially towards their ends. The glands are thought to serve an important function in the nutrition of the embryo prior to implantation and perhaps during the entire gestation period in those animals, *e.g.* the sow, which have a simple diffuse placentation. The number of glands increases in the horns and decreases in the mucosa which lies adjacent to the cervix.

In the ruminants, the mucosa contains non-glandular projections which are known as *caruncles*. The caruncles consist of connective tissue comparable to that found in the cortical stroma of the ovary. The deeper portions of the prominences are rich in blood vessels, but no glands are found under them. They are arranged in a number of rows, extending from the uterine body into the two horns.

In the uterus of the non-pregnant cow, there are 70 to 120 caruncles, each of which measures approximately 1 cm. in diameter. During pregnancy, they may reach a diam-

eter of 10 cm. and attain a spongy appearance, owing to the numerous crypts which receive the chorionic villi from the placenta (Plate IX). These villi develop in localized areas, the *cotyledons*, opposite to the caruncles. The cotyledon and caruncle together form the *placentome*. The mucosa of the ewe contains black pigment which is melanoblastic in origin (Grant, 1933).

In the mare, the mucosa is characterized by a number of conspicuous longitudinal folds which pass into the cervix to form the internal and external orifices. Such folds are less pronounced in the uterus of sows.

Myometrium. The myometrium consists of a thick inner circular layer of smooth muscle fibers and a thin outer longitudinal layer. Between these lies a vascular layer which contains many blood vessels and nerves. The vascular layer is not very distinct in the sow and mare, and may occur within the circular layer in ruminants.

Serosa. The serosa (external serous coat) is formed from the peritoneum and envelops the uterus.

The serosa, the vascular layer and the outer longitudinal muscle of the uterus invests and suspends the uterus from the dorsolateral wall of the body cavity.

2. CYCLICAL CHANGES IN THE ENDOMETRIUM

Each estrous cycle is associated with a build-up of the uterine tissues followed by involution; such changes occur whether fertilization has taken place or not. The cyclical changes are more pronounced in the endometrium of ruminants than in the sow and mare. Such differences may be related to the type of placentation characteristic of the species (see Chapter 10).

The cyclical changes in the endometrium may be considered under several headings. In the *proestrus* phase, when the tissues are under the influence of estrogen (follicular phase), vascularity is increased, the surface epithelium is simple columnar and the uterine glands show some growth, although they are simple and straight, with few branchings.

As a result of the changes in the ovary at estrus, the hormonal control of the endometrium changes from estrogen to progesterone. In early diestrus, when progesterone is acting on the system (luteal phase), the endometrium increases in thickness. The development of the uterine glands reaches its peak; they become larger, more coiled and branched. The glands secrete actively during early diestrus and the surface epithelium becomes high columnar. In the late diestrus, the thickened endometrium shrinks, the secretory activity of glands ceases and they become much smaller.

There is a cyclical shedding of the surface epithelium of the endometrium, followed by regeneration, but this gives rise to no extensive bleeding, such as that observed in primates when a substantial portion of the entire endometrium is lost. During "metestrus bleeding" in the cow, there is a pronounced capillary distention in the caruncles but the epithelium remains intact. In the intercaruncular areas, epithelial disruption and direct capillary hemorrhage into the uterine lumen takes place (Weber *et al.*, 1948).

In the ewe, a sloughing of the endometrium occurs during the early follicular phase of the cycle and is completed in the space of a few days. In the cow and sow, the process takes place during the late luteal phase and is also completed in a few days. In the mare, the cyclical changes in the endometrium appear to be minor.

B. Functions

The uterus serves a number of important functions. At copulation it is an important pathway for sperm, its contractile action being especially important in facilitating the movement of sperm to the Fallopian tubes. Where an ovum is fertilized, it is in the uterus that the developing embryo attaches and remains until its prenatal development is completed. In the early weeks of pregnancy, the embryo is thought to be sustained by the contents of the *uterine luminal fluid*, commonly known as "uterine milk" or "histotroph." The uterine luminal fluid is believed to be an ultrafiltrate of the blood plasma supplemented by secretions from the uterine glands. That some metabolites present in the circulation can be excreted in

the female reproductive tract and then absorbed by the embryo has been demonstrated by Friz & Mey (1959); these workers administered S^{35} to mated rabbits and were then able to detect the isotope in both the secretions and the zona pellucida of the developing embryo. The rate of formation and the biochemical composition of the uterine luminal fluid varies with the species and the stage of estrous cycle.

The uterus is capable of undergoing great changes in size, structure and position to accommodate itself to the needs of the growing conceptus during the gestation period. Its great contractile power remains dormant until time of parturition, when it plays the major role in the expulsion of the fetus and its membranes. Following parturition, the uterus is capable of almost regaining its former size and condition during the process called *involution*.

V. THE CERVIX

The cervix is the sphincter-like segment of the reproductive tract which separates, anatomically and physiologically, the uterine lumen from the vagina. It may be distinguished externally by its thick wall, due to the great thickness of the sphincter muscle, and internally by its constricted lumen. The function of the organ is to close the uterine lumen against macroscopic and microscopic intruders, and it remains closed at all times except parturition. At estrus it serves as a passageway for sperm. In pregnancy, the cervical mucus hardens and seals off the canal by forming the cervical plug which liquefies shortly before parturition. At parturition the cervix dilates, allowing the fetus and fetal membranes to pass out.

Although the structure of the cervix differs in detail among farm mammals, in each the cervical lining is characterized by various prominences. In the cow, ewe and sow, these are in the form of transverse or spirally interlocking ridges, known as *annular rings*. These rings are developed to varying degrees in the different species. They are especially prominent in the cow, where there are usually 4 rings, although this number may vary from 2 to 5. They are also well marked in the ewe, where they fit accurately into

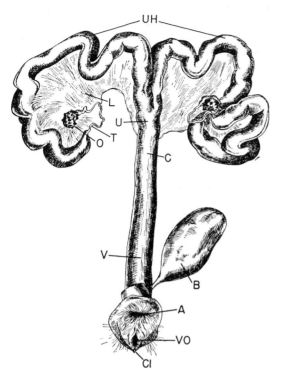

FIG. 4-10.—The reproductive organs of the sow (dorsal view). *A* = anus; *B* = urinary bladder; *C* = cervix; *Cl* = clitoris; *L* = broad ligament; *O* = ovary; *T* = Fallopian tube (uncoiled); *U* = uterine body; *UH* = uterine horns; *V* = vagina; *VO* = vaginal orifice. (*Redrawn from Eckstein & Zuckerman, 1960. In Marshall's Physiology of Reproduction, A. S. Parkes edit., Vol. I, Part 1, London, Courtesy Longmans.*)

each other to close the cervix securely (Plate X). In the sow, the rings are in a corkscrew arrangement which appears adapted to the spiral twisting of the tip of the boar's penis (Chapter 2).

The cervix of the mare is distinguished by conspicuous folds in the mucosa. The cervical canal is not well marked in the mare, but the opening into the vagina, the *os uteri*, is clearly defined. In the cow and ewe, the os uteri is a small opening on a rounded prominence in the anterior extremity of the vagina. The cervix of the sow passes into the vagina without forming an obvious *os uteri*.

A. Histology

The wall of the cervix consists of the mucosa, muscularis and serosa. The mucosa is arranged in high folds, which in turn bear smaller secondary folds. The lumen is lined with tall columnar epithelium. The intricate folds of the mucosa give the cervix its typical "fern-leaf" appearance in microscopic examination. There are numerous mucus-secreting cells in the mucosa and the folds of the tissues give an extensive secretory surface. The mucosa is otherwise non-glandular.

The muscularis is very rich in dense collagenous and elastic tissues and contains many smooth muscle cells. The inner circular layer of muscle is highly developed and forms the main substance of the annular folds.

Cyclical Changes. The greatest secretory activity of the mucus-producing cells of the cervix is shown at estrus; the mucus is least viscous, and blood vessels of the mucosa are congested. In the cow, the surface epithelium is uniform in height 6 days after estrus and few cells are secreting mucus. The edema and congestion of the mucosa, observed at estrus, disappears 8 to 11 days after estrus.

At 14 days post-estrus, the *os uteri* of the cow appears blanched, dry and constricted; the mucus-producing cells are not secreting. At 17 days the epithelial cells are larger and full of mucus, preparing for the copious secretion that precedes and accompanies estrus. At 20 days there is marked congestion of the blood vessels and the *os uteri* is dilated. The epithelial cells then are larger than at any other time in the cycle, and the whole surface is covered by a thin layer of mucus. In the other species, essentially the same changes in the cervical mucosa occur.

VI. THE VAGINA

The vagina is the lowermost part of the internal reproductive tract and serves as the female organ of copulation. In it is deposited the semen at copulation; at parturition it is the dilatable passageway for the fetus. The lining of the vagina shows several longitudinal folds (Plate X). The cow is peculiar in possessing an anterior sphincter muscle in addition to the posterior sphincter (at the junction of the vagina and vestibule) found in the other farm mammals.

A. Histology

The wall of the vagina consists of a mucosa, muscularis and serosa.

Mucosa. The surface epithelium is stratified and is thickened by an increase in the number of layers during proestrus and estrus. In the mare, much of the epithelium consists of polyhedral cells (cells with several sides) with a thin layer of flattened or cornified cells on the surface.

In the cow, surface cells are high columnar and secrete mucus in the upper part of the vagina; there is an absence of cornified cells owing to the low estrogen output in this species. The lower portion of the cow's vaginal epithelium is composed of stratified squamous cells. Tall goblet cells are found in the anterior vagina, but tend to disappear toward the vestibule. The commencement of secretion by the vaginal cells proceeds down the organ in a wave. Shortly after mating the number of leucocytes increases, probably because of semen in the vagina. There are no glands in the vaginal mucosa. Much of the mucus found in the lumen originates in the cervix.

Muscularis. The muscular coat of the vagina is less well developed than in the other parts of the reproductive tract. It consists of a thick inner circular layer and a thin outer longitudinal layer. This latter layer continues for some distance into the uterus. The muscularis is well supplied with blood vessels, nerve bundles and small groups of nerve cells; there is also much loose and dense connective tissue. In the sow, a thin layer of longitudinal muscle is observed within the inner circular layer, but is lacking in the other species.

Serosa. This is a highly compacted tissue, well supplied with elastic fibers. It contains a plexus of blood vessels, branches of which reach the muscularis and vaginal mucosa, and an extensive network of nerves.

Cyclical Changes in the Vaginal Mucosa. The epithelial cells reflect events in the ovaries. They undergo periodic changes, fluctuating between low-cuboidal and stratified squamous. Changes can be followed to some extent by the vaginal smear technique. This is most accurate in animals with short estrous cycles (*e.g.* rats and mice); in the farm mammals, changes in the vagina lag a few days behind ovarian changes and are less reliable indicators of the ovarian cycle.

VII. THE EXTERNAL GENITALIA

The external genitalia comprise the vestibule, the labia, the clitoris and glands that open in the vestibule. During copulation, the penis of the male enters the vagina by way of the vestibule and its associated structures; during the birth of the young, these pass out through this portion of the reproductive tract.

A. Vestibule

The border between the vagina and the vestibule is marked by an annular fold of mucosa, the *hymen* (Plate X). It varies in degree of development in the different species. Normally the hymen is torn and disappears early in the reproductive life of the female. The mature sow and cow have no hymen, but remnants of the hymen are occasionally observed in the young animal.

In the cow, the vestibule extends inwards for approximately 10 cm., and the *external urethral orifice* opens into its ventral surface. Just posterior to this point lies the *sub-urethral diverticulum*, a blind sac (Fig. 4–8). Gartner's ducts (remnants of the Wolffian ducts) open into the vestibule just lateral to the urethral orifice. The ducts from the major vestibular glands (glands of Bartholin) open into the vestibule posteriorly and laterally to Gartner's ducts. A similar arrangement is found in the other three species, although the ducts of Gartner may be absent. These tubo-alveolar glands, which resemble the bulbo-urethral glands of the male, secrete a viscid fluid, most actively at estrus.

The mucosa of the vestibule is lined with stratified squamous epithelium, and branched tubular glands are found in places. The glands are close together in the cow and scattered in the ewe. In the sow, the glands are small and isolated, possessing long, wide excretory ducts. The wall of the vestibule is made up of circular and longitudinal striated muscle.

B. Labia

The integument of the labia is richly endowed with sebaceous and tubular glands and the outer surface shows the same structure as the external skin. The labia contain fat depots and much elastic tissue, as well as a thin layer of smooth muscle. Many large sebaceous glands are found on the surface of the labia.

C. Clitoris

The clitoris is rich in elastic tissue and is made up of the main body, the glans and the prepuce, the latter of which is a continuation of the vestibular mucosa. The organ is the homologue of the penis and is capable of limited erection during copulation. In the cow, the greater part of the glans is buried in the mucosa of the vestibule. The clitoris is well developed in the mare, and in the sow is long and sinuous, terminating in a small point or cone.

The main body of the clitoris possesses a thick tunica albuginea within which lie many vessels and nerves. The end of the clitoris is covered by the glans, which is richly supplied with nerves. The main part of the organ lies in the prepuce, which is composed of the non-glandular cutaneous mucosa of the vestibule.

D. Cyclical Changes in External Genitalia

Various changes are observed, in some species, in the degree of congestion and color of parts of the external genitalia according to the stage of estrous cycle. In the sow, the walls of the labia swell in early estrus, becoming red internally. Late in estrus, the labia become flabby as the muscles relax. In diestrus, the muscles of the labia are contracted and their walls pink and moist. In the cow and mare, there is similar congestion of the labia which also become intensely pink or red during estrus. The swelling subsides after estrus. In the ewe, there are no clear changes in the external genitalia throughout the cycle.

REFERENCES

ANOPOLSKY, D. (1928). Cyclic changes in the size of muscle fibers of the Fallopian tube of the sow. *Amer. J. Anat.*, **40**, 459–469.

ASDELL, S. A. (1960). Growth in the bovine Graafian follicle. *Cornell Vet.*, **50**, 3–8.

BRAMBELL, F. W. R. (1960). Ovarian Changes. *In Marshall's Physiology of Reproduction*. A. S. Parkes (edit.) Chapter 5, Vol. 1, Part 1, London, Longmans.

BURGER, J. F. (1952). Sex Physiology of Pigs. *Onderstep. J. Vet. Res.* Suppl. No. 2, pp. 218.

FRIZ, M. & MEY, R. (1959). Early embryonic death before implantation. *Internat. J. Fertil.*, **4**, 306–308.

GARM, O. (1949). A study of bovine nymphomania, with special reference to etiology and pathogenesis. *Acta Endocrin.*, Suppl. **2**, pp. 144.

GRANT, R. (1933). The pigmentation of the uterine mucosa in the ewe. *Vet. J.*, **89**, 271–274.

GRUENWALD, P. (1942). The development of the sex cords in the gonads of man and mammals. *Amer. J. Anat.*, **70**, 359–389.

HADEK, R. (1955). The secretory process in the sheep's oviduct. *Anat. Rec.*, **121**, 187–206.

HAMMOND, J. & WODZICKI, K. (1941). Anatomical and histological changes during the oestrous cycle in the mare. *Proc. Roy Soc.* (Lond.), **130**B, 1–23.

HISAW, F. L. (1947). Development of the Graafian follicle and ovulation. *Physiol. Rev.*, **27**, 95–119.

LOMBARD, L., MORGAN, B. B. & McNUTT, S. H. (1950). The morphology of the oviduct of virgin heifers in relation to the estrous cycle. *J. Morphol.*, **86**, 1–24.

OLDS, D. & VANDEMARK, N. L. (1957). Composition of luminal fluids in bovine female genitalia. *Fertil. & Steril.*, **8**, 345–354.

REUBER, H. W. & EMMERSON, M. A. (1959). Arteriography of the internal genitalia of the cow. *J. Amer. Vet. Med. Ass.*, **134**, 101–109.

THOMSON, J. D. (1942). Comparative studies on gonad development in the rat, the pig and cattle. *Proc. Iowa Acad. Sci.*, **49**, 475–491.

cattle. *Proc. Iowa Acad. Sci.*, **49**, 475–491.

WEBER, A. F., MORGAN, B. B. & McNUTT, S. H. (1948). A histological study of metorrhagia in the virgin heifer. *Amer. J. Anat.*, **83**, 309–327.

QUESTIONS

1. Draw a diagram showing the reproductive tract of the ewe; label ten organs.
2. Discuss the histological characteristics of the uterus and the two parts of the Fallopian tube.
3. Give a full account of: antrum, cumulus oöphorus, cystic follicle, ovulation fossa, tunica albuginea, caruncle, Müllerian and Wolffian ducts, theca interna, clitoris, fimbriae.
4. In a tabulated form compare the morphology of the female reproductive organs of three farm mammals.
5. Give average measurement for the following organs in the sow and the mare: diameter of mature follicle, weight of ovary, length of uterine horn, length of cervix, length of vestibule.
6. Discuss the anatomy and physiology of the cervix in farm mammals.
7. Describe the histological changes which take place in the Graafian follicle from the time of antrum formation until the time of ovulation. Draw a diagram of a Graafian follicle.
8. Describe the process of ovulation and corpus luteum formation.
9. Give an account of the origin and formation of the female sex organs. Compare their development with that of the male sex organs. Where would you find the female homologues of the vasa deferentia, seminiferous tubules and bulbo-urethral glands?
10. Describe the various structures and glands which comprise the external genitalia. Discuss some of the differences in these which may be observed in four mammalian species.

Chapter 5

Puberty, Breeding Season and Estrous Cycle

By John F. Lasley

Reproduction in the female is complicated and is subject to adverse effects at many stages before and after the initiation of the reproductive cycle. The female must produce viable ova that are released from the ovary at the proper time. She must exhibit estrus (mating desire) near the time that ovulation occurs so the chances of the sperm and ovum uniting in the process of fertilization will be increased. She must supply the proper intra-uterine environment for the young from conception until birth as well as a good environment for her young from birth to weaning. Thus, normal reproduction involves the synchronization of many physiological mechanisms.

It is the purpose of this chapter to outline and discuss the different phases of reproduction in female farm mammals and the physiological mechanisms involved. These reproductive phenomena follow similar general patterns in the different species, although there are some definite and important differences which will be discussed later.

I. PUBERTY (SEXUAL MATURITY)

Puberty is the period of the female's life when the reproductive processes begin to function. In all species of farm mammals, puberty occurs before mature body size is attained and subsequently the young female must supply nutrients for the growth and development of her own body as well as for the growth of her young. This places more of a stress on the very young female if bred than on those that are more mature.

The growth of the ovary and the female reproductive tract is comparatively slow before puberty and these organs exhibit no functional activity. In general, the development of the reproductive organs keeps pace with body weight. A certain degree of body and genital maturity is necessary before the reproductive potential is reached. At a certain age or body weight for each individual female, there is an abrupt appearance of the first estrus and ovulation. This is accompanied by a sudden increase in the size and weight of the reproductive organs (Table 5–1).

A. Hormones and Puberty

Hormonal activity responsible for the occurrence of the first estrus (puberty) in the female is similar to that responsible for subsequent heat periods. The pituitaries of prepubertal animals probably possess large amounts of the gonadotropins but apparently

Table 5–1—Size and Weight of Various Reproductive Organs of Crossbred Gilts Before and After Puberty

(Adapted from Reddy et al., 1958, Mo. Agric. Expt. Sta. Res. Bull. No. 666.)

	Before Puberty	After Puberty	% Increase
Age in days	169	186	
Length of vagina (mm.)	292	318	9
Avg. length of uterine horns (mm.)	383	605	58
Avg. length of Fallopian tubes (mm.)	217	241	11
Avg. weight of uterus (gm.)	153	263	72
Avg. weight of ovaries (gm.)	2.14	2.83	32

lack the ability to release them into the blood stream. The evidence for this is found by the assay of pituitaries of immature females for the hormones and by the ease with which puberty can be induced in such females by the injection of adequate amounts of the gonadotropins. The response of the immature female to the gonadotropins has been known for many years, and the induction of ovarian weight increase in 21-day old rats with pregnant mare serum which contains mostly FSH has been used as the basis of a biological test of pregnancy in the mare. Estrus and ovulation in immature females of several species of farm animals have also been induced by the injection of gonadotropins.

The injection of estrogens in the immature female will also cause the abrupt appearance of symptoms of estrus, although there is some variation between individual females. Thus, it seems that the anterior pituitary gland must first begin secreting or releasing adequate amounts of the gonadotropins into the blood stream to stimulate the production of estrogens by the ovary before puberty is attained.

Although little or no work has been done with farm animals, it is possible that the nervous system may be related to the onset of puberty. A number of pathological conditions affecting the hypothalamus causes precocious puberty in children. In addition, experimental hypothalamic lesions in rats have been reported to hasten the onset of puberty. More work is needed to clarify this relationship.

B. Age and Weight at Puberty

The occurrence of the first estrus is remarkable in its abruptness as if some physiological thermostat has been triggered to initiate reproductive activity. Puberty usually occurs as the mature weight is approached and the growth is declining except in seasonally breeding animals. This suggests that the onset of puberty depends upon a change in the balance between the output of gonadotropic and growth hormones by the anterior pituitary gland.

The age and weight at puberty varies widely between species (Table 5–2). The age of the sow when she gives birth to her first young is dependent to a great extent on her age of attaining puberty. This is of less importance in sheep, cattle and horses because of husbandry practices which usually delay the first breeding season to an older age than in gilts. Gilts are usually bred to farrow their first litters at near one year of age because most pork producers breed to concentrate the time of farrowing in the spring and the fall seasons. Therefore, the gilt usually must conceive by the time she is 8 months of age. Puberty in gilts at an early age is desirable so that by the time the mating season arrives she has passed through one or more estrous cycles. More ova are shed at the second and third heat periods than at the first, and this would favor the production of larger litters at farrowing time.

The age and weight of ewe lambs at puberty are not such an important factor as

Table 5-2.—Puberty, Estrus and Ovulation in Farm Mammals

Phenomena		Cow	Ewe	Sow	Mare
Age at puberty (mo.)		4–14	7–10	4–7	15–24
Weight at puberty (lb.)		350–600	60–75	150–250	Depends on mature size
Duration of estrus	Range	4–30 hrs.	1–3 days	1–5 days	2–10 days
	Avg.	17 hrs.	35 hrs.	2 days	6 days
Length of estrous cycle (days)	Range	14–24	16–21	16–24	10–35
	Avg.	21	17	21	21
Parturition to estrus (days)	Range	16–90	30–59*	3–5	2–30
	Avg.	35	35	4	11
Time of ovulation	Range	2–26 hrs. after end of estrus	12–24 hrs. before end of estrus	16–48 hrs. from beginning of estrus	24–48 hrs. before end of estrus
	Avg.	12 hrs.	17 hrs.	2nd day	
Best time to breed		Late estrus or shortly after estrus	Middle of estrus	2nd day of estrus	Every other day beginning 2nd day of estrus

*Only if still within the breeding season.

in gilts because sheep are seasonal breeders with estrus in mature ewes occurring only in late summer or the early fall. Ewe lambs may be old and heavy enough from the physiological standpoint to reach puberty several weeks or months in advance of the breeding season but do not show outward signs of puberty until the normal breeding season begins.

C. Factors Affecting Puberty

Since puberty is controlled by certain physiological mechanisms involving the gonads and the anterior pituitary gland, it must also be influenced by several factors of both a hereditary and an environmental nature working through these organs.

Season. The influence of the season of birth on the onset of puberty in cattle and horses has received little attention from reasearch workers. More attention has been given in sheep and swine.

An examination of the ovaries of many gilts in a slaughter house showed that the season of slaughter, and thus the season of birth, had a highly significant effect on the age of puberty (Wiggins et al., 1950). The percentage of juvenile tracts in gilts slaughtered in January, April and July varied between 15 and 24 per cent as compared to 45 per cent in gilts slaughtered in October. Gilts farrowed later in the spring reach puberty at an older age. The factors responsible for these observations are not known, although the presence or absence of disease at different seasons could be involved as well as differences in growth rate in the different seasons.

Ewe lambs born earlier in the spring experience a longer breeding season and show more estrous periods during the breeding season than those born late. Many late born lambs do not exhibit estrus at all in their first breeding season. This may be associated with a faster growth rate of lambs born early before the normal seasonal decline in growth rate.

Temperature. The effect of constant environmental temperatures on the appearance of puberty in Zebu (Brahman), Santa Gertrudis and Shorthorn heifers was studied by Dale *et al.* (1959). The calves were raised from one month of age at constant temperatures with a relative humidity of 50 to 70 per cent and with equal periods of light and dark. Puberty was reached at an average age of 398 days in the 80° F. temperature as compared to 300 days at the lower temperature of 50° F. The age of puberty was 320 days in those heifers maintained in an open shed exposed to outside weather conditions. The delay of puberty at the high temperature was attributed to a much slower growth rate.

Nutrition. The level of feeding has a curvilinear relationship with the onset of puberty with an optimal level somewhere between overfeeding and underfeeding. Extreme underfeeding delays puberty probably through a detrimental effect on the pituitary, suppressing the secretion of gonadotropins. Overfatness also is detrimental and will delay the onset of puberty. The physiological effect of overfatness on reproduction is not known. One theory is that the accumulation of fat around the ovaries and the other reproductive organs prevents their normal function. Another theory is that overfatness either interferes with the secretion of the reproductive hormones by the ovary or the fat may absorb estrogens and progesterone from the blood stream so that they are not available in normal amounts. Deficiencies of essential nutrients such as phosphorus in the ration causing slow growth also delay the onset of puberty.

Genetic Factors. Genetic factors affecting the age of puberty are reflected by differences between strains, breeds and by crossbreeding and inbreeding. Some of the dairy breeds of cattle reach puberty before beef breeds. Zebu cattle, in general, reach puberty from 6 to 12 months later than the European breeds. Inbreeding in swine, cattle and sheep delays the age of puberty, whereas crossbreeding causes it to occur at a younger age. These genetic effects in female farm mammals, especially of inbreeding and crossbreeding, indicate that genes which affect this trait are largely non-additive in nature. Therefore, selection for early puberty within a given breed or species would be relatively ineffective.

A genetically sterile strain of mice in which the female reproductive organs do not develop but remain immature as in pre-pubertal females has been reported. This condition is due to a simple recessive gene in the homozygous state. The injection of the various pituitary hormones causes these otherwise sterile females to breed, give birth to young and lactate. The action of this gene seems to be that it causes a failure of the release of the gonadotropins or causes their inactivation after their release. Some gilts with infantile reproductive tracts and ovaries never come into estrus but it is not known if this is due to hereditary or environmental factors.

II. BREEDING SEASON

The term "breeding season" as used here is the period of time during the year when females of a species come into estrus. The non-breeding season (anestrus) is the period of time in which estrus does not occur in the mature female and the reproductive organs are in a state of quiescence.

Most species of wild animals have a definite breeding season which is initiated at a time when environmental conditions are optimum for the survival of the young when they are born. If the duration of pregnancy is 5 months, the breeding season begins in the fall so the young are born in the spring. Where the period of pregnancy is about 9 months, the peak of the breeding season occurs in the early summer so the young will also be born in the spring. The young, then, are born just before green feed becomes abundant so that when the increased supply stimulates a greater milk flow in the mother, the young are old and large enough to handle the increased milk flow to best advantage.

The wild prototypes of the sow, cow and ewe all probably exhibit a restricted breeding season. Domestication of farm animals, covering a period of 5,000 or more years, has resulted in a gradual expansion of the breeding season until most species will now breed at almost any period of the year. Some breeds of sheep are an exception to this.

Several factors may be responsible for the disappearance of a restricted breeding season under domestication. Domesticated animals have had a more constant food supply throughout the year than their wild counterparts. This seems to be borne out by the fact that they are much more prolific than animals in the wild state. Domesticated animals may also have had a more constant environmental temperature because of housing during periods of extreme heat or cold under the watchful eye of man. Another factor is that man has selected for more prolific animals and those which would reproduce throughout the year.

Among farm animals only the sheep are classed as *seasonal breeders*. Sexual activity in domesticated sheep varies from manifestations of a few estrous periods per year in the mountain breeds to year long breeding in the tropical and subtropical breeds. Cows and sows are *continuous breeders* throughout the year. However, there is some evidence, especially in mares, that females show a greater readiness to breed at a time which corresponds to the primitive breeding season of that species (see Chapter 16).

Man now controls the *mating season* in cattle, swine and horses for his own convenience and for economic reasons. Cows are bred to produce spring calves because of the abundance of pasture grasses during the spring and summer months, and because the calves can be weaned in the fall so the mothers will not have the drain of lactation during the winter months when the quality and quantity of feed is low. Sows are usually bred to farrow litters twice each year, in the spring and again in the fall. The time of calving can be set for any season of the year the breeder desires, and the system of multiple farrowing when pigs are farrowed in all seasons of the year has not encountered any difficulty in getting sows to breed.

Dairy cattle vary in their fertility level at different seasons of the year (Mercier & Salisbury, 1947). The lowest per cent of successful services was obtained during winter and spring and the highest during the summer and fall. The average monthly conception rate was correlated with the monthly average day length, there being a lag of approximately 1 to 2 months before the maximum effect was reached.

A. Breeding Season in Sheep

Since sheep exhibit a distinct breeding season, the discussion here will be confined to this species. The factors responsible for the onset of the breeding season in sheep have been an object of considerable study by workers in many parts of the world. Much information has been accumulated to show that the onset of the breeding season is closely related to the length of daylight, although other factors are also involved (Fig. 5-1).

Length of Daylight. That some external factor, or factors, were responsible for the seasonal breeding of sheep was pointed out by Marshall (1937). When sheep were transported across the equator from the northern to the southern hemisphere, the ewes soon altered their breeding season to conform to that in their new environment. This has also been observed in other species. Some females adjust their sexual activity rather quickly to their new environment. Others maintain their internal rhythm for a year or two exhibiting estrus during the season in the country of their origin, but they finally adjust to the breeding season in the new environment. In some females, the change in environment results in the complete lack of stimuli necessary for sexual activity and they never breed. This results in natural selection against such females, because they do not leave young to perpetuate a new generation.

Studies have been made of the breeding season in sheep at different latitudes which gives further evidence that the length of daylight is involved. In general, the breeding season is extended over the whole year at the equator or they have two crops of lambs each year. Breeds of sheep in this area do not react to light because they were developed under comparatively uniform light conditions and do not have the capacity to respond to changes in daylight length as have breeds in other areas.

A study of the breeding season in sheep outside the equatorial region also shows that

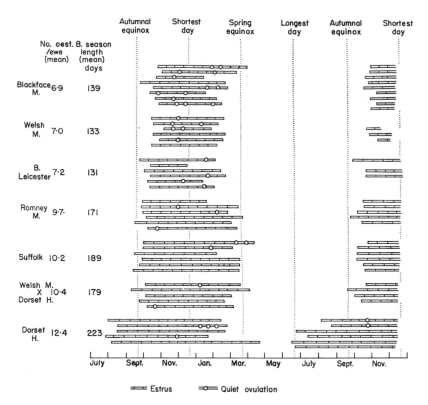

FIG. 5–1.—Breed differences in the duration of the breeding season and non-breeding season in adult ewes in Great Britain. Some breeds such as the Dorset Horn had a prolonged breeding season whereas those such as the Welsh Mountain had a very restricted breeding season. In nearly all cases the breeding season was within the period from the Autumnal equinox and the Spring equinox and the middle of the season corresponded rather closely to the shortest day of the year, or December 21. This illustrates the close relationship between the breeding season and length of day. Note that some estrous cycles double or triple the usual length occurred due to quiet ovulations or to the failure to detect heat in the non-pregnant females observed. (*After Hafez, 1952, J. Agric. Sci. 42, 305.*)

it is related to seasonal changes in day length. The breeding season gradually gets shorter near the poles. The mid-period of the breeding season occurs before the shortest day irrespective of the hemisphere.

Sheep respond to decreasing daylight length and are known as *short day breeders.* Other animals such as poultry respond to increasing day length and are known as *long day breeders* (see Chapter 17). The major role of decreasing daylight in initiating the breeding season in sheep was shown by Yeates (1949). By supplying artificial lighting so that increasing amounts were provided during the winter months and decreasing amounts, using a blacked out pen, during the summer, the breeding season was reversed. The treated ewes came into estrus in May when control ewes were in anestrus. They lambed in October during the regular breeding season of the control ewes.

Hormonal Mechanisms. The foregoing discussion has shown that light in some way increases the activity of the gonads to establish a definite breeding season for many species. The present concept regarding this mechanism is that light acts on the retina of the eyes and the impulse is relayed from there to the hypothalamus via the optic nerves. The hypothalamus then releases a substance into the blood stream that stimulates the release of gonadotropins by the pituitary gland (see Chapter 1). Possibly the proper balance between FSH and LH for ovarian function is brought about by this action. A proper balance seems to be more important for sexual activity than a high level of production of both hormones. One of the reasons for this view is that pre-pubertal and anestrous animals are known to possess normal to high amounts of FSH and LH in their pituitary glands, yet such females do not exhibit normal estrous cycles.

Temperature. Temperature is thought to have little or no influence on the onset of the breeding season in sheep, although it is often difficult to separate temperature and daylight effects. Studies with sheep suggest that temperature may have some influence on the time of onset of the breeding season in this species (Dutt & Bush, 1955). In ewes kept at an environmental temperature between 45° and 48° F. during the summer months, the average date of first estrus occurred 54 days earlier than in control ewes, even though differences between groups in length of daylight were the same.

High ambient temperatures cause a reduction in the number of young produced by females. The loss in sheep has been shown to be due to a lowering in the rate of fertilization and a higher rate of embryonic deaths. In ewes maintained at 70° and 90° F., the rectal temperature and respiration rate were higher and a lower per cent of the ova were fertilized in those maintained at the higher temperature, but estrus was not inhibited nor was the ovulation rate altered (Alliston & Ulberg, 1961). The transfer of embryos between ewes maintained at the two temperatures 72 hours after the onset of estrus showed that embryos originating from ewes maintained at the higher temperature suffered irreversible damage by that time as evidenced by a higher per cent of embryonic deaths. Embryonic deaths were also larger when the transfer was made from the low to the high temperature ewes than when transfers were made between ewes maintained at the low temperature. Thus, it appears that the uterine environment in ewes maintained at the higher temperatures was also less favorable.

Other Factors. Several studies show that there is considerable variation in the onset of the breeding season in the same ewes in different years. A definite difference between breeds in the onset of estrus does exist and this suggests that the trait is influenced by genes. The repeatability coefficient for the onset of the breeding season is low and suggests that selection for this trait would result in slow progress. The action of the genes is probably more of a non-additive nature and would require special methods of selection if progress were to be made. Extreme underfeeding or the feeding of rations lacking in nutrients such as vitamin A and phosphorus may delay the onset of the breeding season in some ewes.

III. THE ESTROUS CYCLE

Once puberty has been reached and the breeding season has been initiated, estrus (heat) occurs in the non-pregnant female in a characteristic rhythmic cycle. The interval between the onset of one estrous period until the onset of the next is known as the *estrous* (*estrual*) *cycle*. These intervals are accompanied by a series of definite physiological changes within the reproductive tract of the female (Chapter 4).

A. Phases of the Estrous Cycle

Some wild animals such as the bear, wolf and fox are *monoestrous* because they have just one (mono) estrous period per year. Females from other species are *polyestrous* because they have many (poly) estrous periods in definite cycles seasonally or throughout the year. Sheep are polyestrous because once the breeding season is initiated and pregnancy does not occur, they have several estrous cycles until the breeding season ends.

The normal estrous cycle in farm mammals consists of four different phases. These are known as *proestrus, estrus, metestrus* and *diestrus*. Proestrus is the phase of the cycle just before the occurrence of estrus in which the reproductive system is beginning preparations for the release of the mature ovum from the ovary. Estrus is the phase of the cycle in which the female will accept copulation. Metestrus is the period im-

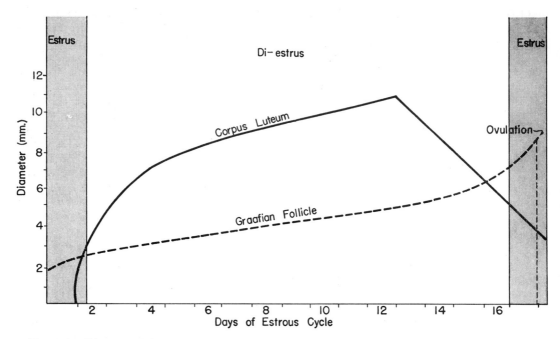

Fig. 5–2.—Diagram of the ovarian changes that take place in the ewe during one estrous cycle. Note that maximum follicular growth occurs when the corpus luteum starts to decline. In the ewe, the maximum diameter of the corpus luteum exceeds that of the follicle. (*Adapted from Warbritton, 1934, J. Morphol. 56, 181.*)

mediately following the estrous period. It is during this phase that the uterus makes preparations for the implantation of the embryo which initiates pregnancy. If pregnancy does not occur, the reproductive tract goes into a period of rest called diestrus. All of these various phases occur in normal females (see Fig. 5–2).

In the cow, sow and mare this period averages close to 20 to 21 days in length, although there is a normal variation of a few days on either side of this average (Table 5–2). Ewes, however, have a shorter estrous cycle averaging between 16 and 17 days in length. Although there are normal variations in the length of the estrous cycle, cycles definitely abnormal in length do occur. Estrous cycles of abnormally short length are definite signs that the ovary is not functioning normally and suggests a hormone imbalance.

B. Physiological Mechanisms

The different phases of the estrous cycle together with the histological and physio-

logical changes which occur are associated with fluctuations in the amounts of gonadotropic and female sex hormones responsible for the changes in the female reproductive tract.

Hormonal Mechanisms. The control of the estrous cycle by the anterior pituitary and ovarian hormones has been demonstrated in many species. Several pituitary and ovarian hormones are interrelated in controlling the events which occur during the estrous cycle (Chapter 1).

FSH is responsible for the growth of the Graafian follicle and the maturation of the ovum. LH initiates the pre-ovulatory enlargement of the follicle, causes ovulation and the subsequent formation of the corpus luteum. FSH in conjunction with LH causes the theca interna cells of the follicle to produce estrogens. The maturing follicle secretes estrogens in increasing amounts until its action on the nervous system produces behavioral estrus (see Chapter 9). Increased amounts of estrogens also inhibit the production of FSH by the pituitary gland.

When ovulation is completed, the corpus luteum is formed and begins to secrete progesterone. As long as the corpus luteum remains active in the production of progesterone, the secretion of FSH remains low and the ovarian follicles show little growth and development. If pregnancy does not occur, progesterone secretion by the corpus luteum wanes, FSH production increases and a new crop of follicles is produced. Apparently, progesterone suppresses the secretion of FSH by the pituitary gland.

Neurohumoral Mechanisms. Evidence is now accumulating to indicate that neurohumoral mechanisms function in the regulation of gonadotropic hormone secretions. By neurohumoral is meant the liberation of a chemical substance by a nervous impulse (humor means liquid; neuro means neuron or nerve). Evidence for this is found in the results of studies showing that (*a*) different lengths of day are responsible for the onset of the breeding season in some species, (*b*) the stimulation of copulation causes a release of LH and ovulation in some species, (*e.g.*, the rabbit), (*c*) gonadal atrophy is often associated with diseases of the brain in humans and (*d*) experimental destruction of the hypothalamus or parts of it has been followed by gonadal atrophy. There is little doubt that the hypothalamus is involved in the control of pituitary hormone secretion. In addition, there seems to be "sexual centers" in the hypothalamus necessary for the occurrence of normal estrus (see Chapter 9).

The neurohumoral mechanisms by which these hormones are released are as follows. In "non-spontaneous" ovulating species (*e.g.* the rabbit), the stimulus of copulation is carried by the nervous system to the ventral portion of the hypothalamus. In those species which ovulate "spontaneously" the stimulators involved are still unknown. The hypothalamus after stimulation releases one or more neurohumoral substances which are carried to the anterior pituitary by the blood stream. These substances stimulate the release of LH which induces ovulation.

Possibly cholinergic (nerve fibers causing effects similar to those induced by acetylcholine) and adrenergic (nerve fibers which produce an adrenalin-like substance at their terminals) components are involved in the neurohumoral release involving ovulation. The injection of atropine, a parasympathetic blocking drug, in heifers at the beginning of estrus will block ovulation (Hansel, 1959). If chorionic gonadotropin was injected along with the atropine at the beginning of estrus, however, ovulation occurred earlier than normal. Thus, it would seem that a neurogenic mechanism having a cholinergic component is involved in the release of pituitary gonadotropins in the cow. More recent work indicates that oxytocin may be one of the neurohumors in the cow. Injections of a purified oxytocin preparation at the beginning of estrus shortened the period between the end of estrus and ovulation. This suggests that oxytocin stimulated the release of LH by the pituitary and hastened ovulation.

Daily injections of oxytocin given during the first 7 days of the estrous cycle shortened cycle length to 8 to 10 days or about one-half the normal length. This appeared to be due to the failure of normal corpus luteum formation and function which in turn may have been due to an inhibition of luteotropic hormone secretion by the pituitary because of the oxytocin injections allowing the estrus inducing substances to be secreted earlier in the cycle than normal. The failure of leutotropic hormone production may have been due to an indirect effect of oxytocin attributable to a reduction of oxytocin secretion by the hypothalamus or by the failure to produce some associated neurohumor (Hansel & Wagner, 1960). Additional work is needed to clarify the mechanisms involved.

IV. ESTRUS AND RELATED PHENOMENA

Estrus and ovulation are more or less synchronized (Fig. 5–2) in females to increase the probability of the ovum and sperm meeting in the process of fertilization to initiate the growth and development of a new individual. Synchronization is necessary because the life of the ovum after ovulation and that of the sperm in the female reproductive tract is limited to a few hours.

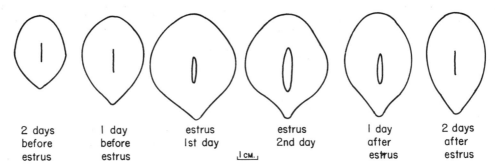

|2 days
before
estrus|I day
before
estrus|estrus
Ist day|estrus
2nd day|I day
after
estrus|2 days
after
estrus|

FIG. 5–3.—Tracings of the vulva in the same sow before, during and after estrus. The lines were smoothed but the size of each is from an actual tracing made on a glass slide. The outside lines show the contour of the vulva and the inside lines and ovals the lumen of the vagina. Note the rapid increase in size of the vulva just before estrus and especially the size of the lumen on the second day of estrus. Also note the decrease in the size of the vulva and lumen following the cessation of estrus.

A. Estrus

The outward signs or symptoms of estrus are somewhat similar in females of the different species of farm mammals, although there are some variations of behavior between and within species (see Chapter 9).

In the cow and especially in the sow, the vulva begins to swell during late proestrus, becomes very much swollen during estrus but the swelling subsides with the end of estrus (Fig. 5–3). As estrus approaches in the cow and sow, they become very active and restless and during heat will mount other females and stand when mounted. Activity and restlessness is less intense in ewes and mares and the mounting of other females is seldom observed in females of these two species.

The swelling of the vulva and the extra secretion of fluids during estrus act as a lubricant for the act of copulation. In the cow, estrus is accompanied by the discharge of considerable amounts of a milky to clear colored gelatinous mucus from the vulva. It is secreted by the cervix.

Duration of Estrus. The duration of estrus varies considerably between species (Table 5–2) and between individuals within a species. Much of this may be due to variations in the frequencies with which checks were made for estrus in each study. This is especially true in studies involving cattle which has the shortest average estrous period of all farm mammals. Whether or not females were checked for estrus with intact or vasectomized males or just by visual appraisal could be a cause of variation.

Breed and strain differences in the duration of estrus have been observed in ewes, cows and sows and draft mares have been reported to have longer estrus than light mares. The duration of estrus, in some areas, is longer in mares in the spring than in the summer when it is hot and dry.

The duration of estrus in range cows seems to be shorter than in cows kept under farm conditions. If this is true, lower levels of nutrition are associated with shorter estrus. Cows with extremely short estrus occurring early in the morning, late in the evening or during the night may be missed entirely when hand mating or artificial insemination are practiced.

Quiet Ovulation. In some females all of the physiological and histological events including ovulation and the different phases of the estrous cycle occur in a normal manner without behavioral estrus. The fact that follicles develop, ovulation takes place and the corpus luteum forms in a normal manner has been verified in cows and mares by palpating the ovary through the rectum and in sheep by observing the ovaries after slaughtering the animals.

Quiet ovulation occurs in ewes just before the onset of the breeding season and just afterward. It occurs more often in ewes on a submaintenance diet than in ewes fed an adequate ration especially during the first half of the breeding season, and has been observed more frequently in young than in adult animals. Quiet ovulation has been observed in all species of farm animals and is indicated when the estrous periods or the time between estrous periods is double or triple the usual length. It has been observed in cows at one or more periods following calving.

Quiet ovulation probably occurs because of a lack of a proper balance among the various hormones affecting the onset of estrus. It is also possible that neurohumoral factors responsible for behavioral estrus might be involved, but the role of these in the expression of estrus is not fully understood.

Anovulatory Estrus. Just as ovulation can occur without estrus, it is possible for estrus to occur without ovulation. This is known as anovulatory estrus and may account for some sterile matings. Anovulatory estrus occurs in all species of farm mammals and mainly during post-partum estrus in swine.

Estrus During Pregnancy. The cessation of estrus after breeding is a good indication that pregnancy has occurred and in the past it was thought that estrus seldom, if ever, occurred during pregnancy. Estrus occurs in cattle in 3 to 5 per cent of the pregnancies mainly during the first 3 months of pregnancy although it can occur at a later time. Ewes, sows and mares also show estrus during pregnancy, although the frequency of occurrence has not been studied as carefully in these species as in cattle where artificial insemination is so widely used. Some growth of follicles has been observed in pregnant females but ovulation seldom occurs. It must occur occasionally, however, because superfetation which is two simultaneous pregnancies with young of different ages in the same female has been reported.

The occurrence of estrus during pregnancy is of practical importance. Repeat breeding females should be inseminated into the cervix and not into the uterus to avoid the possibility of causing abortion. In addition, females which have normal estrous cycles after breeding and are hard to settle should be checked for pregnancy when possible before they are culled and sold.

B. Ovulation

Ovulation may be defined as the discharge of the ovum from the Graafian follicle. Several more follicles begin their period of growth during the proestrous period than normally reach maturity and produce ova. Some of these follicles become atretic, but added injections of gonadotropins during the period shortly before estrus often causes the ovulation (superovulation) of many more ova than the usual number for that species (Chapters 4 & 6).

Although it is generally recognized that LH induces ovulation, the exact mechanism involved is still obscure. Possibly LH initiates changes in the follicular wall which cause it to weaken so that the layers finally burst releasing the ovum and the follicular fluid. An abnormal condition in which the ovary possesses cystic follicles is due to the failure of the follicles to rupture and there is an increased amount of follicular fluid accumulated. The injections of LH often cause these cystic follicles to rupture which further suggests that LH is involved in the process whereby the follicular wall gives way, not because of increased pressure, but more likely because of the increasing susceptibility of the tissues to bursting or separation. The effects of LH are not immediate but require a few hours to result in ovulation. It is known that in the rabbit 10 to 11 hours elapse between LH release or LH injection and ovulation.

Time of Ovulation. The approximate time of ovulation in the different species of farm mammals is summarized in Table 5–2. The time of ovulation is related to the time that LH is released into the blood stream by the pituitary gland. More and more evidence is accumulating to indicate that even in farm mammals which ovulate spontaneously, neurohumoral mechanisms are involved in LH release. The evidence for this is found in the fact that (*a*) copulation in cattle sometimes hastens the time of ovulation by an hour or two, (*b*) injections of LH in mares which normally have a long and extended heat period hastens ovulation and (c) injections of heifers with atropine at the beginning of estrus will block ovulation.

C. Interval from Parturition to First Estrus

The uterus of the female increases greatly in size during pregnancy aside from the contents of the fetus and associated fluids. This increase in size is due to the growth of the endometrium of the uterus to form the maternal placenta which nourishes the fetus. Following parturition, the female must produce milk for her young and prepare the uterus, ovary and other reproductive organs as well as the endocrine system for the resumption of a normal estrous cycle and for a new pregnancy. Complete involution of the uterus in the cow is indicated by the return of the uterus to the normal position (near the pelvic region), size, tone and consistency.

The period from parturition to complete involution in the cow varies considerably and ranges between 30 and 50 days. Involution is usually well completed by the time the first estrous period occurs. Complete uterine involution does not occur in the mare until 20 to 40 days after pregnancy ends. Since the first post-partum estrus occurs within 6 to 13 days in the mare, the uterus has not had sufficient time for complete involution which may be one of the main reasons why the conception rate is low when mares are bred at this time. Little is known about the time required for the involution of the uterus in the sow, but the period of time is probably similar to that required in the cow and mare. Estrus occurs in many sows within 3 to 5 days after parturition, but conception seldom occurs because of a failure of ovulation in most cases. The early weaning of pigs has resulted in the breeding of sows within 4 to 5 weeks after farrowing without any apparent reduction in fertility. However, this point needs further study. The period of time required for involution of the uterus in the ewe is of little practical importance since most ewes have a definite annual breeding season and lamb once each year. This allows enough time for the reproductive system to return to normal before the next pregnancy occurs.

The ability of the female to re-establish an estrous cycle soon after parturition is influenced by several factors. An understanding of these is of importance because optimum breeding efficiency demands that the females be normal and regular in their estrous cycles.

Lactation. The production of milk does not lengthen the interval from parturition to first estrus in the mare, but it does in the cow and sow. The permanent removal of piglets from sows within the first week after parturition results in two-thirds of them coming into estrus within a 3-week period. There is some disagreement as to whether or not sows can be brought into estrus during lactation by separating the piglets from the sows for 4 or 5 consecutive nights. Injections of gonadotropins have successfully initiated estrus in lactating sows especially after the 40th day *post-partum.* Apparently, lactation or the stimulus of suckling has some inhibiting effect on the appearance of estrus in this species possibly through the failure of gonadotropins to be released into the blood stream by the anterior pituitary gland. Studies with cows have shown that the interval from parturition to first estrus is prolonged in cows that nurse their calves as compared to those that are milked twice daily. A large percentage of quiet ovulations has also been observed in cows nursing calves. This strongly suggests that the stimulus of suckling and not the drain of lactation is responsible for the prolongation of the interval from parturition to the first estrous period, although both may be involved when feed is sparse.

Nutrition. The influence of nutritional levels on the interval from parturition to first estrus in cows can be considerable, although it has not received a close study to determine its importance. The interval from parturition to first estrus in range cows where feed is sometimes sparse was 80 days (Lasley & Bogart, 1943). This is about twice as long as the interval observed in dairy cattle and about 20 days longer than that reported for beef cattle under more favorable conditions. Much of the low calf crop on the range (60 to 70 per cent weaned) must be due to a suboptimum level of nutrition during lactation resulting in the failure of cows to initiate a normal estrous cycle during this period.

Heredity. Differences between breeds and strains in the interval from parturition to first estrus have been observed in cows and sows. Undoubtedly genetic effects are present but they may be masked by those of an environmental nature since the heritability of this trait appears to be low.

D. Synchronization of Estrus

The synchronization of estrus means that the estrous cycle is altered so that the estrous period of many females is caused to occur on the same day or within a period of 2 or 3 days. It would have several practical advantages for the livestock breeder. It would be possible to inseminate artificially many females on the same farm on the same day thereby concentrating the efforts to a more limited period of time. In the case of swine where the life of the sperm stored outside the body is limited to a period of 24 to 48 hours, the synchronization of estrus on a large number of females would allow the greater use of semen from a single, superior progeny-tested sire. Another advantage would be that the time of parturition could be confined to a more limited period so that more attention could be given to the young and a larger percentage of them saved. Still another advantage would be that more of the total crop could be marketed at the same time and there would be less need for segregating the young into different age groups during the growing-fattening period.

Efforts to synchronize and control estrus have involved the use of progesterone because this hormone is known to suppress follicular growth, estrus and ovulation. In early experiments, progesterone injections were used and they did not always give a uniform response because of individual variations in the rate of absorption of the hormone, rate of inhibition and the rate of recovery from the inhibition after the supply of the hormone in the body was exhausted.

Various compounds have become available which have an action similar to that of progesterone. Some of these compounds are effective when fed orally and when they are administered in this way they seem to give more uniform results than when given by injections.

The procedure generally followed is to supply the estrus inhibiting compounds in the rations of normal, non-lactating sexually mature females. Most of the studies have been made with heifers and gilts. The feeding period is continued about 15 days and then the compound is withheld from the ration. Within 4 to 5 days after the removal of the hormone from the ration, 70 to 90 per cent of the females come into estrus (Nellor, 1960). Studies of females after autopsy show that ovulation and the number of ova shed from the ovary are normal in the first controlled estrus and the young develop normally if the females are bred. If females are not bred at the first controlled estrus, the next estrous period occurs normally and reproductive efficiency is normal.

The dosage level of progesterone and of the estrus inhibiting compounds is rather critical. If dosages are too high, a high incidence of cystic ovaries occurs especially in swine. If doses are too low there would be no response. Recent results on the synchronization of estrus in farm mammals are very encouraging, although there still are some problems to be solved before the methods can be recommended for practical application.

REFERENCES

ALLISTON, C. W. & ULBERG, L. C. (1961). Early pregnancy loss in sheep at ambient temperatures of 70° and 90° F. as determined by embryo transfer. *J. Anim. Sci.*, **20,** 608–613.

DALE, H. E., RAGSDALE, A. C., & CHENG, C. S. (1959). Effect of constant environmental temperatures of 50° and 80° F. on appearance of puberty in beef calves. *J. Anim. Sci.*, **18,** 1362–1366.

DUTT, R. H. & BUSH, L. F. (1955). The effect of low environmental temperature on initiation of the breeding season and fertility in sheep. *J. Anim. Sci.*, **14,** 885–896.

HANSEL, W. (1959). Further studies on the regulation of the bovine estrous cycle by oxytocin injections. *J. Dairy Sci.*, **42,** 940–941.

HANSEL, W. & WAGNER, W. C. (1960). Luteal inhibition in the bovine as a result of oxytocin injections, uterine dilatation and intra-uterine infusions of seminal and preputial fluids. *J. Dairy Sci.*, **43**, 796–809.

LASLEY, J. F. & BOGART, R. (1943). Some factors influencing reproductive efficiency of range cattle under artificial and natural breeding conditions. *Mo. Agric. Expt. Sta. Res. Bull. No. 376.*

MARSHALL, F. H. A. (1937). On the change over in the oestrous cycle in animals after transference across the equator, with further observations on the incidence of the breeding seasons and the factors controlling sexual periodicity. *Proc. Roy. Soc.*, B, **122**, 413–428.

MERCIER, E. & SALISBURY, G. W. (1947). Seasonal variations in hours of daylight associated with fertility level of cattle under natural breeding conditions. *J. Dairy Sci.*, **30**, 747–756.

NELLOR, J. E. (1960). Control of estrus and ovulation in gilts by orally effective progestational compounds. *J. Anim. Sci.*, **19**, 412–420.

WIGGINS, E. L., CASIDA, L. E. & GRUMMER, R. H. (1950). The effect of season of birth on sexual development in gilts. *J. Anim. Sci.*, **9,**, 277–280.

YEATES, N. T. M. (1949). The breeding season of the sheep with particular reference to its modification by artificial means using light. *J. Agric. Sci.*, **39**, 1–43.

QUESTIONS

1. Define or explain the following terms: puberty, seasonal breeder, estrus, estrous cycle, polyestrous, quiet ovulation, non-spontaneous and spontaneous ovulation, and synchronization of estrus.

2. What factors determine the time of onset of the breeding season in many wild mammals and some species of farm mammals?

3. Outline and explain the hormonal mechanisms involved in the control of the breeding season. Outline and define the different phases of the estrous cycle in farm mammals.

4. What factors determine the age and live weight of puberty in the female of farm mammals?

5. Describe briefly the hormonal mechanisms involved in the control of estrus, ovulation and the estrous cycle.

6. Of what practical importance is the occurrence of estrus during pregnancy?

7. What is meant by involution of the uterus? What physiological processes are involved?

8. Tabulate for the 4 mammalian species (*a*) duration of estrus, (*b*) time of ovulation and (*c*) optimum time to breed during the estrous period.

9. What are some of the abnormalities of the estrous cycle and what are their physiological causes?

10. From the physiological standpoint, how could a submaintenance diet modify the expression of estrus and the estrous cycle?

Chapter 6

Physiology of Mammalian Ova

By E. S. E. Hafez

In this chapter we will discuss the formation of the ovum, the cytological and physiological characteristics of the mature ovum, and our present knowledge of embryo transfer. Mammalian ova were first recognized by de Graaf in 1672, then described and identified by Cruickshank in 1797 and von Baer in 1827.

I. FORMATION OF OVUM

Oögenesis involves the proliferation, growth and maturation of oöcyte, the formation and rupture of the follicle and the release of mature ovum, *i.e.* ovulation. Oögenesis continues cyclically during the breeding season unless interrupted by pregnancy.

A. Proliferation of Oögonium

The ovary of the fetus is made of germinal epithelium from which the *primordial* germ cells are formed as clusters (Plate X). In each cluster, one cell differentiates and forms an oögonium containing cytoplasm with a Golgi apparatus, mitochondria and one or more nucleoli (Fig. 6–1). There is disagreement as to when the formation of oögonia is completed. Two schools of thought exist. One states that proliferation of oögonia is completed by or shortly after birth, *i.e.* the primordial cells of the fetal ovary survive and serve as the sole reservoir of all future ova. The other argues that proliferation of oögonia from the germinal epithelium is a continuous process during post-natal life, *i.e.*, similar to spermatogenesis. The evidence seems to favor the first belief (see Rajakoski, 1960).

B. Growth of Oöcyte

The oögonium starts to develop into a primary oöcyte. This is achieved in three ways: (*a*) the ovum enlarges by accumulating additional cytoplasm; (*b*) an ovum membrane, the *zona pellucida*, develops; and (*c*) the follicular epithelium and adjacent tissue proliferate by mitosis. Granules of deutoplasm (yolk) of different sizes develop in the cytoplasm of the ovum. The follicular cells adjacent to the oöcyte may serve as nurse cells by providing the deutoplasm to the oöcyte. By the time the ovum has reached maturity, it has accumulated reserves of material which later provide energy for development.

The growth of the oöcyte is intimately associated with the development of the

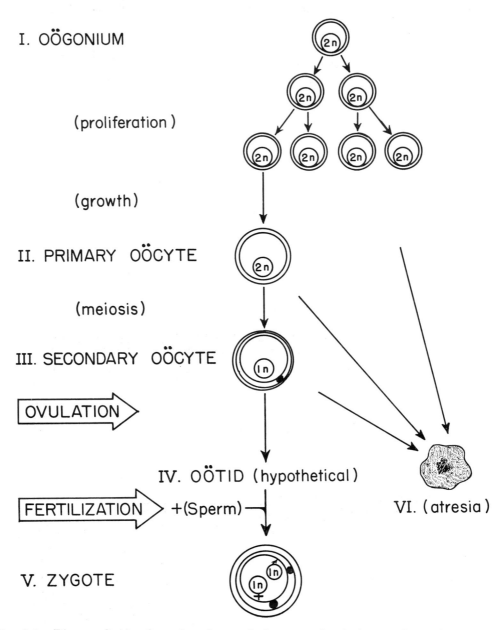

I. OÖGONIUM

(proliferation)

(growth)

II. PRIMARY OÖCYTE

(meiosis)

III. SECONDARY OÖCYTE

OVULATION

IV. OÖTID (hypothetical)

FERTILIZATION +(Sperm)

VI. (atresia)

V. ZYGOTE

Fig. 6–1.—Diagram showing the nuclear changes during oögenesis. (2n) = number of chromosomes in somatic cells (diploid state). (1n) = number of chromosomes in gametes—haploid state.

I. Proliferation of oögonia during pre-natal life.

II. Growth in size of oögonia to form primary oöcyte.

III. The 1st maturation division gives rise to the secondary oöcyte and the first polar body.

IV. The formation of oötid and extrusion of two polar bodies without fertilization is a hypothetical stage.

V. The completion of 2nd maturation division with the extrusion of the second polar body occurs after fertilization. The female pronucleus and the male pronucleus are formed in the zygote.

VI. Atresia of the oöcyte may occur at any stage during oögenesis.

PLATE XI

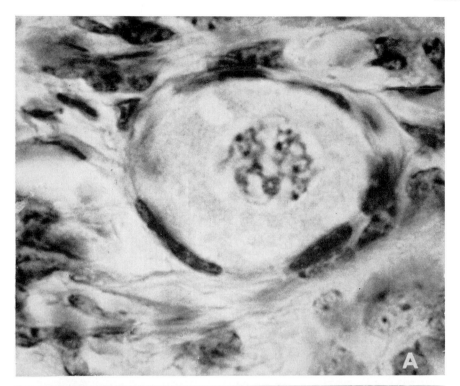

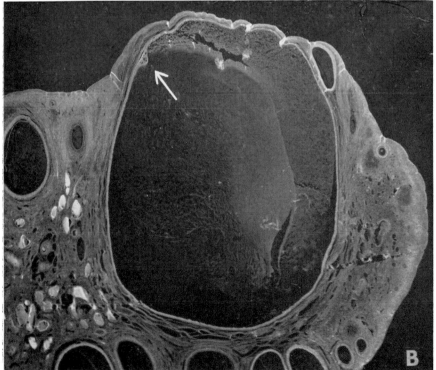

Ovarian oöcytes in cattle

A. Primordial follicle: an eccentric section through the nucleus showing chromosomes in the pachytene stage and a weakly stained nucleolus (× 1800 approximately).

B. Cumulus oöphorus (arrow) in a mature Graafian follicle of 12.5 mm.; a serial section of ovary of a heifer killed on the 21st day of the cycle (× 8 approximately).

(*From Rajakoski, 1960. Acta Endocrin. 34 (Suppl.) No. 52, p. 1.*)

Plate XII

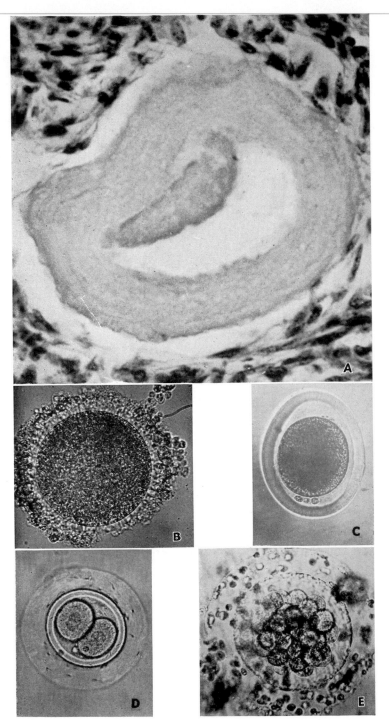

A. Degenerating oöcyte in an ovary of a heifer. Note the hyalinization and thickening of zona pellucida ($\times$ 1900 approximately) (*From Rajakoski, 1960. Acta Endocrin. 34 (Suppl.) No. 52, p. 1.*)

B. Unfertilized horse ovum collected from a large ovarian follicle. Note corona radiata cells attached to the zona pellucida and the abundance of fat droplets in the cytoplasm ($\times$ 230 approximately) (*Photograph by Y. Nishikawa*).

C. One-cell cow ovum showing 3 polar bodies in the perivitelline space; one of the two polar bodies has divided into two ($\times$ 185).

D. Two-cell rabbit embryo; note the thick mucin coat around the zona pellucida, also note the mitotic figures ($\times$ 140).

E. A rabbit embryo transferred surgically, while in 8-cell stage, to the uterus of a cow, and flushed out 24 hrs. later while in the 32-cell stage. Rabbit embryos can survive, for a short time, in the uterus of the cow ($\times$ 185).

ovarian follicle which takes place in two phases. During the first phase the growth of the oöcyte is rapid and is correlated with that of the ovarian follicle. During the second phase, the oöcyte does not grow in size while the ovarian follicle increases very rapidly in diameter (Fig. 6–2). During this latter phase, the oöcyte undergoes the maturation changes.

C. Maturation of Oöcyte

In maturation, the nuclear material and the number of chromosomes are reduced to

maturation divisions, *meiotic* divisions. In the first division, the number of chromosomes is reduced to the haploid, a state which persists through the second division. The two divisions (unlike those occurring in spermatogenesis) are unequal in that one of the daughter cells receives most of the cytoplasm of the mother oöcyte.

The primary oöcyte gives rise to two daughter cells. While each daughter cell gets the same chromosome material, one acquires almost all the cytoplasm, and is known as the *secondary* oöcyte. The other, much smaller cell is known as the *first polar*

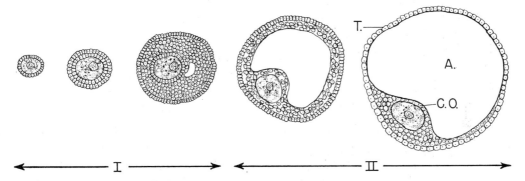

FIG. 6–2.—Diagram showing development of Graafian follicles in relation to maturation of the ovum. *I.* increase in diameter of oöcyte and follicle; *II.* development of follicle with no increase in diameter of oöcyte. *T.* theca externa and theca interna. *A.* antrum filled with liquor folliculi. *C.O.* cumulus oöphorus. (*Adapted from Allan, 1959 in The Endocrinology of Reproduction. J. T. Velardo, edit., New York, Courtesy Oxford University Press.*)

one half the original number. This process is comparable to that which occurs in spermatogenesis (see Chapter 3). In other words the number of chromosomes in the ovum is one half the normal number characteristic of the cells of the body for a given species.

Maturation starts by changes occurring in the nucleus of the oöcyte: the nucleoli and nuclear membrane disappear and the chromosomes condense in a compact form. Then the centrosome (specialized area of dense cytoplasm) divides into two centrioles, around which *asters* (groups of radiations at both poles of oöcyte) appear. These asters move apart and a *spindle* is formed between them. The chromosomes in diploid pairs are set free in the cytoplasm and become arranged on the equatorial plate of the spindle. The primary oöcyte undergoes two

body. At the second maturation division, the secondary oöcyte divides into the *oötid* and a *second polar body* (see Fig. 6–1). The two polar bodies, containing very little cytoplasm, are trapped within the zona pellucida of the oöcyte where they degenerate. One of these polar bodies may divide into two, thus the zona pellucida may contain one, two or three polar bodies (Plate XII).

The two maturation divisions are not completed at the time of ovulation. In the cow, ewe and sow only the first division is completed by the time of ovulation; *i.e.* the ruptured follicle releases the secondary oöcyte containing one polar body. Following liberation of the secondary oöcyte, the second division begins, but is not completed until or unless fertilization takes place; where fertilization does occur, this results in extrusion of the second polar

8

body and the formation of the female pronucleus. In the mare the first maturation division is completed after ovulation; *i.e.* in Fallopian tube (Hamilton & Day, 1945). The cytological changes occurring during maturation of ovum have been studied in detail in sheep (Berry & Savery, 1959) and rodents (Austin, 1959).

It is interesting to note that the stage of the "ovum" proper does not exist in farm mammals. It is not the "mature ovum" but the secondary oöcyte which is liberated at ovulation (primary oöcyte in the case of the mare). Such oöcyte continues the process of maturation until fertilization, when it becomes a "zygote." In oögenesis, *one* primary oöcyte gives rise to one *ovum*; in spermatogenesis, *one* primary spermatocyte gives rise to *four* sperm.

D. Atresia and Degeneration

The estimated number of oöcytes in both ovaries at the time of birth varies from 60,000 to 100,000 according to the species and breed. Not all ova develop to mature stage. For every ovum which is matured and released from the ovary, several never reach maturity. The follicle is called *atretic* if it fails to rupture; the enclosed oöcyte *degenerates*. Consequently every normal ovary contains atretic follicles with degenerating oöcytes. The degenerating oöcyte is characterized by hyalinization and thickening of the zona pellucida or fragmentation of the cytoplasm, *i.e.* separation into segments. The disintegrating oöcyte is engulfed by the ovarian fibrocytes (this phenomenon is called phagocytosis) and eventually the oöcyte shrinks into a scar and disappears.

II. THE MATURE OVUM

Before ovulation, the ovum lies at one side or at the base of the Graafian follicle, embedded in a solid mass of follicular cells, the cumulus oöphorus. The corona radiata (follicular cells immediately surrounding the ovum) are easily observed by the light microscope; further detailed structures can be seen by electron microscopy (Sotelo & Porter, 1959). The corona radiata cells send long processes, through the zona pellucida, to the surface of the ovum where they mingle with thin projections (microvilli) from the oöcyte itself (Fig. 6–3). At the time of ovulation, both types of projections are withdrawn from the zona pellucida. Usually each ruptured follicle releases one ovum. In a few cases, a polyovular follicle may contain double or multiple oöcytes and one or more ova are released from one follicle.

The ovum is a cell especially differentiated for fertilization. It is one of the largest mammalian cells and is incapable of locomotion. The diameter of ovum in farm mammals ranges from 120 to 185 microns (Table 6–1); differences among these species have not yet been established.

A. Cytology

The mammalian ovum is spherical in shape; is surrounded by cellular and noncellular membranes; and contains one nucleus.

Membranes. When the ovum is liberated from the ovary, it is still surrounded by corona radiata cells (Fig. 6–4). Within a few hours, these cells are lost and the ovum is denuded by the aid of a fibrinolytic enzyme secreted by the mucosa of the Fallopian tube. The denudation of the ovum is slower in swine than in cattle, sheep and horses.

In swine, as in other polytocous species such as rats and mice, several ova are shed during estrus. At ovulation, each ovum is still surrounded by a cluster of granulosa cells which are shed with it from the ovarian follicle, and which at this stage are often called *cumulus* cells. The cells are held together by a gelatinous matrix. The cumulus cells surrounding the several ova join together to form a single cluster, the "egg plug." This normally disintegrates soon after ovulation.

During the transport of the ovum along the reproductive tract of the mare, the epithelium deposits a thin coating on the zona pellucida. This coat is quite marked in the tubal ovum of the rabbit, and marsupial and monotreme species. However, in cattle, sheep and swine, the zona pellucida of the tubal ovum is not surrounded by such a coat (Plate XII).

Table 6–1.—Comparative Morphology and Physiology of Mammalian Ova

	Cattle	Sheep	Swine	Horses
No. of chromosomes in ovum (haploid state)	30	27	19	30
Diameter of Graafian follicle before ovulation (mm.)	12–19	5–8	8–12	25–65
Diameter of mature ovum without zona pellucida (μ)	120–160	140–185	120–170	120–180
No. of ruptured follicles at each estrus (ovulation rate)	1–2	1–4	10–25	1–2
Fertilizable life of ovum (hrs.)	12–24	12–24	12–24	12–24
Appearance of vitellus in living ovum	grey	grey	dark grey	blackish

μ = 1 micron. = 10^{-3} mm.

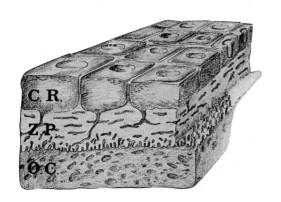

FIG. 6–3.—The structural relationship between the follicular cells and oöcyte in the ovary of the rat as revealed by electron microscopy. The corona radiata (C.R.) cells send long extensions through the zona pellucida (Z.P.) to the surface of the ovum (O.C.). Here they end without establishing any structural continuity with the microvilli which extend from the ovum surface into the material of the zona. (*Redrawn from Sotelo & Porter, 1959. J. Biochem. Cytol. 5, 327.*)

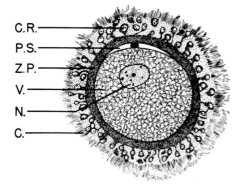

FIG. 6–4.—Structure of a mammalian ovum at the time of ovulation. *C.* cumulus, *C.R.* corona radiata, *Z.P.* zona pellucida, *P.S.* perivitelline space filled with fluid and containing the polar body, *V.* vitellus (cytoplasm), *N.* nucleus.

Vitellus (cytoplasm of ovum). At the time of ovulation, the vitellus fills most of the space within the zona pellucida. After fertilization, a shrinkage occurs and a *perivitelline space* is formed, between the zona pellucida and the vitellus, in which the polar bodies are situated. The vitellus of the living ovum shows a marked difference in appearance within species, mainly due to varying amounts of yolk and number of fat droplets in the cytoplasm. The ovum of horses and swine contains more yolk than that of cattle and sheep. In horses, the vitellus appears black because of the abundance of fat droplets which are highly refractile. In cattle and sheep, the ovum appears grey because there are few fat droplets. The vitellus has a finely reticulated appearance without polarity. It contains mitochondria, Golgi components and sometimes pigmented inclusions.

Nucleus. The large nucleus of the ovum lies in an eccentric position and contains one or more chromatic nucleoli. The nucleus has a distinct nuclear membrane and is frequently surrounded by a clear area of cytoplasm free from inclusions.

Abnormalities. Abnormalities occur in both unfertilized and fertilized ova. Abnormal sizes and shapes of unfertilized ova include: small or giant ova; oval, lentil-like in shape; with a ruptured zona pellucida; ova with large polar bodies or with large vacuoles in the vitellus (Plate XIII). Such abnormalities are a result of faulty or incomplete maturation of the oöcyte, genetic factors or environmental stress. Incomplete maturation may be a failure of the polar body to be extruded; *i.e.* the production of polyploidy (multiple sets of chromosomes). The susceptibility of the ovum to the abnormalities increases with the age of the female and varies among breeds and strains (Braden, 1957). In sheep the percentage of abnormal ova may be higher during the beginning and end of the breeding season than during mid-breeding season (see Laffey & Hart, 1959). Hyperthermia also increases the percentage of abnormal ova in sheep (see Chapter 18).

Developmental abnormalities in zygotes may result from polyspermy (see Chapter 7), different sizes of blastomeres, or inherited defects in the gametes. Either the ova or sperm can carry recessive lethal genes; if the same recessive allele for lethality is present in both gametes, the resulting embryo will degenerate at a particular stage during pregnancy. Embryo degeneration can also result from dominant lethal mutations. The environmental and physiological factors causing prenatal mortality will be discussed in detail in Chapter 7.

B. Biochemistry

Little is known about the biochemistry of the mammalian ovum. When the vitellus of the ovum is freed from nutritional reserves (yolk or deutoplasm), the cytoplasm proper is essentially similar in chemical structure to that of somatic cells. The reserves of deutoplasm contain protein, lipid and carbohydrate. The protein is basically ribonucleo protein, RNP. The lipid is stored as fat droplets of varying size according to the species. Carbohydrate is present in association with protein (mucopolysaccharide) or as scattered granules of glycogen. The ovum also contains basic enzyme systems, *e.g.* cytochrome oxidase and acid phosphatase. The nucleus which contains the chromosomes consists basically of desoxyribo-nucleic acid, DNA, linked with protein. The chemical structure of nucleic acids are discussed in Chapter 3. In general, mammalian ova contain very little nutritional reserves as compared to the ova of birds and reptiles.

The intercellular substance of the cumulus is mainly composed of hyaluronic acid which can be dissolved *in vitro* by addition of the enzyme, hyaluronidase.

III. PHYSIOLOGY OF OVUM

At the time of ovulation, the ovum is picked up by the fimbriae. Then the ovum is transported into the Fallopian tube for fertilization and into the uterus for implantation. Different studies were undertaken *in vitro* and *in vivo* to understand these phenomena (reviewed by Hafez, 1959). The following is a discussion of the physiological mechanisms of the reception, transportation and migration of the ovum. The fertile life of the ovum will be pointed out in relation to the effects of aging of gametes.

A. Reception of Ovum

It is believed that the fimbriae embrace the ovary at the time of ovulation in order to ensure the reception of the ovum. The cumulus containing the ova is expelled from the follicle near the fimbriae and is swept into the opening of the Fallopian tube. This chain of reactions is controlled by anatomical and physiological mechanisms with the hormones playing a major role.

Anatomical and Physiological Mechanisms. The ovary is located inside the ovarian bursa to which the ampulla of the tube and part of the fimbriae are attached. The fimbriae are located at the opened portion of the ovarian bursa. The ovary can move readily from the ovarian bursa to the surface of the fimbriae. This movement is controlled by the *Ligamentum ovarii proprium* and the mesovarium which hold the ovary and Fallopian tube in position (see Chapter 4).

The fimbriae and the infundibulum are basically an erectile tissue which is very rich in vascular and muscular supply—fine blood capillaries interspersed with muscular bands. During estrus the margins of the fimbriae are edematus and translucent; increased blood flow through the fimbriae causes its distension. These mechanisms increase the surface of contact with the ovary and facilitate the reception of the ovum.

Effects of Ovarian Hormones. The contractile activities of the fimbriae, tube and ligaments are partly coordinated by hormonal mechanisms involving the estrogen: progesterone ratio. Ova reception is most effective at about the time of estrus but functions to some degree throughout the cycle. In some species there is evidence to suggest that neuro-hormonal mechanisms at the time of copulation stimulate the contractile activities of the Fallopian tube but these mechanisms are not yet fully established.

B. Transport of Ovum

The fact that the Fallopian tubes, almost simultaneously, conduct the non-motile ovum in one direction and the motile sperm in the opposite direction, has done much to provoke interest in the problem. Moreover, the transport of ova through the Fallopian tubes to the uterus has considerable bearing on fertility, since if the ovum does not reach the uterus within certain well defined time limits, it will fail to develop normally and will perish (see Chapter 7).

Anatomical Mechanisms. The Fallopian tube proper is composed of two more or less distinct parts, the *ampulla* and the *isthmus*

(see Chapter 4). The histology of these two parts reflects the mechanisms and the rate at which the ovum is transported from the infundibulum to the uterus. The ampulla has a thin wall, a thin layer of circular muscle, and a thin mucous membrane forming high branched folds in a wide lumen. The walls of these folds contain numerous blood capillaries interspersed with muscle bundles to form erectile tissue. The epithelial lining of the tube contains secretory and ciliated cells. There are cyclical changes in the histology of the tube characterized by increased vascularity, development of columnar secretory epithelium and the prominence of cilia at the time of estrus.

Physiological Mechanisms. The transport of ova is accomplished by the action of the epithelial cilia which beat toward the uterus; such activity may be stimulated at the time of estrus. Borrell and his associates estimated the rate of ciliary beat in the tube of the estrous rabbit to be 1,500 per minute.

The entire tube shows different types of contractile and peristaltic activities independent of those of the uterus. Ampullary contractions originate in the infundibulum and pass progressively toward the isthmus. The tubal loops, independent of each other, may exhibit segmental contractions. As the segmental contractions subside, they are replaced by a period of intense engorgement with blood, so that the segment may be more than twice its normal size in the relaxed state.

It is not clear whether or not the flow of the tubal secretion helps, directly, the transport of ova. The secretions pass from the infundibulum to the uterus at one stage of the estrous cycle while the secretions may pass in the opposite direction in another stage. Thus if the tube of the rabbit is ligated near the fimbriae, 1 day after copulation, the tubal fluids will accumulate in the ampulla. If ligation is performed 3 days after copulation, the tubal fluids do not accumulate. It is possible that the small size of the sperm and the large diameter of the ova facilitate their transport in opposite directions. The cumulus cells surrounding the ovum at the time of ovulation are probably important in some species (*e.g.* rabbit) for the normal transport from the infundibulum to the ampulla.

Effects of Ovarian Hormones. The rate of tubal contractions is under hormonal control, mainly estrogen and progesterone. The estrogen: progesterone ratio is important for normal transport of ova; the hormonal influence on the transport of the ovum varies with the species. In general, active tubal contractions delay ovum transport, while quiescent tubal musculature accelerates transport. Tubal motility of the right intensity is an important factor in fertility.

Rate of Transport. The embryo reaches the uterus within 2 to $3\frac{1}{2}$ days and its arrival is synchronized with the interval required for the corpus luteum to come into increased activity. Thus, the embryo arrives in the uterus at an optimum time for survival.

The rate of ovum transport is uniform neither in different parts of the tube nor in different species. In ruminants, the rate of transport is very rapid in the upper portion of the ampulla (3 to 6 hrs.) and very slow in the lower portion of the tube (56 to 60 hrs.) (Schilling, 1958). In the rabbit, the ova are transported in the ampulla within a few minutes, then delayed for several hours in the ampullary-isthmic region. The stage of cleavage of the fertilized ovum when it reaches the uterus varies with the species (see Chapter 7). The unfertilized ovum reaches the uterus at the same time as the fertilized one.

C. Fertilizable Life and Aging of Ovum

The fertilizable life of an ovum is the *maximum period during which it remains capable of fertilization and development.* The ovum is capable of fertilization for some 12 to 24 hours in most species (Table 6–1); it rapidly loses its fertilizability when it reaches the isthmus and probably cannot be fertilized after reaching the uterine horn.

The ovum may be fertilized near the end of its fertilizable life as a result of delayed breeding, *i.e.* fertilization takes place in an *aged* ovum. Such fertilized aged ovum may or may not be implanted, and if implanted, it represents mostly a non-viable embryo.

In guinea pigs, as the age of the ovum at fertilization increases, the percentage of abnormal pregnancies increases and the litter size decreases (Fig. 6–5). Fertilization of aged ova in swine is associated with polyspermy (see Chapter 7) and hence abnormal development of the embryo. In single-bearing animals, aging of the ovum may cause abortion, embryonic resorption or abnormal development of the embryo. Similar abnormalities may result from aged sperm (see Chapter 3). In general aging of the gametes involves one of these three possibilities:

aged ovum + freshly ejaculated sperm

aged ovum + aged sperm

freshly ovulated ovum + aged sperm

The non-viable embryos resulting from one or both aged gametes, may be the cause of low conception rates in certain herds and flocks. At present there is insufficient evidence on the relative deleterious effect of aging of gametes on fertilization, implantation, pre-natal development and post-natal development in farm mammals. There is good evidence in poultry that fertilization with aged sperm increases subsequent embryonic mortality; and records from artificial insemination centers suggest that the same phenomenon may occur in cattle.

It is possible that some of congenital abnormalities which persist in the post-natal life of an animal are a result of embryos developed from aged gametes. It is also possible that the incidence of developmental abnormalities, resulting from aging of gametes, is less frequent in farm mammals than in primates where copulation is not restricted to the period of sexual receptivity of the female, and hence more embryos may develop from one or both aged gametes.

If the ovum is not fertilized, it will fragment, *i.e.* breaks into 2 to 20 cytoplasmic segments of unequal size, and in some cases the fragmented ovum resembles the fertilized ones (Plate XIII). All unfertilized ova disappear through complete disintegration or phagocytosis in the uterus.

D. Migration and Loss of Ovum

There is much evidence for the ewe, sow and mare to show that the ovum can

PLATE XIII

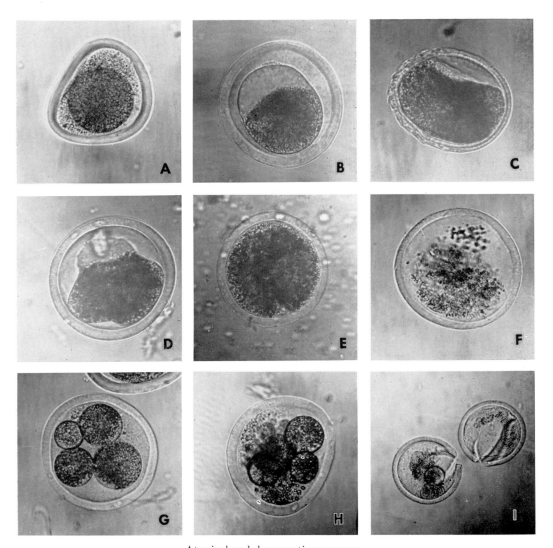

Atypical and degenerating cow ova.

A, B, C, D. Atypical unfertilized ova showing structural abnormalities × 185)

E. Degenerating one-cell ovum; note coarse granulation (× 185).

F. Advanced degree of degeneration (× 185).

G, H. Fragmenting ova; note different sizes of fragments (× 185).

I. Two ova with ruptured zona pellucida; not the escape of cytoplasm (× 63).

PLATE XIV

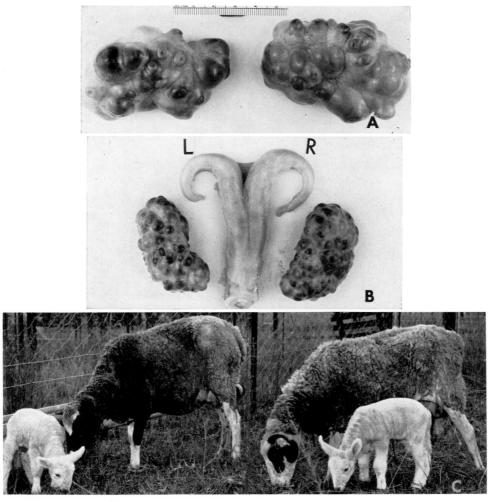

A. Ovaries from beef cattle after superovulation by gonadotropins, 3000 i.u. of PMS followed by 2000 i.u. of HCG 5 days later.   Note the developing corpora lutea.   The cow was slaughtered 5 days after the HCG injection.

B. Superovulated ovary from a 3-month old calf treated with 3000 i.u. of PMS followed by 300 i.u. of HCG 5 days later; 146 ovulation points were counted.   Note the size of ovaries compared with the immature uterus.

C. Border Leicester lambs born in South Africa from embryos obtained in England, flown to South Africa in the uterus of a pseudopregnant rabbit and transferred to Dorper ewes (foster mothers) in South Africa (*Photograph by G. L. Hunter*).

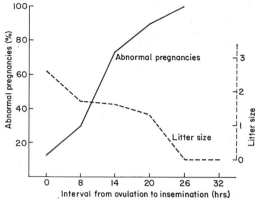

Fig. 6–5.—The effect of aging of ova (delayed insemination) on percentage of abnormal pregnancies and litter size in guinea pigs. Note that the ova were fertilized and implanted when the animals were inseminated at 26 hrs. after ovulation, yet the embryos did not continue development. (*Data from Blandau & Young, 1939. Amer. J. Anat. 64, 303.*)

migrate from one uterine horn to the other through the common body of the uterus, this is known as *trans-uterine migration.* Should one ovary be removed in the sow, for example, approximately half the number of embryos that develop are found in the uterine horn of that side. There is also a tendency in the normal sow for the number of embryos to be equalized within the two horns. In ewes that show double-ovulations in the one ovary, it is usually found that one embryo is present in each horn. In the mare, migration of the ovum is common-place. In the cow, however, it is found that migration may occur in certain cases. The physiological mechanisms that govern the movement of ova, both within individual horns and between horns, is unknown at this time.

Trans-peritoneal migration of ova has been reported under experimental conditions: when one ovary is removed, leaving the fimbriae and tube intact, and the other tube is ligated, a normal pregnancy may follow. In this case, the patent tube has the ability to pick up the ova released by the contra-lateral ovary. Trans-peritoneal migration of ova may be aided by currents created by cilia of the fimbriae, surface tension of the peritoneal fluid and peristalsis of the fimbriae. Dauzier (1962) reported that when ova were transferred to the peritoneal cavity of the rabbit, they were picked up by the fimbriae resulting in normal pregnancy.

On rupture of the mature follicle, the ovum may be entrapped in the follicle during the formation of corpus luteum. The ovum may also be lost in the peritoneal cavity; such an ovum usually degenerates but in rare cases it results in *ectopic pregnancy i.e.* pregnancy not located in the uterus. It is emphasized here that ovum reception is as efficient in farm mammals, with an open ovarian bursa, as in other species, with a closed ovarian bursa. In farm mammals, however, the ovum may be lost in the peritoneal cavity following immobilization of the tube as a result of faulty rectal palpation of the ovaries, post-partum or post-abortum infections, endometritis or non-specific abdominal infections. The ovum may also be lost into the vagina due to different reasons.

III. EMBRYO TRANSFER

As early as 1890, Heape demonstrated that embryos could be isolated from a donor rabbit and transferred to a host rabbit, which served as a foster mother for the production of living young. Embryos have been transferred successfully in cattle, sheep, goats and swine—in all cases by surgical means. Attempts to transfer embryos by non-surgical means through the cervix have not been very successful. Embryo transfer (commonly called ova transplantation) is used in laboratory animals especially the rabbit, rat and mouse, in which considerable success has been achieved with embryo survival.

A. Advantages

The transfer of embryos has scientific and practical advantages. It makes a critical experimental approach possible to problems in physiology and biochemistry of reproduction, genetics, cytology, animal breeding, immunology and evolution. The technique is used to study pre- and post-implantation growth and development, and to evaluate genetic-environmental inter-actions in relation to variability in the phenotype (see Alliston & Ulberg, 1961). In sheep (Hunter, 1956), rabbits (Venge, 1950) and mice (Brumby, 1960), embryos were transferred reciprocally from large breeds to small breeds. It has been demonstrated that the intra-uterine environment affects the size of the young (see Chapter 10).

One of the practical objectives of transfer of embryos in farm animals is to increase the number of offspring which can be obtained from desirable females. This is made pos-sible by superovulation techniques and transferring the embryos to a suitable number of genetically less desirable host-mothers for development of the embryos. The reproductive rate of good genetic material in the female has been limited because some species only produce 1 to 2 young per year. The production of offspring from performance tested females (females tested for productive ability; e.g. feeding efficiency) might be increased markedly by superovulation and transfer of embryos. If embryos could be obtained from immature cows and transferred to sexually mature recipients, the generation time could be reduced by one year; also it should become possible to obtain, for example, beef calves from dairy cows.

Averill et al. (1955) have demonstrated that sheep embryos can remain viable in the reproductive tract of the rabbit for at least 5 days, and can develop from the 2-cell to at least the 8-day blastocyst stage. The use of the reproductive tract of the female rabbit as an "incubator" allows the success-ful long-distance transport of sheep embryos (Adams et al., 1961) (Plate XIV).

While the embryo transfer technique could be used for the rapid multiplication of a specially valuable strain or breed or for the development of inbred lines, it is unlikely at the present stage to be of great general value in livestock improvement as a whole (see section G).

B. Superovulation

The male can produce several million to a few billion sperm each day; the female produces but a few ova at each estrus. However, superovulated immature or ma-ture females can produce 20 to 100 ova at one estrus after the administration of gonadotropins (Plate XIV). The FSH brings about the maturation of several follicles, while the LH causes ovulation.

Superovulation is induced in adult sheep by injecting 600 to 1,100 i.u. of PMS (according to body weight) on the 12th or 13th day of the estrous cycle. There are no standardized techniques for superovula-tion in adult cattle. Several methods give satisfactory but inconsistent results (re-viewed by Hafez, 1961). A common method in cattle is the subcutaneous injection of 2,500 to 3,500 i.u. of PMS on the 16th or 18th day of the cycle, followed by an intravenous injection of 2,000 i.u. of HCG 5 days after the PMS injection. The cow comes in heat 2 to 4 days later, and can then be inseminated or mated to a sire of high genetic value.

Superovulatory Responses. The sensitiv-ity of the immature ovaries to gonadotropins develops gradually and at different rates in different species. The ovaries of immature sheep can be stimulated by gonadotropins at 16 weeks of age, and rabbits at 10 to 20 weeks depending upon the breed and plane of nutrition. Immature animals show superovulatory response as soon as the follicles develop *antra* (*pl.* of antrum). Birth of living young indicates that ova obtained from immature donors are func-tionally normal.

The superovulatory responses of mature animals varies with the species, breed, live weight, stage of estrous cycle, age, post-partum interval, season of the year and plane of nutrition. The number of ova produced by the injection of gonadotropins is also controlled by the potency of hor-mone(s) used, the FSH:LH ratio in the preparation, frequency of successive injec-tions and dosage of hormone. In the rat, the superovulatory response increases with the increase of post-partum interval.

PLATE XV

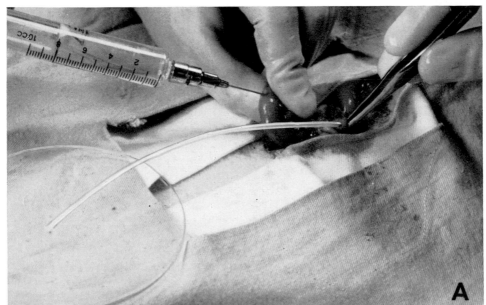

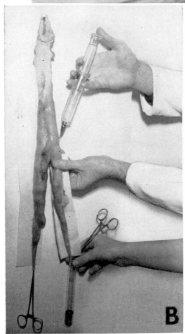

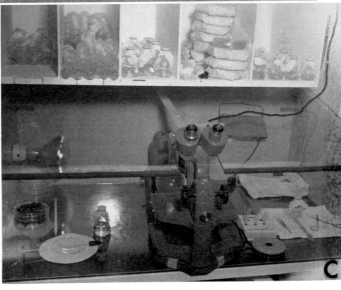

A. The method of collecting embryos *in vivo* from the Fallopian tube of a superovulated ewe after a midline laparotomy. One operator injects serum diluted with saline into the top of the uterine horn and presses on the fluid through the utero-tubal junction. Another operator inserts a polyethylene tube (0.1 inch outside diameter) and holds the Fallopian tube, with wound applicator, to prevent the escape of fluid. The embryos are collected in a watch glass. The procedure is repeated for the other Fallopian tube (*Photograph by C. W. Alliston & L. C. Ulberg*).

B. A method for collecting embryos *in vitro* from the uterus of a superovulated cow. The uterus is dissected and suspended from the cervix. Serum diluted with saline is injected into the uterine horn and embryos collected from the utero-tubal junction.

C. Isolation cabinet used for manipulation of embryos for subsequent storage and transfer. A stereoscopic microscope is mounted in a glass-topped case. The cabinet is equipped with ultra-violet, infra-red and microscope lamps. Autoclaved pipettes, saline, gelatine and watch glasses (inside petri dishes) are on a top shelf for convenience.

At present, there are three limitations to the extensive use of superovulation in cattle. First, the results are inconsistent due to the individual variations in the response to gonadotropins. Second, the number of ova obtained from successive superovulations in the same animals decreases, owing to the refractoriness of the ovaries and the formation of antihormones. Third, the fertilization rate in superovulated cattle is low.

C. Collection of Embryos

The embryos can be collected from superovulated donors using *in vitro* or *in vivo* methods. On the basis of the percentage recovery, *in vitro* methods have been more efficient than *in vivo* methods. However, the latter is essential if the donors are required for future use.

In Vitro Collection. The reproductive organs are obtained immediately after slaughter and the corpora lutea on each ovary are counted. The Fallopian tubes are removed by trimming away the mesosalpinx and then severing them at the utero-tubal junction. A glass pipette is used to flush serum diluted with saline (0.9% sodium chloride solution) through the tube from both the infundibular and then uterine ends. The flushings are collected in watch glasses and examined under a dissecting microscope.

Salpingectomy (surgical removal of the Fallopian tube) can also be used to recover embryos from the tube.

To collect embryos from the uterus, the uterine horns are clamped or ligated at their junction with the uterine body and serum diluted with saline injected through the uterine wall on the side of the occlusion (Plate XV). The flushings are collected from the cut tubal end of the horn into test tubes, allowed to settle for 5 minutes, and transferred with a pipette to watch glasses for microscopical examination.

In Vivo Collection. A high lumbar laparotomy or midline laparotomy is performed and the tube flushed by injecting serum diluted with saline through the uterine wall and the utero-tubal junction. The flushings

are collected from a polyethylene tube inserted into the Fallopian tube at the fimbrial end (Plate XV).

D. Storage of Embryos

Embryos can be stored *in vitro* for 3 to 7 days at low temperature; the best storage temperature is 10°C. At this temperature, the major biological processes slow down and cleavage temporarily stops. "Cold shock" which adversely affects the embryos can be prevented by slow cooling. Different storage media such as blood serum diluted with saline can be used. Rabbit embryos can be stored for one week at 10°C. in diluted blood serum containing 7% gelatine, Ferdows *et al.* (1958) stored rabbit embryos at −79°C. after equilibration in a medium containing 10% glycerine. Sheep embryos can be stored for 5 days in the uterus of the rabbit; no success has been reported for storage of cattle embryos in the rabbit (Hafez & Sugie, unpublished data).

The usual methods of tissue culture (incubation *in vitro* at body temperature) have been used in the cultivation of mammalian embryos. These include the hanging drop with the embryo held in a plasma clot on a coverslip over a fluid-free cavity, or in Carrel flasks kept in an incubator at 38°C. Rabbit embryos can cleave in culture until the blastocyst stage. Little success has been achieved for culture of cattle embryos (see Chapter 7).

E. Transfer Technique

A non-surgical technique for embryo transfer has not been developed yet. A common surgical technique is to apply sedative injections and a local anesthetic to the recipient then using high lumbar or midline laparotomy, the uterine horn is located and the embryos are transferred into the uterine lumen by a glass pipette. Technical details of embryo transfer have been described by Hafez (1958) and Casida (1960).

F. Conception Rate

The conception rate resulting from embryo transfer depends on the proper techniques for superovulation, recovery and selection of embryos, the selection of fertile recipients, synchronization of the donor and recipient, and the mechanics of transfer technique (Moore *et al.*, 1960; Hafez, 1961).

Selection of Embryos. Morphologically normal cleaved ova should be used after discarding embryos showing structural abnormalities previously described. The best stages for embryo transfer seem to be those of 4- to 32-cell. The embryos should be collected not less than 48 hours after the last ovulation since it is sometimes difficult to differentiate between fertilized and unfertilized ova at the one-cell stage. Phase contrast microscopy has been used to identify one-cell fertilized ova of rodents by the presence of sperm within the vitellus; the technique is not yet applicable to ova of farm mammals.

Synchronization of the Donor and Recipient. It is essential for the donor and recipient animals to be in a similar stage of the estrous cycle. Embryos recovered from the Fallopian *tubes* of a given donor should generally be transferred to the *tubes* of the recipients; uterine embryos should be transferred to the *uterus*. Better conception rate is achieved when the donor is one day more advanced in stage of pregnancy than the recipient than *vice versa* (see Chapter 7).

Synchronization can be achieved by one of three methods: (*a*) storage of embryos at low temperature; (*b*) use of a donor and a recipient which come into estrus on the same day; or (*c*) modification of the estrous cycle of the recipient by progesterone treatment (see Chapters 5, 13, 14 & 15). Such treatment holds the animal in diestrus until a few days after progesterone treatment is terminated. Hansel *et al.* (1961) were able to synchronize estrus in cattle by oxytocin and progesterone treatments. The removal of the corpus luteum by rectal palpation in cattle also shortens the diestrous period.

G. Limitations

There are three major limitations to the development of embryo transfer on a practical scale comparable with artificial insemination; (*a*) there are no reliable methods for superovulation and production of fertilized ova on a large scale; (*b*) there is need to synchronize the estrous cycles of the recipient and donor (*c*) there is need for a simple non-surgical technique for collecting embryos from donors and for transferring embryos to the recipients.

In the ewe, the cervix is *S*-shaped and constricted, thus, it is very difficult to penetrate the cervix to transfer the embryos and in this species embryos must be transferred surgically. In the cow, the cervix can be handled by rectal palpation. However, the transfer of embryos through the cervix is unsuccessful perhaps because the uterus, during the luteal phase of the estrous cycle, is susceptible to infection and to the development of pyometra. Harper and his associates, using radioactive "artificial ova," have also shown that one of the reasons for the failure of non-surgical embryo transfers in the cow is the ejection of the embryos about $1\frac{1}{2}$ hours after insertion. This may be due to stimulation of the cervix at the time of the transfer, which causes the release of oxytocin from the pituitary gland, and consequent uterine contractions.

REFERENCES

ADAMS, C. E., ROWSON, L. E. A., HUNTER, G. L. & BISHOP, G. P. (1961). Long distance transport of sheep ova. *Proc. 4th Inter. Congr. Anim. Reprod.* (The Hague, Holland), Physiol. (in press).

ALLISTON, C. W. & ULBERG, L. C. (1961). Early pregnancy loss in sheep at ambient temperatures of 70° and 90° F. as determined by embryo transfer. *J. Anim. Sci.*, **20**, 608–613.

AUSTIN, C. R. (1959). Fertilization and development of the egg. In: *Reproduction in Domestic Animals.* H. H. Cole and P. T. Cupps (edits.) Vol. 1, New York, Academic Press.

AVERILL, R. W. L., ADAMS, C. E. & ROWSON, L. E. A. (1955). Transfer of mammalian ova between species. *Nature* (Lond.), **179**, 238–241.

BERRY, R. O. & SAVERY, H. P. (1959). A cytological study of the maturation process of the ovum of the ewe during normal and induced ovulation. In: *Reproduction and Fertility III Symposium.* F. X. Gassner (edit.) New York, Pergamon.

BRADEN, A. W. H. (1957). Variation between strains in the incidence of various abnormalities of egg maturation and fertilization in the mouse. *J. Genetics*, **55**, 476–486.

BRUMBY, P. J. (1960). The influence of maternal environment on growth in mice. *Heredity*, **14** 1–18.

CASIDA, L. E. (1960). Research techniques in physiology of reproduction in the female. In: *Techniques and Procedures in Animal Production Research.* Monograph, p. 106–121, Amer. Soc. Anim. Prod.

DAUZIER, L. (1962). Nouvelles donnees sur la transplantation des oeufs, chez la lapine, par voie vaginale ou intraperitoneale. *Annales de Biologie Animale, Biochemie Biophysique* (in press).

FERDOWS, M., MOORE, C. L. & DRACY, A. E. (1958). Survival of rabbit ova at −79°C. *J. Dairy Sci.*, **41**, 739 (abstract).

HAFEZ, E. S. E. (1958). Techniques of collection and transplantation of ova in farm animals. *J. Amer. Vet. Med. Assoc.*, **133**, 506–612.

———— (1959). Tubo-ovarian mechanisms of ova reception in mammals. *Cornell Vet.*, **49**, 459–478.

———— (1961). Procedures and problems of manipulation, selection, storage and transfer of the mammalian ova. *Cornell Vet.*, **51**, 299–333.

HAMILTON, W. J. & DAY, F. T. (1945). Cleavage stages of the ova of the horse. *J. Anat.*, **79**, 127–130.

HANSEL, W., MALVEN, P. V. & BLACK, D. L. (1961). Estrous cycle regulation in the bovine. *J. Anim. Sci.*, **20**, 621–625.

HUNTER, G. L. (1956). The maternal influence on size in sheep. *J. Agric. Sci.*, **48**, 36–60.

LAFFEY, N. & HART, D. S. (1959). Embryonic loss from late breeding season matings to ewes. *N. Z. J. Agric. Res.*, **2**, 1159–1166.

MOORE, N. W., ROWSON, L. E. A. & SHORT, R. V. (1960). Egg transfer in sheep. Factors affecting the survival and development of transferred eggs. *J. Reprod. Fertil.*, **1**, 332–349.

RAJAKOSKI, E. (1960). The ovarian follicular system in sexually mature heifers with special reference to season, cyclical and left-right variation. *Acta Endocrin.*, **34** (Suppl.) No. 52, 1–68.

SCHILLING, E. (1958). Untersuchungen über den Eitransport Bei Wiederkäuern. *Verh. Dtsch. Zool. Ges., Zool. Anz.*, **22**, (Suppl.) 283–289.

SOTELO, J. R. & PORTER, K. R. (1959). An electron microscope study of the rat ovum. *J. Biophys. Biochem. Cytol.*, **5**, 327–342.

VENGE, G. (1950). Studies on the maternal influence on the birth weight in rabbits. *Acta Zool.*, **31**, 1–148.

QUESTIONS

1. Discuss the physiological mechanisms of the reception and transport of ova in farm mammals.
2. Describe some of the methods used for: (a) superovulation; (b) synchronization of estrus; (c) storage of embryos.
3. What is the scientific and practical significance of the transfer of embryos.
4. Give a full account of: polyovular follicles; vitellus; secondary oöcyte; deutoplasm; oögonium; zona pellucida; polar bodies.
5. Draw a diagram of a cow ovum and label five cytological structures. List five biochemical substances found in the mammalian ovum.
6. The technique of embryo transfer has been very successful in laboratory mammals, *e.g.*, the rabbit, rat and mouse. Explain why embryo transfer is not used extensively in farm mammals.
7. Give a full account of the fertilizable life and aging of the mammalian ovum. Discuss this in relation to fertility and sterility of farm mammals.
8. In a tabulated form compare:
   (a) the avian egg and the mammalian ovum
   (b) spermatogenesis and oögenesis
   (c) cow ovum and mare ovum
   (d) sperm and ovum
9. Discuss the major nuclear changes which occur in the oögonium until the release of a mature ovum.
10. Explain these phenomena:
    (a) trans-uterine and trans-peritoneal migration of ova
    (b) morphological abnormalities of the embryo
    (c) rate of transport of embryo in the tube in farm mammals

Chapter 7

Fertilization, Cleavage and Implantation

By Anne McLaren

I. FERTILIZATION

THE entire process of sexual reproduction is centered around the act of fertilization: yet fertilization is not itself a reproductive process. On the contrary, it consists essentially of the fusion of two cells, the male and female gametes, to form one single cell, the zygote. Fertilization is a dual process:

(a) In its *embryological* aspect, it involves activation of the ovum by the sperm. Without the stimulus of fertilization, the ovum does not normally begin to cleave, and no embryological development occurs. In some animals, experimental treatments are known which mimic this aspect of fertilization, inducing development in the unfertilized ovum.

(b) In its *genetical* aspect, fertilization involves the introduction into the ovum of hereditary material from the sire. By this means it is possible for beneficial characters arising far apart in time and space eventually to become combined in a single individual. The importance of this process for natural and artificial selection can hardly be overestimated. According to current genetical belief, the essential hereditary material is the chromosomal DNA in the sperm nucleus: fusion of male and female nucleus in the process of *syngamy* is therefore often thought of as the central process of fertilization. Although attempts have been made to inject foreign DNA into the ovum experimentally, this aspect of fertilization has not yet been mimicked in the laboratory.

In fertilization, two cells combine to form one, the first cell of the new individual: yet the number of chromosomes remains constant in every generation. This is because the two gametes each contain only half the number of chromosomes characteristic for the species (see Chapters 3 & 6).

Throughout this chapter, much use will be made of information derived from the study of mice, rats and rabbits, since comparatively little direct work has so far been done on fertilization and early development in the larger and more expensive farm animals. Indeed, the most detailed and exact information which we possess about fertilization relates to the sea-urchin; but how far one is justified in generalizing from sea-urchins to mammals is doubtful, and this work will therefore not be referred to here. Interested readers should consult Austin & Walton (1960) and Hancock (1962).

(124)

A. Description of Fertilization Process

1. The Ovum: Its Position and State

In most mammals, fertilization begins after the first polar body has been extruded, so that the sperm penetrate the ovum while the second reduction division is in progress (see Chapter 6 for description of meiosis). In the horse and dog, however, sperm may enter the ova before the first reduction division has begun.

The site of fertilization in all farm and most other mammals is the lower portion of the ampulla of the Fallopian tube. When it enters the ampulla, the ovum is still surrounded by a cluster of granulosa cells which were shed with it from the ovarian follicle, and which at this stage are often called *cumulus* cells. In swine, the cumulus cells surrounding the several ova join together in the fimbriae of the Fallopian tube to form a single cluster, the "egg plug." This normally disintegrates soon after ovulation, but Spalding and associates report that when ovulation is induced the "egg plug" may persist until after fertilization. In farm animals other than swine, cumulus cells are absent from those ova which have been examined a few hours after ovulation (*e.g.* within 9 to 14 hours of ovulation in the cow). They are probably shed before fertilization begins, as unpenetrated ova recovered from the tube are usually found to be almost or quite denuded.

2. The Sperm: The Encounter with the Ovum

The entry of sperm into the female genital tract, and their transport to the site of fertilization, have been dealt with previously (see Chapter 3). Here we wish to emphasize three points only: (*a*) Although the total number of sperm in an ejaculate is measured in hundreds or thousands of millions, the number travelling as far as the ampulla is relatively small, probably not much more than 1,000 in any mammal. (*b*) Some sperm reach the site of fertilization very quickly, within about 15 minutes of mating. (*c*) In the rabbit, rat, probably cow, and possibly other species, the sperm have to undergo some change or set of changes (called capacitation) before they can activate the ova.

In those species where capacitation is necessary, the ova arrive in the ampulla a sufficient length of time after the sperm to ensure that full capacitation has occurred. As with ova, the fertile life of sperm is fairly short, probably not much more than 24 hours, though successful fertilization 5 days after insemination has been reported in the mare. Possibly sperm may lose their ability to induce viable embryos before they lose their ability to fertilize. The relatively brief fertile life of both sperm and ovum renders timing a matter of the utmost importance in mating (Hammond, 1941) and artificial insemination. For instance in the cow, which normally ovulates about 14 hours after the end of heat, the conception rate from inseminations made at the time of ovulation is very low, and the best time for insemination is from 6 to 24 hours before ovulation (Fig. 7–1).

Fertilization rate in most mammals is remarkably high. In one strain of rabbits, only 1.4 per cent of ova failed to be fertilized, though the overall prenatal loss amounted to 30 per cent. What information we possess on the size of the ampulla of the tube, the number of sperm present, the rate at which they swim, and the surface area of the ovum, suggests that some factor other than chance is probably operating to ensure that ovum and sperm meet. Yet no such factor has so far been demonstrated experimentally. Even the mass of cumulus cells, which might be thought to facilitate contact by trapping sperm in the neighborhood of the ovum, apparently plays no essential role in fertilization. In the rabbit it has been shown that sperm make contact just as readily with ova from which the cumulus mass has been experimentally removed.

It has long been assumed that fertilization is an entirely random process—*i.e.* that there is an equal chance of any sperm fertilizing any ovum. Although direct evidence is hard to come by, this is probably not entirely true. Experiments with mixed inseminations demonstrate that the sperm from different males may differ in their fertilizing capacity. Bateman (1960) has shown that true selective fertilization may in certain circumstances occur in the mouse.

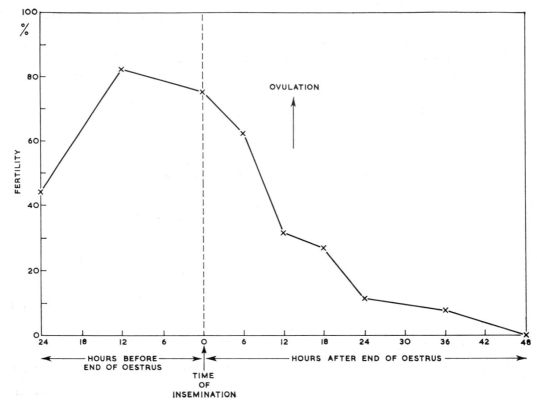

FIG. 7–1.—Relationship between time of insemination and fertility in the cow. (*After Trimberger & Davis, 1943. Neb. Agric. Expt. Sta., Res. Bull. No. 129.*)

When sperm of a particular type were presented with a choice of ova, they united more frequently with one type than with another.

3. ENTRY OF SPERM INTO OVUM

To enter the ovum, the sperm has first to penetrate (*a*) the cumulus mass, if this is still present, (*b*) the zona pellucida, and (*c*) the vitelline membrane.

The sperm makes its way through the cumulus mass by virtue of its own motility, dissolving a tunnel through the hyaluronic acid matrix as it goes. Sperm have been shown to contain the enzyme *hyaluronidase*, and this may help, at least in rodents, to dissolve the cumulus mass. The final disintegration of the cumulus mass is a separate process, which is not necessarily the result of fertilization, and may in fact precede it in farm animals.

The next obstacle to sperm entry is the zona pellucida (Fig. 7–2a). There is some evidence for the existence of a mechanism to ensure that the sperm remains attached at this stage. The ovum is said to produce a substance (*fertilizin*) which reacts with the sperm and specifically agglutinates it. Although well-established in sea-urchins, such a phenomenon has not yet been demonstrated unequivocally in mammals. At any rate the agglutination process cannot permanently immobilize the sperm, since it continues to swim through the zona pellucida, leaving (at least in rodents) a narrow tunnel behind it. At this stage the acrosome, loosened during capacitation, is finally lost, exposing the *perforatorium*. Probably the action of some as yet unidentified enzyme, associated with the perforatorium, facilitates passage through the zona.

The last stage in the penetration of the ovum involves the attachment of the sperm head to the surface of the vitellus (Fig. 7–2b).

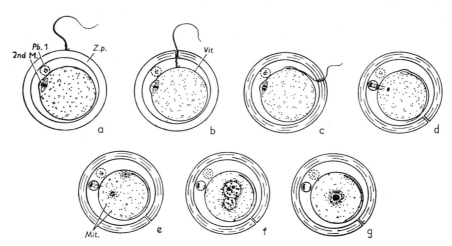

FIG. 7–2.—Diagram illustrating the processes occurring during fertilization in the rat.

(*a*) The sperm in contact with the zona pellucida (Z.p.). The first polar body (Pb. 1) has been extruded; the nucleus of the ovum is undergoing the second meiotic division (2nd M.).

(*b*) The sperm has penetrated the zona pellucida, and is now attached to the vitellus (Vit.). This evokes the zona reaction, which is indicated by shading as it passes round the zona pellucida.

(*c*) The sperm head is taken into the vitellus, and lies just below the surface which is becoming elevated above it. The zona has rotated relative to the vitellus.

(*d*) The sperm is now almost entirely within the vitellus. The head is swollen (see Plate XVI *B*). The vitellus has decreased in volume, and the second polar body has been extruded.

(*e*) Male and female pronuclei develop. Mitochondria (Mit.) gather around the pronuclei.

(*f*) The pronuclei are fully developed, and contain numerous nucleoli. The male pronucleus is larger than the female.

(*g*) Fertilization is complete. The pronuclei have disappeared and been replaced by chromosome groups, which have united in the prophase of the first cleavage division.

(*After Austin & Bishop, 1957. Biol. Rev., 32, 296.*)

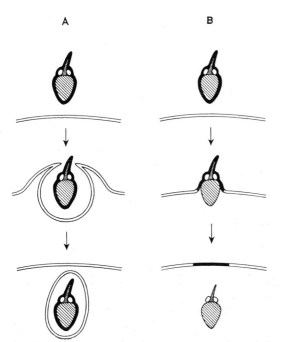

FIG. 7–3.—Entry of the sperm into the vitellus. In *A*, this is represented as a phagocytic process; in *B*, as a process involving rupture and fusion of the plasma membranes of sperm and ovum.

(*After Szollosi & Ris, 1961. J. Biophys. Biochem. Cytol., 10, 275.*)

This period, which lasts for about half an hour in those rodents where it has been measured, is a vital one, since it is at this time that *activation* occurs. Stimulated by the proximity of the sperm, the ovum awakes from its dormancy and development begins. The sperm head, and in some species the tail as well, then enters the vitellus. A projection on the surface of the vitellus marks for some hours the point of sperm entry (Fig. 7–2c).

Electron micrographs of rat ova suggest (Szollosi & Ris, 1961) that the actual process of penetration of the sperm into the vitellus is not, as used to be thought, a phagocytic process, with the vitellus flowing round and engulfing the sperm; rather, the plasma membranes of sperm and ovum appear to rupture and then fuse with one another to form a continuous cell membrane over the ovum and outer surface of the sperm. As a result, the sperm comes to lie inside the vitellus, leaving its own plasma membrane incorporated into the vitelline membrane (Fig. 7–3).

4. PRONUCLEUS FORMATION

One striking result of activation in some species (*e.g.* pig, cow) is that the vitellus shrinks in volume, expelling fluid into the perivitelline space. At the same time the sperm head in the vitellus swells and acquires the consistency of a gel, losing its characteristic shape (Plate XVI *B*, Fig. 7–2d). The perforatorium and the tail drop off. Within the sperm nucleus, a number of nucleoli appear and subsequently coalesce, and a nuclear membrane develops around its periphery. The final structure, which resembles the nucleus of a somatic cell much more closely than it does a sperm nucleus, is termed the male pronucleus (Fig. 7–2e).

Little is known of the subsequent fate of sperm constituents other than the nucleus. In some species the numerous mitochondria of the sperm mid-piece all go to one of the two daughter cells at the first cleavage division, in others they are released into the cytoplasm of the ovum and are distributed equally.

In most species the second polar body is extruded from the ovum soon after sperm entry, and formation of the *female pronucleus*

then begins (Plate XVI *C*). This resembles the male pronucleus in the appearance of nucleoli and the formation of a nuclear membrane. The two pronuclei develop synchronously, increasing in volume during the course of several hours to an extent that was estimated at 20-fold for the rat. In some species, including the pig, the two pronuclei are of roughly similar size (Plate XVI *D*); in others the male pronucleus is the larger (Fig. 7–2f). Pronucleus formation has been studied in detail by phase-contrast microscopy in living rat eggs by Austin (1951). This has not yet been done in farm animals because the texture of the cytoplasm in the living ovum makes the pronuclei almost impossible to see. In farm animals the pronuclei are smaller than in the rat, and the nucleoli are few and small; but in other respects the formation of pronuclei in the rat is probably representative of mammals in general.

5. SYNGAMY

At some stage during their maximum development, the male and female pronuclei come into contact. After a time they begin to shrink, and at the same time to coalesce. The nucleoli and nuclear membrane disappear, and the pronuclei can no longer be seen. In those mammals in which it has been measured, the total life-span of the pronuclei extends over a period of 10 to 15 hours. As the time of the first cleavage draws near, two chromosome groups become visible. These are the maternal and paternal chromosomes respectively. They unite to form a single group, which represents the prophase of the first cleavage mitosis (Fig. 7–2g). Fertilization is now complete.

As in any other mitotic division, each chromosome splits longitudinally, and the halves separate to opposite ends of the cleavage spindle. The fertilized ovum undergoes its first cleavage, to produce a two-celled embryo. Each daughter cell now contains the normal diploid number of chromosomes characteristic of the species, half having been derived from the ovum and half from the sperm.

Because of the uncertainty as to the time of ovulation in spontaneously ovulating mammals, the duration of fertilization, *i.e.*

PLATE XVI

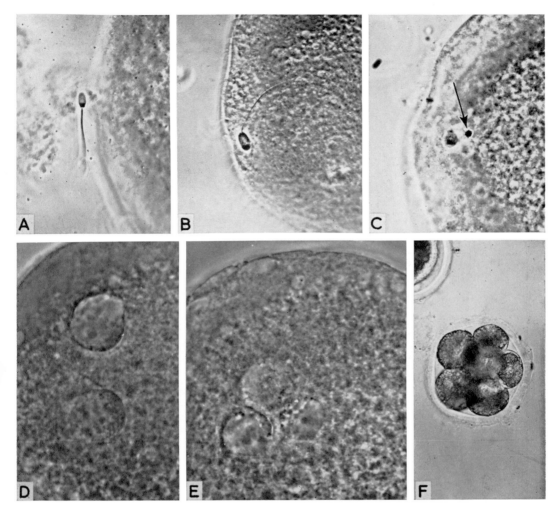

A, B, C. Different regions of a single pig ovum, 8 hours *post coitum*, (× 450). *A* shows a non-fertilizing sperm in the zona pellucida; *B* shows the penetrating sperm which has entered the vitellus (note its swollen head); *C* shows the nuclear apparatus of the ovum, with the recently formed nucleus of the 2nd polar body to the left, and the presumptive female pronucleus (arrowed) to the right.

D. Male and female pronuclei in a normal pig ovum during fertilization (× 500 approx.).

E. Pig ovum 6 hours *post coitum*, with three conjugating pronuclei. The chromatin clumps on the nuclear membranes of the two smaller pronuclei suggest that these are both female (× 460).

F. Unfertilized ovum recovered from a sow's uterus 72 hours after mating to a vasectomized boar. The ovum has fragmented in a manner strikingly reminiscent of normal cleavage (× 185).

(*A, B, C, E from Hancock, 1961. J. Reproduct. Fertil., 2, 307; D from Hancock, 1958. Vet. Rec., 70, 1200; F from Hancock, 1958. Studies on Fertility, 9, 146.*)

PLATE XVII

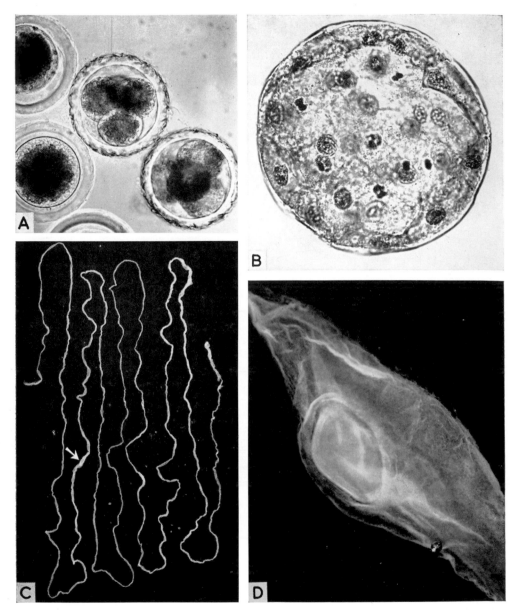

A. Two 4-celled and several uncleaved ova recovered from a sow's Fallopian tube 48 hours after artificial insemination. The two cleaved ova show numerous sperm in the zona pellucida, but no sperm can be seen in the uncleaved ova. The vitellus stains black on account of the dense concentration of yolk platelets (× 185).

B. Late morula of pig, 144 hours *post-coitum*. Several mitotic figures can be seen (× 330).

C. Pig blastocyst 13 days after mating at the beginning of estrus. The total length of this blastocyst was 157 cm. The position of the embryonic disc is indicated by an arrow.

D. Enlarged view of a pig embryonic disc 14 days after mating.

(*A from Hancock, 1958. Studies on Fertility, 9, 146; B from Hancock, 1961. J. Reprod. Fertil., 2, 307; C, D, from Perry & Rowlands, 1962. J. Reprod. Fertil. 3, in press.*)

the total time interval from the penetration of sperm to the time of first cleavage, is not known exactly for any farm animal. It is unlikely to exceed 24 hours.

6. Zona Reaction and Vitelline Block

If ova are classified according to the number of sperm they contain, those penetrated by one sperm only are found to be commoner than would be expected by chance. Often ova are observed with several sperm clustering around the outside of the zona pellucida, but only a single one within. It is therefore inferred that the zona pellucida can undergo some change after the passage of the first sperm which renders it less easy to penetrate subsequently. This change is termed the *zona reaction*. It is further inferred that the reaction is set off when the first sperm makes contact with the surface of the vitellus, and that it is mediated by some substance passing out from the vitellus to the zona.

Extra sperm which succeed in passing through the zona pellucida into the perivitelline space are called *supplementary* sperm. In some species (sheep, dog, hamster) the zona reaction is relatively quick and effective, and supplementary sperm are found rarely if at all. In other species (mouse, rat) they are more common. The rabbit shows no zona reaction, and up to 200 supplementary sperm have been observed in the perivitelline space of the fertilized ovum. Whether or not supplementary sperm play any part in the further development of the embryo is still debated.

The other defense mechanism against entry of more than one sperm is shown by the vitellus itself, and is termed the *vitelline block* or the *block to polyspermy*. The fertilizing sperm is actively engulfed by the vitellus; but subsequently the vitelline surface becomes unresponsive to contact, and no further sperm are engulfed. Sperm which have been damaged by x-irradiation may make contact with the vitelline surface without activating the ovum. In this case the contact also fails to induce the vitelline block.

Extra sperm which succeed in entering the vitellus, in spite of both the zona reaction and the vitelline block, are called *super-numerary* sperm, and the ovum is said to show *polyspermy*. The effectiveness of the vitelline block varies from species to species. When polyspermic ova are found, but supplementary sperm are seldom or never seen (*e.g.* sheep, dog, hamster), the vitelline block must either be absent or must be delayed until after the zona reaction is in operation. On the other hand in a species such as the rabbit, with many supplementary sperm in the perivitelline space but a very low incidence of polyspermy, there must exist a rapid and efficient vitelline block.

In mice, the incidence of polyspermy depends upon the strain of the female; on the other hand the proportion of ova containing supplementary sperm is related to the strain of the male, and does not depend on the female.

B. Polyspermy

The existence of the zona reaction and the vitelline block would lead one to expect that polyspermy in mammals was a disadvantageous state. This is indeed so. All the processes of fertilization, including the factors which regulate the number of sperm reaching the ampulla, are coordinated to ensure that, while every ovum is fertilized, polyspermy is kept to a minimum. The incidence of polyspermic ova in most mammalian species is normally only 1 to 2 per cent. In birds, on the other hand, polyspermy is usual.

The incidence of polyspermy may be increased experimentally, either by increasing the number of sperm in the ampulla, or by lowering the barriers which prevent extra sperm from entering the ovum. Conditions which reduce the zona reaction also tend to reduce the vitelline block. These include aging of the ovum, or heating of the ovum or of the whole animal. Delayed copulation, since it leads to fertilization of aged ova, is an effective method of increasing the incidence of polyspermy in pigs and rabbits.

When polyspermy does occur, the one or more supernumerary sperm often form pronuclei in the normal way, though in such a case all the pronuclei are reduced in size. Ova with three or occasionally four pronuclei have been observed in many species, including the cow, sheep and pig (Plate

9

XVI *E*). Sometimes it is possible to prove that two of the three pronuclei are male in origin and hence that polyspermy has occurred; sometimes, however, the extra pronucleus will be female in origin, having arisen through failure of polar body formation at one or other reduction division. At syngamy the three pronuclei, whatever their origin, give rise to three chromosome groups which then unite. In this way a *triploid* embryo is formed, with three sets of chromosomes in every cell instead of the normal two sets. Triploid rat embryos can survive to mid-gestation, and a boy with three sets of chromosomes in most of his cells has been reported; but the great majority of triploid embryos die at a very early stage of development. The disadvantage of polyspermy to the organism is thus that it leads to triploidy, which is a lethal condition.

C. Parthenogenesis, Gynogenesis, Androgenesis

In *parthenogenesis* the ovum is activated by some means other than by a sperm. In *gynogenesis* the ovum is activated by a sperm which takes no further part in fertilization. In *androgenesis* the ovum is activated by a sperm in the normal manner, but the nucleus of the ovum takes no part in fertilization. In all three phenomena only a single pronucleus is formed, female in origin in the first two, and male in the third. Gynogenesis and androgenesis rarely if ever occur spontaneously in mammals, but may be induced experimentally, for instance by irradiating either the sperm or ova. The embryos that result are *haploid*, with only a single set of chromosomes, and do not survive beyond the early stages of development.

Spontaneous cleavage of unfertilized ova has been reported in a large number of mammalian species. In some of these cases, degenerative fragmentation may have been mistaken for parthenogenetic development. True activation has been induced by chemical treatment, heating or cooling of unfertilized ova *in vitro* (rabbits), and by cooling, anesthesia, and oxygen lack *in vivo* (rabbits, mice, rats, sheep). Development may proceed to blastocyst stage or even to implantation, but a report that induced parthenogenesis in rabbits led to the birth of live young has not been confirmed. According to the nuclear mechanism involved, parthenogenetic embryos may be either haploid or diploid. In the second case, they would be difficult to distinguish from normal young.

Gynogenesis, androgenesis, parthenogenesis and other abnormalities of fertilization are discussed at length by Beatty (1957).

D. Fertilization in Vitro

If a reliable procedure were developed for achieving fertilization of mammalian ova outside the body of the female, experiments on the mechanism of fertilization in mammals would become much easier. Numerous attempts to obtain fertilization *in vitro* were made before the phenomenon of sperm capacitation had been discovered. These were largely vitiated by the use of uncapacitated sperm. When cleavage of the supposedly fertilized ovum was observed in culture, the possibility exists that the ovum had been activated parthenogenetically; while ova treated with sperm *in vitro* and shortly afterwards transferred to the Fallopian tubes of a recipient female might have had sperm attached to their surfaces which only achieved fertilization after transfer.

These difficulties have been overcome in the work of Thibault and his colleagues on rabbits. Rabbit ova were removed at body temperature, to lessen the risk of parthenogenetic activation. They were mixed with sperm which had been previously capacitated in the genital tract of female rabbits. Subsequent microscopical examination showed that the ova had been penetrated by sperm, and were undergoing pronucleus formation and apparently normal cleavage. Chang, using the same technique, returned the embryos to recipient female rabbits and obtained live young. The percentage of embryos which developed successfully was rather low.

E. Sex Determination

Every cell in the mammalian body except the gametes contains a pair of *sex chromo-*

		O V A		
		Normal	Non-disjunctive	
		x	xx	o
S P E R M — Normal	x	xx (= normal female)	xxx	xo
	y	xy (= normal male)	xxy	yo
Non-disjunctive	xy	xxy		
	o	xo		

Fig. 7–4.—Diagram showing how normal and abnormal sex-chromosome constitutions can arise at fertilization. An O sperm or ovum is one which carries neither an X nor a Y chromosome. Non-disjunctive gametes arise through faulty sharing out (non-disjunctive) of the sex chromosomes; *yo* individuals are probably not viable; *xxx* individuals, in man, are sterile females.

somes. In females the two members of the pair resemble one another and are known as X chromosomes; in males the sex chromosomes differ, one being an X chromosome, the other smaller, known as a Y chromosome. The sex chromosome constitutions of females and males are therefore referred to as XX and XY respectively. The gametes, being haploid, contain only a single sex chromosome: an X chromosome in the female (*homogametic* sex) and either an X or a Y chromosome in the male (*heterogametic* sex).

In normal fertilization, the embryo develops as a female or as a male according to whether the ovum (carrying an X chromosome) is fertilized by a sperm carrying an X or a Y chromosome. If the two types of sperm are present in equal numbers, the ratio of males to females at conception (the *primary sex ratio*) should be equal to one. Attempts to control the sex ratio in farm animals usually depend on treating the semen in such a way as might be expected to alter the proportions of X-bearing and Y-bearing sperm (see Chapter 3).

Rare individuals have been detected in Man and in the mouse whose cells contain two X chromosomes *and* a Y chromosome (XXY), and others whose cells contain only a single X chromosome (XO). These must have arisen through faulty sharing out of sex chromosomes either to the gametes (Fig. 7–4), or, after fertilization, to the products of early cleavage. XXY indi-

viduals are male, and XO individuals female, proving that maleness must be determined in the first instance by factors on the Y chromosome. Both types show some abnormalities of sexual development in Man.

XXY and XO individuals probably also occur occasionally in farm animals, though none have been reported so far. The best-known case of abnormal sexual development in farm animals is the free-martin condition found in cattle and occasionally also in sheep and pigs. This is not due to any abnormality of fertilization, but arises during gestation as a result of a female fetus sharing its blood supply with a male (see Chapter 10).

II. CLEAVAGE

After syngamy is completed, there ensues a period of several days during which the fertilized ovum, zygote or *embryo* as it should be called once development has started, leads a free-living existence in the Fallopian tubes and uterus of the mother. During the latter part of this period, the embryo may be nourished by uterine secretions; but not until implantation has taken place does the embryo derive any nourishment from the maternal bloodstream.

At the beginning of the free-living period the ovum is a single cell, of relatively enormous volume compared with other cells of the body, and therefore with a very large ratio of cytoplasm to nuclear material. Reserve nutrients are stored in the cytoplasm in the form of yolk (deutoplasm). This single cell divides and redivides many times without any accompanying increase in volume of cytoplasm, though some increase in volume occurs through the uptake of water. The total amount of cellular material in the embryo actually decreases by about 20 per cent in the cow, and by as much as 40 per cent in the sheep. The process of cellular division without growth is called *cleavage*. It continues until implantation, by which time cell size has been reduced more or less to the size characteristic of the species. During the early stages of cleavage, up to the appearance of the blastocoele, the embryonic cells are often known as *blastomeres*.

A. Normal Course of Cleavage

The unfertilized ovum already possesses some polarity and an axis of symmetry. The nucleus lies in the *animal pole*, where the cytoplasm is usually dense and rich in ribonucleoproteins and mitochondria. In the opposite half (*vegetal pole*) the cytoplasm is more vacuolated and contains fewer mitochondria. In species (*e.g.* guinea-pig) where the ovum contains fat globules, it is in the vegetal pole that they chiefly accumulate.

The plane of the first cleavage division is not related to the plane of symmetry of the ovum. It usually passes through the area where the male and female pronuclei were situated at the beginning of syngamy, passing from the animal to the vegetal pole. The second cleavage divisions occur at right angles to the first, the third more or less at right angles to the second. But the divisions are not perfectly synchronized, so that 3-celled and 5-, 6-, 7-celled stages may be found. Nor are the divisions always equal, since the cells containing the more vacuolated cytoplasm tend initially to be larger than those at the animal pole. (This tendency is less marked in the cow than in other farm animals). All the divisions are mitotic, and consequently each cell of the embryo, from the fertilized ovum onwards, contains the diploid number of chromosomes

($2n$). Considerable amounts of DNA are synthesized during cleavage.

By the 16- to 32-celled stage, the cells are crowded together into a compact group within the zona pellucida. The embryo is now known as a *morula* (Plate XVII *B*). Fluid begins to collect in the intercellular spaces, and an inner cavity or *blastocoele* appears. Once this has begun to expand, the embryo is known as a *blastocyst*.

In swine and horses, where the ovum is very rich in yolk, the surplus is eliminated (*deuto-plasmolysis*) into the perivitelline space during cleavage, and later is found in the blastocoele. In the horse, this yolk is extruded asymmetrically, on the side of the ovum which is farthest from the nucleus.

1. FATE OF CLEAVAGE PRODUCTS

In mammals, cleavage is of the *indeterminate* type. This implies that, up till quite a late stage of development, it is impossible to tell which particular organs of the body are going to be formed by which cells. It also implies that all the cells of the early embryo retain all their original potentialities, in the sense that any cell would be capable of giving rise to an entire new embryo if the environmental conditions were suitable.

How indeterminate the mammalian embryo is at different stages we do not yet know. Tarkowski (1959) has destroyed one blastomere of a 2-celled mouse embryo, and has shown that the remaining one is capable of developing into a normal adult mouse. (The resulting embryo remains smaller than normal throughout the first part of gestation, but is of normal size by the time it is born). Whether both the first two blastomeres, if separated, could develop as completely as this is not known, though earlier work on rat embryos suggest that they are certainly both capable of undergoing some further development after separation. In the mouse, blastomeres isolated at the 4-celled stage will also sometimes develop up to the blastocyst stage, but show a good deal of variation in their developmental potentialities. This supports the idea, put forward by Dalcq (1957) on cytochemical grounds, that even at very early stages considerable cytological differentiation exists within the embryo.

Tarkowski (1961) also fused together pairs of 8-celled mouse embryos, which then developed into single, abnormally large blastocysts, and finally (after transfer to the uterus of a recipient female) into adult mice of compound origin. This important experiment shows that, at least up till the 8-celled stage, the blastomeres are capable of *regulating*, that is of adapting themselves to the cellular environment in which they are situated.

In the morulae of many species, including the sheep, goat and swine, small actively dividing cells can be seen grouped together

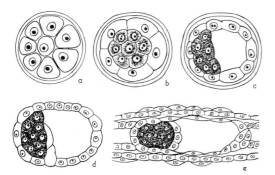

at one pole, and larger, less actively dividing cells at the other. Subsequently the smaller cells, which probably are derived from the vegetal half of the ovum, come to form the outer layer of the embryo which in turn gives rise to the *trophoblast*. The larger cells from the animal half of the ovum, lie in the middle, to one side of the blastocoele cavity, and are known as the *inner cell mass*. It is from the inner cell mass that the fetus will develop after implantation. Dalcq (1957), who has made an intensive study of the cytochemistry of the developing rat embryo, finds that proteins, nucleoproteins and alkaline phosphatase are concentrated in the inner cell mass (see Figure 7–5), while the outer, vegetal layer produces the greater part of the mucopolysaccharides and acid phosphatase of the embryo.

2. Cleavage Rates

Approximate estimates of the times taken by the embryos of various farm mammals to reach certain stages of development are given in Table 7–1. All these species ovulate

Table 7–1.—Rates of Development. Times, which are Approximate, are Given in Days After Ovulation

Species	2-cell	8-cell	Enters uterus	Blastocyst	Birth
Cattle	1–1½	2½	4	7–8	284
Sheep	1–1½	2	3	5½–6	150
Goat	1½	3	3½	6–7	150
Swine	1–1½	3–4	2–2½	5–6	112
Horse	1	3	4–6	–	335

Fig. 7–5.—Distribution of alkaline phosphatase enzyme (shaded) in rat embryos. At the 8-celled stage (*a*) none is detectable; at the morula, (*b*) and blastocyst (*c*, *d*) stage the reaction appears in the inner cell mass. The trophoblast (*e*) is negative. (*After Dalcq, 1957. Introduction to General Embryology, New York, Oxford University Press.*)

spontaneously and little accurate information is available concerning the time of ovulation. Estimates of cleavage rate are therefore subject to an error of unknown magnitude. In addition, of course, developmental rate will be subject to considerable real variation, both among individuals and, probably, among different breeds. The rate of cleavage up to the blastocyst stage tends to be faster in species where the total gestation period is short.

Passage of embryos down the Fallopian tubes is slow, taking 2 to 3½ days in most species (see Chapter 6). The pig embryo enters the uterus relatively early, at the 4-celled stage, while in most other mammals the embryo has reached at least the 8- to 16-celled stage before passing from the Fallopian tubes into the uterus. Species differences in the cleavage stage at which the embryos reach the uterus may be due to differences either in rate of cleavage or in rate of tubal transport.

3. THE BLASTOCYST

The respiratory activity of ova, as judged by oxygen uptake *in vitro*, does not alter until the blastocyst stage is reached. Biochemical studies (Fridhandler, 1961) suggest that during this initial period, glucose is oxidized mainly via the hexose monophosphate oxidation pathway. Then, at the early blastocyst stage, respiration rate suddenly rises, and the route of glucose oxidation changes to the Embden-Meyerhof pathway and the tricarboxylic acid (TCA) cycle.

As the embryo swells up with fluid, the blastocoele enlarges. The extent of this enlargement varies from species to species. In farm mammals it is considerable, the blastocyst becoming within a few days a thin-walled fluid-filled sac, more or less filling the uterine lumen. During this period, the zona pellucida is shed. In some species (*e.g.* guinea pig), remnants of the zona can be seen adhering to the blastocyst wall. Shedding of the zona occurs also in blastocysts cultured *in vitro*, and is probably due to the activity of the trophoblast itself rather than to any factor of the uterine environment.

The biochemistry of the fluid in the blastocoele has been studied in the rabbit before and during implantation. Use of radioactive tracers makes it possible to determine the passage of substances into and out of the blastocyst. Before implantation the blastocoele fluid is very rich in potassium and bicarbonate, which appear to be actively drawn into the blastocyst from the uterine fluid. As implantation proceeds, potassium and bicarbonate fall to the levels found in the maternal serum. At the same time protein and glucose, previously present in small amounts only, increase up to maternal serum levels. Phosphorus and chlorides also increase greatly in concentration. Water-soluble vitamins (thiamin, riboflavin, B_{12}, nicotinic acid) are present in small amounts in the blastocyst fluid before implantation.

The fall in bicarbonate concentration in the blastocoele fluid around the time of implantation may be a result of the increase in *carbonic anhydrase* in the endometrium, which was shown by Lutwak-Mann and Adams (1957) in the rabbit to be mediated by progesterone. Accumulation of carbonic anhydrase would lead to increased conversion of carbonic acid to CO_2, which would be removed by the maternal circulation. Transfer of bicarbonate from the blastocyst would be facilitated, and the attendant local liberation of alkalinity would make both the membranes and the trophoblast sticky and thus promote implantation (Böving, 1959).

It is clear that the blastocyst cannot be considered as a passive vesicle into which substances enter by simple diffusion. It possesses a high degree of metabolic selectivity, actively controlling the rate of entry of substances from the surrounding fluid. The role of uterine secretions in embryonic nutrition is discussed below.

B. Twinning

Two distinct types of twins are known: *monozygotic* (*identical*) twins and *dizygotic* (*fraternal*) twins.

Dizygotic twins originate from a double ovulation in a normally *monotocous* species. Two ova may be shed in the same estrous period, and fertilized by two different sperm. The resulting young do not resemble one another genetically any more closely than do ordinary brothers and sisters. In fact a pair of dizygotic twin lambs of opposite sex differ on average more from one another in birth weight than do male and female lambs born in twin pairs of like sex. This is known as the *enhancement effect*, and is probably due to some form of competition between embryos in the uterus.

Multiple ovulation may be induced, and hence the frequency of dizygotic twins increased, by the injection of pituitary or chorionic gonadotropins. This technique is already finding practical application in sheep breeding. Monozygotic twins, on the other hand, originate from a single fertilized ovum. In theory they could occur in all species, including species such as the pig which normally bear several young at a time, but so far they have been recognized in only a few species, notably man and cattle. Even here they are relatively rare: up to 5 per cent (depending on breed) of all births in cattle will be twin births, but only about one in every thousand births will be monozygotic twins. There is no evidence that any twin births in sheep or swine are monozygous.

Since monozygotic twins represent, as it were, two halves of a single individual, they resemble one another very closely indeed in all genetically determined characteristics. For instance, they are always of the same sex. Because of their identical hereditary equipment, monozygotic twin pairs of cattle, for instance, are particularly valuable experimental material for studying the effect of varied environmental conditions on such characters as milk yield in dairy breeds, and weight gain and conformation in beef breeds (European Association for Animal Production, 1960).

Many cases of monozygotic twinning probably originate fairly late in development, after implantation. A single blastocyst implants, and the single inner cell mass then differentiates two primitive streaks, giving rise to two separate individuals. Such twins have a common amnion. Alternatively, the inner cell mass in a single blastocyst may duplicate before implantation. This condition has been reported in both sheep and pigs. The resulting embryos will have separate amnions and placentas. It is not impossible that some monozygotic twins may originate still earlier, as a result of blastomeres separating inside the zona pellucida.

In swine, the simultaneous presence of more than one embryo in the uterus is normal. There is rarely fusion between either the allantois or the chorion of neighboring embryos. In sheep, where more than one embryo occurs frequently but not always, there is fusion of the chorion but not of the allantois; while in cattle, where multiple pregnancies are found relatively seldom, there is usually fusion of both chorion and allantois, with consequent anastomosis of blood vessels between neighboring embryos. This means that in cattle the majority even of dizygotic twins have a common blood circulation, while in other farm mammals the proportion is much lower. Where the twin partners are of opposite sex, the common blood circulation leads to the development of free-martins; where they are of different genetic constitution they become mutually

tolerant of one another's tissues, with the result that skin grafts can be freely exchanged between them in later life.

This fusion of the embryonic blood vessels is responsible for an unexpected difficulty in distinguishing monozygotic from dizygotic twins in cattle. In general, monozygotic twins are recognized by their striking similarity in all traits that depend mainly or only on heredity. Sex, coat color and pattern, nose prints, serum-globulin type, and presence or absence of horns are particularly useful traits for this purpose in cattle. But the genetically determined blood groups have to be used with caution in classifying cattle twins, because the common embryonic circulation results in a mixture of the blood-forming cells, so that each dizygotic twin shows not only his own blood group but also that of the other twin. If detected, this mosaicism is of course itself evidence of dizygosity. It has been estimated that, if all diagnostic tests are used, the error in diagnosing monozygosity in cattle twins can be reduced to about 1 per cent.

C. In Vitro Culture of Embryos

Detailed knowledge of the biochemistry and metabolism of early mammalian embryos can only be obtained from embryos grown in culture outside the body. Techniques for this purpose are slowly being developed.

Rabbit embryos will develop from early cleavage stages to mature blastocysts *in vitro* provided that the culture medium contains blood serum, plasma, or certain proteins. Mouse embryos will develop from the 8-celled up to the blastocyst stage in a simple buffered saline with added glucose and crystalline bovine albumin. Earlier stages need sodium lactate in the medium as well. A wide range of tonicity is tolerated, but small variations in pH will swiftly terminate development. Mouse embryos require a relatively high concentration of CO_2 in the atmosphere of the culture vessel, perhaps because early development *in vivo* is semi-anaerobic. The temperature of the cultures is usually maintained at about 37°C.

Cleavage and blastocyst formation often take place more slowly *in vitro* than *in vivo*. But the blastocysts produced are apparently normal, and in the case of mice have been shown to give rise to normal young when transferred to uterine foster-mothers. This suggests that the tubal environment does not contain any specific factors essential for the nutrition of the early embryo. Development of the embryo beyond the blastocyst stage has not been obtained *in vitro*.

Little work has so far been done on the culture *in vitro* of the embryos of farm mammals. Pincus reported that early cow embryos would not undergo more than a small amount of cleavage *in vitro*. Wintenberger and her colleagues cultured sheep embryos in homologous blood serum, and found good development of 1-celled to 8-celled stages and of 16-celled stages to blastocysts. Goat embryos gave similar results.

D. Pre-implantational Mortality

Prenatal mortality in farm mammals represents a considerable source of economic loss (see Robinson, 1957). In cattle and horses, which normally bear only one young at a time, it is often hard to distinguish between embryonic mortality and infertility, since all one observes is the proportion of matings which are not followed by the birth of live young. This is commonly as high as 33 per cent in cattle. If mortality occurs early, before the embryo has affected the corpus luteum, estrus may recur at the normal time, as though fertilization had not taken place. In polytocous species, the loss of whole litters sometimes occurs. More often only some individuals in a litter die, and hence the effect of prenatal mortality is to lower the average litter size.

If a female of a polytocous species is killed during pregnancy, the number of live and dead young in the uterus can be counted. A rough indication of the number of ova which failed to be fertilized or which died before implantation can be got by subtracting the total number of implanted embryos from the total number of corpora lutea in the ovaries. Since fertilization is an efficient process, most of this difference will be due

to pre-implantational mortality. This method of estimating prenatal mortality takes no account of the loss of whole litters.

In laboratory rabbits, Adams found that total prenatal mortality amounted to about 30 per cent. One-third of this loss occurred before implantation, most of it probably at the blastocyst stage. Five per cent of does lost all their embryos before implantation; more than half suffered some pre-implantational mortality. Exact figures are not available among farm mammals but the level of mortality in swine is probably even higher than in the rabbit.

Little is known of the causes of pre-implantational mortality. Most fertilized ova develop into blastocysts. Failure to develop further may be due to some deficiency either of the embryo or of its environment. Parthenogenetic activation of ova by chemical or physical treatments, for instance, or fertilization of stale ova, commonly gives rise to embryos which die at the blastocyst stage. Similarly, in crosses between closely related species, *e.g.* rabbit (*Oryctolagus cuniculus*) × hare (*Lepus europaeus*) and rabbit × cottontail rabbit (*Sylvilagus floridanus*), a hybrid embryo is often produced which develops up to blastocyst stage but no further. Possibly development up to the blastocyst stage is more or less independent of the embryo's nuclear apparatus, and it is only when a normal nucleo-cytoplasmic ratio has been restored as a result of cleavage that deficiencies or chromosomal imbalances in the embryonic nucleus make themselves apparent in development.

Inadequacies in the maternal environment may also lead to death of blastocysts. For instance, Bruce finds that exposure to the odor of males belonging to a different strain from the fertilizing male causes failure of pregnancy in 70 to 80 per cent of recently mated mice. The embryos develop up to blastocyst stage and then perish. Presumably the olfactory stimulus from the strange male causes some endocrine disturbance in the female, which produces an unsuitable tubal or uterine environment. In sheep, maintaining the ewes at a high environmental temperature has been shown by Alliston and Ulberg to kill the embryos

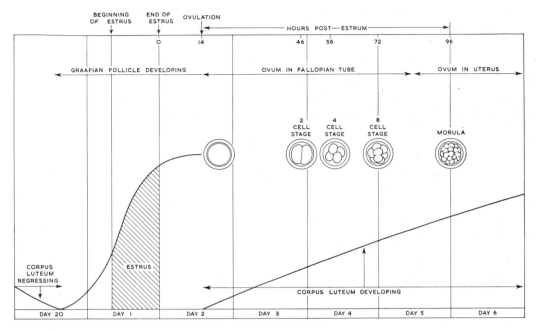

FIG. 7–6.—Diagram of events at and about estrus in the cow, showing the synchronization between the development of the embryo and the development of the corpus luteum. (*After Hammond, 1953. Ann. Ost. Ginecol., Milan, 6, 17.*)

during their first 3 days of life (see Chapter 18).

Death of embryos before implantation may also be due to pathological conditions such as bovine genital *vibriosis*, or infection of cattle with *Trichomonas foetus* (see Chapters 19 & 20).

The most critical period for the survival of the embryo is that of implantation itself. Normally, the developing corpus luteum, under the influence of luteotropic hormone from the pituitary, secretes progesterone, the action of which on the female tract is thus closely correlated with the development of the embryos (Fig. 7–6). Even under natural conditions, the failure of embryos to implant may often be due to the absence of receptivity in the uterine mucosa at the appropriate time. The consequences of experimental interference with the delicate synchronization between embryonic development and the maternal environment will be considered more closely in a later section.

The role of nervous pathways in implantation has recently been demonstrated by Nalbandov and associates. In sheep, implantation and pregnancy can be prevented

either by partial resection of the pituitary stalk, or by total section of the nerves going to the uterus. These procedures interrupt the neural pathways from hypothalamus to pituitary gland and from uterus to hypothalamus respectively, in either case preventing the signal for release of luteotropic hormone from reaching the pituitary gland, and hence interfering with the production of progesterone.

III. IMPLANTATION

The embryo is said to be *implanted* or *attached* when it becomes fixed in position, and no longer floats freely in the uterine lumen.

The term implantation seems most appropriate for those species where the embryo becomes buried in the wall of the uterus. In many rodents, for example, the blastocyst comes to lie in a pocket (crypt) of the uterine wall, forming a very intimate association with the maternal tissues; while in other species, including man, the blastocyst implants by passing through the uterine epithelium and is thus entirely cut off from the uterine cavity. In farm mammals, on the other hand, the embryo remains in the uterine cavity, and *whatever attachment it forms with the wall of the uterus prior to the formation of the placenta is of an extremely loose nature.* Movement of the blastocyst within the uterus becomes increasingly restricted as it expands; and in the sheep, a mucous substance sticking the blastocysts to the uterine wall has been reported. The possible role of carbonic anhydrase in rendering the rabbit blastocyst sticky during the period of implantation has already been mentioned.

The loose and gradual nature of the attachment process in farm mammals has led to considerable controversy as to when implantation actually begins. Estimates range from the 10th to the 22nd day *post-coitum* for the sheep, and from the 11th to the 40th day for the cow.

A. The Embryo

1. Spacing

In polytocous species, the blastocysts become distributed down the length of the uterine horn as a result of the muscular churning movements of the uterine wall. In swine, the blastocysts can also pass freely between the two horns; though this is not so in many rodents.

Whether there exists any more precise mechanism for spacing the embryos during implantation is still debated. The distribution of embryos between the two horns of the sow is much more even than would be expected by chance. On the other hand there is no evidence that an implanting blastocyst exerts any inhibitory influence on the implantation of another blastocyst close by. When the muscular movements which normally promote mixing of the uterine contents are inhibited, mouse blastocysts will successfully implant in close proximity to one another. After implantation embryos often become more uniformly spaced in the uterus, owing to differential growth of the uterine wall later in pregnancy.

The apparent absence of any inhibitory effect of an implanting blastocyst upon its neighbors implies that the upper limit to the number of embryos which can implant in a single uterus may be very high, at any rate in normally polytocous species. Implantation rate is therefore unlikely to be a limiting factor in any attempts to increase litter-size artificially in swine (for instance by inducing superovulation with gonadotropic hormones). Such attempts are more likely to founder at a later stage of pregnancy, owing to the inadequacy of the vascular supply or to the mechanical effects of crowding on the embryos; while the young which are born may well be under-sized and difficult to rear.

In sheep, on the other hand, Robinson has studied prenatal mortality in multiple ovulated females, and finds that the number of embryos surviving is reduced to a fairly constant number ($2\frac{1}{2}$ to 3 embryos per female) within the first 3 weeks of pregnancy. This implies that embryonic loss increases as the number of ova shed increases. The work of Moore and associates on transferring different numbers of embryos in sheep confirmed Robinson's findings, and indicated that the embryonic mortality associated with increased numbers occurs during the early stages of the attachment process, about day 14. Mortality did not seem to be due to a deficiency of progesterone.

2. Orientation

In any given species, the position in which the blastocyst implants is usually fixed. In swine the embryonic disc is always situated on the anti-mesometrial side of the uterine horn. On the other hand the embryos at the end of pregnancy are equally likely to be facing up or down the uterine horn.

If the mesometrial-antimesometrial axis of the rat uterus is reversed surgically, blastocysts still implant on the anti-mesometrial edge. The position of implantation is therefore determined by the relationship between blastocyst and uterine wall, rather than by the action on the blastocyst of any external factor such as gravity. That it is the uterus itself which plays the chief determining role is shown by the recent work of Wilson. Using pseudo-pregnant female mice as recipients, he showed that pieces of muscle or tumor put into the uterus at the appropriate time would become "implanted" on the anti-mesometrial edge just as do blastocysts in a normal pregnancy.

3. Gastrulation

Gastrulation is a stage of embryonic development occurring, though in various different guises, in all vertebrates. It succeeds formation of the blastocyst and precedes organ formation. Essentially, gastrulation consists of movements of cells or groups of cells in such a way as (*a*) to convert the embryo from a two-layered into a three-layered structure, and (*b*) to bring the future organ-forming regions into their definitive positions in the embryo.

In mammals, gastrulation involves the cells of the embryonic disc only. From the embryonic disc three types of tissue differentiate, *endoderm, mesoderm* and *ectoderm*. From these, all the fetal tissues develop, and also the embryonic membranes which connect the embryo and fetus to the mother. Cells migrate or split off from the inner cell mass of the embryonic disc to give rise to a layer of endoderm which spreads round the interior of the blastocyst, forming the *bilaminar omphalopleure*. At the same time the notochord and mesoderm are formed by invagination of cells in the *primitive streak* region of the embryonic disc.

4. Delayed Implantation

The duration of the blastocyst's free life in the uterine lumen, *i.e.* the interval between its entry into the uterus and its subsequent implantation, ranges from 2 days in the mouse and 10 to 20 days in the sow, to about 8 weeks in the mare. In some species (*e.g.* badger, roe deer, certain weasels and bears) the blastocyst may undergo a still longer period of dormancy after entering the uterus, implantation being postponed for several weeks or even months. This is known as *natural delayed implantation.*

In some rodents and insectivores, implantation may also be delayed for a week or two, and the gestation period thereby prolonged, if the mother is lactating. This is known as *physiological delayed implantation.* The larger the litter which is being suckled, the greater the prolongation of pregnancy. Rat and mouse blastocysts may be induced experimentally to remain dormant in the uterine lumen, without implanting, either by the hormonal induction of ovulation and mating in females too

young for implantation to occur, or by removing the ovaries subsequent to ovulation. In the latter case, small amounts of progesterone may have to be given to keep the blastocysts alive. No deterioration in the condition of such experimentally dormant blastocysts has been observed over a period of several weeks. The endocrinological basis of delayed implantation is still a subject of debate. The balance between estrogen and progesterone is probably of critical importance.

Seasonal variations of gestation period have been recorded in cows, sheep and goats, but the differences are small, and probably due to nutritional influences on rate of embryonic development or time of parturition (see Chapter 10). In the mare, on the other hand, season of breeding accounts for nearly half of the considerable variations in gestation period that have been reported. Since the horse blastocyst anyway undergoes a period of dormancy in the uterus, these variations may well be due to seasonally determined variations in the time of implantation.

B. The Uterus

1. Pre-implantational Changes

While the embryo is undergoing cleavage and blastocyst formation, the uterus too is undergoing changes, preparing the way for implantation.

During this *progestational* period, there is a decrease in the muscular activity and tonicity of the uterus, which may help to retain the blastocysts in the uterine lumen. At the same time, an increased blood supply develops to the uterine epithelium. In some species the increased vascularity is greatest along the side of the uterus at which implantation takes place. Associated with the increased blood supply, nutritive material (mainly glycogen and fats) accumulates in the uterine epithelium. This material, along with cellular debris and extravasated leucocytes in the uterine lumen, forms the *histotrophe* (uterine milk) which provides nourishment for the embryo in the early period of uterine life, before the chorio-allantoic placenta is established. There is evidence that histotrophe plays an important role in embryonic nutrition from about 80 hours *post coitum* in the rabbit, and from the 9-day blastocyst stage onwards in the sheep. In farm animals, where the placenta is of the epitheliochorial or syndesmochorial type (see Chapter 10), the association between fetal and maternal blood is not very close. Histotrophic nutrition is therefore important not only in the early stages of uterine life, but throughout gestation.

The epithelial lining of the uterus undergoes striking histological changes during the estrous cycle (see Corner 1921). Proliferation of the epithelium during the progestational phase provides increased uterine surface and also increased glandular activity. In the absence of fertilization the epithelium regresses. Progesterone plays the leading part in determining the preimplantational changes in the uterus, just as at an earlier stage in the cycle estrogen predominated. The balance between estrogen and progesterone is probably more important than the absolute levels of either alone. In almost all mammals, removal of the ovaries immediately after ovulation prevents both implantation and the uterine developments associated with it.

2. Relative Roles of Embryo and Uterus

Should implantation be considered an active process from the point of view of the embryo? Or is the role of the embryo a purely passive one, with the maternal tissues of the uterine wall as the active agent?

In support of the second point of view are the following observations: (*a*) Wilson's report that the mouse uterus at the appropriate stage of progestational development will "implant" pieces of muscle or tumor inserted into it, in the same antimesometrial position as the embryo would occupy in a normal pregnancy; (*b*) in some species, when the uterine epithelium is sensitized by progesterone (*e.g.* during pregnancy, pseudopregnancy, or lactation), it reacts to mechanical or electrical stimulation by the formation of *deciduomata*, even if no blastocyst is present. These experimentally induced deciduomata are very similar in histology and vascular pattern to those which in normal pregnancy form the maternal part of the placenta.

That the embryo plays an active role in implantation is suggested by the following observations: (*a*) in the guinea-pig, pseudopodia-like processes have been observed cinematographically to project out from the blastocyst and to penetrate the uterine epithelium; (*b*) blastocysts are capable of "implanting" in situations other than the normal one (*e.g.* in the anterior chamber of the eye; or under the capsule of the spleen, kidney or testis). Glenister (1961) has observed that rabbit blastocysts cultivated *in vitro* on strips of uterine endometrium will form an attachment to the endometrium, with the embryonic trophoblast cells penetrating and eroding the maternal tissues as in normal implantation. This *"in vitro* implantation" occurs just as readily if the endometrial strips are reversed, so that the blastocysts are in contact with the endometrial stroma, without any uterine epithelium intervening. In many species, ectopic pregnancies are occasionally found— that is, embryos which have spontaneously implanted outside the uterus, usually either on the broad ligament, or on some band of intraperitoneal muscle. Such embryos rarely survive long; but in Man some continue their development to full term, when they have, of course, to be delivered surgically.

The evidence suggests that, as in many biological and especially developmental processes, a system of "double assurance" operates in implantation. Both the embryo and the uterus play an active role, and in a normal pregnancy the activities of the two are harmoniously synchronized.

3. Relation Between Embryo and its Maternal Environment

The importance of the tubal environment in embryonic development has been underlined by the findings of Wintenberger-Torres (1956). If the passage of sheep embryos through the Fallopian tubes to the uterus is hastened by hormone treatment, development is slowed down, and cleavage rate does not return to normal for 9 days. If, on the contrary, the embryos are retained in the tubes by a ligature, they continue to develop normally for a week; for the next

2 days they develop more slowly but will recover if transferred to the uterus; while if they remain for more than 10 days in the tubes, they will undergo no further development even if transferred to the uterus.

In species other than the sheep, the role of the tubal environment has been little studied. Data on the role of the uterine environment, on the other hand, have been obtained by experiments on embryo transfer (see Chapter 6). The chief point which emerges is the critical importance of *synchronization* between the stages of development of the embryo and of the uterus if successful implantation is to take place. Embryo transfers to the uterus give a high success rate if donor and recipient female are at the same stage *post-coitum*; or better still (since transfer may slightly retard embryonic development) if the donor is somewhat more advanced in development than the recipient. But if the embryo is "younger" than the recipient uterus, so that it is not ready to implant at the moment when the uterine endometrium is ready for implantation, the success rate is usually very low.

Details of this synchronization have been worked out for the rat by Noyes & Dickmann (1960). Implantation in this species normally takes place on the 5th day *post-coitum*. The conditions for successful embryonic survival and implantation after transfer were that both the donor and the recipient should be at the 3rd, 4th or 5th day *post-coitum*, and in addition, that the donor should be at the same post-coital stage as the recipient, or one day in advance. Embryos that were in advance delayed their development and did not implant until the uterus was ready; those that were "younger" developed at the normal rate until the 5th day, but then rapidly degenerated.

In farm mammals, the period of implantation accounts for a significant proportion of all reproductive losses. Delayed development of the embryos, their delayed passage into the uterus, or precocious development of the endometrium, will all lead to failure of synchronization between blastocyst and endometrium at the critical time, and hence may be responsible for failures of implantation.

C. Course of Implantation

It has been stressed earlier that implantation is a gradual process in all farm mammals, and that the early attachment of the trophoblast to the endometrium is of an extremely loose nature. We shall now briefly consider the morphological processes concerned in implantation in farm mammals. The differentiation of the embryonic membranes, by which the embryo is connected to the mother, and the subsequent formation of the chorio-allantoic placenta, will be described in Chapter 10.

Swine. The initial period of attachment lasts from about the 12th to the 24th day after fertilization. By about the 7th day, the zona pellucida surrounding the blastocyst has been shed, so that the trophoblastic cells are in direct contact with the uterine epithelium. The trophoblast now starts to proliferate rapidly, which leads to a folding of the trophoblast wall, presumably because the accumulation of fluid in the blastocyst cavity does not keep pace with the expansion of the wall. Endoderm appears and the blastocyst changes in the course of a few days from a small spherical vesicle to an exceedingly elongated thread-like tube, sometimes attaining a length of several feet (Plate XVII). The embryonic disc (Plate XVII) occupies a short enlarged section in the central part of this tube (Heuser & Streeter, 1929). At this time the wall of the uterus is deeply folded, and the outer layer (*chorion*) of the elongated blastocyst is apposed to the uterine epithelium, following the course of the folds. Throughout this period the nutrition of the embryo depends on the absorption of histotrophe or "uterine milk." The great length of the pig blastocyst provides a large absorptive surface for this purpose.

Sheep. The early development of the sheep blastocyst is similar to that of the pig. Some degree of attachment has been reported as early as the 10th day. Elongation is less extreme, and does not start till the 12th day, but the blastocyst may still attain a length of 4 cm. by the end of the 3rd week. The process of implantation is different from that of the pig, since the sheep uterus contains permanent "attachment organs" the *cotyledons*. By about the 18th day, the chorion has expanded until it fills the uterine lumen, bringing the trophoblast into close contact with the uterine epithelium over the cotyledons. Trophoblast cells invade and eventually destroy this epithelium, and later, all other uterine epithelium with which they are in contact. This destructive process lays the foundation for a more intimate relationship between chorion and maternal tissue than is formed in the pig or horse. By about 4 to 5 weeks, the process of implantation is completed.

Cow. The course of implantation in the cow is essentially similar to that in the sheep, but starts later. The zona pellucida is shed at about 8 days, in the early blastocyst stage, and a few days later the blastocyst begins to elongate. Gastrulation is complete at 13 days. By the 33rd day, the chorion has formed a fragile attachment with 2 to 4 of the cotyledons surrounding the fetus; and within a few days maternal and fetal tissues have become so intimately interdigitated that the embryo is being nourished by these cotyledons. Growth of the cotyledons is probably stimulated by progesterone.

Horse. For nearly two months the horse blastocyst, although pressed up against the uterine epithelium by the pressure of its own fluids, is not attached in any way. It attains a diameter of at least 5 cm. and elongates only very slightly. During the third week, the blastocyst acquires an albumen coat, 3 to 4 mm. in thickness. At the end of the third week, groups of columnar cells, the *trophoblastic discs*, can be seen on the trophoblastic wall of the chorion. Some of the cells have processes which are thought to be phagocytic. The discs may help in attachment, but are more likely to be concerned with the ingestion of "uterine milk." By the 10th week, projections (or *villi*) from the chorion are penetrating into the mucosal folds of the uterine wall, and by the 14th week attachment is complete.

REFERENCES

AUSTIN, C. R. 1951. The formation, growth and conjugation of the pronuclei in the rat egg. *J. Roy. micr. Soc.*, **71**, 295–306.

AUSTIN, C. R. & WALTON, A. 1960. Fertilization, Chap. 10 in *Marshall's Physiology of Reproduction*, A. S. Parkes (edit.), Vol. I, Part 2, pp. 310–416. London, Longmans.

BATEMAN, N. 1960. Selective fertilization at the T-locus of the mouse. *Genet. Res., Camb.*, **1**, 226–238.

BEATTY, R. A. 1957. *Parthenogenesis and polyploidy in mammalian development.* Cambridge, University Press.

BÖVING, B. G. 1959. Endocrine influences on implantation. In: *Recent Advances in the Endocrinology of Reproduction*, C. W. Lloyd (ed.), pp. 205–226. New York, Academic Press.

CORNER, G. W. 1921. Cyclic changes in the ovaries and uterus of the sow, and their relation to the mechanism of implantation. *Contr. Embryol. Carneg. Inst.*, **13**, 117–146.

DALCQ, A. M. 1957. *Introduction to General Embryology.* London, Oxford University Press.

EUROPEAN ASSOCIATION FOR ANIMAL PRODUCTION. 1960. Research work with monozygotic cattle twins. Publn. No. 9.

FRIDHANDLER, L. 1961. Pathways of glucose metabolism in fertilized rabbit ova at various pre-implantation stages. *Exp. Cell Res.*, **22**, 303–316.

GLENISTER, T. W. 1961. Organ culture as a new method for studying the implantation of mammalian blastocysts. *Proc. roy. Soc. B.*, **154**, 428–431.

HAMMOND, J. 1941. Fertility in mammals and birds. *Biol. Rev.*, **16**, 165–190.

HANCOCK, J. L. (1962). Fertilization in farm animals. *Anim. Breeding Abst.*, **30**, No. 3, (in press).

HEUSER, C. H. & STREETER, G. L. 1929. Early stages in the development of pig embryos, from the period of initial cleavage to the time of the appearance of limb-buds. *Contr. Embryol. Carneg. Inst.*, **20**, 1–30.

LUTWAK-MANN, C. & ADAMS, C. E. 1957. Carbonic anhydrase in the female reproductive tract. 2. Endometrial carbonic anhydrase as indicator of luteoid potency: correlation with progestational proliferation. *J. Endocrin.*, **15**, 43–55.

NOYES, R. W. & DICKMANN, Z. 1960. Relationship of ovular age to endometrial development. *J. Reprod. & Fertil.*, **1**, 186–196.

ROBINSON, T. J. 1957. Pregnancy. Chap. 18 in: *Progress in the Physiology of Farm Animals*. Vol. 3, pp. 793–904., J. Hammond (ed.) London, Butterworths.

SZOLLOSI, D. G. & RIS, H. 1961. Observations on sperm penetration in the rat. *J. Biophys. Biochem. Cytol.*, **10**, 275–283.

TARKOWSKI, A. K. 1959. Experiments on the development of isolated blastomeres of mouse eggs. *Nature* (Lond.), **184**, 1286–7.

——— 1961. Mouse chimaeras developed from fused eggs. *Nature* (Lond.), **190**, 857–860.

WINTERBERGER-TORRES, S. 1956. Les rapports entre l'oeuf en segmentation et le tractus maternel chez la brebis. *Proc. 3rd. Int. Congr. Anim. Repr.*, (Cambridge) **1**, 62–64.

QUESTIONS

1. A cow is artificially inseminated, but comes on heat again 3 weeks later. List the possible reasons.
2. Define implantation. In what way is the term inappropriate when applied to farm animals?
3. Discuss the vital importance of synchronization, with reference to (*a*) fertilization, (*b*) implantation.
4. With reference to a named species, describe in detail a hypothetical experiment to demonstrate the occurrence of fertilization *in vitro*.
5. In what ways does cleavage resemble cell division in an adult animal? In what ways is it different?
6. What obstacles does a sperm meet in fertilizing a mammalian ovum, and how does it overcome them?
7. What sex would you expect a parthenogenetic embryo to be in (*a*) mammals, (*b*) birds? Why?
8. Write brief notes on: pronuclei; zona pellucida; trophoblast; monozygotic twins; histotrophe; cotyledons; delayed implantation; freemartins.
9. Distinguish between polyspermy and the presence of supplementary sperm. Mention the possible consequences of each, and describe mechanisms which decrease the frequency of their occurrence.
10. "The blastocyst is a metabolically inert bag of fluid into and out of which substances passively diffuse." Discuss.

Chapter 8

Artificial Insemination

By G. W. TRIMBERGER

ARTIFICIAL insemination aroused only scientific interest in its application to mammals, when the Italian physiologist, Lazzaro Spallanzani, applied the method to dogs in 1780. Some practical use of artificial insemination was made in horse breeding about 1890. Wide use of artificial breeding for improvement in farm animals was first made in U.S.S.R. through the work of Ivanoff. He started the program with horses about 1900, and soon included cattle and sheep; by 1938 the technique was in common practice for breeding mares, cows, and ewes. Recently this method has been widely used for providing service to swine in the Far East and Europe. In several countries over 50 per cent of the sows are now bred by artificial insemination.

From artificial breeding programs started in Denmark, U.S.A., U.K., and U.S.S.R., this advanced system of breeding has spread to every country in the world. Cooperation between countries and between colleges of agriculture and livestock breeders was at its best in the development of artificial insemination. Within 20 years this program has developed so rapidly that 100 per cent of the dairy cattle in Denmark are now bred artificially. Comparative figures for other ranking countries are: Japan 95 per cent,

Holland 75 per cent, England 55 per cent, Western Germany 45 per cent, the United States 40 per cent, and France 40 per cent.

The fundamental reason for this unparalleled development is that artificial insemination provides the opportunity to breed genetically superior males with females anywhere in the world. Although artificial insemination techniques progressed most rapidly for breeding dairy cattle, the method soon was developed for all classes of farm animals, poultry, and nearly every other species, including bees.

The discussion in this chapter deals with semen collection, processing of semen, frozen semen, and insemination techniques.

I. SEMEN COLLECTION

When properly fed and managed, a young bull is ready for service at 12 months, a ram at 6 to 9 months, a boar at 8 months, and a stallion at 24 months of age (see Chapter 3 for age of puberty).

A. Preparation of Males

Production of high quality semen depends on the care and management given the male long before the time of actual semen collection.

1. Nutritional Requirements

The nutritional requirements for growth in the male are different from those in the female. A young dairy bull will need much more grain than a growing heifer when both are fed liberal amounts of forage. The amount of total digestible nutrients (TDN) required to develop young Holstein bulls to semen-producing age is a constant in the order of about 1700 lb. of TDN. Reduced TDN intake causes lack of sexual expression, an increase in age for onset of semen production and reduced sperm output. This is due

show no difference in semen production (Flipse & Almquist, 1961).

Bulls changed from a high to a low level of feeding during early life show no ill effects in quality or quantity of semen produced later. Thus for practical application, there are advantages in moderate to heavy feeding up to 18 months of age, and then in restricting the ration to prolong the useful life of the bull. Even severe underfeeding does not impair sperm production in a mature bull. Overfeeding at this age, regardless of the feeding regime during early life, results in weaknesses of the feet and legs and a decrease in sexual expression. This limits the animal's reproductive life. At comple-

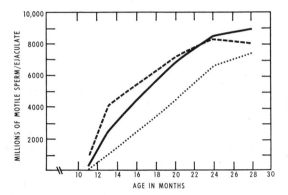

Fig. 8–1.—Number of motile sperm (million) per ejaculate from Holstein bulls at different ages on a high (– – –), medium (———), and low (· · ·), level of feeding. (*Data from Bratton et al., 1961, Cornell Univ. Agric. Exp. Sta. Bull. No. 964.*)

to a slower development of the testes until sufficient TDN is provided to meet the basic requirements. Fertility in terms of conception rate is not affected by underfeeding, but age of producing semen, quantity of semen produced, and concentration of motile sperm temporarily show a marked effect. Bulls raised on low, normal, and high daily TDN intakes came into semen production at an average age of 39, 46, and 58 weeks, respectively.

A young bull that will not serve because he has been underfed usually shows a marked response from additional feed. Underfed bulls less than 18 months of age will produce less than 50 per cent of the expected number of sperm per ejaculate, but when changed to a standard ration at 18 months they produce a normal number at 30 months (Fig. 8–1). But after 30 months of age even bulls given continuous low levels of feeding from birth

tion of the growth period, the aged bull becomes fairly well stabilized in semen production and fertility. There is little effect from changes in TDN allowances, source of protein in the ration, and levels of vitamins included. However, there are variations in sperm fertility between bulls and between different ejaculates from the same bull.

Rams fed at different planes of nutrition during the growing stage showed no difference in semen production or fertility. The effects of plane of nutrition in boars receiving 50, 70, and 100 per cent of the recommended energy intake during the growing period were reflected in a larger volume of semen from the boars on the high plane, but there were no observable differences in libido and semen characteristics (Dutt & Barnhart, 1959).

Restricted nutrient intake in boars does reduce the volume of seminal plasma as

10

well as its citric acid, fructose, ergothioneine, and inositol content, but has no effect on daily sperm production, sperm quality and fertility (Stevermer *et al.*, 1961). However, a 50 per cent feeding level in mature boars will finally result in lethargy and reduced sperm output.

A few weeks before the start of the breeding season, the ram should be changed from an all-forage ration to one with 1 to 2 lb. of 14 per cent total protein grain mixture. For the boar, the usual ration of 4 to 5 lb. of grain daily should be increased by 1 to $1\frac{1}{2}$ lb. several weeks before the breeding season starts, and it is best to have the boar gain weight during this time. However, neither overfeeding nor severe underfeeding can be tolerated from the standpoint of physical condition of the boar. The stallion should gain slightly in weight during the mating season. The optimum amount of grain fed depends on the amount of exercise, breed, and individual differences.

2. EXERCISE

Exercise serves as a special aid toward keeping males in optimum breeding condition. Some bulls can stand continuously tied in a stall and maintain a record of active service. However, most bulls keep in better physical condition with improved muscle tone from moderate exercise. This can be provided in several ways, such as: a paddock in which a bull can exercise at his leisure; a fixed cable between two posts or buildings; a mechanical exerciser driven by an electric motor.

Exercise is no problem for rams, but for the boar it must be considered in a good management program. It is usually provided by pasture lots or with feeding and housing facilities at opposite ends of a long pen when boars are housed in a restricted area. Exercise is most important in the stallion, and the equivalent of a half-day's work under the saddle or in the harness each day is recommended.

3. TEASER FEMALES

The use of a teaser female or another male has proved most successful for long-term semen collections. Estrous females serve as an incentive during the training period or for the sluggish or more discriminating male. As a protective measure against service to the female and possible infection of the male, a clean towel or apron is used to cover the vulva of the teaser female. Restraint of the teaser by use of ingenious devices such as horse collars and breeding stall is helpful. The artificial vagina is held by hand at the proper position on the animal.

With good handling and proper training, it is possible to collect semen by use of a dummy resembling a female of the species. Usually a hide is placed over a strong framework of either metal or wood, capable of supporting a large male. The sides and top should be well padded. The artificial vagina can be handled manually or suspended and held in place by a spring or elastic bands (Fig. 8–2). Boars are very adaptable to a "dummy sow" (Fig. 8–3).

4. TEASING

The active part of successful semen collection starts with the "teasing" procedure (see Chapter 9). Teasing can be instrumental in increasing quantitative powers (semen production) in a male. Sexual preparation and stimulation by false mounts also improve semen quality; for example, in the bull one false mount produces 50 per cent more sperm per ejaculate than can be obtained without teasing, three false mounts produce 100 per cent more. Procedures for producing a rejuvenating effect on bulls include: (*a*) change of teaser, (*b*) change in location of teaser, even moving the teaser 3 feet back, forward, or to the side, (*c*) leading another bull to the collecting area. For best results, a change of teaser or location is required for about every 12 ejaculates, regardless of whether a bull is collected from twice or 6 times per week.

B. Techniques and Equipment

The technical skill of the operator is important. Not only may such skill prevent injury to the animal, but it may have a favorable effect on the volume, concentration, and purity of semen sample. Appreciation of the prolonged period required for the complete ejaculation of semen in the boar and stallion is important for efficient per-

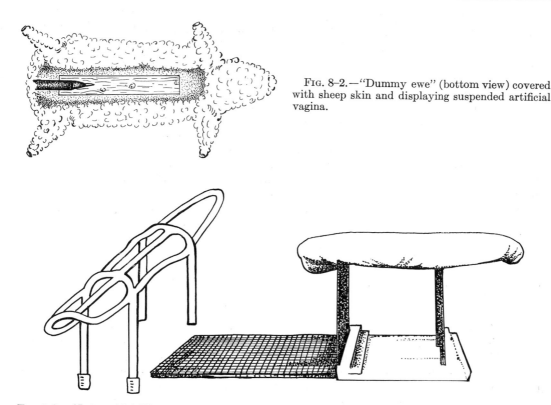

Fig. 8–2.—"Dummy ewe" (bottom view) covered with sheep skin and displaying suspended artificial vagina.

Fig. 8–3.—(*Left to right*) "Dummy sow" frame constructed from steel pipe.   Side view of ready-to-use 4-foot dummy covered with padding.   (*After Aamdal & Hogset, 1957, J. Amer. Vet. Med. Assoc., 131, 59.*)

formance when collecting semen artificially. The following is a discussion on the methods of collecting and handling of semen and the frequency of collections.

1. Artificial Vagina

Although several methods are available, the use of the artificial vagina is usually the choice for semen collection.   Various sizes and shapes are used, but all consist of a heavy rubber or metal outside cylinder with a rubber lining on the inside.   This enables a clean, complete ejaculate to be collected in the glass tube fitted on the lower end of the artificial vagina.   The entire process simulates natural copulation.

Bull.   For the bull, temperature is much more important than pressure.   The latter is usually controlled by the amount of water added rather than by blowing in air. The temperature inside the vagina should be between 40° and 45° C. at the time of collection.   The initial temperature of the water added to the artificial vagina should be increased to achieve the correct temperature at the time of collection.   This depends on prevailing ambient temperatures and the time interval between adding the water and collection.   Sometimes the temperature of the water is increased for bulls difficult to collect from.

The underline and preputial hairs are cleaned by brushing or washing and drying. Some of the long hair on the prepuce may be clipped; but since it protects against irritation, it should not be cut too short.   Proper teasing helps in cleaning the path for the semen.

During collection, the artificial vagina should be held parallel to the cow close to the actual site of collection in a slanting position in line with the expected path of the bull's penis.   The penis should be guided into the artificial vagina by clasping the sheath with the flat of the hand immediately back of the orifice (Plate XIX). The protruded penis itself should never be grasped; this usually causes immediate retraction and may spread disease; also it may cause an immediate ejaculation before the penis enters the artificial vagina.

Insertion of the penis is usually best accomplished on the upward movement or during the "jabbing" act. Precise timing produces best results. As the bull thrusts forward for ejaculation, the operator allows the artificial vagina to move forward and gently tips it in the opposite direction so the semen can run into the collecting tube. At this stage the skill of the operator is important in avoiding sharp bending of the penis, which may cause discomfort or even injury to the bull. The intelligent operator caters to the likes and dislikes of each individual male during semen collection.

Ram. The recommended temperature of the smaller-sized artificial vagina for the ram, is identical to that described for the bull. The technique of collection is also similar, but the forward thrust is less vigorous, thus reducing the possibility of injury and requiring less emphasis on skill in the collection process.

Boar. In the boar the collection period must be prolonged since the emission of semen, as in natural service, lasts from 5 to 20 minutes. Best results are brought about by exerting continuous pressure near the distal end of the "corkscrew"-like penis. Temperature is not important for collecting semen from the boar. The application of the proper pressure can be accomplished by grasping the rubber liner (preferably smooth) with the penis inserted, and providing sufficient stimulation from continuous pressure by a firm grip near the tip of the penis (Plate XVIII). Once ejaculation is started, the boar will usually remain quiet until ejaculation is completed (Polge, 1956). Pulsations or relaxation of pressure on the end of the boar's penis will result in a cessation of the sperm-rich fraction and a return to thrusting by the boar, increased seminal fluid emission, and renewed ejaculatory gelatinous secretions. The boar ejaculates from a penis locking sensation when it is firmly engaged in the sow's cervix, the artificial vagina, or the operator's hand. If the engaging pressure is relaxed, even slightly, sperm ejaculation temporarily ceases.

The ejaculate from the boar consists of three fractions. The first fraction contains mostly seminal fluids with a high bacterial content and a gelatinous pellet-like material from the vesicular glands which serves to seal the cervix of the sow during mating. This pre-sperm fraction is best discarded before the sperm-rich fraction is collected. The sperm-rich fraction is followed by another seminal fluid fraction which also contains some gelatinous material. The gelatinous material (about 20%) may be discarded at the time of collection and/or removed by straining the semen through gauze. Usually the boar emits only one sperm-rich fraction at a collection; however, some boars may ejaculate a series of two or

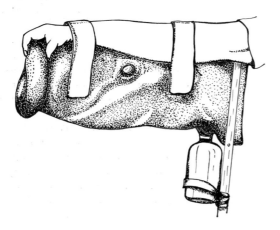

FIG. 8–4.—Artificial vagina (Mississippi model) for stallion. (*Adapted from Berliner, 1940. J. Amer. Vet. Med. Assoc., 96, 667 and Berliner, 1960. Horses and Jackstock, In The Artifical Insemination of Farm Animals, E. J. Perry edit., New Brunswick, N. J., Courtesy Rutgers University Press.*)

three sperm-rich fractions which are interrupted by seminal fluid emission.

Stallion. Because the artificial vagina for the stallion is larger than that for the bull, two operators may hold the equipment for semen collection. Temperatures similar to those described for the bull are used, but the stallion's penis is not as sensitive to temperature, and proper pressure to produce friction is more important (Fig. 8–4). When the pulsations characteristic of ejaculation in the stallion begin, the position of the artificial vagina is changed from the original angle, with the entrance held slightly downward, to an angle that allows the semen to flow toward the collecting bottle (Berliner, 1940).

2. ELECTRO-EJACULATION

Electrical stimulation is the preferred method for males that refuse to serve the artificial vagina, or when injuries and infirmities make this impossible. Whenever inability to serve is due to non-genetic factors, insemination of semen collected by this method is justified, and provides the best means for using such males. It can be used very successfully in the bull and ram, and is acceptable in obtaining a semen sample of reduced volume from the boar. It is often used for routine collection of ram semen.

Bull. A rectal probe with either ring or straight electrodes is used to provide the electrical stimulation. (Sometimes feces in the rectum will prevent full stimulation). However, by this method, the penis usually erects and the semen is collected without the possibility of contamination in the prepuce. When finger electrodes are used, full erection of the penis is seldom achieved, and there is a possibility of contamination from bacteria in the prepuce.

Secretion from the accessory sex glands takes place at the lower voltage level and ejaculation at the higher voltages. Excessive stimulation at the lower sub-ejaculatory level may make it difficult to obtain an ejaculation. If the increase is too rapid and the recommended procedure is not carefully followed, a pre-erection ejaculation is obtained which is subject to the disadvantage mentioned in the previous paragraph. The low voltage used at first is gradually increased to a higher level. Repeated rhythmical stimulation periods are alternated with short rest periods, when the voltage is momentarily returned to zero after each increase.

The bull responds favorably to this method of collection with no apparent ill effects, even after continuous routine collections over a period of a year or more. This is surprising in view of the reaction usually observed. The bull stiffens, arches his back and tends to push forward; thus a suitable restraining rack with good footing should be used. Sometimes bulls will bellow, giving the impression that the technique is painful, but other observations indicate that this is not the case.

Semen samples obtained from a bull with an electro-ejaculator are usually of larger volume with less concentration of sperm, but the fertility and total sperm numbers are the same as samples obtained with an artificial vagina.

Ram. The ram responds exceptionally well to electrical stimulation, and the response is much more rapid than in the bull. Sometimes only three stimulations of 2-, 5-, and 8-volt peaks are required for ejaculation. The semen can be collected with the ram in the standing position, or in a recumbent position on a table (Plate XIX). Semen collected from the ram by use of an electro-ejaculator is comparable in density and other characteristics to that collected from the ram with an artificial vagina. This is a difference between the bull and the ram.

Boar. An electro-stimulator designed for use in the ram can also be used in the boar. The bipolar rectal electrode, with a terminal pole and 3-ring electrodes spaced 2 inches apart, is placed 14 inches within the rectum of the boar. The current is applied gradually from zero to 30 volts, with stimulations of 5 to 10 seconds. Ejaculation is induced at 25 to 30 volts. Sperm motility, morphology, and concentration are good, but the volume is decreased with a low proportion of gelatinous material. The ejaculate is not fractionated as in natural service or when collected with an artificial vagina.

3. MASSAGE METHOD

The operator's hand is inserted about 10 inches into the rectum of the bull. By feeling carefully through the rectal wall, the vesicular glands are picked up with the fingers and stroked gently toward the center and backwards. This massage causes a slightly turbid fluid, usually about 5 ml., to flow from the prepuce. The vesicular fluid contains only cells of the mucous membrane with no sperm, and cleanses the path through which the semen will flow. After the assistant changes test tubes, the operator massages the ampullae of the vas deferens until a turbid fluid (the semen) is obtained; this contains great numbers of active sperm (Miller & Evans, 1934).

Best results are obtained in massaging the ampullae by placing a finger on each side of the tube and using the floor of the pelvis on the other side. Each ampulla is massaged its entire length from front to back about 12 times. Then both are picked up and massaged further. A semen sample is obtained in about 5 minutes. The massaging must be done gently because if the tube is irritated the secretion may contain blood; skill is more important than pressure. Samples obtained by this method have only about half the sperm concentration as semen collected with the artificial vagina. The bacterial content is usually higher and the survival time of the sperm during storage is shorter. However, if the massage technique is good the fertility of recently collected semen is comparable to semen collected with the artificial vagina.

4. HANDLING THE SEMEN AT TIME OF COLLECTION

Clean collecting equipment is essential to prevent any possibility of contamination by dust, dirt and chemicals. Water and rain drops should be kept out of the samples and the rubber liner of the vagina should be examined periodically for small leaks.

Preventing cold shock is important in handling semen during collection and processing. Cold shock during collection in cold weather can be avoided by: (a) an insulated covering for the test tube, (b) a special vagina with a complete inner liner terminating in a funnel (this permits the test tube to be carried inside the cylinder where the temperature is constantly warm), (c) holding the collection tube in the hand to control temperature, (d) surrounding the collection tube with a plastic tube containing warm water.

Precautions during cooling are also important. Soon after collection, the semen is partially diluted with a diluent at the same temperature as the semen. Diluents offer protection to the sperm during temperature change. All cooling should be gradual, at a rate of about 1° C. every 4 minutes. This is accomplished by placing the tubes of partially diluted semen in a beaker of water at room temperature and placing it in a refrigerator at 5° C.

5. FREQUENCY OF SEMEN COLLECTION

Frequently ejaculated sperm are not measurably different from infrequently ejaculated sperm in respect to livability during storage at temperatures ranging from 25° to −80° C. vital staining, morphological abnormalities, and fertilizing capacity. Mature bulls ejaculated once daily over a period of 8 months required more teasing and an additional false mount for sexual stimulation before each ejaculation, compared with bulls ejaculated once a week (Table 8–1). Changes in method and location of teasing and in the individual used for teasing, had to be made more frequently for bulls on a daily semen-collection schedule. However, no difficulty was experienced in obtaining semen samples because 96 and 98 per cent of the ejaculations respectively for daily and weekly collection frequencies were obtained within 1 minute after the bulls were given the opportunity to serve the artificial vagina (Hafs et al., 1959).

Regardless of collection frequency, the average practical maximum sperm harvest from mature bulls is approximately 35 billion per week. One or two ejaculations per week tap only a small percentage of the potential. A higher frequency of ejaculation results in more efficient use of bulls. Daily ejaculation of aged bulls is neither harmful to the bulls nor to the quality of the sperm.

PLATE XVIII

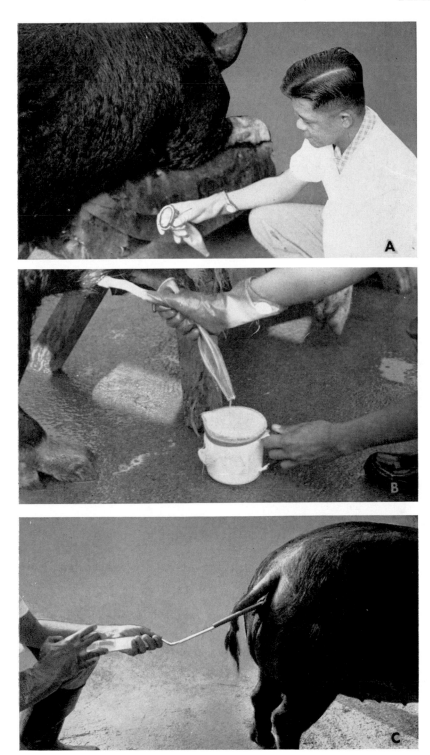

A. Boar mounting a dummy in preparation for semen collection.

B. Semen collection from boar by use of a smooth rubber liner and continuous pressure exerted by hand near distal end of penis.

C. Artificial insemination of sow (*Courtesy of L. L. Clamohoy*).

PLATE XIX

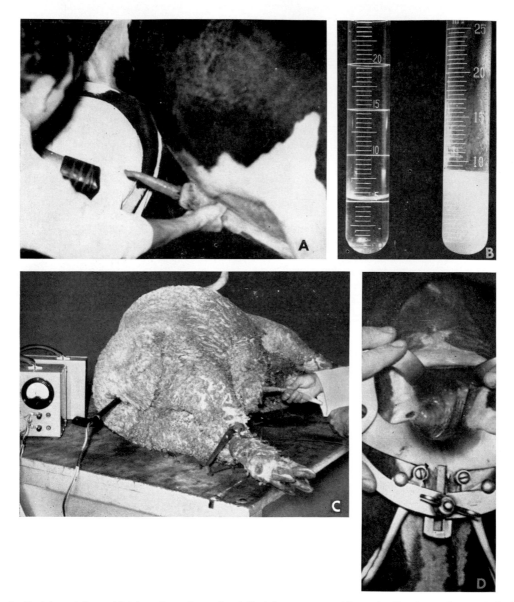

A. Position of the artificial vagina reflects the skill of the operator with good collection technique inducive to good serving habits in the bull.

B. *Left*: Vesicular fluid obtained from vesicular glands by massage method (or during teasing of male). *Right*: Semen obtained by massage of the ampullae (or by ejaculation) in the bull.

C. Semen collection by electro-ejaculation with rectal probe in the ram (*Courtesy of C. W. Emmens, and Sir John Hammond*).

D. The normal cervix in the cow tightens due to straining when a speculum (glass or metal) is used for artificial insemination but usually relaxes when the recto-vaginal technique is used.

Table 8–1.—Effect of Daily and Weekly Ejaculation of Bulls on Sperm Output and Fertility*

(Hafs et al., 1959, J. Dairy Sci. 42, 626.)

Frequency of ejaculation	Volume of Semen		Sperm Concentration (Billion/ml.)	Total Sperm		Motile Sperm		Fertility
	Per ejac. (ml.)	Per week (ml.)		Per ejac.	Per week	Per ejac.	Per week	60–90 day % N.R.
				(Sperm in billions)				
Daily	6.2	43.3	0.81	5	34	3	24	73
Weekly	9.5	9.5	1.89	18	18	11	11	70

*Total of 10 bulls for a period of 8 months.

Collecting semen with several ejaculations on 2 or 3 days a week makes it possible to provide liquid semen with satisfactory fertility at all times from a particular bull (Foote et al., 1960).

The ram can be used much more frequently during the breeding season, with 5 or more ejaculates each half day, but at least 15 minutes should be allowed between ejaculates. For the boar, about the same picture prevails for frequency of collection as for the bull. If necessary, a boar can be ejaculated daily for an entire month, but the number of sperm per ejaculate will decline about 50 per cent. Collections taken every 2 or 3 days produce approximately the same and 90 per cent of the maximum number of sperm respectively per week as do those taken daily. Stallions can serve twice daily, but it is best to provide the equivalent of one or two days of rest during the interval of a week.

6. DEPLETION TEST

Exhaustion tests deplete the extra-gonadal sperm reserves. A depletion test removes about half of the total sperm reserve in a bull, which on the average is approximately 70 billion (Almquist & Amann, 1961). Recovery depends on sperm output to replenish the reserves. Thus indices of estimated sperm production can be established. For accurate measurement of sperm production, it is important that preliminary depletion must be adequate to remove essentially all initially present sperm reserves, and the numbers of sperm subsequently removed must exceed the anticipated production. Thorough depletion in the bull can be accomplished by three consecutive daily collections of 20, 15, and 10 ejaculates, and sperm output (approximately 7 billion per day) can be estimated by two collections daily for a minimum period of 1 week (Hale & Almquist, 1960). Intensive sexual preparation (2 minutes of restraint and 3 false mounts) is necessary for reliable results. If there is a drop in sex drive or if it ceases entirely during a depletion test, it can be revived by supplying a new teaser (stimulus animal) and/or by a change in location of the collection site.

A bull apparently exhausted of sperm, after frequent collections in a depletion test, recovers and returns to normal in approximately one week. Semen volume is still low, but sperm concentration is higher; thus the number of sperm per ejaculate is about normal and indicates nearly complete replenishment of sperm reserves. Results of depletion tests show that repeated ejaculations produce no harmful effects on the sperm-producing capacity of the bull nor any deleterious effect on semen quality or fertility. The decrease in sperm concentration during depletion trials in bulls results in a gradual decline in freezability of sperm beyond the 10th ejaculate. A wide range exists for individual differences among bulls in sperm production and extra-gonadal sperm reserves. Dairy bulls produce a larger volume of semen and are sexually more active than beef bulls; they serve the same female more frequently and have more total services per day and per season in natural service.

II. PROCESSING OF SEMEN

A. Semen Evaluation

The greatest efficiency in artificial insemination is achieved by using the minimum number of viable sperm for each female, in contrast to the extravagent waste of sperm typical of natural service. Consequently, semen evaluation is of great importance and permits intelligent processing of the sample.

Volume and Appearance. The volume of the ejaculate varies among individuals and between different collections from the same male. The volume is much smaller in young males, and the correlation with body size is largely responsible for breed differences. Young dairy bulls usually start with 2 or 3 ml. per ejaculate, whereas a mature bull has an average of 8, but a maximum of 14, ml. or more. Breed, age, level of nutrition, climate, teasing time, technical skill of the operator, management, special handling, frequency of collection, individual differences, and temperament of the male contribute to the variations observed in the volume of semen collected. After a sexual rest, the semen qualities in the second ejaculate are better than in the first. A comparison between beef and dairy bulls used at artificial breeding studs showed that, collectively, beef bulls are inferior in volume and quality of semen produced, but that they surpass dairy bulls in conception rates (60 to 90 days non-returns) obtained when the semen is used for routine artificial insemination.

Normal bull semen is milky white in color (Plate XIX). An opaque, viscous appearance indicates a good sample. Usually, the greater the viscosity the higher the sperm concentration; a relatively clear and translucent sample would have a low sperm concentration. Some bulls produce semen that has a yellow tinge; this is caused by a riboflavin pigment in the semen.

Motility of Sperm. The percentage of motile cells may be determined by using a microscope, warm slide, and a microscope stage at 37° C. The motility is recorded in terms of percentage at intervals of 10, from 0 to 100. A percentage greater than 80 is seldom observed, but an occasional sample may have only motile sperm present.

Three main types of sperm motility are possible; progressive motion, rotary or circular motion, and oscillatory motion without change of position. Rate of motility, especially in contaminated semen samples and after storage of semen, reveals the quality of semen. Rates of motility may be recorded on the following basis:

0—No progressively motile sperm.
1—Sluggish motility, slow forward progress, with many undulating sperm.
2—Motility somewhat sluggish, still progressive but not rapid and flashy.
3—Intermediate motility, not the best but fairly rapid progressive motility.
4—Maximum progressive motility, very rapid and flashy; only found in a small percentage of samples.

When evaluated by the experienced technician, the above ratings may be broken down to intervals of 0.5.

Concentration. The concentration, or number of sperm per ml., of semen varies considerably among males and depends on some of the factors listed for differences in volume.

The equipment and chemicals needed to determine sperm concentration are: photoelectric colorimeter, test tubes checked for light transmission (standardized), 0.1-ml. and 10-ml. serological pipettes, 0.9 saline solution (NaCl) or citrate buffer, and a hemacytometer. A number of samples, with different concentrations, are counted with a hemacytometer (calibrated slide used for blood cell count) and also measured in the photoelectric colorimeter to prepare a representative calibration curve of sperm concentration. Determinations for any particular sample are then possible by comparing photoelectric colorimeter readings with the prepared curve. The sperm concentration multiplied by the percentage of observed motility gives the number of motile sperm per ml. of semen (Salisbury *et al.*, 1943).

Photometric methods are extremely variable for the determination of boar and stallion sperm concentration because the ejaculate contains a varying amount of non-sperm cellular material which decreases the accuracy of the results.

Abnormal and Defective Sperm.   After low magnification is used to get a general picture of representative fields, the high-power ($\times$ 440) is used to observe individual sperm. Since this is done with diluted semen, only about 10 to 40 sperm appear in one field. Only a rough estimate can be obtained this way; for accurate results, it is necessary to prepare a stained slide for microscopic examination and for counting the percentage of normal and abnormal sperm in representative fields. Percentage of normal sperm is expressed at intervals of 10 units, from 0 to 100, and 60 to 80 per cent normal is common for males with high fertility.

pH of Semen.   Semen with a high sperm concentration is usually slightly acid, with a pH of 6.3 to 6.8. Samples obtained by the massage method may have a pH of 8 or more. In contrast, high quality semen collected with an artificial vagina may have a pH as low as 6 after a very intense period of teasing. The pH becomes lower in semen samples as the time after collection increases because fructose is changed to lactic acid (see Chapter 3). The pH of diluents is adjusted to approximately 6.8.

B. Semen Diluents

Semen diluents provide: nutrients for the metabolic process of sperm, cold-shock protection, buffer effects against the lactic acid produced by sperm metabolism, a reducing substance for the protection of certain enzymes, and (certain diluents only) CO_2 gas which stops motility and reduces sperm metabolism. They also help to maintain proper osmotic pressure and proper mineral balance.

Composition of Diluents.   The composition of recommended buffers and diluents for the semen of farm mammals is shown in Table 8–2. The buffer ingredients are all weighed into an Erlenmeyer flask and dissolved in boiling redistilled water, because in

Table 8–2.—Composition of Buffers and Diluents Recommended for Artificial Insemination of Farm Mammals

(*Adapted in part from Foote et al., 1960, J. Dairy Sci., 43, 1330 & Dzuik, 1958, J. Anim. Sci., 17, 548.*)

Ingredient	Bull	Ram	Boar	Stallion
Buffers*				
Sodium citrate dihydrate (g) ($Na_3C_6H_5O_7 \cdot 2H_2O$)	14.5	28.0	—	—
Sodium bicarbonate (g) ($NaHCO_3$)	2.1	—	2.1	—
Potassium chloride (g)	0.4	—	—	—
Potassium sodium tartrate (g)	—	—	—	1.0
Glucose (g)	3.0	8.0	42.9	82.3
Glycine (g)	9.4	—	—	—
Gelatin (g) (as capsule)	—	—	—	25.7
Citric acid (g)	1.0	—	—	—
Sulfanilamide (g)	3.0	—	—	3.0
Distilled water (ml) (final volume)	1000	1000	1000	1000
Diluents*				
Buffer (% by volume)	80	80	70	70
Egg yolk (% by volume)	20	20	30	30
Penicillin (units/ml.)	1000	—	—	100
Dihydrostreptomycin (μg./ml.)	1000	1000†	1000	200

*The buffers and diluents listed give the best results on fertility and survival of sperm during storage.   Milk is a satisfactory diluent for bull, ram, boar, and stallion semen.
†Or penicillin 500 units/ml. and dihydrostreptomycin 500 μg./ml.

glycine containing diluents, the glycine adheres to the outside and partially decomposes when direct heat is applied. The buffers are prepared previously and stored in the dark (to avoid change of sulfanilamide in bull and stallion semen diluents) at room temperature or in the refrigerator. The diluents are prepared daily by combining egg yolk with the buffers and adding antibiotics to the final diluent.

Milk has been successfully used as a diluent for bull, ram, boar, and stallion semen. Either fresh homogenized milk or pasteurized skim milk can be used with the following method: the milk is heated to 92° C. over water in a covered boiler, held between 92° and 95° C. for 10 minutes, cooled to room temperature; antibiotics are added, and diluent then mixed with semen (Almquist *et al.*, 1954). Further improvements are obtained by adding 10 per cent glycerol to milk diluents.

Differences in diluent composition may reflect the requirement of the sperm of a particular species. For dilution of stallion semen, glucose is added to supplement the low sugar content of the semen.

Temperature Requirements. Careful attention to temperature is particularly important in processing semen. The upper limit for survival is about 45° C., which is important from the standpoint of temperature inside the artificial vagina. At low storage temperatures, metabolic activity and sperm motility are reduced and the life of the sperm extended (see Chapter 3). Requirements for slow cooling (to avoid cold shock) are met by mixing 1 part of semen with 3 parts of diluent at room temperature.

Rate of Dilution. The extent to which semen should be diluted for insemination depends on the concentration of motile sperm in the ejaculate. The ultimate objective is to have at least the minimum number or more of motile sperm prescribed for the standard insemination dose of diluted semen. Information on this for farm mammals is presented in Table 8–3. An example of the calculations used to determine the dilution rate of any particular sample of bull semen follows:

Volume of ejaculate = 8 ml.
Concentration of sperm = 1,200,000,000 per ml.
Percentage of motile sperm = 70
Then, 1 ml. of semen contains 1,200,000,000 $\times$ $\frac{70}{100}$ or 840,000,000 live sperm.

Number of motile sperm required in 1 ml. of diluted bull semen = 8,000,000.

Thus dilution rate = $\dfrac{840,000,000}{8,000,000}$ = 105

Then 8 ml. of semen can be diluted (8 $\times$ 105) to 840 ml.

Antibiotics. Addition of antibiotics to semen prevents the decline in fertility by inhibiting bacterial growth and killing some of the harmful pathogenic organisms (*e.g.* *Vibrio fetus*). Sulfanilamide (6 gm./100 ml. of buffer solution) depresses the respiration rate of sperm and also reduces bacterial growth. It is customary to use penicillin (bull and stallion) and streptomycin in semen diluents and to include sulfanilamide (bull and stallion) in the buffer solution.

The marked decrease in embryonic mortality in cows (as indicated by a smaller percentage of delayed returns) when antibiotics are added to semen diluents, has produced a noticeable improvement in the accuracy with which final non-returns can be predicted at an early date. Difference in late returns that existed among bulls at one time have been eliminated because the antibiotics added to semen control *Vibrio fetus* infection and eliminate other infectious organisms that frequently cause early embryonic mortality.

C. Storage of Diluted Semen

Liquid diluents maintain good fertility in bull semen stored at 5° C. for 3 or 4 days. Ram semen is ordinarily used within a day or two after collection, although a few samples have maintained some fertility for a week when stored at 5° C.

Boar semen cannot be successfully stored for more than 24 to 48 hours, and for best results, the semen should be used within a

Table 8–3.—Insemination Requirements and Related Phenomena in Farm Mammals

Item	Cattle	Sheep	Swine	Horses
Frequency of semen collection (per week)	3–5	7–25	3–5	7–10*
Characteristics of average ejaculate† Volume (ml.)	8	1	215	125
Sperm concentration (million/ml.)	1200	3000	270	120
Total sperm/ejac. (million)	9600	3000	58,000	15,000
Motile sperm (%)	70	75	60	70
Morphological normal sperm (%)	80	90	60	70
Recommended diluent	yolk-citrate + modifications	yolk-glucose-citrate	yolk-glucose-bicarbonate	glucose-gelatin
Storage temperature for liquid semen (°C.)	5	5	15 to 5	15
Rate of dilution‡ (1 ml. of semen diluted to — ml.)	105	9	4	2
Storage of liquid semen (days)	4	1 or 2	1	1
Optimum time to inseminate	middle or end of estrus	toward end of estrus	first and/or second day of estrus	third day of estrus
Dose of insemination (volume, ml.)	1	0.2	50	20–40
(motile sperm no., million)	8	50–60	2000	1500
Deposition of semen	cervical	cervical	cervical	uterine
No. of possible females bred/ejaculate	800	40	17	7
No of possible females bred/week	3200	600	80	60
Conception on 1st insemination (% pregnant)	65	70	70	65

*One or two days of rest should be provided each week.
†Normal and healthy mature males with nearly ideal collection techniques.
‡Adjusted to concentration of sperm—practical rate listed.

day after collection. A storage temperature of 12 to 15° C. produces better results with boar semen than the lower temperature routinely used for bull semen. If boar semen is not fractionated for removal of the gelatinous material, the sperm die when stored at 5° C. but remain viable at 15° C. Boar semen diluted with yolk-glucose-bicarbonate or a milk diluent stores well at temperatures of 5 to 8° C. but with yolk-citrate diluents a storage temperature of 12 to 15° C. produces the best fertility and motility maintenance. It has now been demonstrated that citrate is not a satisfactory ingredient in boar semen diluents.

Stallion semen does not store well and is usually used during the first day after collection. It can be stored at 5 to 15° C., but the higher temperature produces better results.

Although one successful pregnancy has been achieved using freeze-dried bull semen, subsequent attempts have repeatedly failed. However, a diluent that permits successful storage of semen at room temperature has been produced; this has special application in countries where mechanical refrigeration is not readily available. The Illini variable temperature (IVT) diluent has been modified by various investigators (VanDemark & Bartlett, 1958; Foote *et al.*, 1960). The method of storage at room temperature is based on the fact that CO_2 gas inhibits sperm motility and reduces metabolism so that fertility is maintained.

After the semen is diluted, cooled, and placed in suitable vials, it is ready for shipment. The vials of semen are wrapped in a paper cover and placed alongside a rubber balloon or a metal can of ice. By wrapping the vials with an insulating cover, a uniform temperature of 5° C. can be maintained for some 24 hours. An insulated box of a size to accommodate the vials, refrigerant, and insulating wrapper is used for shipment. Technicians performing artificial insemination in the field use an ice chest to maintain proper temperature.

Special handling should always be indicated for shipment of semen because the sperm are fragile and susceptible to mechanical injury. Shipping of boar and stallion semen is impractical until the methods are improved.

III. FROZEN SEMEN

The freezing of semen for storage over long periods has erased all barriers of time and distance in artificial breeding. Developed by British scientists, the procedure has been very successful in the artificial insemination of cattle, but additional research is required before practical application of the method can be made with ram (First *et al.*, 1961), boar, or stallion semen (Parkes, 1957). Within 10 years after the development of this method, more than 40 per cent of the artificial breeding associations in the United States were using frozen semen for all services. This included the American Breeders Service at Madison, Wisconsin, which inseminated more than a million cows each year. In capable hands, results with frozen semen have proved as successful as those with liquid semen.

The technique of freezing semen has made it possible to have the same sire (planned mating) easily available throughout the entire year anywhere in the world. It also has a great advantage in the storage of semen after death of outstanding sires. It has promoted international exchange of genetic material and has increased the efficiency of progeny testing at artificial insemination centers. It has improved the allocation of daily semen demands. Frozen semen provides an opportunity for genetic improvement of breeds with small numbers.

A. Diluents

Successful preservation of bull sperm during freezing depends on: an optimum concentration of glycerol (7 or 8% in the final diluent), prevention of "osmotic shock" by adding the glycerolated diluent slowly, and providing the minimum time required for equilibration before the freezing process is started.

The diluent used for dilution of semen for freezing may consist of yolk-citrate with 7 per cent glycerol, heated homogenized milk with glycerol, or heated skim milk with 10 per cent glycerol. Half of the yolk-citrate diluent is added without glycerol and half with 14 per cent glycerol (see D, Freezing).

Sulfanilamide is not included among antibiotics added to diluents for freezing semen because it is toxic to sperm during freezing. But penicillin and streptomycin in either yolk citrate or milk produce no adverse effects on the sperm.

B. Equipment

The usual freezing equipment consists of a cooling bath, a mechanical agitator, a dial thermometer ($-100°$ C. to $+40°$ C.), an automatic timing clock, flasks, beakers and graduated cylinders for measuring materials in the preparation of diluents. Also, ampules, labels with name of sire, automatic labeling machine, automatic sealing machine, wire racks to hold ampules during freezing alcohol baths, utensils required to handle dry ice (solid CO_2) during freezing, and equipment for holding frozen semen when the process is completed.

C. Storage Facilities

When semen has been frozen by the recommended processing technique, it can give satisfactory fertility results for a long time. Low constant temperature must be maintained however. A storage temperature of −80° C. (*i.e.* dry ice) is so close to the temperature level at which sperm cell damage occurs that any intermittent temperature fluctuations usually cause sperm damage.

Dry Ice and Alcohol. The ampules of semen are kept in a bath of alcohol containing solid CO_2. The alcohol acts as a buffer against rapid temperature changes when the chest is opened. The alcohol must always contain some dry ice, because its presence insures low temperatures, and the bubbles of gas it gives off keep the alcohol in circulation, thus giving a uniform temperature. This refrigerant is used most widely, especially by individual herd owners, where cost is a factor. A liberal supply of dry ice should always be kept available. Ice chests designed to use air for conductivity are not satisfactory.

Electric Freezer Storage Chests. Automatically controlled, mechanically operated cabinets have the advantage of a lower temperature, but may present a problem during power failures or difficulties with the machine itself.

Liquid Nitrogen. The use of liquid nitrogen for the storage of frozen semen at −195° C. is the most advanced method (Plate XX). It is safe because despite variations, the temperature is always well below the prescribed one. Although under ideal conditions, fertility results are the same whether semen is stored in liquid nitrogen or dry ice; liquid nitrogen has the advantage of eliminating the factor of human carelessness—a cause of temperature variations when the dry ice supply is low.

Different-sized storage freezers are used. One large commercial freezer has a capacity of 45,000 ampules—170 gallons of liquid nitrogen—the total weight is 1 ton, and the approximate holding time 2 months. The freezers used in the field have a capacity of 500 ampules, 7 gallons of liquid nitrogen; the total weight is 120 lb. and the approximate holding time 3 weeks.

Liquid Air. This method is used extensively in Europe. It provides a holding temperature below −150° C. and has the same advantages, with respect to equipment and temperature, as liquid nitrogen.

Liquid CO_2. A storage cabinet using liquid CO_2 as the refrigerant maintains the frozen semen at about the same temperature as does dry ice. It is economical to operate and free from mechanical problems.

D. Freezing

Dilution. Immediately after collection, the semen is diluted 1:4 with a non-glycerol diluent at 30° C. composed of a 2.32 per cent sodium citrate dihydrate buffer, 20 per cent egg yolk, 1000 units of penicillin, and 1000 μg. of dihydrostreptomycin per ml. of diluent. The sample is cooled to 5° C. over 75 minutes and made up to half the final volume with the non-glycerol diluent at 5° C. The final volume is determined by the percentage of motile sperm and the concentration of sperm so that approximately 8 million motile sperm per ml. will be obtained for use in insemination. Allowance is made for the expected 20 to 30 per cent of sperm killed during the freezing process. Since there are great differences among individual bulls relative to the livability of sperm in the freezing process, the percentage of expected mortality is based on the previous average survival figures for sperm from each bull.

Glycerolation. In the next step—the glycerolating and equilibrating procedure—the glycerol diluent, at a temperature of 5° C., is slowly added, at 20 minute intervals, in increments of 10, 20, 30, and 40 per cent of the remaining volume. Each added increment is mixed with the partially glycerolated semen by gentle end-over-end rotation of the container (Bratton *et al.*, 1957). Sperm cells are allowed to equilibrate in this final, 7 per cent glycerol diluent for 6 hours before being frozen. This improves the quality of the frozen semen and assures sufficient time to kill *Vibrio fetus* and other micro-organisms.

Ampuling. About 1.1 ml. of diluted glycerolated semen is placed in cold, 2-ml. ampules at 5° C. during the equilibration period (Plate XX). The ampules are sealed with an automatic sealer and placed in wire baskets made of $\frac{1}{8}$-inch mesh hardware cloth.

Freezing. The ampules are placed in an alcohol bath adjusted to 5° C. Then both alcohol bath and ampules at 5° C. are cooled by being placed directly in a freezing bath ranging in temperature from -20 to -40°C. This saves time and labor and produces better results (Kennelly *et al.*, 1960). The ampules are frozen by further reducing the temperature 10° C. or more per minute to -80° C. or lower, depending on the storage facilities used.

Fast freezing procedures, now recommended, give higher survival of sperm, because it is apparently near the optimum between thermal shock and osmotic shock. Freezing removes water as ice and causes an increase in salt concentration which damages the protein and the lipo-proteins in the sperm. In addition to the protective properties provided against cold shock, the glycerol can be utilized by sperm.

E. Shipping and Handling

Shipping. Frozen semen can be transported long distances when stored in chests containing dry ice or liquid nitrogen. Transporting frozen semen in liquid nitrogen is the safest method of shipment for sperm preservation. However, weight is a factor and dry ice equipment is lighter and will maintain low temperatures for a few days.

Thawing. The frozen semen sample may be warmed immediately to body temperature without special care at the time of insemination. The ampule of semen can be placed in a vacuum bottle containing iced water about 5 or 10 minutes before insemination. The sample should be used soon after thawing because reduced fertility has resulted from keeping thawed semen at 5°C. for several hours before insemination.

IV. INSEMINATION TECHNIQUE

To successfully practice artificial insemination, it is necessary to have information on the following: (*a*) signs of estrus, (*b*) time of onset of estrus and ovulation, (*c*) duration of estrus, (*d*) optimum time to inseminate, (*e*) expected rate of conception if it is not possible to inseminate at the optimum time, (*f*) proper insemination technique.

A. Optimum Time for Insemination

An interval of 60 days should be allowed before the first service after calving, even for cows with excellent genital health at the time of parturition. Cattle should be inseminated during the middle or toward the end of the estrous period. Satisfactory conception rates are obtained from artificial insemination within 6 hours after the end of estrus (standing when mounted is used as an indication of estrus). Insemination during the first 6 hours of an average 18-hour estrus is too early, and conception rates decrease (see Chapter 7). It is therefore recommended that cows be checked twice daily for estrus and reported as "a.m. or p.m. cows." The following timing of artificial insemination is recommended:

Cows first showing estrus	Should be bred	Too late for good results
In the morning	same day	next day
In the afternoon	next day-morning or early afternoon	after 3 p.m. next day

In the ewe, insemination should take place at the middle or during the second half of estrus. Sows come into estrus about 3 to 5 days after farrowing, but they should not be bred at this time. Since sows ovulate about 30 to 36 hours after the beginning of estrus, with rapid loss of fertility after ovulation, it is best to inseminate either late on the first day or early on the second day of estrus (Chapter 5). Some advantage is gained by inseminating on both the first and second day of estrus. Inseminating a mare during foal heat, about 9 days after foaling, is not advised (see Chapter 16). Since

PLATE XX

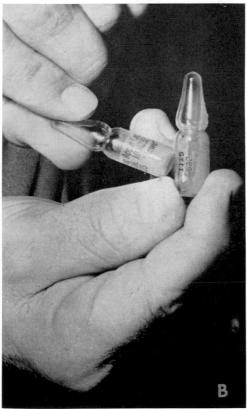

A. An automatic ampuling machine places the required amount of semen into each ampule and this is followed with automatic sealing by machine in assembly-line procedure.

B. Individual ampules of semen properly sealed in preparation for freezing.

C. Liquid nitrogen storage container with 500 ampules and holding time of 3 weeks for routine insemination with frozen semen. (*Photographs by American Breeders, Madison, Wis.*)

mares have a long estrus period, it is best to inseminate on the 3rd day of estrus, with a repeat service to the same stallion only if the mare is still in estrus on the 5th or 6th day.

Detection of Estrus. A heat expectancy list, based on an estrus 18 to 22 days before, can assist with the difficult task of detecting estrus. Dairy cows listed can be turned out into a paddock as a group and beef cattle can be placed in a separate pasture for close observation. At best, about 20 per cent will not be detected in estrus at the expected time (Trimberger, 1956). Paint or chalk colors on the brisket of teaser rams with aprons or on the brisket of vasectomized rams, is an efficient way of detecting estrus in ewes.

B. Preparation of the Female

The dairy cow is usually inseminated while standing in a stanchion or stall. Pens or corrals are used for holding beef cows in estrus, and a squeeze chute (restraining stall) is used to restrain the individual during insemination. The ewe is best held securely by placing her in an elevated crate during insemination. Sometimes a rotating plat-

form arrangement is used to inseminate more than 100 ewes per hour. This permits one man to put a ewe on the platform, another to inseminate, and a third man to release the ewe.

The sow is best inseminated without being restrained, thus avoiding the struggle that makes it difficult for the semen to flow through the cervix. With some rubbing and stroking, the sow may stand calmly during insemination (Plate XVIII). If she will not, the operator may sit on her rump or hips (see Chapter 9) and, facing the rear, make the insemination. In contrast, the mare is restrained by hobbles or backed against a board wall, preferably in a breeding chute; this offers protection from kicking during insemination.

C. Insemination Site

Originally in artificially inseminated cattle, the semen was deposited in the cervix with the aid of a speculum. In the recto-vaginal technique, used widely at present, the inseminating catheter is passed through the spiral folds of the cow's cervix (Fig. 8–5). For some years, part of the semen was deposited in the uterus, just inside the cervix, and the remainder in the cervix as

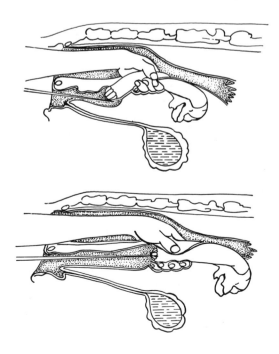

Fig. 8–5.—(*Top*) Wrong way of holding cervix for recto-vaginal technique of inseminating cow. If cervix is tipped and/or is not pulled forward it is almost impossible to insert end of catheter in opening of cervix. (*Bottom*) By using correct procedure, it is relatively easy to deposit semen in middle of cervix. (*Redrawn from Bonadonna, 1957, Nozioni Di Fisiopatologia Della Riproduzione E Di Fecondazione Artificiale Degli Animali Domestici, Milan, Courtesy of T. Bonadonna.*)

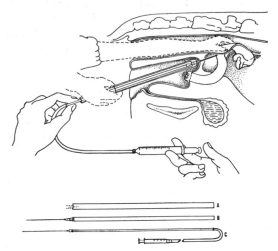

Fig. 8–6.—Special technique for direct uterine horn insemination when cervix is closed completely by abnormal condition. *A*—outer tube, *B*—middle tube with No. 18, 4″ sharp needle, and *C*—inner tube with No. 22, 5″ blunt needle. (*Drawings by E. S. E. Hafez & T. Sugie.*)

the catheter was withdrawn. Also for some time, the uterine insemination was made by depositing one-third of the semen in each horn of the uterus and the remaining one-third in the cervix. There is no difference in conception rates between cervical and uterine deposition of semen by artificial insemination. However, cervical deposition of semen by the recto-vaginal technique is now recommended for the following reasons: (*a*) the uterine mucosa is easily injured by the end of the catheter, thus increasing the possibility of uterine infection; (*b*) the cervical secretions provide the most favorable environment for sustained life of the sperm, and the antibacterial properties of the cervical secretions provide decided advantage in avoiding infection; (*c*) with cervical deposition of semen, the pregnancy in cows artificially inseminated will not be disrupted, but uterine inseminations usually result in abortion (approximately 5% of pregnant cows show estrus and occasionally there is mistaken identity of cows by the farmer or technician); (*d*) even with mid-cervical insemination, the sperm are transported rapidly throughout the reproductive tract of the cow (VanDemark & Moeller, 1950).

In rare cases, the cervix may be entirely closed by abnormal growth and/or injury. For this situation, Hafez & Sugie have developed a special technique to deposit the semen in the horn of the uterus through a long needle which pierces the vagina and uterine horn (Fig. 8–6).

The cervical method is necessary in the ewe because of the numerous cervical folds, like those in cattle. When the sow is artificially inseminated, the tube is automatically guided into the opening of the cervix, because the vagina tapers directly into the cervix. Although the boar's penis frequently penetrates the cervix in natural service, this is usually not possible with an inseminating tube, which is manipulated by gentle pressure as far into the cervix as possible (past one or more of the cervical folds), and the semen then flows into the uterus. However, frequent and careful observations are made for wastage caused by backflow during insemination.

In the mare, the smooth cervix has no spiral folds and is not well adapted to hold the sperm. Therefore, uterine insemination is practiced, corresponding to the deposition in natural copulation.

D. Volume of Semen Inseminated

Volume of semen injected is not important for cattle and sheep, although a minimum number of sperm per insemination is required for normal fertility. In the ewe a small number of sperm are more effective if inseminated in a small volume (.1 to .2 ml.) than in a large volume. However, for the sow and mare, both a minimum volume and a minimum number of sperm are essential (Table 8–3).

It is easy to establish and explain the minimum sperm numbers for various farm animals, but the way in which volume influences conception and embryo survival is not fully understood. A larger volume may: (*a*) initiate a neurogenic stimulus which may trigger the neurohypophysis to release a substance that exerts an influence; (*b*) stretch the uterine myometrium and initiate a contractile response which assists in sperm transport; (*c*) activate some other response caused through action on the cervix (Stratman & Self, 1960).

E. Cleaning of Equipment and Sanitary Precautions

Equipment can be sterilized by rinsing in 65 to 70 per cent ethyl or isopropyl alcohol, by boiling for 15 minutes, or placing it in an oven at a temperature of 120 to 180° C. (250 to 350° F.) for one hour. Synthetic organic detergents have bactericidal properties which are injurious to sperm and they should not be used for washing artificial insemination equipment. Sperm are very sensitive to toxic substances and it is difficult to remove all traces even by rinsing. Sodium hexa-meta-phosphate and other inorganic salts such as tetra-sodium pyrophosphate are recommended for washing the equipment used in artificial insemination. If traces of these compounds remain, they will decompose into simpler sodium phosphates which are not harmful but correspond to ingredients in buffer nutrient diluents.

Technological improvements through research at all levels, from semen collection to cleaning of equipment, have made possible the rapid expansion of artificial insemination. From a humble beginning, regarded with skepticism, criticism, and pessimism, this has developed into a tool of inestimable importance to the program of modern livestock improvement.

REFERENCES

ALMQUIST, J. O. & AMANN, R. P. (1961). Reproductive capacity of dairy bulls. II. Gonadal and extra-gonadal sperm reserves as determined by direct counts and depletion trials; dimensions and weight of genitalia. *J. Dairy Sci.*, **44**, 1668–1678.

ALMQUIST, J. O., FLIPSE, R. J. & THACKER, D. L. (1954). Diluters for bovine semen. IV. Fertility of bovine spermatozoa in heated homogenized milk and skimmilk. *J. Diary Sci.*, **37**, 1303–1307.

BRATTON, R. W., FLOOD, J. C., FOOTE, R. H. & WEARDON, S. (1957). Fertility of bovine spermatozoa stored at minus 79° C. for one week and for seventeen weeks. *J. Dairy Sci.*, **40**, 154–162.

BERLINER, V. R. (1940). An improved artificial vagina for the collection of stallion and jack semen. *J. Amer. Vet. Med. Assoc.*, **96**, 667–670.

DUTT, R. H. & BARNHART, C. E. (1959). Effects of plane of nutrition upon reproductive performance of boars. *J. Anim. Sci.*, **18**, 3–13.

FIRST, N. L., SEVINGE A. & HENNEMAN, H. A. (1961). Fertility of frozen and unfrozen ram semen. *J. Anim. Sci.*, **20**, 79–84.

FLIPSE, R. J. & ALMQUIST, J. O. (1961). Effect of total digestible nutrient intake from birth to four years of age on growth and reproductive development and performance of dairy bulls. *J. Dairy Sci.*, **34**, 905–914.

FOOTE, R. H., GRAY, L. C. & YOUNG, D. C. (1960). Fertility of bull semen stored up to four days at 5° C. in 20% egg yolk extenders. *J. Dairy Sci.*, **43**, 1330–1334.

HAFS, H. D., HOYT, R. S. & BRATTON, R. W. (1959). Libido, sperm characteristics, sperm output and fertility of mature dairy bulls ejaculated daily or weekly for thirty-two weeks. *J. Dairy Sci.*, **42**, 626–636.

HALE, E. B. & ALMQUIST, J. O. (1960). Relation of sexual behavior to germ cell output in farm animals. *J. Dairy Sci.*, **43** (Suppl.), 145–169.

MILLER, F. W. & EVANS, E. I. (1934). Technique for obtaining spermatozoa for physiological dairy studies and artificial insemination. *J. Agric. Res.*, **48**, 941–947.

KENNELLY, J. J., HOYT, R. S., FOOTE, R. H. & BRATTON, R. W. (1960). Survival rates of rapidly frozen bovine spermatozoa. *J. Dairy Sci.*, **43**, 1140–1146.

PARKES, A. S. (1957). The development in Great Britain, 1949–52, of the technique of preserving bull semen in the frozen state. *Vet. Rec.*, **69**, 463–464.

POLGE, C. (1956). Artificial insemination in pigs. *Vet. Rec.*, **68**, 62–76.

SALISBURY, G. W., BECK, G. H., ELLIOTT, I. & WILLETT, E. L. (1943). Rapid methods for estimating the number of spermatozoa in bull semen. *J. Dairy Sci.*, **26**, 69–78.

STEVERMER, E. J., KOVACS JR., M. F., HOEKSTRA, W. G. & SELF, H. L. (1961). Effects of feed intake on semen characteristics and reproductive performance of mature boars. *J. Anim. Sci.*, **20**, 858–865.

STRATMAN, F. W. & SELF, H. L. (1960). Effect of semen volume and number of sperm on fertility and embryo survival in artificially inseminated gilts. *J. Anim. Sci.*, **19**, 1081–1088.

TRIMBERGER, G. W. (1956). Ovarian functions, intervals between estrus, and conception rates in dairy cattle. *J. Dairy Sci.*, **39**, 448–455.

VanDemark, N. L. & Moeller, A. N. (1950). Spermatozoan transport in the reproductive tract of the cow. *J. Dairy Sci.*, **33**, 390–391.

VanDemark, N. L. & Bartlett, F. D. Jr. (1958). Prolonged survival of bovine sperm in the Illini Variable Temperature diluent. *J. Dairy Sci.*, **41**, 732–733.

QUESTIONS

1. What is the reason for the rapid expansion of artificial breeding?
2. (*a*) Describe the effects of overfeeding or underfeeding at different ages on the sperm output of the bull. (*b*) What differences are observed in semen production with various frequencies of collection?
3. (*a*) How is the motility of sperm evaluated? (*b*) Contrast the characteristics of semen collected from the bull and ram by electro-ejaculation.
4. On what basis is the dilution rate of a semen sample determined and what calculations are involved?
5. (*a*) What determines the number of females that can be inseminated from a single ejaculation? (*b*) What is the number for the bull, ram, boar, and stallion?
6. Discuss recommendations on frequency of semen collection for the bull, ram, boar, and stallion.
7. What factors should be considered for making recommendations on the site of insemination?
8. (*a*) Why is proper teasing so important in collecting the semen sample? (*b*) What procedures can be used for teasing males?
9. Describe glycerolation in the procedure for freezing semen.
10. Discuss the optimum time for insemination during estrus of the cow, ewe, sow, and mare.

Chapter 9

Sexual Behavior in Farm Mammals

By E. S. E. Hafez

In the course of evolution, sexual behavior has become increasingly complex. The main function of sexual behavior and copulation is, of course, to bring the male and female gametes together to ensure fertilization, pregnancy and the propagation of species. In farm mammals, sexual receptivity of the female is restricted to the period of estrus; thus copulation is synchronized, roughly, with the time of ovulation. In primates, peaks of sexual receptivity are not defined throughout the sexual cycle; thus conception takes place only when an attempt is made to synchronize copulation with the time of ovulation.

In this chapter we will discuss the patterns, intensity and mechanisms of typical and atypical sexual behavior. It is convenient to discuss the sexual behavior of the two sexes separately, but it is emphasized that they normally act in concert.

I. SEXUAL BEHAVIOR OF MALES

A. Copulatory Locomotor Patterns

Copulation and the events leading up to it may be divided into the following phases: sexual arousal, courtship (sexual display), erection, penial protrusion, mounting, intro-

mission, ejaculation, orgasm-like reaction and dismounting. If the female is receptive, copulation may occur within a few minutes; if she is not completely receptive, the male follows her and may make repeated attempts to mount. The duration of courtship and of actual copulation varies with the species; but both events are shorter in cattle and sheep than in swine and horses.

Courtship. The male makes frequent displays of masculinity, especially in the presence of an estrous female or another male. He nuzzles the perineal (genito-anal) region of the female and emits a characteristic type of vocalization. Different species exhibit characteristic patterns of courtship (Table 9-1). In some cases, the male attempts to separate a particular female from the other females, or chase away young or subordinate males; this is a type of territorial behavior.

Mounting. In the presence of a proestrous female, the male attempts several mounts, the penis becomes partially erected and protrudes from the prepuce. These mounts are usually unsuccessful because the female does not allow copulation. Before mounting, the male (especially in bulls)

Table 9-1.—Anatomy of the Reproductive Organs in Relation to Courtship and Ejaculation in the Male of Farm Mammals

Male	Anatomy			Courtship			Site of semen ejaculation
	Penis	Scrotum	Accessory glands	Locomotor Patterns	Duration	Vocalization	
Bull	fibro-elastic	pendulous	vesicular gland large, prostate and Cowper's glands proportionally small	"guards" female (stands with female, head to tail); paws and throws dirt over back and withers; extends his neck in the air with up-curled lip; rests chin and throat on female's rump with slight pressure	very brief	snort with head lowered and nostrils distended	near or on os cervix
Ram	fibro-elastic with filiform process	pendulous	same as in bull	sniffs urine of estrous female; runs tongue in and out; nudges and steps back; extends his neck in the air with up-curled lip; moves along side of female rubbing her wool	very brief	several series of staccato grunts prior to mating	filiform process rotates and semen is sprayed near or on os cervix
Boar	fibro-elastic (spiral tip)	close to body	vesicular gland and Cowper's glands very large, prostate proportionally small	noses female's sides and flanks; pokes snout between hind legs of female with a sudden jerk; lifts her hind quarters; grinds teeth; moves jaws from side to side; foams at mouth	long	regular series of soft gutteral grunts	uterus and cervix
Stallion	vascular-muscular	close to body	vesicular glands and prostate large, Cowper's glands proportionally small	smells groin of mare; grasps the folds of skin near the mare's rump with his teeth; extends his neck in the air with up-curled lip	medium	snort	uterus and cervix

secretes "dribblings" of *accessory fluid* derived from the Cowper's glands. Such accessory fluid is different from the seminal plasma secreted, during ejaculation, from the vesicular glands.

In the presence of an estrous female, the male mounts, "fixes" his forelegs around the female, grasps her firmly (Fig. 9-1) and begins rhythmic pelvic thrusts. Some males, especially boars and stallions, mount and dismount the female repeatedly before copulation; others mount once and copulate.

sheep or in the uterus and cervix as in swine and horses. Abortive ejaculation may take place if the female refuses intromission or if the male's penis fails to penetrate the vulva. Upon ejaculation, the muscles of the hind legs of the male contract, respiration quickens, the head droops and the whole body relaxes (so-called orgasm reaction). After ejaculation takes place the male dismounts and the penis is soon retracted into the prepuce.

Among farm animals, the boar and stallion

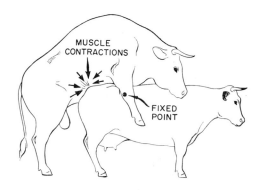

FIG. 9-1.—Copulatory locomotor patterns. Note the contraction of the abdominal muscles and fixing the front feet of the male around the pelvis of the female (*Diagram redrawn from C. A. H. Hultnäs, Personal Communication*).

Intromission. When the male mounts the female, the abdominal muscles, particularly the *rectus abdominis* muscles, contract suddenly. As a result, the pelvic region of the male is quickly brought into direct apposition to the external genitalia of the female. Once the tip of the erect penis contacts the moist walls of the vagina, maximum intromission is accomplished. Often the force of muscular contraction is so strong that the hind legs of the male are often lifted off the ground, giving the appearance of an active leap. The boar, with the penis partially out of the prepuce, thrusts his pelvis until the tip of the penis penetrates the vulva; only then is the penis fully unsheathed and intromission occurs. In the stallion, intromission takes place after several pelvic oscillations which stimulate engorgement of the penis with blood and make it rigid for maximum intromission. In farm mammals, one intromission takes place per copulation.

Ejaculation. The semen is ejaculated near the *os cervix* in the case of cattle and

have the longest ejaculation time and produce the greatest volume of semen; *i.e.* 150 to 500 ml. (see Chapter 8). The frequency of ejaculation varies between species and individuals and is easily modified by pre-coital stimulation (teasing). A new female is a very effective stimulus to elicit repeated ejaculations and Hale & Almquist (1960) have collected 70 ejaculates per week for 6 weeks from a bull by this method. Using the same technique, Jakway & Sumption obtained 5 successive ejaculates within 2 hours from a boar. The physiological mechanisms involved in pre-coital stimulation are not yet known.

B. Mechanisms

1. ANATOMY OF THE PENIS

The copulatory patterns of the male are primarily governed by the neuro-muscular anatomy and blood supply of the penis (see Chapter 2). In the bull, ram and boar, the penis is of the fibro-elastic type, relatively small in diameter, and rigid when non-erect. The amount of contractile tissue is limited.

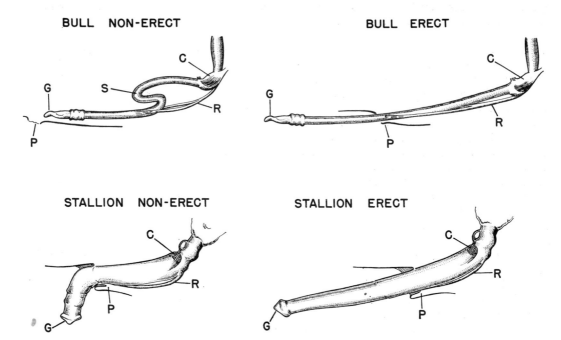

BULL   NON-ERECT

BULL   ERECT

STALLION   NON-ERECT

STALLION   ERECT

Fig. 9–2.—Diagram of the anatomy of fibro-elastic type penis (bull) and a vascular-muscular type penis (stallion) in the non-erect and erect positions. The anatomy of the penis determines, to a great extent, the ejaculatory responses of the species. *C.* cavernous muscle. *G.* glans. *P.* prepuce. *R.* retractor penile muscle. *S.* sigmoid flexure. (*Redrawn from Hafez, 1960. Cornell Vet., 50, 384.*)

Although the penis becomes more rigid upon erection, it enlarges very little. Protrusion is effected mainly by a straightening of the S-shaped sigmoid flexure and by relaxation of the retractor muscle. Erection is also rapid.

On the other hand, the stallion has a typical vascular-muscular penis (comparable with the penis of humans) with no sigmoid flexure. The function of the penis as an organ of intromission depends on the power of erection as a result of sexual excitement. The size, shape and length of the penis varies greatly between the flaccid and the erect state (Fig. 9–2). The retractor penile muscle is relatively undeveloped and adheres to the ventral surface of the penis. Erection and protrusion of the horse penis are effected by gradually increasing tumescence of the erectile vascular tissue in the penis (Walton, 1960). The erectile mechanisms of the stallion includes the synergism of two processes: (*a*) expansion of the helicine arteries and the contraction of corresponding venules under nervous control; this per-

mits additional blood to enter the erectile tissue but slows its exit, and (*b*) compression of the dorsal vein of the penis by the ischio-cavernosus muscle, thus limiting total blood flow from the penis (Julian & Tyler, 1959).

The basic neural components of sexual behavior are *innate* (inborn) and are controlled by complex pathways from the central nervous system. Electrical stimulation of the sacral nerves results in erection and/or ejaculation. This fact has been put to practical use in collecting semen. Broadly speaking, the anterior (frontal) portion of the cerebral cortex appears to co-ordinate the locomotor activities involved in copulation, while the posterior (occipital) region of the cortex, including the visual areas, is involved mainly in sensory control of copulation.

2. Sex Hormones

Males show sexual behavioral responses to estrous females before the onset of puberty and spermatogenesis; *i.e.* some males mount and mate before sperm are present in the ejaculate. The gonadal hormones and early experience, both sexual and social, act jointly to control the onset, maintenance and persistence of sexual behavior.

Castration eliminates, or at least greatly decreases, sexual activity; but when exogenous androgen is injected or implanted subcutaneously, sexual activity is restored. The administration of sex hormones affects the sexual behavior of individuals differently. Young and associates measured the sexual activity of guinea-pigs; they then castrated them after which sexual activity dropped to a minimum. Administration of androgen 4 months later raised the males to the same level of sexual activity that had characterized them before castration regardless of the amount of hormone injected (above a certain threshold). These results may be interpreted to indicate that an inherited capability to respond to androgen, rather than supply of androgen, was the limiting factor determining the level of sexual activity.

3. EARLY EXPERIENCE

Valenstein & Young (1955) found that guinea-pigs raised in social groups developed higher levels of sexual activity than those raised in isolation. When castrated, both groups dropped to the same minimal level. Androgen replacement therapy, however, caused the sexual activity level of each group to rise to the level which had characterized it before castration. Such results indicate that early experience of the male helps determine the type of effect that exogenous hormones will have on behavior.

It is often observed that the latency of ejaculation (reaction time to ejaculation) is longer in inexperienced males than in the experienced. Pubertal males may not show any sexual excitement in the presence of a dummy, while adult males exhibit normal sexual behavior. This suggests the importance of associations developed during "copulation experience" and "sexual anticipation." With a dummy, specific stimuli tend, in fact, to be replaced by conditioned reflexes in adult males. The importance of conditioned reflexes has been shown in castrated adult stallions which maintained normal sex desire for 516 days, and the potential for

erection for 618 days following castration (Nishikawa, 1954).

The initiation of copulation in males is controlled by a central excitatory mechanism (CEM) which reacts to sexual stimuli when sensitized by an appropriate androgenic hormone (Beach, 1942). At a threshold excitatory level, the CEM discharges into locomotor centers which mediate copulation. Studies with rodents have shown that sexual arousal is facilitated by previous copulatory experience when the males initially are of low excitability or when the stimuli for sexual arousal are inadequate.

4. SENSORY CAPACITIES

Visual, olfactory, tactile and auditory sensations contribute to sexual attraction, identification of the sexual partner and facilitation of copulation. The separation of the sensory components of sexual behavior is complicated by several factors: (a) the variation among species of the relative importance of the different sensory capacities; (b) interactions between sensory stimuli on the one hand and early experience, learning and conditioned reflexes on the other; (c) interactions between sensory capacities themselves. The individual stimuli are additive, i.e. the response to one stimulus is accelerated by an additional stimulus. If one sense is inhibited, it may be augmented by another sense which is ordinarily used to a lesser degree. Thus, when visual stimuli are inhibited, the male makes use of tactile and olfactory stimuli. Auditory stimulation of sexual behavior is probably more important in the female than in the male.

Visual Stimulation. Males may be stimulated by the sight of an estrous female, a castrate, part of the body of an animal (Plate XXI) or an inanimate object, e.g. a dummy. Bulls for instance have been known to mount a person in a bending position, a car and a padded sawhorse. Barker has noted that congenitally blind bulls develop sexual behavior at a much later date than normal sighted bulls. However, sexual behavior may be elicited when the male is blindfolded. This reaction is readily shown if the male has had previous sexual experience (Plate XXI).

Olfactory Stimulation. Olfactory stimulation of the male may be derived from the urine of the estrous female and from different parts of the female's body, *e.g.* the external genitalia, the muzzle and, in horses, from the groin and the neighboring parts (Berliner, 1959). Some males refuse to copulate when the female has a young at foot, presumably because of inhibitory olfactory (and possibly visual) stimuli. Young stallions usually show poor or negative sexual response to a dummy, yet sexual behavior is elicited from the same stallion when the dummy is sprinkled with urine from an estrous mare (Wierzbowski, 1959).

Though important, sense of smell usually plays a secondary role in sexual stimulation. Semen can be collected from stallions whose noses are masked.

Tactile Stimulation. Intromission and ejaculation are elicited by tactile stimuli (warmth of vagina and slipperiness of mucus) acting on receptors in the penis. The penis of the bull and ram is quite sensitive to temperature and that of the stallion is more sensitive to pressure exerted by the vagina and fornix than to temperature. By applying tactile stimulation to the chest region, Hale has induced blindfolded experienced bulls to mount in the absence of stimulus object.

C. Sex Drive (Libido)

Sex drive is the potential intensity of sexual behavior. The intensity of sexual behavior expressed by the male may not reflect the potential intensity because the latter is greatly modified by exteroceptive factors impinging on the male. For example, when a male repeatedly copulates with the same female under the same setting, sexual indifference may occur; this concept is called "sexual satiety." The time required to reach, and recover from, sexual satiety varies with the species, individual and surroundings. We should not confuse "sexual satiety" with "sexual exhaustion;" the former is a mental state, while the latter is a physical state which results from too frequent copulation regardless of female or setting.

1. MEASURES OF SEX DRIVE

Indices designed to measure sex drive in the male are relative values based on the frequency and spacing of mounts, intromissions and successful copulations. Under range conditions one may count the number of females mated by a given male per unit of time. In this situation the index of sex drive is dependent on several factors, *e.g.* the number of estrous females, the total number of males and the antagonistic interactions between them. A second method is to measure the *latency of ejaculation, i.e.* the time from the introduction of the female until ejaculation occurs. In this situation the *stimulus pressure* (total sexual stimulus to the male) should be maximized and recovery from any sexual satiety or exhaustion complete. A third method is the *exhaustion test* in which one measures the maximum possible number of ejaculates and the time required for sexual exhaustion. In artificial insemination centers, routine semen collections do not represent the maximum number of ejaculates obtainable from a given male. Although the common practice is to collect semen from bulls twice a week, Hale & Almquist had collected 77 ejaculates from one bull in 6 hours. A fourth method to evaluate sex drive is to measure recovery time (*i.e.* the time required to attain a normal frequency of ejaculations) after sexual exhaustion.

2. FACTORS AFFECTING SEX DRIVE AND SEXUAL EXPRESSION

The potential sex drive of the male is determined by genetic factors. As mentioned above the expression of sexual behavior is readily modified by several factors mainly environment, sexual experience, and stimulus pressure.

Genetic Factors. Bane (1954) observed the sexual pattern of several pairs of identical twin bulls: there were great similarities in the sexual pattern of identical twin brothers and great differences between twin pairs (Fig. 9–3). Bulls of European breeds mount

PLATE XXI

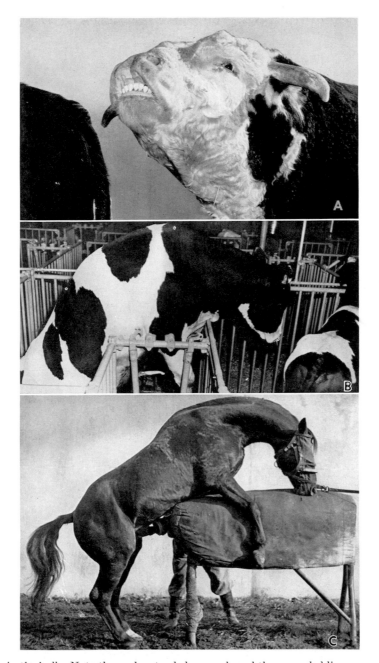

A. Courtship in the bull. Note the neck extended upwards and the up-curled lip.

B. Twin bulls, 19 months old, housed in adjacent stalls. Visual cues alone sufficed to elicit sexual responses, mounting and erection. Stall partitions did not inhibit mounting. (*From Hafez & Schein, 1962 in The Behaviour of Domestic Animals, E. S. E. Hafez, edit., London, Courtesy of Bailliere, Tindall & Cox.*)

C. Adult experienced stallion showing sexual behavior, to an artificial vagina, even when blindfolded. The absence of visual cues did not prevent mounting, erection and ejaculation of sexually experienced male. (*Photograph by W. Plewinski & S. Wierzbowski, Krakow, Poland.*)

PLATE XXII

A. Copulatory behavior of the boar. The boar's haunches are clenched forward. (*Photograph by L. J. Sumption.*)

B. Homosexual activity in boars. A male stands passively for mounting and rectal intromission. (*From Hafez et al., 1962 in The Behaviour of Domestic Animals, E. S. E. Hafez, edit., London, Courtesy of Bailliere, Tindall & Cox.*)

C. A sow in estrus showing the mating stance when the attendant applied pressure to her back.

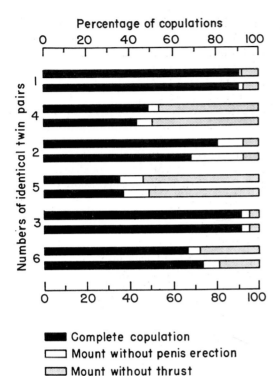

Percentage of copulations

Numbers of identical twin pairs

FIG. 9–3.—Ejaculatory behavior in identical twin dairy bulls showing percentage distribution of complete copulations, mounts without penis erection and mounts without thrust. Note the great similarities in the ejaculatory pattern of the twin brothers and the great variability between the twin pairs. (*Adapted from* Bane, 1954. *Acta. Agric. Scand.*, *4*, *95*).

■ Complete copulation
□ Mount without penis erection
▨ Mount without thrust

other bulls and cows not in estrus; Zebu (Brahma) bulls exhibit a well marked sexual sluggishness and only mount cows in estrus. Among European breeds, differences are evident during semen collection by an artificial vagina; Shorthorn and Guernsey bulls react more slowly than Friesians. The broader differences among breeds are only brought out clearly in carefully controlled experiments.

Climate, Nutrition and Disease. The expression of sexual behavior is reduced by hot conditions and very high altitudes (see Chapter 18). The plane of nutrition, *per se*, does not seem to affect sexual responses appreciably. On low planes of nutrition, however, males are easily exhausted sexually. Protein deficiency, over-consumption of water, too little daylight, vitamin A deficiency and food poisoning may affect sexual behavior. Any physical trouble, no matter how irrelevant clinically, may seriously affect sexual expression, *e.g.* inflammation of the hooves or joints, change of teeth,

eczema, pains from accidents or certain diseases.

Sexual Experience. In A. I. centers, young inexperienced males are usually awkward to handle at their first semen collection. They approach the female hesitantly, spend a long time exploring the external genitalia, mount without erection, descend, and try to mount again. Erection and ejaculation are weak, and the volume of the semen is small, the sperm concentration low and motility poor. On repeated use at intervals under the same conditions, with the same attendant, males gradually become conditioned to their surroundings and copulate vigorously.

Stimulus Pressure. The intensity of sexual behavior in the male is dependent upon visual, olfactory and tactile cues which make up the *stimulus pressure*. The relative body size of the female, color, appearance and odor of coat, size and shape of horns, time from recent parturition and cleanliness may all, to a variable extent, modify the expression of sexual behavior of the male.

II. SEXUAL BEHAVIOR OF FEMALES

Sexual behavior of females is intimately related to the estrous cycle and pregnancy. Each major phase of the estrous cycle is characterized by certain elements of behavior which are discussed separately in the following section.

A. Locomotor Patterns

Pro-estrus. During pro-estrus, the female shows interest in the male but refuses to be mounted. The female becomes restless and moves on the slightest disturbance, *e.g.* the switching on of lights or in the handling of gates. When the female refuses the attention of the male, he soon loses interest, particularly if other fully receptive females are present. Later in pro-estrus, the female shows a special interest in the male and nuzzles some parts of his body, *e.g.* scrotum and flanks.

Estrus. At the onset of estrus, the female becomes restless and her position in the social hierarchy is temporarily ignored; *i.e.* the female may indiscriminately approach both dominant and subordinate herd-mates. The estrous female urinates frequently and may smell and lick the male's prepuce and the attached accessory fluids. The primary criterion of estrus is receptivity to the male. The species-specific locomotor patterns during behavioral estrus are shown in Table 9–2. With the exception of the ewe, the estrous female makes a variety of vocalizations, *e.g.* the sow gives a rapid succession of short, quiet grunts.

The responses of the female during and after copulation are less elaborate than in the male. When the female is ready to copulate, the hind legs may be spread and the pelvis lowered. The sow, on applying pressure on her back (by the boar or attendant) assumes the *mating stance* (Plate XXII); this behavior is often used to detect estrus in sows for mating or artificial insemination. It is believed that the female of farm mammals exhibits an "orgasm-like" response after copulation; this, however, is not essential for conception.

Table 9–2.—*Species-specific Behavioral and Physiological Changes in Female Farm Mammals During Estrus*

Female	Behavioral changes*	Physiological changes	
		External genitalia	Mucus secretions are visible
Cow	attempts to mount or solicits mounts from other females; vulva sniffed by other females; raises and switches her tail; may become separated from other females; roams in search of male	congested vulva	yes
Ewe	rubs neck and body against male; roams around male and sniffs his genitalia; shakes tail vigorously	no	no
Sow	attains mating stance (stationary attitude) when touched or pressure is exerted on her rump by the chin of the male or hands of the attendant	swollen and congested vulva	no
Mare	allows stallion to smell and bite her; extends hind legs; lifts tail sidewise; lowers croup (some mares without signs)	swollen, partly everted labia; elongated vulva; erect clitoris; clitoris frequently exposed by contraction of labia	yes (varies markedly in degree)

*Other patterns of behavioral estrus common to all species are mentioned in the text

Diestrus and Pregnancy. During diestrus, the female is not receptive to the male and often escapes when the male attempts to mount her. The degree of non-receptivity varies from female to female; some are not permissive while others are very aggressive. During pregnancy, the female displays limited sexual response. Occasionally pregnant cows, in late stages of pregnancy, exhibit a "false estrus" with typical behavioral estrus.

B. Mechanisms

The expression of sexual behavior of the female is controlled by hormonal and neural factors as well as sensory capacities.

thalamus and other parts of the central nervous system also regulates behavioral estrus. Certain hypothalamic loci (centers) participate in the display of sexual behavior independently of those involved in the regulation of pituitary-gonadal axis (Fig. 9-4). For example, lesions induced experimentally in certain loci in the hypothalamus will inhibit behavioral estrus; lesions induced in other loci will inhibit the gonadal activity.

Sensory Capacities. Behavioral estrus is readily modified by olfactory, visual and auditory sensations. Odorous substances may play a part in the initiation and maintenance of behavioral estrus or in the identification of partners. The perineal glands

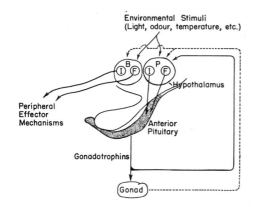

Fig. 9-4.—A diagram to depict both facilitative (F) and inhibitory (I) hypothalamic mechanisms, influencing sexual behavior (B) as well as pituitary function (P). These mechanisms serve independently as target areas for the gonadal, and possibly for the gonadotropins in the production of sexual behavior and in the feed back system regulating the anterior pituitary mechanisms. The particular regions involved vary greatly among species (*From Johnson et al., 1962 in the Behaviour of Domestic Animals, E. S. E. Hafez, edit., London, Courtesy Bailliere, Tindall & Cox.*)

Sex Hormones. Behavioral estrus depends primarily on the pituitary-gonad stimulating functions and the build up of adequate ovarian hormones. In the absence of the ovary, behavioral estrus is either not manifested at all or not manifested as regularly and frequently as by an intact female. Normal sexual behavior is restored in ovariectomized females by the injection of estrogen and progesterone.

Neural Mechanisms. The secretory activity of the ovary depends on suitable hormonal stimulation by the gonadotropins of the anterior pituitary. The rate of production and the rate release of gonadotropins are controlled by nervous activities within the hypothalamus which is anatomically related to the anterior pituitary (see Chapter 1). The nervous activity within the hypo-

of boars are modified sebaceous glands which secrete a lipophilic substance, probably muscone and the odor is extremely penetrating. Different feeds seem to produce different odors, *e.g.* boars fed on garbage may be rejected by estrous sows fed on grain. Also the females may be able to distinguish male from female by face-to-face contact without first smelling the genitalia.

Signoret and associates were able to show that the rhythm of the boar's *chant de cour* (song of courtship) is important. They tested estrous gilts which did not assume a mating stance on applying pressure to the back. When a recording of a boar's grunts was broadcasted, half the gilts assumed a mating stance. The number of positive responses decreased when the tempo of the grunts was slower. Thus auditory stimuli are involved in the expression of estrus.

C. Intensity of Behavioral Estrus

The intensity of behavioral estrus is subjectively classified into intense, medium, and weak, according to excitability and the observed cyclical changes in the external genitalia, *e.g.* relaxation or congestion of the vulva, secretion of vaginal mucus. The intensity of behavioral estrus varies throughout the cycle and between breeds and individuals. In the mare, the intensity reaches its peak just before ovulation; following ovulation, sexual receptivity decreases until estrus ceases (Fig. 9–5). In the cow, sexual

A. Homosexuality and Bisexuality

Homosexuality refers to sexual behavior between individuals of the same sex. Thus a male mounting another male is behaving homosexually (Plate XXII). The partner who is being mounted, is also engaging in homosexual behavior but his part is feminine. Homosexual behavior occurs among males to a greater extent than among females, but even then it is relatively uncommon. In males it occurs chiefly at puberty during the development of sexual behavior (Rosenblatt & Schneirla, 1962). Segregation of the sexes

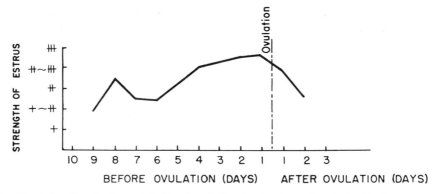

Fig. 9–5.—The intensity of estrous behavior in relation to the time of ovulation in the mare; maximum intensity occurs just before ovulation. Vertical axis is a ranking scale (from + to +++) without actual quantities. (*Redrawn from Nishikawa, 1959. Studies on Reproduction in Horses, Tokyo, Courtesy of Y. Nishikawa.*)

receptivity usually ceases 14 hrs. before ovulation.

Given equal opportunity, females differ in the frequency of mating, presumably owing to variations in the intensity of behavioral estrus. The intensity of estrus does not seem to be related to conception rate, except that weak estrus may pass unnoticed by the male, especially under range conditions, thus copulation does not take place.

III. ATYPICAL SEXUAL BEHAVIOR

Atypical sexual behavior may be classified into homosexuality, hypersexuality, hyposexuality and auto-erotic behavior. Some of these patterns are a result of genetic factors causing disturbance in the gonads or the endocrine or nervous systems. Other anomalies may be due to sexual inhibition and faulty management of animals.

often results in homosexual relationships as observed in young bulls and boars housed together. The hormonal, neural and experiential factors involved in the expression of homosexuality are not known in farm mammals.

Bisexuality refers to the ability of a male to perform elements of the female sexual pattern as well as the male patterns, and conversely, the ability of a female to act like a male sexually (as in the case of cattle virilism).

B. Hypersexuality

Hypersexuality in males consists of heightened sexual excitement, increased frequency of copulations and attempted copulation with males and young females of the same species or with other species. Nymphomania (prolonged periods of behavioral estrus) occurs in cows and mares. Nymphomania in cows is characterized by prolonged estrus at irregular intervals, pawing, bellowing and mounting. Prolonged estrus may last from 10 to 40 days, especially in mares which have failed to conceive or have aborted, and those used for heavy draft work.

C. Hyposexuality

Hyposexuality in males is manifested by abnormalities in the ejaculatory pattern. Hyposexual males may fail to ejaculate in spite of protrusion or erection. Some males may not even be able to mount.

In females, different types of hyposexuality

of the pelvis and abortive ejaculation. The bull arches his back, performs pelvic movements and passes the penis in and out the preputial orifice; such tactile stimulation causes abortive ejaculation. Dairy bulls, during masturbation, may use the skin fold between their forelegs as a vagina. Masturbation is uncommon in rams and boars but is more commonly observed among bulls on high protein rations, *e.g.* bulls prepared for shows. Hultnäs suggests that as a result of such diets, the peripheral mucosa of the penis becomes more sensitive to tactile stimulation.

Spontaneous emission of sperm which is commonly observed in some species has not been recorded for farm mammals.

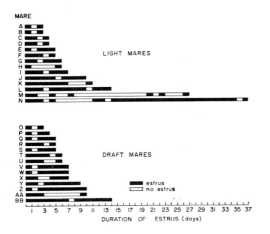

Fig. 9–6.—The occurrence and duration of "split estrus" in draft and light mares. "Split estrus" was characterized by an initial heat period followed by a non-receptive period of 1 or 2 days followed by a subsequent return of estrus. Graafian follicles were present in the initial heat period and continued to develop during the non-receptive interval (*Redrawn from Andrews & McKenzie 1941, Mo. Agric. Exp. Sta. Res. Bull. No. 329*).

include quiet ovulation (commonly called, "silent heat"), irregular estrus, anestrus (absence of both estrus and ovulation), and split estrus. Split estrus occurs in mares; the mare is apt to go off estrus for a short period and to become receptive again during what would be one full estrous period (Fig. 9–6).

D. Auto-Erotic Behavior

Auto-erotic behavior refers to the self-arousal of sexual responses in males which is called *masturbation*. The locomotor patterns vary with the species. The stallion rubs his rigid erected penis against the hypogastrium (lower median anterior of abdomen), and lowers the croup (loin region) rapidly; this is followed with several forward movements

IV. SEXUAL BEHAVIOR AND FERTILITY

In natural mating and semen collection, one must prevent sexual inhibition of the male and stimulate sexual desire in both sexes whenever possible.

Natural Mating. Farm mammals are *promiscuous* breeders: pair-bonds are very loosely established during estrous periods and depend solely upon the ability of the male to keep other males away from the female. Under free-roaming conditions there is considerable competition between males and the dominant male performs the majority of copulations. Such a male prevents other males from copulating, even when temporarily unable to copulate. Unfortunately, there seems to be no correlation between social dominance and fertility of the male. Thus a "boss" male who is infertile or diseased may depress the conception rate of the herd. On the other hand competition between rams when a number are present results in most if not all ewes being bred, and most by more than one ram. This presumably would result in greater opportunity for conception.

The size of the pasture also affects the number of matings per female. Lindsay & Robinson (1961) have reported that the proportion of ewes bred by three rams, compared to those bred to one ram was higher in a $\frac{1}{5}$-acre pasture than a 17-acre pasture.

Some males prefer certain females to the exclusion of others; this may lower the fertility of a herd (under range conditions) if several females manifest estrus at the same time. The proportion of females showing "weak" estrus also reduces the conception of the herd. Improved management during the mating season increases the chances for females with a short or "weak" estrous period to be mated by the male (see Chapter 13). Frequently, it is necessary to try several teaser males before such animals are bred.

In sheep, manifestation of estrus is influenced by the presence of the male and this has been employed in an attempt to initiate earlier onset of the breeding season. Australian scientists have studied the effect of introducing the ram to ewes during transition from the non-breeding to the breeding season. It is claimed that association with the ram under such conditions increases the number of ewes showing behavioral estrus early in the season. In horses, the discontinuous association of the two sexes also affects fertility in a similar way. The hormonal and neural factors involved in this phenomenon are not entirely clear.

Semen Collection. Little is known about the behavioral responses during semen collection in the ram, boar and stallion and the following discussion is concerned with the bull.

Sexual inhibition may develop as a result of fear or repeated frustration at the time of semen collection. The individuality of the male, the teaser female, the time and methods of applying the artificial vagina and the semen collector himself are factors that should be considered when collecting semen. Certain males are sensitive to semen collections while others will endure considerable rough handling. In very sensitive males, inhibitions may arise quickly, even when semen is collected with care. Removing the source of trouble is insufficient to release such inhibition; it is necessary to remove conditioned stimuli which are usually visual. Sometimes inhibition is released by moving the teaser female to a different situation. Walton was able to release inhibitory conditioned reflexes in bulls during semen collection by changing the white overalls of the collector to brown ones. A completely inhibited bull was accidentally blinded in one eye; after this he performed satisfactorily provided the collector approached from the blind side. Some males refuse to mount when the collector stands too close to the teaser female. Inhibition may also occur if the collector takes any part in operations associated with pain, *e.g.* blood sampling or testing for disease. Inhibitions are only removed from some males by long abstinence, a temporary return to natural mating or by use of electro-ejaculation.

The intensity of stimulation required for semen collection by an artificial vagina varies with the species, breed and age of male. Thus the degree of thermal, pressure and tactile stimulation should be adjusted accordingly. Thermal sensation can be increased by raising the internal temperature of the artificial vagina 5 to 10° C. above normal body temperature; this will stimulate intromission and may compensate for deficiencies in other stimuli. If the water in the artificial vagina is too cold, peripheral stimulation does not reach threshold and ejaculation is inhibited. If it is too hot the male withdraws his penis and dismounts. The pressure stimulus at the base of the penis is very slight in the usual form of artificial vagina; a further increased pressure is recommended. An inner liner (for the artificial vagina) with a rough surface is recommended for old bulls and with a smooth surface for young bulls.

In collecting semen, the male should be

conditioned gradually to the surroundings, the collector and the technique. The latency of ejaculation can be shortened by exclamation, calling the male by his name, scratching his shoulders, or showing the artificial vagina.

The wrong timing for applying the artificial vagina may cause inhibition; also if it is held at a wrong angle, the penis will be slightly bent. Sharp and rough withdrawal of the artificial vagina may irritate the penis.

In general, the expression of sexual behavior of the male is not correlated with the quality and quantity of sperm per ejaculate. Sperm concentration may be increased by pre-coital stimulation (teasing); particularly in males with an otherwise low sperm output. Pre-coital stimulation also increases the volume of ejaculate, the fructose concentration, sperm motility and the percentage of live sperm. A high stimulus pressure is necessary to ensure maximum sexual response and several techniques have been developed for pre-coital stimulation during semen collection (see Hafez, 1960; Hafez & Schein, 1962). Thus the frequency of ejaculation can be increased by changing the stimulus female at intervals.

REFERENCES

BANE, A. (1954). Studies on monozygous cattle twins. XV. Sexual functions of bulls in relation to heredity, rearing intensity and somatic conditions. *Acta. Agric. Scand.*, **4**, 95–208.

BEACH, F. A. (1942). Analysis of factors involved in the arousal, maintenance and manifestation of sexual excitement in male animals. *Psychosom. Med.*, **4**, 173–198.

BERLINER, V. R. (1959). The estrous cycle of the mare. In *Reproduction in Domestic Animals*. H. H. Cole & P. T. Cupps (edits.) Vol. I, New York, Academic Press.

HAFEZ, E. S. E. (1960). Analysis of ejaculatory reflexes and sex drive in the bull. *Cornell Vet.*, **50**, 384–411.

HAFEZ, E. S. E. & SCHEIN, M. W. (1962). The behaviour of cattle. In *The Behaviour of Domestic Animals*. E. S. E. Hafez (edit.) London, Bailliere, Tindall & Cox.

HALE, E. B. & ALMQUIST, J. O. (1960). Relation of sexual behavior to sperm cell output in farm animals. *J. Dairy Sci.*, **43** (*Suppl.*), 145–169.

JULIAN, L. N. & TYLER, W. S. (1959). Anatomy of the male reproductive organs. In *Reproduction in Domestic Animals*. H. H. Cole & P. T. Cupps (edits.) Vol. I, New York, Academic Press.

LINDSAY, D. R. & ROBINSON, T. J. (1961). Studies on the efficiency of mating in sheep. II. The effect of freedom of rams, paddock size and age of ewes. *J. Agric. Sci.*, **57**, 141–145.

NISHIKAWA, Y. (1954). Strength of sexual desire and properties of ejaculate of horse after castration. *Bull. Nat. Inst. Agric.* Japan, Ser. G. No. 8, 161–167.

ROSENBLATT, J. S. & SCHNEIRLA, T. C. (1962). The behaviour of cats. In *The Behaviour of Domestic Animals*. E. S. E. Hafez (edit.) London, Bailliere, Tindall & Cox.

VALENSTEIN, E. S. & YOUNG, W. C. (1955). An experiential factor influencing the effectiveness of testosterone proprionate in eliciting sexual behavior in male guinea pigs. *Endocrinology*, **56**, 173–177.

WALTON, A. (1960). Copulation and natural insemination. In *Marshall's Physiology of Reproduction*. A. S. Parkes (edit.) 3rd Ed., Vol. I, Part 2, London, Longmans.

WIERZBOWSKI, S. (1959). The sexual reflexes of stallions. *Rocan. Nauk. Roln.*, B, **73**, 753–788.

QUESTIONS

1. Explain the species differences in locomotor copulatory patterns of the male.
2. Give a full account of the techniques used to avoid sexual inhibition during semen collection in the bull.
3. Discuss the effects of sensory capacities and early experience on sexual behavior in the male; give three examples.
4. Discuss the practical significance of sexual behavior in relation to the fertility of farm mammals. Outline three problems of sexual behavior in which fundamental research is needed.
5. Define the following: stimulus pressure, sex drive, homosexuality, bisexuality, auto-erotic behavior, latency of ejaculation, "orgasm."
6. Tabulate some of the locomotor patterns of behavioral estrus of three mammalian species. Discuss the mechanisms and stimuli involved in behavioral estrus.
7. Describe two methods to measure sex drive in the male. What are the precautions to be considered in order to obtain accurate values?
8. Give a full account on (a) mating stance in the sow, (b) erection in the stallion, (c) competition between males, (d) pre-coital stimulation (teasing).
9. Discuss the effects of hormonal and neural factors on sexual behavior in the two sexes.
10. Give evidence of genetic variations in sexual behavior in farm mammals.

Chapter 10

Gestation and Parturition

By E. B. Harvey

GESTATION, pregnancy, begins with fertilization, penetration of sperm into the ovum, and is completed at parturition, expulsion of the fetus and placenta. The period of gestation can be conveniently divided into three phases: cleavage of the fertilized ovum to blastocyst formation; implantation and development of the embryo; and development of the fetus to birth of the young. Until birth the embryos and fetuses are totally dependent on the placenta for their uptake of nutrients and excretion of metabolic wastes.

The duration of gestation, the maintenance of the embryo and fetus *in utero*, the physiological interplay between the conceptus and mother, and finally the physiology of parturition form the substance of this chapter.

I. GESTATION

A. Duration of Pregnancy

The period of gestation varies considerably among species of farm mammals. But, differences between breeds is more pronounced in mares than cows, sows and ewes (Table 10–1). The small variations in duration of pregnancy that exist within breeds may be due to the effects of the season and

locality where bred and variations within an individual from pregnancy to pregnancy. The wide variations in duration of pregnancy of mares may be due to delayed implantation (Chapter 7). Both genetic and environmental factors influence the duration of pregnancy, but it is difficult to determine which of these play the predominant role particularly since the differences between breeds tend to be small.

Genetic Effects. The genotype of the fetus as inherited from both the sire and dam plays a part in the duration of pregnancy. The effect of the sire on duration of pregnancy in cows has been recognized for a long time, but it is now known that the genotype of bovine fetuses is a factor in duration of pregnancy (Rollins *et al.*, 1956). These workers have also shown that a sex-linked gene in mares and fetuses affects the duration of pregnancy in Arabian breeds. The differences in gestation length between mutton breeds of sheep with different wool types have been accounted for by genetic factors (Terrill & Hazel, 1947). Other studies have also shown that the genetics of the fetus play some part in gestation length of beef cattle and goats.

(176)

Table 10–1.—*Differences in Gestation Periods of Farm Mammals*
(*From the Literature*)

Animal	Range	Average
Cattle (dairy breeds)		
Ayrshire		278
Brown Swiss	270–306	290
Dairy Shorthorn	322	282
Friesian	240–333	276
Guernsey		284
Holstein-Friesian	262–359	279
Jersey	270–285	279
Swedish-Friesian	260–300	282
Zebu (Brahman)		285
Cattle (beef breeds)		
Aberdeen-Angus		279
Hereford	243–316	285
Beef Shorthorn	273–294	283
Sheep	140–159	148
Swine		
Domestic	102–128	114
Wild Pig	124–140	
Horse		
Arabian	301–371	337
Belgian	304–354	335
Clydesdale		334
Morgan	316–363	344
Percheron	321–345	
Shire		340
Thoroughbred	301–349	338

Environmental Effects. Environment as it affects the gestation period includes the internal and external environmental factors that act during gestation. The internal environment includes the physiological condition of the mother (*i.e.* age, weight, and inherent reproductive glands and structures), size, sex and weight of the fetus, and litter size. The weight or size of the fetus or fetuses has a small effect on the duration of pregnancy in cows and ewes but is apparently without effect in sows. Twins of cattle are carried 3 to 6 days less than are single fetuses and twins of sheep are carried 0.6 days less than singles. Litter size may have no effect on gestation length in sows. The sex of the fetus may also determine gestation time, since male fetuses in some dairy and beef cattle as well as the mare are carried 1 to 2 days longer than females. The duration of pregnancy is shortened 8 to 12 days when a she-ass is carrying a hinney.

The size and sex of the fetus presumably affects gestation length by hastening the time of onset of parturition. What the factors are that do this and how they act have not been isolated.

The external environment (*i.e.* length of day, temperature, and nutrition) also plays a part in duration of pregnancy. Dairy calves born in the spring are carried 2 days longer than those born in the fall. Gestation length is 4 days shorter in mares on a higher nutritional plane than those on pasture and oat-hay, but conversely the period of gestation of sheep maintained on low levels of nutrition during the latter third of pregnancy is reduced as much as 5 days.

The season when Arabian mares are bred has a significant effect on duration of pregnancy. Breeding during December through May results in 10 days longer gestation than breeding in June through November (Howell & Rollins, 1951). This prolonged gestation

12

of mares following winter breeding however is presumably the result of delayed implantation (Chapter 7).

B. Extra-embryonic Membranes and Fluids

The early blastocyst of farm mammals lies free in the uterine lumen. During this period nutrients and metabolites pass to and from the embryo by way of extra-embryonic membranes. Broadly speaking the placenta is an intimate apposition or fusion of embryonic or fetal organs to the maternal tissues for physiological exchange. Thus the *troph-ectoderm*, the single layer of cells making up the early blastocyst and *chorionic-sac* is a placenta. Extra-embryonic membranes which later form the vascularized *chorio-allantoic placenta* are derived from the *germ-disc* which is at one pole of the blastocyst.

1. Extra-embryonic Membranes

Yolk-sac Membrane. The inner border of the single layer of troph-ectoderm cells of the blastocyst enclosing a blastocoele is lined by endoderm which grows from the germ-disc. The blastocoele is thus enclosed by the yolk-sac membrane and thereby converted to the yolk-sac cavity.

Amnionic and Chorionic Membranes. During formation of the yolk-sac membrane, *ectoderm* and its underlying layer of *lateral mesoderm* at the periphery of the *differentiating* embryo fold over the embryo. These folds meet, fuse and give rise to an inner membrane, the *amnion*, which encloses the *amnionic cavity* and the embryo. The outer membrane, the *chorion*, is also derived from these folds. The newly formed chorion and contiguous troph-ectoderm form the outer layer of tissue which make up the *chorionic sac*.

In early stages the chorion encloses a large cavity, the *exo-coelom*, which lies between the chorion and amnion. In later stages, the *amnionic membrane* fuses with the chorion in the cow, ewe and sow to form an *amnio-chorionic* membrane. A characteristic feature of the inner aspect of the amnionic membrane of farm mammals are heaped up growths of amnionic tissue, *amnionic pustules* (Fig. 10–1).

Allantois. The *allantoic* membrane begins as an envagination from the posterior region of the gut and is an extension of the urinary bladder of the fetus. In farm mammals, the allantoic membrane grows into the exocoelom and surrounds the amnion. During this period the yolk-sac regresses. In all placental mammals, the allantois which is highly vascularized by fetal vessels fuses with the chorion thereby bringing fetal vessels to the periphery of the chorionic sac and thus into closer apposition with maternal tissue.

Allanto-chorion. Fusion of the vascular allantois with the chorion forms the *allanto-chorionic membrane*.

Attention has been drawn to the allanto-chorion by Lillie's theory of the cause of *"free-martins"* in cattle (Lillie, 1917). According to this theory, a sterile female-calf born as a co-twin with a male-calf is the result of male calf hormones passing to the female twin by way of a common circulatory pathway which results when fusion of their respective allanto-chorions occur (Plate XXIII). Although fusion of allantoida is common in twin calves, it is less common in ewes and rare in pigs because the tips of the chorions become necrotic earlier than in the cow, thereby decreasing the chances for fusion between chorions. Twins of the mare are aborted too early for analysis of the effects of the crossed hormones on fetal gonads.

2. Amnionic and Allantoic Fluids

The necessity of a watery medium for life is probably nowhere so marked as in the development of young of all organisms. Immediately surrounding the embryo is amnionic fluid which is contained within the amnionic membrane. Surrounding this membrane is the allantoic fluid contained within the allantoic membrane.

The total quantity of fetal fluids rises rapidly in early pregnancy in all species, but there is considerable variation between volumes of allantoic and amnionic fluids in different species and often between individuals of the same species. In the cow the amnionic fluid increases rapidly in volume during the first half of pregnancy, although not so rapidly as the allantoic fluid (Swett

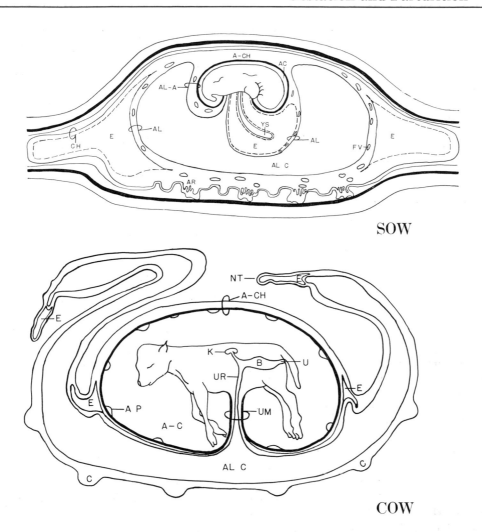

SOW

COW

FIG. 10–1.—(*Top*) Diagram of chorionic-sac of sow embryo in the uterus at an early stage. The yolk-sac has regressed and the allantois is growing into the exo-coelom. (*Adapted from Mossman, 1939. Carnegie Institute of Wash. Publ. 479, Courtesy of Carnegie Inst. of Wash., Wash., D.C.*)

(*Bottom*) Diagram of a chorionic-sac typical of the cow or ewe late in the fetal period. Urinary bladder opens to the amnionic cavity by way of the urethra and allantoic cavity by way of the urachus. (*Adapted from Harvey, 1959, in Reproduction in Domestic Animals, H. H. Cole & P. T. Cupps edits., New York, Courtesy Academic Press.*)

A-C	Amnionic cavity	*AR*	Areolae	*K*	Kidney
A-CH	Amnio-chorion	*B*	Bladder	*NT*	Necrotic tips of chorion
AL	Allantois	*C*	Cotyledon	*U*	Urethra
AL-A	Allanto-amnion	*CH*	Chorion	*UM*	Umbilicus
AL.C	Allantoic cavity	*E*	Exo-coelom	*UR*	Urachus
AP	Amnionic pustule	*FV*	Fetal vessel	*YS*	Yolk-sac

et al., 1948).   In the ewe the amnionic fluid reaches its maximum in the 3rd month (Cloette, 1939) and as in the cow, allantoic fluid reaches its maximum at term (Table 10–2).

One important function of amnionic fluid during prenatal development is to provide a watery medium in which the embryo can develop symmetrically and free from distortions that would arise from being pressed by its weight against surrounding structures. This fluid also prevents adhesions of embryonic skin to the amnionic membrane. The initial steps of implantation may also be aided as the volume of the fluids increase thereby expanding the chorionic sac and

and the bladder is connected to the allantoic cavity by way of a canal, the *urachus*, in the umbilical cord (Fig. 10–1).

Dark brown masses, *hippomanes*, composed of cell debris, globules of fat and degenerating blood cells can be found floating free in amnionic and allantoic fluids. These are often ingested by the fetus and may be found lodged in its mouth.

C. Chorio-allantoic Placenta

During the long intra-uterine existence, the embryo and fetus must carry on the same complex metabolic functions as the adult and in addition it must be adequately

Table 10–2.—Approximations of the Placental Fluid Volumes and Placental Weights of Farm Mammals

(*From the literature*)

	Cow	Ewe	Sow	Mare
Amnionic fluid (maximum volume, ml.)*	1250	700	50–280	3000–5000
Allantoic fluid (maximum volume, ml.)*	320	760	10–240	8000–15000
Weight of Placenta at Parturition (lb.)	8.58	0.44	0.44	—
Birth Weight (lb.)	88	11	4	—
Ratio between Placental Weight and Birth Weight	1:10	1:25	1:10	—

*The values for volumes of fluids are extremely variable between individuals as indicated by the ranges shown for the sow. For the ewe, amnionic fluid reaches maximum at about mid-pregnancy, then decreases to about 200 ml. at term. Allantoic fluid increases to maximum at term.

bringing it into closer apposition with the uterine epithelium.   At parturition dilatation of the cervix may be aided by pressure of fetal fluids within their membranes and it may also serve to lubricate the fetus in its passage through the vagina when the membranes break.

Amnionic and allantoic fluids are slightly alkaline. In sheep the amnionic fluid ranges in pH from 8.50 to 7.08 while allantoic fluid ranges from 7.87 in the first month to 6.86 in the 5th month of pregnancy.   The specific gravity ranges from 1.0026 to 1.0045 for amnionic fluid and 1.0075 to 1.0127 for allantoic fluid (Cloette, 1939).

Both fluids contain proteins, fats, glucose, fructose and inorganic salts. The presence of urea and creatinine in these fluids supports the hypothesis that they have a urinary origin. The *buccal* cavity and *urethra* of the fetus open into the amnionic cavity

supplied with nutrients and readily freed of metabolites to permit normal development of its new tissues, organs and system. The *chorio-allantoic placenta* serves these functions by permitting a ready exchange of nutrients and metabolites between the circulatory systems of the fetus and mother in all placental mammals.

The compound vascularized allanto-chorionic membrane together with uterine tissue is designated the *chorio-allantoic* placenta, and is classified according to its form and also the number of tissues separating the fetal and maternal vascular system. Although our interest in this chapter centers about the farm mammals, the reader should be aware of the placental types in other species. The preferred method of classification of the placenta is based on the number of tissue layers separating fetal and maternal vascular systems (Table 10–3).

Table 10-3.—Tissues of Mature Placentas Separating Maternal and Fetal Blood

(Adapted from Mossman, H. W., 1937, Contr. Embryol. 26, 129. Carnegie Inst. Wash. Pub. No. 479, Wash., D.C.)

Morphological type	Maternal tissue				Fetal tissue			Gross form	Example
	Endo-thelium	Connective† tissue	Epi-thelium	Uterine lumen	Tropho-blast	Connective tissue	Endo-thelium		
Epithelio-chorial	+	±	+	+	+	±	+	Diffuse type Cotyledonary or multiplex	Pig, horse Ruminants
Endothelio-chorial	+	±	−	−	+	±	+	Zonary to discoid	Carnivora, most bats, beaver
Hemo-chorial	−	−	−	−	+	±	+	Discoid	Many insectivora Most rodents *Tarsius dasypodidae* Molossidae
Endothelio-endothelial	+	+	−	−	−	+	+	Discoid	Soricidae, Crocidura
Hemo-chorial with hemo-endothelial areas	−	−	−	−	−	−	+	Discoid cup-shaped	Geomyidae and higher rodents Lagomorpha

†Basement membranes of maternal endothelium surrounding vessels varies greatly in thickness in different species.

1. Epithilio-chorial Diffuse-Type Placentas

The *epithelio-chorial* type of placenta is found in farm mammals. In these at least six layers of tissue separate fetal and maternal bloods: fetal vascular endothelium, connective tissue of the allanto-chorion, chorionic epithelium, uterine epithelium, connective tissue of the endometrium and maternal vascular endothelium. Its gross form is classified as *diffuse* because of the extensive and relatively smooth apposition of the chorion with uterine epithelium (Table 10–3). Interlocking of allanto-chorionic and uterine folds together with tumescence of these tissues (through increased vascularity) appears adequate to anchor the chorionic sac in the uterine lumen.

There are specialized areas of the allanto-chorion of the sow called *areolae* that overlie glands and are adapted for the absorption of the glandular secretions (Fig. 10–1). The mare placenta also differs slightly from the sow by the growth of *chorionic villi* at about the 7th week from the allanto-chorion into folds of the uterine mucosa (Fig. 10–2). Prior to formation of the villi (6th week) abortion of the foal may take place, thus the growth of villi is considered important to anchor the conceptus in the uterus. At about the 50th day of pregnancy *endometrial cups* form in the endometrium of the mare These contain a coagulum rich in degenerate epithelial cells, red blood cells, leucocytes and a high concentration of gonadotropin. The high level of equine-gonadotropin in pregnant mare serum (PMS) occurs when endometrial cups form (Cole & Goss, 1943) (Plate XXIII).

2. Epithelio-chorial Cotyledonary-Type Placenta

The placental-type found in the cow, ewe, and goat formerly called the *syndesmochorial*-type is characterized by the absence of the uterine epithelium overlying *caruncles* (see Chapter 4). In these highly specialized areas there are five layers of tissues separating fetal and maternal blood: fetal vascular endothelium, connective tissue of the allanto-chorion, chorionic epithelium, connective tissue of the caruncles, and maternal vascular endothelium (Table 10–3). The carun-cles are specialized circular areas of uterine mucosa that project into the uterine lumen. The number of caruncles varies in different ruminants. The ewe has from 88 to 96, while the cow has from 70 to 120. Shapes of the caruncles also vary in the ruminants. They are convex in the cow and concave in the ewe (Fig. 10–2). *Cotyledons* of the allanto-chorion attach to the caruncles by invasive villi and together they form the *placentome*. *Fetal cotyledons* develop only over caruncles but not all caruncles are invaded by chorionic villi, thus the placentome number is usually less than the number of caruncles. During pregnancy the caruncles enlarge becoming several times their original diameters. In the cow invasion of the caruncles by villi of the allanto-chorion begins on the 30th day of pregnancy and is completed by the 90th day, while in the ewe invasion begins on the 31st day and is completed by the 78th day. In the intercotyledonary areas of the cow and ewe uterus there is a smooth apposition of the allanto-chorion and the uterine epithelium as in the sow and mare.

D. Development of the Embryo and Fetus

The neonate is the result of a series of orderly processes that transform a single-celled ovum into an organism typical of the species. *Differentiation* is the process by which cells of the embryo become destined to form either one or other of the many types of cells comprising the embryo or fetus. The increase of dimensions resulting from increased number of cells or increase in cell size through addition of protoplasmic substances is *growth*.

1. Differentiation

Undifferentiated cells at one pole of the blastocyst, the germ-disc, give rise to 3 separate layers of cells. The innermost layer, the *endoderm*, in the region of the germ-disc forms the lining of the gut, its glands and the bladder.

The outermost layer of the germ-disc, the *ectoderm*, differentiates early by forming an elongated ridge in the central axis of the germ-disc. This elongated ridge of ectoderm, *neural ectoderm*, subsequently gives rise to

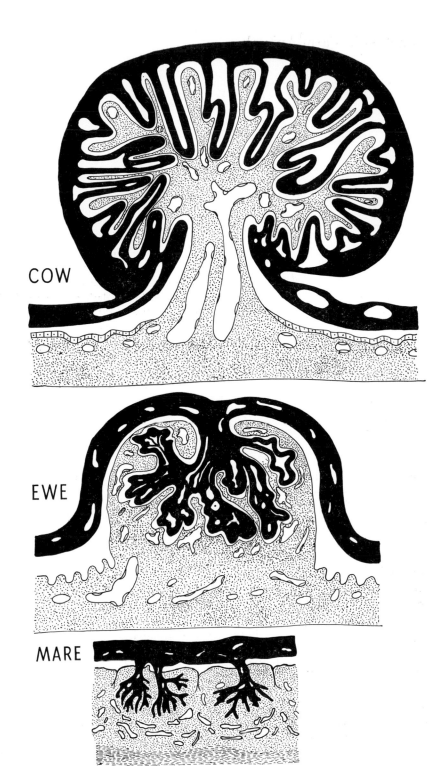

FIG. 10–2.—(*Top*) Placentome of cow. Allanto-chorion of fetus (black) surrounds and villi invade the convex maternal caruncle (stippled). (*Middle*) Placentome of ewe. Allanto-chorion (black) is surrounded by convex caruncle. (*Bottom*) Villi of mare allanto-chorion (black) invade uterine tissue (stippled) at about the 6th month. (*Adapted from Mossman, 1937. Contributions to Embryology Carnegie Inst. 26:129, Courtesy the Carnegie Institution of Washington, Wash., D.C.*)

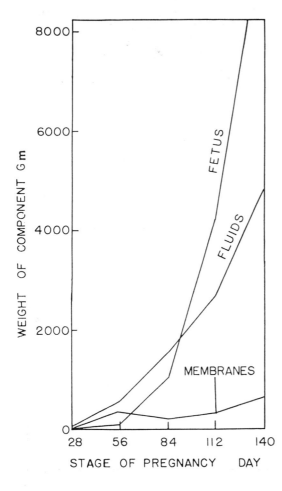

FIG. 10–3.—Weight changes of fetuses, fetal fluids and membranes during pregnancy in ditocous ewes. (*From Wallace, 1948. J. Agric. Sci., 38, 93.*)

the brain and spinal cord and all other derivatives of the nervous system, *i.e.* optic vesicles, posterior pituitary, ganglia and adrenal medulla. Ectoderm lateral to the neural ectoderm gives rise to the skin and all of its derivatives, *i.e.* mammary glands and other skin glands, nails, hair, hooves, anterior pituitary, and lens of the eye. The third germ-layer, the *mesoderm*, forms between the ectoderm and endoderm. The mesoderm gives rise to connective tissues, vascular systems, bones and muscle as well as the adrenal cortex. The *primary sex-cells* may also be derived from mesoderm, however there is more evidence that they are derived from endoderm. For details of embryonic and fetal development as it would occur in farm mammals the interested ader should refer to Patten (1948).

2. Growth of the Fetus

The embryo remains small until formation of extra-embryonic membranes, differentiation of the tissues, and development of the organs (*organo-genesis*) and systems has taken place. Comparison of Table 10–4 with Figure 10–3 shows that after differentiation and organogenesis there is a very rapid increase in linear dimensions and weight of the fetus. These changes in dimensions reflect addition of cell numbers and in some instances cell size.

Two designations for describing growth are useful; *absolute* growth and *relative* growth. Absolute growth is the increment increase in dimensions (volume, crown-rump length, weight, *etc.*) of the fetus in a unit of time, while relative growth is the increment change in dimension for a unit time divided by the dimension attained at the time of measurement. Absolute growth increases continuously throughout development, but relative growth begins to decrease about mid-way in pregnancy.

The large increase in the size of the uterus does not necessarily reflect uterine growth. The changes in uterine dimensions of the cow during pregnancy are illustrated in Plate XXIV. Some of the increase in size of the uterus in the first month of pregnancy is due to an increase in vascularity and fluid accumulation in tissue of the uterus. The large increase in uterine size between the 1st and 2nd month of pregnancy is in a large part accounted

of the fetus (crown-rump, C–R). Cloette has shown that the most reliable measurement to correlate with fetal age in sheep is one taken from the tip of the nostril to the tip of the tail over the back in a sagittal plane (Fig. 10–4). In primates, studies are under way to correlate the age of the embryo and fetus according to the stage of differentiation and development of the tissues, organs and systems. All of these methods have disadvantages that make them difficult to use for ageing embryos and fetuses of farm mammals. Often the copulation time or ovulation times are not known; weight and length of the fetus are influenced by breed and strain, maternal age, and litter

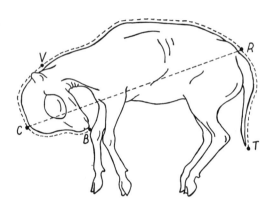

Fig. 10–4.—Diagram to illustrate measurements used for estimation of age and growth rate of mammalian fetuses. (*From Harvey, 1959, in Reproduction in Domestic Animals, H. H. Cole & P. T. Cupps, edits., New York, Courtesy Academic Press.*)

BCVRT   Total Length
C–R   Crown-Rump
CVR   Curved Crown-Rump
VR   Vertebral Column Length
VRT   Vertebral Column and Tail Length

for by the increase in fluid of the chorionic sac which in turn distends the uterine horn. Between the 5th and 6th month of pregnancy most of the apparent increase in uterine dimensions can be accounted for by fetal growth. Nevertheless, there is a small and consistent increase in uterine tissue throughout gestation (Fig. 10–3).

During the first two-thirds of gestation, growth of the embryo is apparently independent of the nutrition of the dam and of the litter size. In the latter one-third of pregnancy there is marked variation in fetal weights which reflect variations in genetic factors, litter size, nutritional status and health of the dam.

3. Age Determination of Embryo and Fetus

Criteria for age determination of embryos and fetuses have been based on copulation and ovulation time, and weight and length

size. Genetic effects and possibly season of breeding may also result in significant variations in determination of age. The ideal method for determining the age of embryos and fetuses would be based on differentiation and development of embryonic and fetal structures, *"developmental horizons,"* (Streeter, 1942), but little of this information is available for farm mammals. In Table 10–4 are listed some of the outstanding horizons in the development of embryos and fetuses of the cow, ewe, and sow.

E. Hormonal Mechanisms During Pregnancy

All hormones are necessary for the well-being of the mother and are in this sense necessary for maintenance of a "normal" pregnancy (see Chapter 1). Maintenance of pregnancy is dependent on the proper balances of hormones. However, with the

Table 10–4.—Some Outstanding Horizons in Development of Embryos and Fetuses of Farm Mammals

(Adapted from Salisbury & Van DeMark 1961 Physiology of Reproduction and Artificial Insemination of Cattle, 1961. San Francisco Freeman, for the cow; Cloette, 1939. Onderstep. J. Vet. Sci. Anim. Ind. 13, 417, for the sheep and Patten, 1948 Embryology of the Pig, 1948 Philadelphia, The Blakiston Co., for the sow.)

Developmental Horizons	Cow (Days)	Ewe (Days)	Sow (Days)
Morula	4–7	3–4	3.5
Blastula	7–12	4–10	4.75
Differentiation of germ layers	14	10–14	7–8
Elongation of chorionic vesicle	16	13–14	9
Primitive streak formation	18	14	9–12
Open neural tube	20	15–21	13
Somite differentiation (1st)	20	17 (9 somites)	14 (3–4 somites)
Fusion of chorio-amniotic folds	18	17	16
Chorion enters non-pregnant horn	20	14	—
Heart beat apparent	21–22	20	16
Closed neural tube	22–23	21–28	16 (11 somites)
Allantois prominent (anchor shaped)	23	21–28	16–17
Forelimb bud visible	25	28–35	17–18
Hindlimb bud visible	27–28	28–35	17–19
Differentiation of digits	30–45	35–42	28+
Nostril and eyes differentiated	30–45	42–49	21–28
Cotyledons 1st appear on chorion	30	—	—
Allantois replaces exocoelom of pregnant horn	32	21–28	—
First attachment (implantation)	33–	21–30(?)	24–
Allantois replaces all of exocoelom	36–37		25–28
Eyelids close	60	49–56	
Hair follicles first appear	90	42–49	28
Horn pits apparent	100	77–84	—
Tooth eruption	110	98–105	(160 mm. pig)
Hair around eyes and muzzle	150	98–105	—
Hair covering body	230	119–126	—
Birth	280	147–155	112

advent of the placenta and of the fetal endocrine glands, an interplay of hormones occurs among the placenta, fetus and mother. Although the extent of these relationships has not been determined, there is evidence that placental and fetal hormones are both important in maintenance of pregnancy (Cole, 1953).

Hormones shown to be necessary for the maintenance of pregnancy are estrogen and progesterone from the ovary and gonadotropin and prolactin from the anterior pituitary. There is evidence that these can all be produced either in the maternal or fetal portion of the chorio-allantoic placenta. Those involved in parturition are relaxin from the ovary and oxytocin from the posterior pituitary. Although adrenal cortical hormones and thyroxin are important in some animals, the extent of the activity of these in farm mammals has not been ascertained (Chapter 1).

Gonadotropins are found in high concentration in endometrial cups of the mare and pregnant mare serum (PMS) between the 55th and 110th day of pregnancy. In the cow, ewe, sow and goat, however, there is no measurable quantity in the serum. Prolactin (lactogenic or luteotropic hormone) is necessary for maintenance of corpora lutea and the presence of maternal behavior.

The hormones of the adrenal cortex, the cortical steroids, belong to two classes: those controlling carbohydrate metabolism (corticosterone) and those controlling mineral metabolism (deoxycorticosterone) both of which increase in the mother during gestation.

The placenta is independent of the fetus, but like the fetus depends upon the proper uterine environment for its existence. The contribution of the placenta to maintenance of pregnancy other than as a passage way of nutrients and metabolites for the embryo has been under intensive investigation in recent years. The placenta of the cow, ewe, sow and mare is rich in estrogens and the placenta of the mare is also rich in progesterone and gonadotropin. Three steroids, deoxycorticosterone, cortisol and tetrahydrocortisol have also been isolated from the placenta.

F. Pregnancy Diagnosis

There are at least three major methods used for diagnosis of pregnancy in farm mammals: (a) clinical diagnosis (b) biological assay (bioassay) and (c) chemical diagnosis (chemo-assay) (Cowie, 1948).

Clinical Diagnosis. In the cow, pregnancy can be determined by rectal palpation for the amnionic vesicle as early as 34 days and after this time palpation for placentomes (cotyledons) is a highly reliable method. These methods are not useful for ewes or sows, but x-ray films after the 55th day of pregnancy in ewes have proven to be an accurate method of pregnancy diagnosis but have no practical value to the farm operation (Benzie, 1951). For the mare, pregnancy may be determined by the 21st day by examination of cervical mucus and rectal palpation of the ovaries and uterus when done by a highly skilled technician. Between the 90th and 100th day, rectal palpation has proved highly successful (see Chapter 16).

Biological Assay (Bioassay). Bioassay has proven of particular value for diagnosis of pregnancy between the 50th and 100th day in the mare. This diagnosis is dependent on detection of gonadotropin in the pregnant mare's serum (PMS) by injection of the serum into immature female rats, mice or rabbits. Formation of follicles in the ovaries of these test animals assures the diagnosis of pregnancy.

Chemical Diagnosis (Chemo-assay). After 120 days of pregnancy, detection of urinary estrogens by the *Cuboni fluorescence test* of the urine of the mare also signals pregnancy. Because of the low levels of serum gonadotropins and urinary estrogens in the pregnant cow, neither bioassay methods nor chemical analysis have proved effective in early pregnancy diagnosis of cows.

G. Transfer of Nutrients and Metabolites Across the Placenta

Nutrients, substances utilized by the cells of the embryo and fetus in the production of energy and structure, and metabolites, end-products of metabolism, are transferred across the fetal membranes by several processes. Simple diffusion, movement of molecules from a place of high activity (concentration) to a place of lower activity (concentration) of those molecules was formerly thought to be of prime importance for the early blastocyst. However, it is now recognized that most molecules are transferred across living membranes by activity of the cells. *Phagocytosis*, engulfing food, and *pinocytosis*, ingesting water, are two of the methods by which cells of the blastocyst obtain nutrients. Although these and other means of *active transport* utilize energy, they have the advantage of being able to move substances against an activity (concentration) gradient. Thus, the embryo can store nutrients in higher concentrations than exist in maternal blood (Barcroft, 1944).

The mechanisms involved in the transfer of large quantities of nutrients and excretion of metabolites by the placenta is one of the interesting problems of fetal and placental physiology. Hammond proposed the "Theory of Partition of Nutrients" to help explain how the embryo is able to grow even when the mother is losing weight. In this theory he proposed that *partition* of *nutrients* was determined by the relative metabolic rates of the tissues. Those tissues with higher metabolic rates have priorities over those with lower rates. Presumably fetal tissues have higher metabolic rates than maternal tissues. Under extreme nutrient deprivation to the mother, the order of descending effect on fetal tissue is fat, muscle, bone and finally the nervous system and fetus.

Inorganic Nutrients. Water moves freely between the mother and fetus. But a curious problem of placental physiology arises from the fact that water moves from the mother to the fetus even against an osmotic gradient and in the face of a lower plasma protein concentration in the fetal blood. Of the 78 grams of weight that a 115–day sheep fetus gains daily, 60 gm. is water.

Sodium ion is restricted in its passage across the placenta, however there appears to be an equal balance of this ion between fetal and maternal blood (Flexner & Gellhorn, 1942). Iron tends to be higher in the fetuses of the cow, ewe and sow than in the mother. Iron is transferred from maternal circulation to the uterine lumen, reaching the sow fetus by way of the areolae (Fig. 10–1) and the cow fetus by way of the chorion in the intercotyledonary areas. Iron is subsequently stored in the fetal liver, spleen and bone marrow and is utilized by the suckling neonate since milk contains little iron. Copper like iron tends to increase in concentration in the fetal liver but its pathway to the fetus is across the chorio-allantoic placenta. Manganese is found in the liver of the cow fetus but does not accumulate like iron. Calcium and phosphorus both enter fetal blood against an activity (concentration) gradient and maternal reserves will be depleted if dietary levels of these are low in the mother. Decalcification of the mother's bone will even occur when feeds are too low in calcium.

Oxygenated hemoglobin of the mother is dissociated readily in presence of the lowered pH that exists in the placenta, thereby increasing the availability of oxygen for fetal circulation. Fetal hemoglobin also has a greater affinity for oxygen than maternal hemoglobin. Maternal and fetal bloods move in opposite directions in the placenta. The resultant counterflow maintains a concentration gradient that favors the embryo.

Organic Nutrients. The blood sugar level of ruminant fetuses is higher than in the mother. Peculiarly, fructuose comprises about 70 to 80 per cent of the blood sugar of fetal blood, while only glucose is present in maternal blood. One can account for passage of glucose from the mother to the fetus by the fact that the concentration is higher in maternal blood than in the fetus, but the absence of fructose in maternal blood does not explain how the placenta can act as a barrier to passage of fructose from fetal blood to the mother. There is evidence that the fructose is formed in the placenta, stored in the fetal liver and utilized as a reserve energy source for ruminant fetuses. Glycogen concentration is higher in the maternal portion of the placenta and is independent of blood sugar levels (Barcroft, 1946).

Lipids are higher in the maternal blood of sheep than in the fetuses. A similar result is observed in sows when fed a high bacon fat diet. The placenta does not permit passage of fat as such, but fatty acids and glycerols pass freely. Unaltered fats, however, may be phagocytized by cells of the trophectoderm from "uterine milk."

Nitrogenous substances may also be taken up readily from "uterine milk" by trophectoderm prior to implantation. During implantation some proteolysis occurs at attachment points and the tissue debris is engulfed by the cells of the chorionic sac, thus permitting passage of unaltered proteins. After implantation and formation of the chorio-allantoic placenta, proteins for purposes of nutrition pass across the placental barrier in their simplest form, amino acids. It is emphasized here that studies on nutrition for the embryo and fetus of farm mammals are lacking.

The fat soluble vitamins A, D and E seem to be impeded by the placental barrier, thus at birth the concentration of these is lower in fetal livers than that of the mother. A new born calf has only 600 *B.U.* of vitamin A in its body but acquires 55,000 *B.U.* from colostrum after birth. The role that water soluble vitamins play in fetal nutrition has not been studied to any extent in farm mammals since these are formed in the rumen and are in high concentration in normal feeds of sows.

Fetal Excretion. Our primary concern to this point has been fetal nutrition, however, it is also essential that excretion of metabolites occurs. There have been only a few studies on this topic; however, it appears that there is a relation between the size and early formation of the allantois and the time of formation of a functional embryonic kidney (*mesonephros*). The sow and mare of the mammals have the largest allantois and earliest developed mesonephros, as well as the most tissues separating fetal and maternal circulation. The slow but constant excretion of urine by fetuses adds to the accumulation of allantoic fluid that occurs throughout fetal development.

CO_2 according to Barcroft is transferred readily from the embryo to the mother by diffusion with the gradient favoring the embryo. To what extent the amnionic and allantoic fluids serve to retain or detoxify fetal excretions and secretions has not been ascertained for farm mammals and little has been done in other placental mammals.

H. Disorders of Pregnancy

The fetus can mobilize its essential nutrients at the expense of the mother except for vitamin A, possibly vitamin D and iron supplies. It is characteristic of placentas of all species that maternal and fetal bloods flow in opposite directions, thus maintaining a gradient of metabolites between fetal and maternal blood. But it appears that even when the mother is in a good condition, her reserves are not sufficiently labile to permit maximum growth of the fetus when the maternal food intake is limited. In the ewe, pregnant 2 months, the combined weights of the fetal membranes and the placenta account for 40 per cent of the gravid weight of the uterus (Wallace, 1948). The fetal growth may be dependent on the growth of the fetal placenta because the weight of the lamb at birth is related to the number of fetal cotyledons. Some literature of mammals other than farm mammals points to essential nutrient lack at various stages of embryonic development as a causal factor in fetal abnormalities. For farm mammals, however, under-standard management practices, nutritional disorders during pregnancy involve the maternal organism and not the fetus.

Subterranean clover of Western Australia is rich in gonadotropin-like substances and this feed has been implicated in large outbreaks of *dystocia* and sterility in ewes.

Pregnancy toxemia (twin lamb disease) of sheep appears to be related to a low calorie intake during the last 2 months of pregnancy, and is not common when an adequate intake permits a small but consistent increase in live weight during gestation. The cause of "toxemia" has been attributed to additional energy demands by the fetus, placenta and mother during the latter part of pregnancy. The fetal liver- and blood-sugars remain high in spite of almost complete exhaustion of these in the mother. The ewe utilizes fat for an energy source thus freeing toxic substances of partial fat oxidation *i.e.* ketone and acetone bodies in excess. These toxins though fatal to the ewe do not traverse the placenta. Complete control of this disease can be effected by adequate feeding throughout gestation.

Fetal death and abortion occur during vitamin A and D deficiency in cows, ewes and sows. A high incidence of fetal death in cows has also been attributed to faulty calcium and phosphorus ratios. Piglets of vitamin A deficient mothers are often born with a cleft palate and without eyes and calves from cows on iodine deficient rations have high incidences of goiter (see Chapter 18).

II. PARTURITION

Parturition, the normal conclusion of a pregnancy, may be divided into three stages: (1) preparatory stage (2) expulsion of the fetus and (3) expulsion of the placenta. Although we describe the physical events as they occur, the mechanisms underlying the cessation of tolerance for the fetus and the placenta by the mother are not clearly understood.

A. Normal Labor

Several days before parturition relaxation of pelvic ligaments is brought about by the synergistic action of the ovarian hormone relaxin and the high titer of pre-parturitional estrogens. Before normal labor begins, the fetus usually assumes a position in the uterus characteristic of the species. Mare, cow and

Table 10–5.—Time (Hours) Required for Various Stages of Parturition in Farm Mammals

(*From Robert's Veterinary Obstetrics and Genital Diseases, 1956.   Pub. by the author, Ithaca, N.Y.*)

Animal		Preparatory stage	Expulsion of fetus(es)	Expulsion of placenta(s)	Involution of uterus (Days)
Cow	range	0.5–24	0.5–3 to 4	0.5–8	9
	average	2–6	0.5–1	4–5	
	trouble if		in pluriparous		
	more than	6–12	2–3	12	
Ewe	range	0.5–24	0.5–2	0.5–8	30
	average	2–6	–	–	
	trouble if				
	more than	6–12	2–3	12	
Sow	range	2–12	1–4	1–4	10
	trouble if				
	more than	6–12	6–12	–	
Mare	range	1–4	10–30 min.	0.5–8 to 12	13–25
	average	–	–	0.5–3	
	trouble if				
	more than	4	20–30 min.	12	

ewe fetuses are on their backs during intrauterine life but before labor they rotate so that they are in an upright position with their nose and forelegs directed posteriorly to the dam.   Fetuses of sows may be born in any position as occurs in other polytocous species.

The time for the 3 stages of parturition vary between species and breeds and between individuals of a breed.   The time for expulsion of fetus is the shortest of the 3 stages and for the farm mammals the mare has the shortest expulsion stage (Roberts, 1956) (Table 10–5).

1st Stage (Preparatory Stage).   The preparatory stage is characterized by dilation of the cervix and rhythmic contractions of the longitudinal and circular muscles of the uterus with the expulsive motion toward the cervix.   In uniparous animals the contractions start at the apex of the cornua while the caudal part remains quiescent.   In multiparous animals, contractions begin just cranial to the fetus nearest the cervix and the remaining part of the uterus remains quiescent.   The fluid-filled allantois and the fetus push against the cervical opening which tends to aid in expanding the cervix.   The amnion with its fluid serves

this same purpose when the allantoic sac ruptures.   In this stage and in the second stage of parturition, there is an increase in the rate and strength of uterine contractions. These contractions are the result of extrinsic autonomic neural reflex mechanisms and the characteristic automatic contractility of smooth muscle.   The neural reflex is enhanced by fetal motility, while the intrinsic mechanism is enhanced by hormonal effects, particularly oxytocin.   Unusual disturbance of a parturient female may cause inhibition to uterine muscle contractions thereby slowing or inhibiting parturition.   The rhythmicity is superimposed on the intrinsic motility of the uterine musculature by lumbar nerves.

The first stage is followed shortly by the second stage; however, a prolonged first stage (beyond 6 hours in the mare and cow) indicates that some difficulty of presentation of the fetus exists (Table 10–5).

2nd Stage (Expulsion of Fetus).   This stage is characterized by the completing of dilation of the cervix and entrance of the fetus into the cervix and vagina.   During this phase muscle contractions of the uterus increase in rate with a prolonged contraction and shortened relaxation periods.   It is

PLATE XXIII

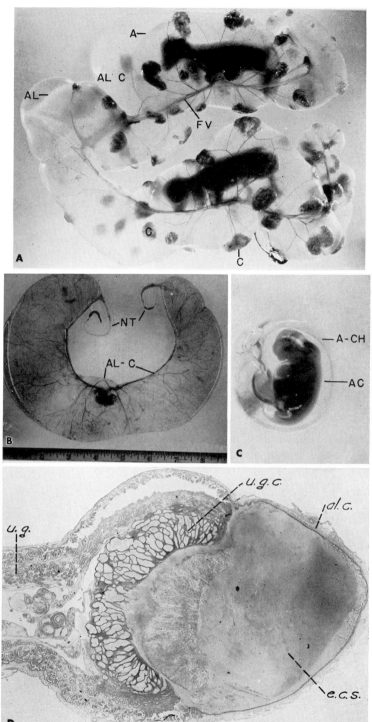

A. Chorionic-sac of the cow with twin fetus. The chorion and allantoida are fused. (*Photograph by G. W. Trimberger.*)

B. Chorionic sac with a 26-day embryo. (*Photograph courtesy University of Missouri, Columbia, Mo.*)

C. Normal 26-day old pig embryo enclosed in the amnion. (*Photograph courtesy University of Missouri, Columbia, Mo.*)

D. Endometrial cup from mare sacrificed on 105th day of pregnancy. (*From Harvey, 1959. In Reproduction in Domestic Animals, H. H. Cole & P. T. Cupps edits., New York, Courtesy Academic Press.*)

A	Amnion	Al.C	Allanto-chorion	NT	Necrotic tip of chorion;
AC	Amnionic cavity	C	Fetal cotyledon	UG	Uterine gland
ACH	Amnio-chorion	ECS	Endometrial cup secretion	UGC	Uterine gland in area of
AL	Allantois	FV	Fetal vessels		endometrial cup

PLATE XXIV

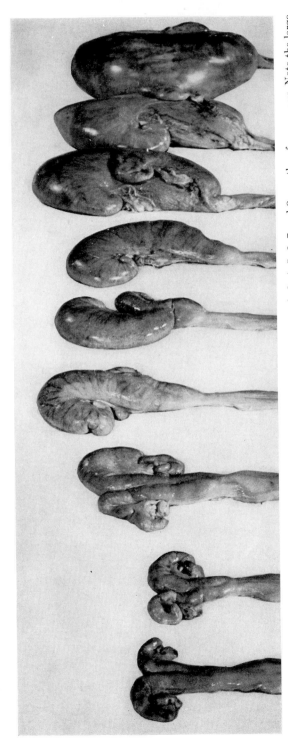

Cow uteri at monthly intervals of pregnancy. *Left to right:* non-pregnant uterus, 1, 2, 3, 4, 5, 6, 7 and 8 months of pregnancy. Note the large increase in size of uterine horn between the non-pregnancy condition to 1 month pregnant; progressive increase in size to the 5th month; and large increase in size between 5th and 6th month. Note difference in size of the two uterine horns, the embryo is located in the larger horn. (*Photograph by G. W. Trimberger.*)

also during this stage that the fetus becomes free of its placental tissues and begins to carry on respiration free of the mother. In the mare there is complete separation of the chorion from the uterine wall, thus effectively depriving the fetus of oxygen from the maternal vasculature. Any delay in parturition may result in anoxia and death of the foal. In the cow and ewe oxygen may be supplied by way of the placentome during expulsion and until breakage of the umbilical cord.

3rd Stage (Expulsion of Placenta). During this stage the chorio-allantoic placenta is expelled from the uterus. Strong and continuous contractions of the uterus occur normally during this stage. Removal of fetal blood and consequent de-tumescence of the fetal cotyledons in the cow and ewe permit separation of fetal cotyledons from maternal caruncles.

Involution of the Uterus. Following expulsion of the fetus and placenta the uterus returns to normal size of non-pregnancy. This stage is termed *involution* and might logically be considered the *4th stage* of parturition. For a period of 26 to 47 days contractions of the uterus occur at a rate greater than normal. During this time the caruncles return to normal size and epithelium is replaced (9 days in the cow). In the ewe involution takes about 30 days and in the mare 13 to 25 days (Table 10–5).

Hammond found that uteri of anestrous ewes which had lambed 4 to 6 weeks earlier were filled with a viscous brown pigmented fluid which appeared to be blood undergoing autolysis. The size of the uteri varied from a non-pregnant type to that of one about 35 days pregnant. Such an observation suggests that involution of uterus is not a simple process as considered earlier for farm mammals. If a similar condition exists in uteri of cows, this may account for the low level of fertility of cows bred or inseminated shortly after parturition.

B. Initiation of Parturition

The several theories which account for normal cessation of pregnancy, center around the hormonal, neural, physical and biochemical changes that occur during gestation in the mother, fetus, and placenta. Whether only one, several, or all of these mechanisms are involved in parturition has not been determined.

Hormonal Mechanisms. The evidence for hormonal mechanisms as responsible for parturition is based on observations that uterine motility *in vivo* or *in vitro* is greater in the presence of estrogen. It is known that toward the end of gestation the estrogen levels rise, and uterine motility may be the result of direct action by estrogen on uterine muscle or it may act synergistically with oxytocin, from the posterior pituitary or placenta, which has a stimulating effect on uterine motility. This theory depends on the assumption that progesterone which inhibits uterine motility decreases at the end of gestation. Such an event has not been reported in farm mammals.

Neural Mechanisms. Distension of the uterus and pressure on the cervix may bring about stimulus by way of the nervous system to the hypothalamus and a subsequent release of oxytocin from the posterior pituitary, but physiological levels of oxytocin will not act alone as an initiator of parturition.

Physical Mechanisms. Distention of the uterus during rapid fetal growth may bring about an increased sensitivity of the uterine musculature to both estrogen and oxytocin. It is known that twins of cows and ewes are born sooner than singles, thus it appears that the mass of conceptus as a result of fetal motility may play a part in initiation of uterine contractions and subsequent parturition. Distention may so alter the blood supply to the uterus as to bring about early aging of the placenta with a resultant anoxia of the fetuses.

Integrated Mechanisms. From the above mentioned facts we can derive the following tentative picture of initiation of parturition. As the fetus enlarges *in utero* it distends the uterine musculature and stimulates sensory nerves of the uterus and cervix. This stimulus causes an increase in secretion of oxytocin from the posterior pituitary. Oxytocin working synergistically with the increased estrogen level at term and acting on the uterine musculature increases its irritability. Progesterone levels subside thus removing inhibition to muscle contraction. The fetus increases in motility near term because of anoxia resulting from reduced vascular flow when the uterus is distended. This fetal motility further stimulates uterine contractility until the contractions reach an expulsive force. Expulsion is permitted by relaxation of the cervix and vagina and enhanced by contraction of uterine and abdominal muscles of the mother during labor.

REFERENCES

BARCROFT, J. (1944). The nutritional functions of the placenta. *Proc. Nutr. Soc.*, **2,** 14–25.

———— (1946). *Researches on Pre-Natal Life.* Vol. I, Oxford, Blackwell Scientific Publications.

BENZIE, D. (1951). Use of X-ray for determination of pregnancy in sheep. *Brit. Vet. J.*, **107,** 3–10.

CLOETTE, J. H. L. (1939). Prenatal growth in merino sheep. *Onderstep. J. Vet. Sci. Anim. Ind.*, **13,** 417–460.

COLE, H. H. (1953). Problems in the field of physiology of reproduction of farm animals. *Iowa State Coll. J. Sci.*, **28,** 133–138.

COLE, H. H. & GOSS, H. (1943). The source of equine gonadotrophin. In: *Essays in Biology.* Berkeley, Calif., Univ. of Calif. Press.

COWIE, A. T. (1948). *Pregnancy diagnosis tests:* A review. Joint Pub. 13, Edinburgh, Imper. Bur. Anim. Breed. & Gen.

FLEXNER, L. B. & GELLHORN, A. (1942). The comparative physiology of placental transfer. *Amer. J. Obstet. Gynec.*, **43,** 965–973.

HOWELL, C. E. & ROLLINS, W. C. (1951). Environmental sources of variation in the gestation length of the horse. *J. Anim. Sci.*, **10,** 789–796.

LILLIE, F. R. (1917). The freemartin; A study of the action of sex hormones in the foetal life of cattle. *J. Expt. Zool.*, **23,** 371–452.

PATTEN, B. M. (1948). *Embryology of the Pig.* Philadelphia, The Blakiston Co.

ROBERTS, S. J. (1956). *Veterinary Obstetrics and Genital Diseases.* Ithaca, New York, S. J. Roberts.

ROLLINS, W. C., LABEN, R. C. & MEAD, S. W. (1956). Gestation length in an inbred Jersey herd. *J. Dairy Sci.*, **39,** 1578–1593.

STREETER, G. L. (1942). Developmental horizons in human embryos. *Contribs. Embryol. Carnegie Inst.*, **30,** 211–240.

SWETT, W. W., MATHEWS, C. A. & FOHRMAN, M. H. (1948). Development of the fetus in the dairy cow. *U.S. Dept. Agr. Tech. Bull.* No. 964.

TERRILL, C. E. & HAZEL, L. N. (1947). Length of gestation in range sheep. *Amer. J. Vet. Res.*, **8,** 66–75.

WALLACE, L. R. (1948). The growth of lambs before and after birth in relation to the level of nutrition. *J. Agric. Sci.*, **38,** 243–302 & 367–401.

QUESTIONS

1. Define: gestation, parturition, placenta, extra-embryonic membrane, embryo, fetus, epitheliochorial placenta, diffuse-type *vs.* cotyledonary-type, caruncle, cotyledon, placentome, endometrial cups.
2. What is the origin of the amnion, yolk-sac membrane, chorion and allantois in farm mammals?
3. Give the length of gestation periods in the mare, cow, ewe and sow.
4. How are the gestation periods affected by heredity and environment?
5. How are the hormones of the adrenal, pituitary, ovary and placenta involved in maintenance of gestation and initiation of parturition? Discuss the origin, time of action and organ on which each acts.
6. What is the significance of "partition of nutrients?"
7. Describe one method of pregnancy diagnosis for the mare, cow, ewe and sow.
8. What are some of the nutritional disorders and their causes during pregnancy?
9. Describe in brief the stages of parturition.
10. Integrate the theories on the causes of parturition.

Chapter 11

Lactation

By RALPH P. REECE

MAMMALS are distinguished by the presence of mammary glands, present in both male and female although usually functional in the female only. Mammary glands are modified skin glands and are found in primitive mammals, the duckbill (*Ornithorhynchus anatinus*) and spiny anteater (*Echidna aculeata*), although teats are not present. Each mammary gland of all other mammals, with the exception of certain males (mouse, rat, and horses), is provided with a teat. Mammary glands secrete milk for the nourishment of young and in some species colostrum has a high antibody titer which protects the young against disease for several weeks after birth. As the mammary gland becomes more highly developed a greater percentage of the milk protein is made up of casein. The gland is most highly developed in the dairy cow and in other farm mammals the amount of milk secreted influences considerably the efficiency of meat production. Unless indicated otherwise the dairy cow is used as a model in presenting the material in this chapter.

I. ANATOMY OF THE UDDER

A. Gross Anatomy

1. EXTERIOR OF UDDER AND TEATS

In cattle the udder consists of four glands (quarters) and is located in the inguinal region. It is posterior to the umbilicus and extends backward between the hind legs. The skin of the udder is covered with hair, however, the teats are devoid of hair. The number of gestations, breed, and functional activity influence empty udder weight which vary from 7 to 165 lb. The amount of fluid that a post-mortem udder will hold is about 140 per cent of its empty weight. In one study of 10 mature Jersey cows, estimated udder capacity (maximum amount of milk that could be secreted and stored) was 54 lb. (Tucker *et al.*, 1961). Insufficient capacity is the most serious defect limiting milk secretion.

Supernumerary teats are observed in about 40 per cent of the cattle population and occur in one of three positions: (*a*) to the rear of normal teats (*caudal* teats); (*b*) between normal teats (*intercalary* teats); and (*c*) attached to or branching from normal teats (*ramal* teats). Caudal teats occur with equal frequency on the right and left side and are usually removed surgically from heifer calves. Rudimentary teats are present in the male and are located either anterior to or on the anterior surface of the scrotum.

In the ewe the udder consists of two halves with a single gland in each half, and is located in the inguinal region. Fine hairs are found on the teat and there may be

13

extra or supernumerary teats. When supernumerary teats are present they are located anterior to the two normal teats.

In swine the mammary glands are located in two rows on the abdomen and numbers vary from 8 to 18 with an average of 12. Teats are classified as normal, supernumerary, or rectal and are short, blunt, wrinkled, and free of hair and of sebaceous glands. Defective teats are occasionally observed; they appear hollow or inverted and may evert during late stages of pregnancy or at parturition. The defect, however, is usually permanent and milk cannot be removed from the gland through the teat. Teats may be exactly paired, left and right; one of a pair may be missing (suppressed teat); or one teat may be placed midway between the opposite two (triangular pattern).

The udder is located in the inguinal region in the mare and consists of two glands. The teat is flat and broad with a blunted tip. The teat and skin of the udder are covered with fine hair and is usually pigmented. Both sweat and sebaceous glands are present in the skin of the udder.

2. Internal Structure of Teat and Udder of Adult

At the tip of the teat one observes a slight depression in the center of which the teat orifice is located. The orifice leads to the streak canal which varies in length from 8 to 12 mm. and is kept closed by an involuntary sphincter muscle. Dorsal to the streak canal is the teat cistern (*sinus papillaris*) which has a capacity of 30 to 45 ml. Between the streak canal and teat cistern there are a number of folds (4 to 8) which radiate in many directions to form a structure called *Furstenberg's rosette*. There may be a constriction between the teat cistern and gland cistern in the form of a *cricoid* (annular) fold. It has either a central or off center circular opening and consists of dense connective tissue. The gland cistern (*sinus lactiferous*) is located above the teat cistern; it is a cavernous opening with a capacity from 115 to 400 ml. Leading into the gland cistern are from 8 to 12 large milk ducts (*galactophores*). The large ducts branch irregularly and, in good producing animals, extend throughout the udder. Ducts

usually constrict at the point of branching which is followed by a sinus-like enlargement. Ducts continue to branch and terminate in an enlargement called an *alveolus*. Teats of cattle and sheep have one streak canal whereas those of swine and horses are traversed by two. The internal structure of a cow's udder is shown in Figure 11–1.

The udder is supported in a variety of ways. The skin plays a minor role in suspending and stabilizing the udder. The skin in turn is attached to underlying tissue by a loose connective *areolar* tissue. A cord-like tissue helps to keep the dorsal surface of the fore quarters in close proximity to the abdominal wall. Two pairs of lateral sheets, a superficial layer and a deep layer, arise from the subpelvic tendon and extend downward and forward over the udder. Numerous *lamellae* (plates) extend from the deep lateral sheet into the secretory tissue of the udder. The *median suspensory ligament*, consisting of yellow elastic connective tissue, arises from the abdominal wall and attaches by lamellae to the medial surface of the two halves. The lateral suspensory ligaments and the median suspensory ligament join on the ventral surface of the udder to form the *intermammary grove*. The comparative anatomy of mammary glands in farm mammals is presented in Table 11–1.

3. Vascular System

A mammary artery enters each half of the udder dorsal to the rear teats. The mammary artery branches to form the cranial and caudal mammary arteries which continue to branch and become smaller until they become capillaries surrounding each alveolus. The cranial and caudal mammary veins, with their anastomosing branches, form the venous circle at the base of the udder. The mammary vein arises from the union of the cranial and caudal mammary veins and leaves the udder as the external pudic vein. Anterior to the base of the udder the right and left cranial mammary vein become the right and left subcutaneous abdominal mammary veins. A third vein, the perineal vein, originates from the anastomotic branches of the caudal mammary veins and pursues a tortuous course in the perineal region toward the vulva. The

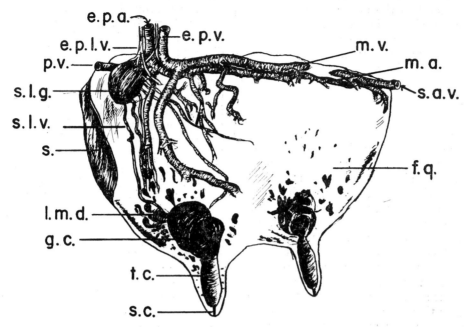

FIG. 11-1.—Section of bovine udder showing internal structure. *e.p.a.*, external pudic artery; *e.p.l.v.*, external pudic lymph vessel; *p.v.*, perineal vein; *s.l.g.*, supramammary lymph gland; *s.l.v.*, subcutaneous lymph vessels; *s.*, skin; *l.m.d.*, large milk ducts; *g.c.*, gland cistern; *t.c.*, teat cistern; *s.c.*, streak canal; *f.q.*, fore quarter; *s.a.v.*, subcutaneous abdominal vein; *m.a.*, mammary artery; *m.v.*, mammary vein; *e.p.v.*, external pudic vein. (*After Turner, 1939. The Comparative Anatomy of the Mammary Gland. Columbia, Mo., University Cooperative Store. Courtesy C. W. Turner.*)

Table 11-1.—Comparative Anatomy of Mammary Glands

	Mammary Glands			Teats			
				Streak Canals			
Species	Location	Number	Location of extra teats	No. per teat	Color	Hair present	Tissue closing teat orifice
Cattle	inguinal	4	caudal, intercalary, ramal	1	white	no	muscular (circular) tissue
Sheep	inguinal	2	anterior to normal teats	1	darkly pigmented	yes	elastic connective tissue
Swine	abdominal	12*	between normal teats	2	–	no	elastic connective tissue
Horses	inguinal	2	–	2	black	yes	muscular (circular) tissue

*Range from 8 to 18

perineal vein, however, does not convey venous blood from the udder but carries venous blood to the udder from the vulva and anal region (Linzell & Mount, 1955). Therefore there are two arteries (external pudic) and one vein (perineal) conveying blood to the udder and four veins [external pudic (2) and subcutaneous abdominal (2)] conveying blood from the udder.

4. Lymphatic System

The lymphatic system is a one-way system conveying materials from but not to the tissues. It aids the venous system in absorbing tissue juice and returning it, as lymph, to the blood vascular system. The system consists of capillaries, ducts, and lymph nodes or glands. Capillaries surround alveoli and combine to form ducts which pass upward and backward to a large supramammary lymph gland, one in each half. In addition to the lymphatics of glandular tissue there are lymphatics of the skin of the udder and teats. The lymph glands are kidney-shaped, have a weight of 22 to 1458 gm. and are located on the postero-dorsal surface of the udder. A large lymph duct passes through the inguinal canal, combines with other lymph ducts to form the lumbar trunk and continues as the thoracic lymph duct which opens into the anterior vena cava just behind the angle of the jugular veins.

Absorption of tissue juice from intercullular spaces by lymphatic capillaries to constitute lymph is aided by pressure in blood capillaries and intercullular spaces. Lymph flow is aided by: (a) blood capillary pressure; (b) contraction of muscles; (c) valves in lymph vessels which prevent back flow of lymph; and (d) breathing; with each inspiratory movement lymph is moved forward in the thoracic duct into the anterior vena cava.

5. Nervous System

The activities of various parts of the body are coordinated by the nervous system and by the endocrine system. Although there is no evidence that nerve fibers directly influence the secretory activity of the udder they do influence it indirectly by dilating or contracting blood vessels. The innervation of the udder consists of sensory fibers (conducting nervous impulses from udder) and motor fibers (conducting impulses to udder).

The sensory fibers originate from four different sources and they innervate the skin of the udder and teats and the glandular tissue. Motor impulses are conveyed to the udder by nerve fibers incorporated in the inguinal nerve and which are of sympathetic (a division of the autonomic nervous system —involuntary system) origin. Cutting the inguinal nerve causes a temporary vasodilation of the external pudic artery and a relaxation of the teat sphincter. Hence the udder is innervated by spinal and by sympathetic nerves (St. Clair, 1942).

B. Microscopic Anatomy

The skin of the udder consists of the epidermis and dermis or true skin. The epidermis is a stratified squamous epithelium in which six layers can usually be identified. The dermis is made up of a superficial papillary layer and a deep reticular layer.

The streak canal is lined by stratified squamous epithelium which is similar in structure to the epidermis of the skin. The epithelium is a glistening white in color. Beneath this epithelium are longitudinal and circular muscle fibers, the circular fibers constituting the teat sphincter. Dorsal to the streak canal is Furstenberg's rosette which may aid in preventing the escape of milk from the udder.

The teat cistern is lined with a two-layered epithelium, the outer layer consisting of columnar cells whereas cuboidal cells make up the basal layer. The epithelium is yellow in color and contrasts markedly with the white epithelium of the streak canal. The epithelium rests upon a basement membrane beneath which is found the tunica propia. In the middle section of the teat wall one finds longitudinal, circular, and oblique muscle fibers among which is found an abundance of elastic connective tissue. The middle section of the teat wall is called the teat corpus cavernosum because of the abundance of longitudinal blood and lymph vessels. Accessory glands, little tubulo-alveolar glandules with a single-layered epithelium, have been described in the wall of the teat cistern.

The ducts of the udder are similar in structure to the gland cistern wall. Working from the lumen outward one encounters a two-layered epithelium, a myoepithelial layer which is longitudinally arranged, and a basement membrane. Arteries and veins are found in the tunica propia of the large ducts, however, capillaries are not abundant since secretory activity is nil. As the ducts extend from the gland cistern there is a gradual decrease in the mixed muscle fiber layer and an increase in connective tissue. A terminal duct enlarges to form an alveolus and both are lined by a single layer of epithelial cells.

Alveoli. The secretory units of the udder are lined by a single row of epithelial cells. The epithelial cells are either cuboidal or columnar in shape, depending on amount of accumulated secretory products. *Myoepithelial* cells, cells with branching processes and an irregular arrangement and disposed in whorls, surround the epithelial layer of alveoli (Plate XXV). The cells lie on a delicate basement membrane and although no one has seen them contract the effects of their contraction have been observed by direct microscopic study of the mammary gland. Around the alveoli the supporting tissue (*stroma*) is delicate, loose, and rich in capillaries.

A group of alveoli and their ducts constitute a lobule. These ducts (terminal) unite to form intralobular ducts (ducts within a lobule) which empty into an intralobular collecting space. Each lobule is surrounded by a connective tissue layer (septum). Where the intralobular milk-collecting space joins the septum it narrows and passes through to become an interlobular duct (duct between lobules). A group of lobules are surrounded by a broader septum to constitute a lobe. The interlobular ducts empty into an interlobular milk-collecting space which is continued as an intralobar duct (duct within a lobe) as it passes through the septum. This duct continues in interlobar septa of connective tissue and is termed an interlobar duct (duct between lobes). A number of interlobar ducts join to form a milk-collecting space, the duct from which constitutes a galactophore that empties into the gland cistern (Fig. 11–2). The connective tissue of the udder is termed stroma and is white in color whereas the secretory tissue is orange in color and is called parenchyma.

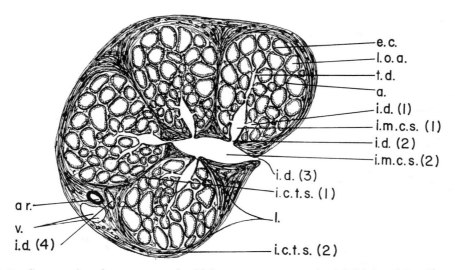

FIG. 11–2.—Cross-section of a mammary gland lobe.   *ar.*, artery; *v.*, vein; *i.d.* (*4*), interlobar duct; *i.c.t.s.* (*2*), interlobar connective tissue septum (*2*); *l.*, lobule; *i.c.t.s.* (*1*), interlobular connective tissue septum; *i.d.* (*3*), intralobar duct; *i.m.c.s.* (*2*), interlobar milk collecting space; *i.d.* (*2*), interlobular duct; *i.m.c.s.* (*1*), intralobular milk collecting space; *a.*, alveolus; *t.d.*, terminal duct; *l.o.a.*, lumen of alveolus; *e.c.*; epithelial cells. (*After Turner, 1939. The Comparative Anatomy of the Mammary Gland. Columbia, Mo., University Cooperative Store. Courtesy C. W. Turner.*)

II. UDDER GROWTH

A. Embryonic and Fetal Period

The secretory tissue of the mammary gland develops from the ectoderm and the first discernible evidence of mammary gland development is two parallel lines on the ventral surface, posterior to the umbilicus. The mammary lines consist of several layers of cells which are derived from the Malpighian layer of the ectoderm. These cells have a greater affinity for dye than adjacent ectodermal cells. At intervals on the mammary line further proliferation results in the formation of mammary buds, the number of which determines the number of glands that will develop. In cattle two mammary buds form in each line and they develop into the secretory tissue of a fore and rear quarter of the udder.

A downgrowth of the mammary bud into the mesenchyme (embryonic connective tissue) results in the formation of primary sprouts, the number of which determines the number of ducts in the mature teat. One primary sprout develops in cattle and sheep and two in swine and horses. At about the same time, mesenchymal cells surrounding the mammary bud proliferate rapidly and force the bud above the general body surface. Teats resulting from this type of activity are termed *proliferation* teats. *Canalization* (canal formation) of the primary sprout then occurs due to its increase in circumference, thus resulting in the formation of a *lumen* (space). A primary sprout is the antecedent of the streak canal, teat cistern, and gland cistern. Secondary sprouts grow out at angles from the primary sprout, canalize, and later divide into *tertiary* (third in order) sprouts. These sprouts are the *anlagen* (first discernible cells) of the duct system of the udder. At birth the duct system, in relation to the size of the udder, is limited indeed, being confined to a small area around the gland cistern. Although there is little growth of glandular tissue during pre-natal life nevertheless udder form in cattle is outlined 5 months after fertilization. Distinct differences in the shapes of udders can be observed in bovine embryos (Turner, 1930, 1931).

B. Birth to Puberty

In general udder development parallels increases in body weight. Development consists of an extension of the duct system, deposition of fat, and an increase in connective tissue. There is a greater development of the duct system in dairy calves than in breeds less highly developed for milk production (*i.e.* beef calves).

The glandular tissue in the udder of heifer calves can be palpated to identify the stage or stages of development and to determine the dimensions of these glands (Swett *et al.*, 1955). There is a highly significant correlation between palpation grade and body weight in heifer calves. If the extent of glandular tissue growth is to be used as a means of predicting potential producing capacity udder palpations should be made at 5 months of age for Holsteins and at 4 months of age for Jerseys. There is only slight growth of glandular tissue from birth to puberty in the lamb at which time it can be palpated.

C. Puberty to Conception

The glandular tissue undergoes cyclic changes during the estrous cycle which correspond to, but lag behind, those of the corpus luteum. In dairy heifers udder capacity increases approximately 0.4 lb. a month between 9 and 30 months of age. During these recurring estrous cycles there is growth of the duct system but no development of alveoli. Similar changes occur in the udder of other farm mammals.

D. Pregnancy

In cattle duct proliferation characterizes mammary growth during the first 3 months of pregnancy. During this time the proportion of glandular tissue to adipose tissue is small. Ducts grow out from interlobular ducts, replacing fatty tissue, to form eventually the lobule-alveolar system (Fig. 11–3). From the 3rd month on there is rapid growth of the lobule-alveolar system with greatest mitotic activity at mid pregnancy. Growth of alveoli is noted first near the gland cistern and large ducts with the peripheral (outer) region being the last to show alveolar growth.

PLATE · XXV

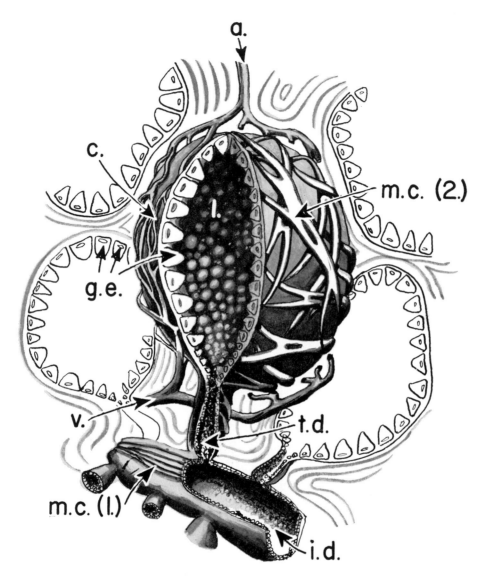

Diagram of capillaries and myoepithelial cells surrounding an alveolus. *a.*, arteriole; *c.*, capillary; *g.e.*, glandula r epithelium; *v.*, venule; *m.c. (1)*, duct wall with myoepithelial cell; *i.d.*, intralobular duct; *t.d.*, terminal duct; *l.*, lumen; *m.c. (2)*, myoepithelial cell. (*After Turner 1952. The Mammary Gland. I. The Anatomy of the Udder of Cattle and Domestic Animals. Columbia, Mo., Lucas Brothers. Courtesy C. W. Turner.*)

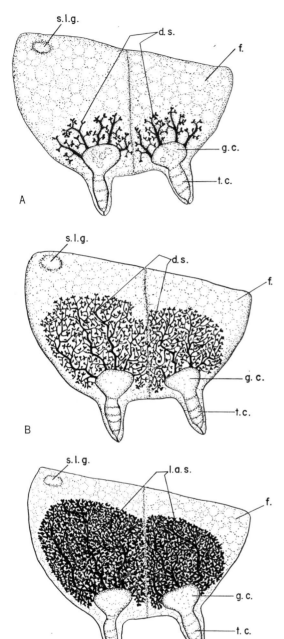

A

B

C

Fig. 11–3.—Schematic drawing of bovine udder. *A*, Prior to puberty: note limited development of duct system.

B, Prior to conception: note extent of duct development.

C, During pregnancy: note development of lobule-alveolar system. *s.l.g.*, supramammary lymph gland; *d.s.*, duct system; *l.a.s.*, lobule-alveolar system; *f.*, fat; *g.c.*, gland cistern; *t.c.*, teat cistern.

(*After Turner, 1939. The comparative Anatomy of the Mammary Gland. Columbia Mo., University Cooperative Store. Courtesy C. W. Turner.*)

Lobular outline is more definite by the 4th month and connective tissue increases in denseness. In the 5th month, although lobules are small they are definitely formed and the connective tissue contains numerous blood capillaries. The lobules increase greatly in size during the 6th month due to distension of alveoli with a honey-like secretion. During the last 3 months of gestation additional alveoli form, but at a reduced rate, and secretory activity of the alveolar epithelium increases. About 20 days prior to parturition there is further increase in secretory activity which accounts for the increase in udder size at this time. In the ewe most of the glandular development occurs during pregnancy and marked enlargement of the udder is usually associated with pending parturition.

E. Lactation

One must rely on studies conducted with laboratory mammals to answer the question: Is there an increase in the number of secretory cells during lactation? Mitotic figures are rarely seen in histological sections of mammary glands of lactating rats. When colchicine, however, is injected $9\frac{1}{2}$ hours prior to sacrifice cells that are dividing during this period are arrested in the metaphase stage. Using this technique a few mitotic figures can be observed up to 4 days after parturition but rarely thereafter. Deoxyribonucleic acid (DNA) content of mammary glands is used as an estimate of the total number of cells in mammary glands (Griffith & Turner, 1961). The DNA content of the mammary gland increases for 3 days following parturition and thereafter remains constant during lactation.

F. Neural Mechanisms

Growth of the mammary gland occurs in the absence of nerves to the gland. This is demonstrated when the gland is autotransplanted (transplanting to a part of the body tissue taken from another part of the same body), provided a procedure is employed whereby all nerves to the gland are severed. In goats, mammary glands grow almost normally following autotransplantation.

G. Hormonal Requirements

Duct System. Estrogens are the primary stimulators of duct growth, they being responsible for the more rapid growth of the duct system which occurs at puberty. Estrogen administration to ovariectomized animals will induce duct growth comparable to that in intact animals. Estrogens have a direct effect on the mammary gland as can be shown by applying estrogen to the skin of individual mammary glands which results in localized mammary growth provided the dosage is sufficiently low. Whether or not estrogens act indirectly on the mammary gland through the anterior pituitary remains to be ascertained.

Estrogens are noneffective in hypophysectomized animals (Reece *et al.*, 1936). Estrogen administered in conjunction with either prolactin or growth hormone will induce duct growth.

Lobule-alveolar System. Estrogen and progesterone, when injected in the proper ratio into ovariectomized mammals, will induce growth equal to that which occurs during pregnancy. In certain mammals (cow, goat, and guinea-pig) estrogen alone induces considerable lobule-alveolar growth whereas in others it stimulates none (mouse). Mammary growth does not occur in hypophysectomized animals following estrogen and progesterone administration. In order to induce mammary growth in hypophysectomized animals, equal to that which occurs during pregnancy, one must inject estrogen, progesterone, prolactin, and the growth hormone (Lyons, 1958).

III. INITIATION OF LACTATION

The function of the secretory cells of the mammary gland is the secretion of milk. Small quantities of milk can be secreted by an extensively developed duct system, however, appreciable amounts of milk are secreted only after the development of the lobule-alveolar system. Although there is a tremendous surge in secretory activity at the time of parturition, nevertheless there is activity prior to that time.

A. Secretory Activity Prior to and Following Parturition

The fluid in the udder during the early stages of gestation in first-calf heifers is similar to that before conception and the secretory activity of the gland appears to be confined to the duct system. Secretion in the udder at the 15th week of pregnancy in the cow is similar to that in the udder of either nulliparous heifers or heifers several weeks after conception. Casein can be detected in udders of heifers after 24 weeks of gestation but not before 20 weeks of pregnancy.

The secretory activity of the alveolar epithelium, which begins at mid-gestation, is characterized by a gradual change in shape of epithelial cells from cuboidal to columnar. Later on, the lumina of alveoli begin to fill, a process that results in the gradual expansion of the udder. The udder fluid is thick and viscous and has a high solids content which is chiefly protein. There is a gradual increase in secretory products which is followed by a striking increase 20 days before parturition.

Following parturition milk secretion increases rapidly, the rate of increase being greater in multiparous than in primiparous mammals. A 6-year old Jersey produced 50 lb. of milk on the 4th day of lactation. The amount of milk secreted per day usually increases for 2 to 4 weeks after parturition and many factors influence the length of time required to attain maximum production.

B. Neural Mechanism

It is essential to consider whether or not the secretory tissue of the mammary gland is innervated since either sensory or motor impulses could be factors in initiating lactation. Nerve fibers are limited to the stroma and blood vessels of the gland, none ending on the secretory epithelium. That normal nervous connections to the mammary gland are not essential for the initiation of lactation is indicated by experiments in which mammary glands were transplanted; after parturition secretion can be expressed from a transplanted mammary gland. Nevertheless the nervous system plays a role in the initiation of lactation.

Stimuli arising from suckling or milking are not required for the initiation of lactation since it occurs in animals not suckled or milked following parturition (Reece & Turner, 1937). Increasing quantities of prolactin (LTH) are released at the time of parturition and there is evidence that stimuli arising from the cervix can induce this release. Electrical stimulation of the cervix in the rat induces release of LTH since the corpora lutea become functional. Moreover, cervical stimulation initiates secretory activity in mammary glands of estrogen-primed rats.

C. Hormonal Requirements

The first evidence that the endocrine system is involved in the initiation of lactation appeared in 1928. The injection of an aqueous extract of the anterior pituitary induced lactation in rabbits pseudopregnant for 10 days. Extensive work on extraction, isolation, and purification of the active substance shows it to be distinct from other anterior pituitary hormones and is termed prolactin (LTH). Lactation can be induced in a large number of mammals, including heifers, by injecting either crude pituitary extracts or more highly purified LTH preparations.

Animals adrenalectomized during pregnancy may deliver normal litters but they rarely lactate sufficiently to raise them. The failure to lactate sufficiently is not due to a deficiency of pituitary LTH since adrenalectomy does not prevent the post-partum rise in pituitary LTH content.

The importance of the anterior pituitary in initiating lactation is indicated by experiments with hypophysectomized animals. In some animals hypophysectomized during pregnancy a transient milk secretion follows parturition, due to fetal anterior pituitary or placental hormones, but lactation is not initiated.

Thyroidectomy during pregnancy does not prevent the initiation of lactation following parturition. There is, however, a complete failure of lactation in goats thyro-parathyroidectomized during pregnancy. Insulin is the only factor in the pancreas necessary for the initiation of lactation.

Since lactation does not occur during pregnancy in primiparous animals it has been suggested that some factor(s) restrains lactation at this time. A number of concepts have been developed to account for this lack of lactation and the one that appears most attractive is presented. In the latter half of gestation the stimulus to the mammary gland to grow becomes less and less whereas the stimulus to secrete becomes greater and greater. Changes occur at parturition that result in a sudden increase in the stimulus to secrete whereas the stimulus to grow decreases. The removal of the stimulus to grow is not sufficient to initiate lactation since ovariectomy at the end of pseudopregnancy (rat and rabbit) is not followed by lactation. The anterior pituitary discharges factors which are essential for the initiation of lactation since it does not occur in hypophysectomized animals. Some stimulus around the time of parturition brings about the discharge of these pituitary factors (LTH and ACTH).

Hormonal Induction of Lactation. The injection or pellet implants of estrogen, estrogen and testosterone propionate, or estrogen and progesterone will induce growth of secretory tissue and initiate lactation. The quantity of milk secreted varies from negligible amounts to quantities that would be considered normal following parturition. The response of nulliparous animals, for unknown reasons, is more consistent than that of multiparous ones.

IV. MAINTENANCE OF LACTATION

Milk production increases rapidly following parturition, reaches a peak in 2 to 4 weeks where it remains for a short period of time, and then gradually declines. In the rising segment of the lactation curve the increase in milk yield becomes less and less. After maximum milk production is passed the decline in yield is exponential, *i.e.*, the decline in milk production in unit time is a constant percentage of the previous production of unit time.

Many factors influence the shape of the lactation curve. After the 5th month of gestation pregnant cows decline more rapidly in milk production than do non-pregnant cows. Dairy cows normally milk for 10 to 12 months yet there is a report of one cow that lactated for 5 consecutive years following parturition. There is need for a better understanding of the factors that make a prolonged lactation possible.

A. Neural Mechanisms

The nervous system plays an important role in the maintenance of lactation. Stimuli arising from either suckling or milking bring about the release of LTH, ACTH, and the milk let-down hormones, oxytocin and vaso-pressin. Hence nervous stimuli make available factors required for milk synthesis and milk removal from the udder.

Motor impulses are conveyed by the inguinal nerve to the blood vascular system and teats of the udder. Stimulation, by induced electrical current, of the inguinal nerve produces a marked contraction of the teats and a marked vasoconstriction but milk let-down is not induced. Vasoconstriction reduces blood flow to the udder and in this manner influences milk synthesis and milk let-down.

B. Hormonal Requirements

Anterior Pituitary. The anterior pituitary gland is essential for lactation, *i.e.*, hormones of the gland must be available before the epithelial cells of the mammary gland can synthesize milk. Removal of the pituitary gland in lactating animals results in the immediate cessation of lactation. In order to maintain lactation in hypophysectomized animals one must inject LTH and ACTH. LTH acts directly on the alveolar epithelium whereas ACTH probably acts by maintaining the necessary levels of milk precursors in the blood. If the posterior lobe is removed along with the anterior lobe then one must inject oxytocin in conjunction with LTH and ACTH in order to maintain lactation.

Other hormones of the anterior pituitary influence the level of milk production but they are not considered essential for lactation. STH is a galactopoietic agent (enhances established lactation) and undoubtedly the amount of TSH released influences the level of milk production.

Adrenal Cortex. Lactation ceases or is greatly impaired following adrenalectomy of lactating animals. In order to maintain lactation in adrenalectomized animals it is necessary to administer an adrenal steroid that influences protein and carbohydrate metabolism and an adrenal steroid that influences electrolyte metabolism. Lactation can be maintained in the adrenalectomized goat by implanting pellets of cortisone acetate and deoxycorticosterone acetate.

Thyroid. The thyroid gland is not essential for lactation since it continues, although at a lower level, in thyroidectomized animals. Milk yields can be restored to normal levels in thyroidectomized animals and augmented in intact ones by either injecting or feeding L-thyroxine and by feeding thyroprotein (active substance is thyroxine). Indeed it is possible to increase maximum daily milk production in dairy cattle by feeding thyroprotein and additional grain.

Parathyroids. There is a greatly increased demand for calcium during lactation and it is possible that the parathyroids are essential for optimal milk yield. There is an increase in weight of the parathyroids during lactation in rabbits and parathyroidectomy depressed lactation in the rat almost as much as thyro-parathyroidectomy. There is a lack of udder development and complete failure of lactation in goats thyro-parathyroidectomized during pregnancy.

Pancreas. The hormonal factor in the pancreas required for the maintenance of lactation is insulin since lactation is maintained in pancreatectomized bitches receiving adequate amounts of insulin. The administration of large doses of insulin to lactating cows lowers blood sugar and milk yield whereas small doses have a galactopoietic effect.

V. MILK SECRETION

A. Cytological Aspects

The secretory cycle of the epithelial cells of the mammary gland is similar to that of secretory cells in general. After suckling or milking, lumina of alveoli are relatively free of milk, the alveolar epithelium appears to be folded, and the epithelial cells are cuboidal in shape and devoid of secretion. With milk biosynthesis, the epithelial cells become columnar as secretory products accumulate in the apical (the top) region. Prior to suckling alveoli are distended with milk and secretory cells are low cuboidal and free of secretory products.

That the *Golgi apparatus* is involved in the secretory process is suggested by several observations. The amount of Golgi material varies with the secretory intensity of the epithelial cells. It decreases in size when suckling is suspended and it fragments following weaning. Other cytoplasmic structures are demonstrable and they undoubtedly participate in the secretory process.

Fat droplets, which are about 4 μ in diameter and highly *osmiophilic* (affinity for osmic acid), appear either in the region of the Golgi apparatus or in the ergastoplasmic zone. It is thought that protein granules are formed in the *ergastoplasm* (substance disposed in the cytoplasmic matrix in a fibrillar form) and then accumulate in the Golgi apparatus. The electron microscope reveals protein granules within smooth-walled vacuoles approximately 150 $m\mu$ in diameter and which are less osmiophilic than fat droplets.

B. Milk Biosynthesis

Milk biosynthesis occurs during the milking interval, *i.e.*, between milkings or suckling bouts. Intramammary pressure is zero following a complete milking and for 1 to 2 hours thereafter. It increases very slowly and then more rapidly as the milking interval lengthens. The secretion of milk is more rapid after milking and the average secretion rate after an 8-hour interval is greater than it is after a 12-hour interval.

Milk is formed from blood constituents, some of which exist in milk in the same form as they do in blood. On the other hand some milk constituents are synthesized by the glandular epithelium. Undoubtedly enzymatic action plays an important part in the biosynthesis of milk. Milk can be considered as an emulsion of fat in a colloidal solution of protein with crystalloids in true solution. Two milk constituents, casein and lactose, are not found elsewhere in the body and glyceride combinations of milk fat are peculiar to it. It has been estimated that about 450 volumes of blood are required to produce one volume of milk.

Carbohydrate. Milk sugar, lactose, consists of 1 molecule of glucose plus 1 molecule of galactose minus 1 molecule of water. The mammary gland takes up sufficient glucose to account for lactose formation, however, glucose is also used for other purposes by the gland. About 80 per cent of lactose carbon originates from either blood glucose or substances which can be changed rapidly to glucose.

Fat. Although milk fat can be affected by dietary fat, nevertheless the cow is not dependent on dietary fat for the production of milk fat since she can use carbohydrates and proteins for such purposes. It has been estimated that around 25 per cent of fatty acids in milk is derived from dietary fat.

The milk of herbivores is especially rich in short-chain fatty acids (C_4 to C_{14}) and there is evidence that these acids result from condensation of C_2 chains. For the biosynthesis of short-chain fatty acids in the mammary gland acetate appears to be the primary source of carbon in ruminants and glucose in non-ruminants.

Protein. Casein and β-lactoglobulin make up about 90 per cent of the protein nitrogen in cow's milk. A very large proportion of the essential amino acids of casein and β-lactoglobulin is derived from essential amino acids in the blood. Fifty to 90 per cent of the non-essential amino acids of casein and β-lactoglobulin comes from the same free amino acids of the blood and less than 20 per cent of certain non-essential amino acids is synthesized in the mammary gland from blood glucose. There is also evidence that a-lactalbumin is synthesized in the gland, the process being similar to that for casein and β-lactoglobulin.

It is believed that most of the globulin fraction of colostrum is synthesized by plasma cells in the mammary gland from free amino acids of the blood. On the other hand milk globulin and milk serum albumin are derived directly from the blood.

VI. MILK DISCHARGE

From the Cell. Fat droplets secreted in the ergastoplasm accumulate in the apical region of the cell and leave the cell surrounded by a double cytoplasmic membrane. The fat droplet is discharged from the cell by a process of constriction without exposure of the cytoplasm. Vacuoles containing protein granules, appear to collect in the apical region of the cell and open under the cell membrane. The fat and protein, along with other substances, are taken up by water to constitute milk; fat droplets appearing as an emulsion of fat globules in a colloidal solution of protein.

From the Gland. In order for most of the milk to be removed from the mammary gland there must be an increase in intramammary pressure and the teat orifice must be opened. When there is a sudden increase in intramammary pressure it is said that milk has been *let-down*. At this time most of the milk in the gland is available to the young. The teat orifice is opened by creating a vacuum at the end of the teat by suckling.

In milk let-down both the nervous and endocrine systems are involved. Sensory impulses arising from various stimuli are conveyed by diffused afferent pathways directly to the hypothalamus. The hypothalamus in turn, via nerve fibers to the posterior lobe of the pituitary gland, brings about the release of oxytocin and vasopressin. These two hormones are transported to the udder by the blood where they stimulate contraction of the myoepithelial cells. These contractions increase intramammary pressure, forcing milk from lumina of alveoli and terminal ducts into large ducts, thus making most of the milk available to the young.

When an animal becomes frightened after milk let-down intramammary pressure decreases and it is not possible to remove normal quantities of milk from the udder. This is the result of epinephrine being released from the medulla of the adrenal glands which causes vasoconstriction, thus reducing the amount of blood available to the udder. The end result is an insufficient quantity of oxytocin and vasopressin to maintain myoepithelial cells in a contracted state.

VII. INVOLUTION OF SECRETORY TISSUE

In a disease-free mammary gland the secretory tissue remains intact as long as milk is regularly removed and sufficient

LTH is released from the anterior pituitary to stimulate the alveolar cells to secrete. When the amount of LTH released is insufficient to stimulate all alveolar cells to secrete then there is a gradual loss of these cells. The mammary glands of lactating and pregnant animals do not *involute* (loss of secretory tissue) to any great extent since there is little mitotic activity in glands of such animals. If involution were extensive there would have to be extensive cellular division to supply epithelial cells for the subsequent lactation period.

Alveoli involute in non-pregnant animals following the removal of the suckling or milking stimulus. After involution the mammary gland is similar to that of a nulliparous animal; however, the duct system may be somewhat more ramified following involution than it is in a nulliparous animal. This slight difference in mammary tissue can be accounted for by the fact that some duct growth occurs during the first part of gestation. When the suckling or milking stimulus is removed LTH is no longer released from the anterior pituitary and this accounts for the loss of alveoli. The injection of LTH into lactating animals from which the young have been removed maintains the lobule-alveolar system of the mammary gland.

There is need for a more complete understanding of factors controlling the growth and secretory intensity of epithelial cells of the mammary gland. Much work remains to be done in order to determine the optimum level of milk production in farm mammals.

REFERENCES

GRIFFITH, D. R. & TURNER, C. W. (1961). Normal growth of rat mammary gland during pregnancy and early lactation. *Proc. Soc. Exp. Biol. & Med.,* **106**, 448–450.

LINZELL, J. L. & MOUNT, L. E. (1955). Variations in the direction of venous blood-flow in the mammary region of the sheep and goat. *Nature,* **176**, 37.

LYONS, W. R. (1958). Hormonal synergism in mammary growth. *Proc. Roy. Soc. B.,* **149**, 303–325.

REECE, R. P., & TURNER, C. W. (1937). The lactogenic and thyrotropic hormone content of the pituitary gland. *Mo. Agric. Exp. Sta. Res. Bull.* No. 266.

REECE, R. P., TURNER, C. W. & HILL, R. T. (1936). Mammary gland development in the hypophysectomized albino rat. *Proc. Soc. Exp. Biol. & Med.,* **34**, 204–207.

ST. CLAIR, L. E. (1942). The nerve supply to the bovine mammary gland. *Am. J. Vet. Res.,* **3**, 10–16.

SWETT, W. W., BOOK, J. H., MATTHEWS, C. A., & FOHRMAN, M. H. (1955). Evaluation of mammary-gland development in Holstein and Jersey calves as a measure of potential producing capacity. *U.S.D.A. Tech. Bull.* 1111.

TUCKER, H. A., REECE, R. P. & MATHER, R. E. (1961). Udder capacity estimates as affected by rate of milk secretion and intramammary pressure. *J. Dairy Sci.,* **44**, 1725–1733.

TURNER, C. W. (1930). The anatomy of the mammary gland of cattle. I. Embryonic development. *Mo. Agric. Exp. Sta. Bull. No.* 140

—————— (1931). The anatomy of the mammary gland of cattle. II. Fetal development. *Mo. Agric. Exp. Sta. Bull. No.* 160.

QUESTIONS

1. (a) What is the most serious defect in the udder of cattle?
   (b) Where are supernumerary teats located in: cattle; sheep; and swine?
2. (a) What are the secretory units of the udder?
   (b) Distinguish between a lobule and a lobe. Draw diagrams.
3. (a) Define the term "mammary gland." Is there growth of the duct system of the mammary gland from birth to puberty?
   (b) When does the lobule-alveolar system develop?
4. Are nerves to the mammary gland necessary for mammary growth?
5. What is the primary stimulator of mammary duct growth?
6. Following ovariectomy what hormones would you inject in order to stimulate lobule-alveolar growth of the mammary gland?
7. (a) What is the role of the nervous system in the initiation of lactation?
   (b) What is the contribution of the anterior pituitary in the initiation of lactation?
8. (a) What anterior pituitary hormones are essential for the maintenance of lactation? Is the thyroid hormone essential for lactation?
   (b) What brings about the release of LTH for the anterior pituitary?
9. (a) When does milk biosynthesis occur?
   (b) What blood constituents are utilized by the mammary gland in synthesizing: lactose; milk fat; and casein?
10. Define milk let-down. What factors are operating in bringing about milk let-down?

Chapter 12

Reproductive Physiology in Poultry

By J. E. PARKER

THE physiology of reproduction in domestic poultry differs from that of mammals in a number of important respects, among them being the development of the progeny outside the body of the dam made possible by the inclusion of a large amount of yolk within the egg, the maturation and ovulation of a single egg day after day, the development of only the left ovary and oviduct in the female, the absence of a true penis and of counterparts to the mammalian male accessory reproductive glands, and the capacity of avian sperm to retain their fertilizing capacity for weeks within the reproductive tract of the female.

Since over 95 per cent of the income from domestic poultry is from chickens and turkeys the content of this chapter is limited primarily to these two species. Wherever information based on other species is included, the species is indicated. The chapter is divided into four principal sections. The first two, which constitute the major part, are concerned with *reproductive physiology* in the male and in the female fowl, the third with *sexual behavior*, and the last with *fertilization* of the egg and subsequent *pre-oviposital embryonic development*.

(206)

I. THE MALE FOWL

A. The Reproductive Organs

The reproductive system consists of paired testes with epididymides, two vasa deferentia or sperm ducts and the *copulatory apparatus* which is very dissimilar to the mammalian penis (Plate XXVI). The male fowl does not have counterparts to prostate, Cowper's glands, and vesicular glands which are the accessory glands in mammalian males, but avian semen from the vas deferens is diluted with fluid from *vascular bodies* located near the posterior ends of the vasa deferentia. Fowls also differ from farm mammals in that the testes remain in the body cavity, never descending into an external scrotum.

The testes are bean-shaped and are suspended on both sides of the vertebral column just below the anterior end of the kidneys. In mature males the testes are partially surrounded by the thin membranes of the posterior thoracic air sacs. The testes are usually creamy white in color, although in some cases they may be partially or entirely black. In heavy breeds the testis of sexually active adults averages 15 to 20 gm. and in egg-type breeds about 10 to 15 gm. in weight. Testes of sexually active turkey males are about the same size as those from heavy breed chicken males. The testes within one male are not often the same size, but neither the right nor left is consistently larger than the other. Located on the dorso-medial surface of each testis is the epididymis which is small or rudimentary in comparison with other farm animals.

The testis is made up of thousands of seminiferous tubules which contain germ cells in the several stages of spermatogenesis (Plate XXVI). The sperm are in clusters with their heads attached to the Sertoli cells and their tails projecting into the tubule lumina. The intertubular spaces contain blood vessels and the interstitial cells which, in the sexually active adult, are very scant. The testis is enclosed by the thin tunica albuginea.

The vasa deferentia are convoluted ducts extending from the epididymides to the cloaca and are located on each side of the vertebral column. As the ducts continue posteriorly their diameters increase noticeably, and where they enter the wall of the *cloaca* they become up to 3.5 mm. in diameter in chicken males. Much of this enlargement of the lower vas is due to an increase in the thickness of the walls, especially the musculature. Histologically the avian vas deferens is somewhat similar to that of the mammal, one difference being that the longitudinal and circular muscle fibers are not organized into definite layers. The vas deferens transports sperm from the testis and epididymis to the copulatory apparatus and also acts as a reservoir for semen. More detailed information on the histology of the avian reproduction system is described by Gray (1937).

The copulatory apparatus of the male chicken and turkey consists of two *papillae* and the *rudimentary copulatory organ* (Plate XXVI). The papillae, each with a lumen through which semen is emitted, are the posterior terminations of the vasa deferentia and are located in the ventral floor of the cloaca. Slightly posterior to the papillae is the rudimentary copulatory organ. In the duck and goose this latter organ is well developed and erectile in nature, but as in the chicken there is no lumen in it. It is the rudimentary copulatory organ that is observed in determining the sex of day-old chicks and turkey poults by the Japanese or vent inspection method.

B. Sexual Development and Spermatogenesis

While many wild birds and some domestic fowls do not produce sperm until they are about a year old, chickens and turkeys attain sexual maturity at considerably younger ages because they have been bred and selected for early sexual maturity due to its economic importance.

From time of hatching the growth rate of chicken testes is relatively greater than body growth—the combined testes weight being about 0.02 per cent of body weight at hatching and about 1.0 per cent of adult body weight (Parker, 1949). The testes grow slowly during the first 8 to 10 weeks but thereafter their growth is accelerated. In Leghorns and other egg-type breeds the testes attain mature weights generally at 24 to 26 weeks of age whereas most of the heavier breeds will require 1 to 3 weeks longer. Periods of fastest comb growth tend to coincide with the periods of fastest testis growth (Fig. 12–1). As with the testes, combs of egg-breed males develop faster than those of the heavier breeds; breed differences in rate of comb growth show up as early as 4 weeks of age. Males with the fastest growing combs fertilize hens at younger ages than males with a slower rate of comb development, but there is evidence that there is no difference in their fertilizing capacity after both groups have attained full sexual maturity.

At the time of hatching the male chick has spermatogonia within the relatively indistinct seminiferous tubules of the testis. There appear to be 4 rather distinct stages of spermatogenesis according to Kumaran & Turner (1949). During the first 5 weeks the tubules become more organized or distinct in outline and multiplication of the single basal layer of spermatogonia occurs. The second stage begins with the appearance of primary spermatocytes at about 6 weeks of age and continues for 2 to 3 weeks. At this

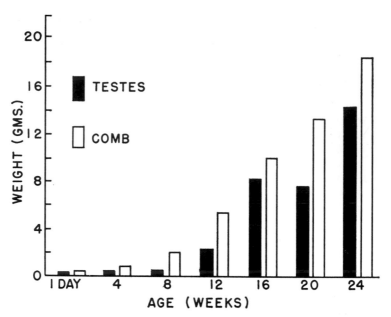

Fig. 12–1.—Growth of testes and combs of White Leghorn cockerels. Testes weights are for both testes. Note the close relationship between testis and comb growth. (*Redrawn from Parker et al., 1942. Poult. Sci., 21, 35.*)

stage there is a layer of primary spermatocytes upon the basal layer of spermatogonia. In the third stage, commencing with the 10th week, secondary spermatocytes appear as a result of the meiotic (reduction) division of the primary spermatocytes. During the fourth stage, which begins at about 12 weeks of age, the secondary spermatocytes divide into spermatids which subsequently metamorphose into sperm. Spermatids and mature sperm are observed in tubules of most males by 20 weeks. Great growth in the length of the seminiferous tubules occurs during this stage. While the above are representative ages for the several stages of spermatogenesis in one breed of chickens, White Rocks, the ages of these stages vary with different strains, breeds and species of poultry.

In some very precocious individuals sperm appear as early as 8 to 9 weeks and semen has been collected from males only 10 to 12 weeks old. However, satisfactory volumes of semen and satisfactory fertility in natural matings do not occur usually until the males are 22 to 26 weeks of age. There is considerable variation among breeds and individuals in this respect.

The testes of turkey males approach maximum weights at about 7 months at which age semen is being produced and reasonable fertility can be expected; however, some early maturing individuals produce semen as early as 5 months of age. The growth and functional development of the turkey testes are more greatly influenced by season than are those of chickens. Testes of spring hatched turkeys often regress in size and activity during the decreasing day lengths of the fall and winter unless the males are exposed to additional artificial light.

C. Sperm and Semen of Domestic Fowls

Sperm of domestic fowls are dissimilar in shape to those of other farm animals in that they have long cylindrical heads equipped with pointed acrosomes (Plate XXVI). The head, midpiece and tail of avian sperms measure approximately 15, 4 and 80 μ, respectively, in length; the entire length being about 100 μ. The head and midpiece are about 0.5 μ in diameter and the tail considerably less. Electron microscope studies show that the acrosome is composed of two parts, an apical spine

PLATE XXVI

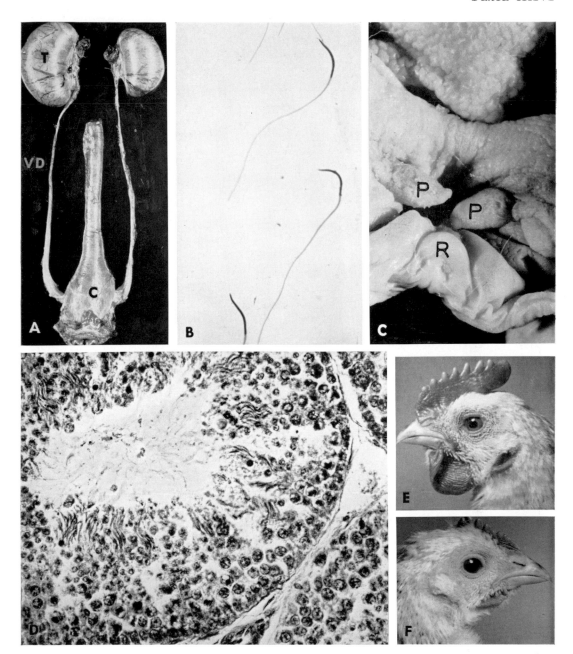

A, Reproductive organs of the male domestic chicken. The vas deferens (VD) leads from the testis (T) to the cloaca (C) ($\times$ 0.48).

B, Sperm from the domestic chicken showing the slender cylindrical head with pointed acrosome ($\times$ 600).

C, Copulatory apparatus located in the posterior ventral cloaca of the male chicken showing papillae (P) and the rudimentary copulatory organ (R) ($\times$ 5.6).

D, Seminiferous tubule of a cock showing the several stages of spermatogenesis. Note the group of interstitial cells at lower center ($\times$ 440).

E & F, Showing the effect of male hormone on comb growth of 5-week old Delaware chicks. F was untreated and E was treated with testosterone propionate ($\times$ 0.55).

(Photos A, B, D, from Parker et al., 1952. Mo. Agric. Expt. Sta. Res. Bull. No. 347. Photo C from Taylor, L. W. 1949. Fertility and Hatchability in Chicken and Turkey Eggs, New York, Courtesy of John Wiley. Photos E & F courtesy of Ore. Agric. Expt. Sta.)

PLATE XXVII

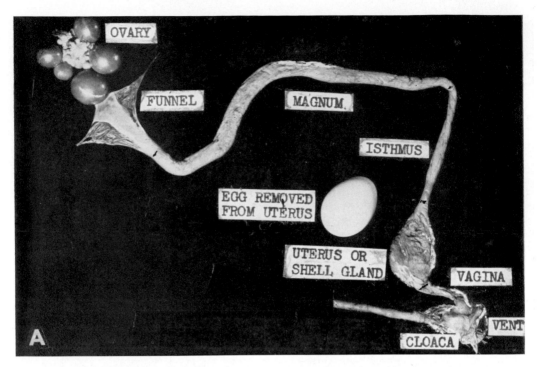

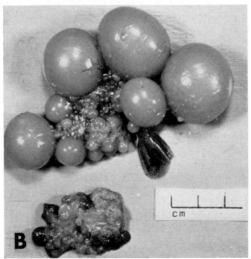

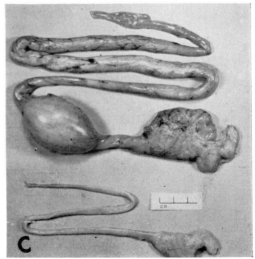

A, Reproductive organs of a laying chicken hen. Note the stigma on the largest follicle next to the funnel of the oviduct ($\times$ 0.25).

B, Showing the effect of hypophysectomy on the ovary of the avian female. Top picture shows the active ovary of a normal chicken hen and below is the ovary of an hypophysectomized hen 6 days after the operation. ($\times$ 0.70).

C, Oviducts of laying hen (top) and of hypophysectomized hen 6 days after operation (bottom) ($\times$ 0.38).

(Photo A courtesy of Tenn. Agric. Expt. Sta. Photos B & C from Opel & Nalbandov. 1961. Proc. Soc. Exp. Biol. & Med. 107, 233.

and its conical axial cap covering; and that the axial filament contains 11 fibrils (Grigg & Hodge, 1949). Also in contrast with mammalian sperm there is no helically wound cord surrounding the axial filament in the tail (see Chapter 3). Those interested in species variations in morphology and in the spermatogenesis of avian sperm are referred to the review of Romanoff (1960).

1. SEMEN CHARACTERISTICS

Semen from domestic fowls varies from a dense opaque suspension to a watery fluid, the relative sperm density being positively correlated with the opaqueness and viscosity of the sample. Chicken semen is white in color, unless contaminated, whereas turkey semen often has a brownish or yellowish color. Semen in the vas deferens is composed of sperm plus secretions from the seminiferous tubules, the epididymis and the vas deferens itself. However, in collecting semen, especially by the abdominal massage technique, it is mixed with secretions of the lymph folds and vascular bodies in the cloaca, and it may be contaminated to varying degrees by urates, feces or blood depending upon the excitability of the males and the experience of the person ejaculating them.

In comparison with farm mammals the volumes of semen ejaculated by chickens and turkeys is small but the concentration of sperm in the semen is high (Table 12–1). Semen volumes vary with the breed or

species of fowls and with the method of collection, volumes being greater when obtained by the massage technique than when intercepted during natural mating. Males of the egg-type breeds of chickens such as Leghorns generally produce smaller volumes when massaged than those shown in the table, averaging about two-thirds as much or about 0.6 ml. per ejaculate. It is surprising that turkey males which are 3 to 4 times as heavy in body weight as the chicken males produce less than half as much semen. With both chickens and turkeys many apparently normal matings are incomplete. No semen is obtained by interception in 14 to 32 per cent of natural matings in chickens. Chicken males have been observed to mate with as many as 35 to 40 females per day, but less than a third of the females were fertilized.

Turkey semen contains a higher concentration of sperm per unit volume than that of chickens—usually more than twice as many. Sperm counts of 8 to 11 million sperm per mm.^{3} are not unusual in turkeys. Because of this high concentration the total number of sperm per ejaculate from turkeys compares favorably with the number from chickens when ejaculates are obtained by the massage technique. The average intercepted ejaculate from the chicken male contains slightly less than a billion sperm.

Abnormal types of sperm are common in the semen of both chickens and turkeys (Fig. 12–2). Sperm with coiled, broken and missing tails are the most common abnormal

Table 12–1.—Some Semen Characteristics of Chickens and Turkeys

(Chicken data from Parker et al., 1942. Mo. Agric. Exp. Sta. Res. Bull. No. 347; turkey data from Parker, 1946, Poult. Sci., 25, 65.)

Species and method of collection	Volume (ml.)	Sperm concentration per mm.^{3} of semen (millions)	No. of Sperm per ejaculate (billions)
Chicken			
Intercepted	0.36	3.1	0.9
	(.05 to 1)*	(0 to 10)	(0 to 5.3)
Massage	0.88	3.4	3.3
	(.3 to 1.5)	(.03 to 11)	(.01 to 15)
Turkey			
Massage	0.33	8.4	2.8
	(.2 to .5)	(3.6 to 13)	(1.3 to 5.4)

* Figures in ( ) are ranges.

14

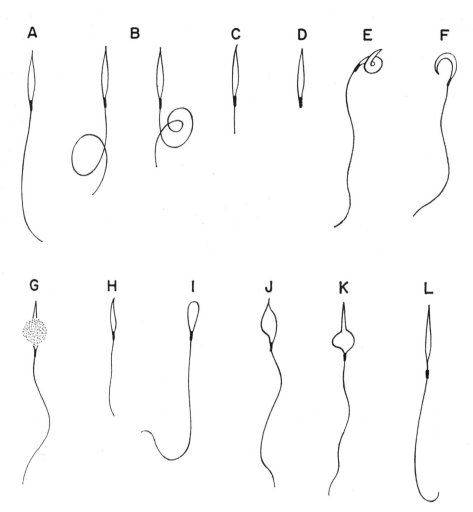

Fig. 12–2.—Types of abnormal sperms in cock semen. Deformities of the tail occur more frequently than those of the head. *A*, Normal. *B*, Coiled tail. *C*, Broken tail. *D*, Tailless. *E*, Coiled head. *F*, Hooked head. *G*, Ruptured head. *H*, Small. *I*, Blunt head. *J*, Swollen head. *K*, Balloon head. *L*, Filiform midpiece. (*Redrawn from Parker et al., 1942. Mo. Agric. Exp. Sta. Res. Bull. No. 347.*)

types and appear in 80 to 90 per cent of all ejaculates. Deformities of the head are less common. In most ejaculates the percentages of abnormal sperm range from 5 to 20 per cent (Parker *et al.*, 1942).

Fresh semen is usually slightly alkaline— the average in pH ranging from 7.0 to 7.6. In storage the pH decreases with increase in temperature and time.

Relatively little is known about the biochemistry of avian semen. The glucose or fructose level of chicken and turkey semen is low. This is particularly true of semen taken from the vas deferens and free from *transudates* from blood sometimes occurring in ejaculates obtained by the massage technique. In contrast to mammals, Lake *et al.*, (1958) found no citric acid in chicken semen and determined that the average concentration (mg./100 ml.) of sodium was 393; potassium, 43; calcium, 8; chloride, 205; creatine, 92; ascorbic acid, 3; ergothionine, 2; and glutamate, 1033. Avian semen also contains small amounts of zinc and copper and traces of other amino acids in addition to glutamic acid. For information on the metabolism of avian sperm see Lorenz (1959).

2. Motility of Sperm

Microscopic examinations of ejaculates show that only in exceptional cases are sperm non-motile. A high percentage of ejaculates, usually over 80, shows vigorous motility. Avian sperm are motile over a wide range of temperature—from a low of 2°C. to a high of 43°C.—the movement increasing with an increase in temperature. Sperm cooled no lower than 2°C. regain their initial motility when rewarmed, but motility is permanently lost after several hours exposure to temperatures of around 40°C. Although chicken and turkey sperm remain motile *in vitro* at refrigerator temperatures for 3 to 5 days generally, and in exceptional instances for 15 to 24 days, this motility is not associated with fertilizing capacity since the sperm usually lose their fertilizability in only a few hours under such conditions. Sperm seem to maintain their motility longer in an environment that is neutral to slightly alkaline, although good motility has been maintained at pH ranges of 6.5 to 8.

3. Maturation of Sperm

After the sperm are formed in the seminiferous tubules they pass through the epididymal ducts and the vas deferens before being ejaculated. As with mammals avian sperm undergo a maturing or ripening process as they pass through these excurrent ducts during which they acquire the ability to fertilize eggs. Sperm taken directly from the cut testis and artificially inseminated into hens resulted in practically no fertility, whereas sperm taken from the epididymis fertilized 19 per cent and those taken from the lower vas deferens fertilized 65 per cent of the eggs laid (Munro, 1938). Motility of sperm taken from these locations shows an increase corresponding to fertilizing capacity. Sperm pass from the testis to the lower vas deferens in as short a time as 24 hours. Chicken sperm remain motile for as long as 4 weeks when forced to remain in the vas deferens by ligating both ends of the duct. Removal of the testes does not influence the duration of sperm motility in the ligated ducts indicating that the testis hormone, androgen, does not preserve the length of life of sperm in the avian vas. In

mammals injected androgen extends the life or motility of sperm stored in the epididymis.

D. Hormones Related to Reproduction in the Male

Besides producing sperm the other principal function of the testis is to produce and secrete the male hormone, androgen. The bulk of the evidence shows that the hormone is secreted by the Leydig cells in the intertubular tissue and not by the seminiferous tubules. Rate of androgen secretion increases as the testes grow and, as pointed out already, there is a high correlation between testis size and comb size in developing cockerels. The immature male chicken's comb is a secondary sex organ and is so sensitive to androgen that it has long been used to assay the potency of androgenic substances (Table 12–2 & Plate XXVI). Following *caponization* (castration) the comb atrophies but its growth can be stimulated by feeding or injection of androgen, the degree of growth recovery being proportional to the dose of the hormone used.

Table 12–2. Effect of Feeding Methyl Testosterone on the Comb Growth of Delaware × New Hampshire Chicks to 4 Weeks of Age

(Parker & Arscott, 1962. Unpublished data, Ore. Agric. Exp. Sta.)

Treatment	Comb weights (mg.)	
	Males	Females
Controls	480	95
Methyl-testosterone 20 mg./lb. feed	1484	920
% increase due to hormone feeding	209	868

In addition to comb growth androgen controls other secondary sexual characteristics such as crowing in chickens, and gobbling, strutting and the development of the *snood* and *caruncles* in turkeys. Male-type sexual activity also is influenced by androgen; copulatory actions can be induced by it in either chicks or turkey poults at only a few weeks of age. Social rank or *peck order* in chickens of both sexes is related to the rate of androgen secretion. Caponization of male chickens results in loss of social rank which can be restored by androgen injections.

The avian testis is stimulated into growth and activity by the FSH and LH from the pituitary. In contrast with farm mammals there is substantial evidence that in the fowl either avian LH is different or that two LH-like hormones are involved. Nalbandov and his associates have shown that mammalian LH stimulates the already

otherwise it has a depressing effect brought about by a reduction in gonadotropic hormone output. Similarly, injections of either estrogen or prolactin depress spermatogenesis by reducing the output of gonadotropic hormones.

Since the growth and development of both the seminiferous tubules and the interstitial cells are controlled by hormones from the pituitary, hypophysectomy results in the interruption of spermatogenesis and causes testicular atrophy. Injection of

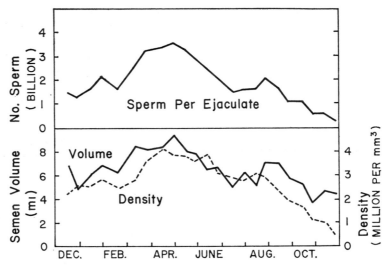

Fig. 12–3.—Seasonal variation in semen characteristics. Influence of season on volume and sperm density of semen and total numbers of sperm produced by RIR chicken males. (Tennessee, U.S.A., latitude 36°N. *Adapted from Parker & McSpadden, 1943. Poult. Sci., 22, 143.*)

formed interstitial Leydig cells of the cock to secrete androgen, but it lacks the factor contained in avian pituitary extracts that is necessary for the formation of new Leydig cells. Comb growth of hypophysectomized cocks can be induced only temporarily with mammalian LH, after which comb size regresses; however, comb growth can be maintained indefinitely with chicken pituitaries.

The growth of the testes and the seminiferous tubules is stimulated by FSH from the pituitary. LH, by controlling androgen production, indirectly contributes to complete spermatogenesis. Androgen in small doses stimulates spermatogenesis if the testes are already producing this hormone and if secondary spermatocytes are present,

adequate levels of cortisone stimulates spermatogenesis but adrenalin, at least in chickens, has a depressing effect. Feeding of thyroid at low levels increases testis weight and stimulates spermatogenesis, whereas thiouracil, which depresses the thyroid, decreases the number and fertilizing capacity of sperm. For a comprehensive report on the hormones influencing reproduction in birds, including wild species, the reader is referred to Parkes & Marshall (1960).

E. Factors Affecting Spermatogenesis and Semen Production

By stimulating the pituitary to increase

its output of gonadotropic hormones artificial light has a pronounced influence on spermatogenesis in fowls. Increasing daily light periods stimulates spermatogenesis whereas decreasing light periods has an opposite effect. Increments or decrements in the daily light periods are more important than the actual lengths of the light periods. Although there is evidence that a minimum of 12 hours of daily light is required for maximum testis growth and spermatogenesis, chicken males mature sexually and produce semen capable of fertilizing eggs on as little as 1 to 3 hours of light daily. After exposure to light for prolonged periods, even when

tion in both chickens and turkeys varies seasonally. With chickens in the northern hemisphere semen volume, sperm density and total sperm ejaculated increase from December through April and then decrease during the late spring and summer (Fig. 12–3). Sperm production in turkeys also is highest in the spring months. Many turkey males become completely aspermic or infertile during the subsequent late summer and fall months.

Environmental temperatures also affect sperm production; however, within normal ranges their effects are less dramatic than those of light. Spermatogenesis commences

Table 12–3.—Effect of Frequency of Collection by the Massage Technique on Semen Characteristics from Male Chickens

(Adapted from Parker et al., 1942, Mo. Agric. Exp. Sta. Res. Bull. No. 347.)

Interval between collections (days)	Av. volume per ejaculate (ml.)	Av. number of sperm per mm.³ semen (millions)	Av. number of sperm per ejaculate (billions)
$\frac{1}{4}$	0.80	0.53	0.49
$\frac{1}{2}$	0.70	0.80	0.55
1	0.75	2.36	1.74
2	0.87	3.85	3.33
3	1.20	3.85	4.65
8	0.98	4.54	5.34

the days are artificially lengthened, sperm production in both chickens and turkeys eventually decreases. Whether this refractoriness to light stimulation is due to exhaustion of the gonad-stimulating mechanism or to the inability of the testes to respond to the pituitary hormones is controversial.

Since light affects reproduction in fowls seasonal changes in testis size, spermatogenesis and semen production would be expected. In wild birds testis size increases of 50 to more than a 1000 fold occur from the resting to the sexually active period in the spring; however, in improved strains of chickens there is relatively little seasonal variation. Turkey testes are more sensitive to season although there are individual and possibly strain differences. Sperm produc-

sooner when chicks are reared at temperatures of around 30°C. than at lower temperatures of 0 to 10°C. In mature chicken males temperatures up to 30°C. have no deleterious effect on sperm production but higher temperatures (to 38°C.) have a depressing effect.

Although a vast amount of experimental work has been conducted on the effect of inheritance and nutrition on egg production in female domestic fowls very little attention has been directed toward the influence of these two factors on the reproductive characters in males. The information available indicates that sperm production in both chickens and turkeys is inherited, and that males from high egg-production strains of chickens produce more semen than those from low-production strains. The limited data on nutrition show that inanition results in decreased sperm production, and that prolonged feeding of rations deficient in vitamins A or E has an adverse effect on sperm production.

Numbers of sperm tend to decrease with successive natural matings during the day. Also the total sperm per ejaculate obtained with the massage technique increases noticeably with an increase in the time interval between collections (Table 12–3). Such physical characteristics as body shape, weight and general appearance are not reliable indices of sperm production. Confining either chicken or turkey males to wire floored cages does not affect adversely the volume or fertilizing capacity of their semen.

Exposing adult male chickens to x-ray doses of about 1300 r affects spermatogenesis adversely and doses of about 2200 r to 2800 r stops sperm formation in adults and prevents subsequent spermatogenesis in sexually immature males. The fertilizing capacity of semen exposed to dosages ranging from 231 to 5544 r declines consistently with increased dosage and is lost at 6488 r (Kosin, 1944).

II. THE FEMALE FOWL

A. The Reproductive Organs

Female fowls normally have only one ovary and one *oviduct*—the left (Plate XXVII). During incubation the right ovary and oviduct develop to some extent but by the time of hatching they have degenerated and only rudiments remain. Occasionally a female chicken or turkey will be found with two oviducts, a condition more prevalent in some strains than in others. More rare is the presence of two ovaries.

1. OVARY

The ovary is located at the anterior end of the kidney and slightly left of the midline in the sublumbar region of the abdominal cavity. It is suspended from the dorsal wall by a fold in the peritoneum.

In the sexually active female chicken the ovary is a cluster of many follicles which range from approximately 1 to 35 mm. in diameter. Each follicle contains an oöcyte and is attached to the ovary by a slender stem or stalk. The number of visible follicles in the ovary varies from about 1000 to 3000, depending upon the breeding of the chickens. Through selective breeding the number of follicles in the domestic hen has been greatly increased during the past century, however, the ability of the hen to lay at a rapid rate probably is influenced more by other factors than by the number of follicles present in the ovary. The smaller follicles are pale in color becoming more intensely colored with yellow pigment as they grow to mature size. The ovary of the laying hen usually has from one to five ruptured follicles. The weight of the ovary in the mature laying chicken hen is 40 to 60 gm. and in the laying turkey hen 125 to 200 gm. (Table 12–4).

Table 12–4.—Weights and Measurements of the Reproductive Organs of Laying Chicken and Turkey Hens

Weights of oviducts are free of attachments and oviducal eggs. (*Harper & Parker, 1962. Unpublished data, Ore. Agric. Exp. Sta.*)

Organ	Chicken	Turkey
Ovary		
Weight, gm.	46	165
Oviduct		
Weight, gm.	47	119
Length, cm.	74	108
Funnel, cm.	10	16
Magnum, cm.	37	49
Isthmus, cm.	12	18
Uterus, cm.	8	14
Vagina, cm.	7	11

Histologically the avian ovary is somewhat similar to the mammalian ovary in that there is an inner medulla covered with an outer cortex from which the follicles develop. The follicular membrane is lined with granulosa cells, and the theca interna and theca externa contain cells that are similar in appearance and arrangement to those in mammals. In contrast with mammalian follicles the avian follicle has no antrum.

2. OVIDUCT

The oviduct in the laying hen is a long

convoluted tube which occupies a large part of the left side of the abdominal cavity. Its anterior end is near the ovary and the posterior end opens into the cloaca. The oviduct of the laying hen is about 70 to 80 cm. long and varies in width from 1 to 5 cm., whereas in nonlaying hens it is only 10 to 15 cm. long and 1 to 7 mm. in diameter. Oviducts of laying turkey hens are considerably longer, measuring from 90 to 115 cm. in length (Table 12–4). The oviducal walls are well supplied with blood vessels and are elastic to facilitate great changes in diameter to accommodate the developing egg. There are five rather clearly defined regions of the oviduct each having its specific function in egg formation, namely: (a) the *funnel* or *infundibulum* that lies just posterior to the ovary and engulfs or picks up the yolk following ovulation, (b) the *magnum* that secretes the thick *white* or *albumen*, (c) the *isthmus* that secretes the shell membranes, (d) the uterus or *shell gland* that secretes the shell and (e) the *vagina* that aids in the expulsion of the fully formed egg.

Histologically the walls of the oviduct consist of an outer layer of muscles which run longitudinally, a layer of circular muscles and glandular epithelial lining. The epithelial lining is thrown into folds which greatly increase the secretory surface area. Size and shape of these folds vary in the different regions. The glands that secrete all parts of the egg except the yolk are located in the epithelial lining of the oviduct.

B. Age and Seasonal Changes in Ovary and Oviduct

Sexual maturity or the laying of the first egg is reached in the female chicken at about 6 months of age and in turkey females about 7 months. At the onset of egg production the ovary is 5 or 6 times as large as it was a few weeks earlier. The ovarian weight of chickens increases from 0.02 gm. at time of hatching to about 40 gm. at sexual maturity when the first egg is laid. Because the growth of the oviduct is controlled by estrogen from the ovary, its growth parallels that of the ovary. The chicken oviduct increases in weight from 0.2 gm. at 3 months of age

to approximately 45 gm. at sexual maturity and in length from 0.5 cm. at time of hatching to 65 to 70 cm. at sexual maturity.

There is less seasonal variation in the sizes of ovaries and oviducts of chickens than those of turkeys and waterfowl which are more seasonal than chickens in reproduction. When egg laying ceases the ovary and oviduct weights drop sharply. During the rest or non-productive period the ovary of the hen is 10 to 15 times and the oviduct about 10 times lighter in weight than when laying. Seasonal variation in egg production will be discussed in detail in Chapter 17.

C. Oögenesis and Yolk Formation

About midway of the incubation period the germ cells of the female chick multiply rapidly to form smaller cells, the oögonia. When the oögonia stop multiplying they enter a growth phase and become primary oöcytes. Changes take place within the nucleus of the primary oöcyte during subsequent incubation and afterwards, but the reduction division of the nucleus to form secondary oöcytes does not take place until 1 to 2 hours before ovulation (Olsen 1942). It is the secondary oöcyte that is ovulated, and if it is not subsequently fertilized, the egg is laid as a secondary oöcyte. Further discussion of maturation is included in the last section of this chapter.

The yolk of the fowl's egg is a large mass of non-living material which is deposited with the microscopic germ cell or oöcyte. The first true yolk material is passed into the oöcyte when the chick is about 2 months old. At first the oöcyte grows slowly by accumulating light colored yolk material. As sexual maturity is approached and the yolks reach 5 to 6 mm. in diameter a few of them, one after another, begin to grow at a greatly accelerated rate. In 7 to 9 days the yolk reaches mature size, increasing its weight approximately 100 fold in this short period. The yolk material is deposited in concentric layers—a layer of dark yolk and a layer of light yolk being formed each 24 hours. As the yolk enlarges the germinal disc migrates to the surface or periphery. Light yolk fills in its path and forms the neck of the *latebra*; the latebra being the

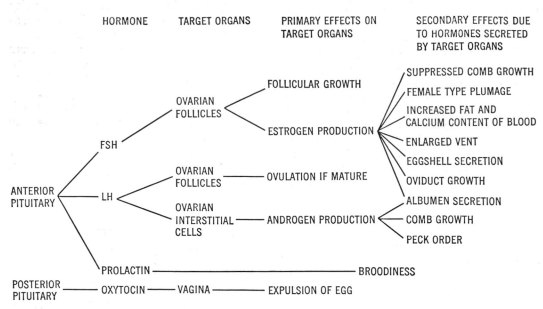

| HORMONE | TARGET ORGANS | PRIMARY EFFECTS ON TARGET ORGANS | SECONDARY EFFECTS DUE TO HORMONES SECRETED BY TARGET ORGANS |

FIG. 12–4.—Diagram showing some of the principal effects of hormones on reproduction in the female fowl. Note the many secondary effects of the hormones from the anterior pituitary.

original central position of the germinal disc filled also with light yolk. Before the accelerated deposition of yolk begins the *vitelline membrane* is formed by secretions of the follicle and cytoplasm of the oöcyte. It is the vitelline membrane that encloses the yolk after it is ovulated.

Follicular growth in domestic fowls is stimulated by FSH from the anterior pituitary gland (Fig. 12–4). Hypophysectomy results in atrophy of the ovary and oviduct within a few days (Plate XXVII). Opel & Nalbandov reported that ovarian degeneration commences first in the smallest of the rapidly growing follicles, then in the nearly mature ones and lastly in those of intermediate size. All follicles are affected within 24 hours after the operation. In contrast to mammals the ovaries of immature chickens are not stimulated by FSH of mammalian origin until 20 to 30 days before sexual maturity would normally be reached; however, injection of crude chicken pituitaries results in the growth of yolks to almost ovulatory size in sexually immature pullets. Also, gonadotropins of avian origin are more effective in maintaining the ovaries of hypophysectomized hens than mammalian gonadotropins, although neither is effective

for an indefinite period of time. As in males increments in the amount of daily light have a stimulating effect on gametogenesis in the female by increasing the gonadotropic hormone output by the pituitary.

There is a relation between the thyroid and egg formation, hens laying at a slow rate secreting less thyroxin than hens laying at a faster rate. Also, both rate of lay and thyroxin secretion are decreased at high temperatures. Thyroid administration reduces yolk size. There is some evidence that thyroprotein increases the rate of egg production when fed toward the end of the laying year. Prolactin administration results in inhibition of yolk formation, regression of the ovary and *broodiness*. Progesterone when administered in sufficient amounts results in inhibition of yolk growth and cessation of egg laying.

D. Ovarian Hormones

In addition to producing yolks another important function of the ovary is to produce the female sex hormone, estrogen. Estrogen stimulates the growth of the oviduct, causes the pubic bones to spread apart and the vent to enlarge in anticipation of egg laying. Estrogen modifies the shape and pigmentation of feathers to the female type. The neck and back or saddle feathers of the female are relatively short and rounded whereas those of the male and castrates are long and tapering. Estrogen also increases the levels of fat, calcium and phosphorus in the blood facilitating the deposition of these substances in developing eggs.

The red blood cell count of both intact males and capons is reduced by estrogen administration. Injection of sufficient amounts of the hormone into adult males causes decreases in testis and comb size, increased fat deposition and less aggressiveness. Implantations of 12 or 15 mg. pellets of diethylstilbestrol chemically caponize chicken males. Estrogens or stilbestrol bring about castration effects by inhibiting the secretion of gonadotropins which are necessary for maintenance of normal testis size and the secretion of the male sex hormone. The castration effects of estrogens are temporary, the males becoming normal again several weeks after the termination of treatment.

The ovary also secretes androgen. In the developing female androgen stimulates comb growth, whereas estrogen by its suppressing effect modifies it to the female type. Androgen is important in the female because it functions in combination with other hormones—its synergistic action with estrogen to stimulate albumen secretion being a notable example.

E. Ovulation

When the yolk attains full size the follicle ruptures along the *stigma* and the yolk is released or ovulated into the *ovarian pocket*, a small cavity formed about the ovary by surrounding organs. The stigma is a macroscopically nonvascular area or band extending about half the circumference of the follicle and opposite the follicular stalk (Plate XXVII). Microscopically, however, the stigma has small arteries and veins. The rupture usually begins at one end or pole of the stigma and extends rapidly to the other, releasing the yolk almost instantaneously. The stigma becomes wider just prior to ovulation due to increased pressure

within the follicle on the blood vessels near the stigma. Ovulation in the chicken normally occurs about 30 minutes after laying of a previous egg—the time interval varying from 7 to 74 minutes. Under usual conditions most yolks are ovulated in the morning and very few after 2 P.M.

After the chicken yolk is ovulated the ruptured follicle regresses rapidly and in 30 to 35 hours it is about half of its original weight and barely visible after a week. In pheasants the ruptured follicles persist in recognizable form for as long as 3 months after ovulation. The ruptured avian follicle is neither structurally nor physiologically similar to the corpus luteum of mammals; however, it does play a role in the timing of *oviposition*, the laying of the egg.

As in mammals ovulation in fowls is induced by LH from the anterior pituitary and indications are that this hormone is released into the blood stream 4 to 8 hours before ovulation. Fraps and associates have demonstrated experimentally that ovulation is induced in laying hens 6 to 8 hours after LH injections, and that hens hypophysectomized 8 hours or more prior to expected time of ovulation fail to ovulate, whereas the majority of those hypophysectomized within 3 hours of expected ovulation time ovulate. Also, follicles excised from ovary an hour or so before expected ovulation proceed to ovulate *in vitro* (Olsen & Neher, 1948). Progesterone injections in small amounts induce ovulation; however, since progesterone does not induce ovulation in hypophysectomized hens this hormone induces ovulation indirectly, probably by stimulating the pituitary to release LH.

F. Cycles or "Clutches"

The number of eggs laid by a hen on consecutive days is known as a cycle or "clutch" (Fig. 12–5). A cycle is terminated the day an egg is not laid. Poor layers have short cycles of 1 or 2 eggs, whereas good layers lay cycles of from 4 to as many as 200 eggs. It is likely that in good layers gonadotropin secretion by the pituitary is greater than in poor layers since injecting hens with short cycles with mammalian

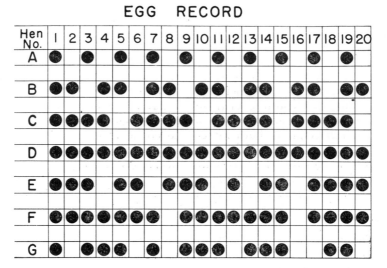

FIG. 12–5.—Diagram showing different egg laying cycles or clutches in chickens. Hens *A*, *B* and *C* have regular cycles of 1, 2 and 4 eggs respectively, while *D* shows a continuous cycle characteristic of high producers, *E* an irregular cycle, *F* and *G* are actual records of a good and mediocre layer.

gonadotropins increases the cycles in many of them significantly.

The oviduct has an effect on the timing of ovulation. Suspending a foreign object, to simulate a yolk, in the magnum or isthmus stops ovulation immediately. This indicates that a foreign body or developing egg in the oviduct inhibits the pituitary, probably by a neural mechanism, from releasing the amounts of LH required for ovulation (Nalbandov, 1953). Disturbance or any other factor that delays laying and causes the egg to be retained in the oviduct longer than normal time delays ovulation. Premature expulsion of the egg from the oviduct, on the other hand, does not speed up ovulation.

As previously pointed out ovulation normally occurs about 30 minutes after the laying of the previous egg. However, if laying happens after 2 P.M. ovulation of the next yolk does not take place until about 16 to 18 hours later, therefore, no egg is laid the following day. This results in a termination of the cycle. If hens are kept under constant uniform 24-hour artificial illumination they will lay at all hours of the day, there being no onset of darkness to delay ovulation and terminate the cycle. The exact manner by which the onset of

darkness delays ovulation is not known but it may influence the timing in the release of the luteinizing hormone which induces ovulation (Fraps, 1959). Under controlled lighting, reversing the day and night will cause the hens to switch their laying schedule to the lighted period in 3 to 4 days. Time of feeding also influences time of laying. Hens kept under continuous light and fed during the day lay most of their eggs during the day; however, if feeding is done during the normal night time the hens adjust and lay many of their eggs then.

G. Formation of Non-Yolk Components of Egg

All components of the fully formed avian egg (Fig. 12–6) with the exception of the yolk, are formed in the oviduct. At the time of ovulation there is much peristaltic activity of the anterior portion of the oviduct which undoubtedly aids the funnel in picking up the ovulated yolk. Contact of the funnel with the bare yolk appears to be a matter of chance, the time required for the engulfment process varying from 5 to 25 minutes. After entering the oviduct the yolk is passed along by wave-like contractions of the oviducal muscles. The approximate times spent and

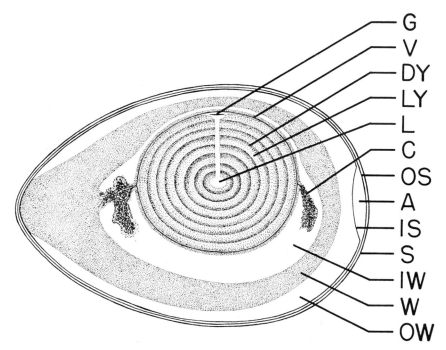

Fig. 12-6.—Diagram showing in vertical section the parts of the hen's egg. Note the concentric layers of light and dark yolk and the germinal disc which floats to the top in a short time. *G* is the germinal disc or germinal vesicle, *V* the vitelline membrane, *DY* the dark yolk, *LY* the light yolk, *L* the latebra, *C* the chalaza, *OS* the outer shell membrane, *A* the air cell, *IS* the inner shell membrane, *S* the shell, *IW* the inner thin white or albumen, *W* the thick white, and *OW* the outer thin white. (*Adapted from Card, 1961. Poultry Production, 9th Ed., Philadelphia, Courtesy Lea & Febiger.*)

Table 12-5.—Egg Formation in Domestic Chickens

Part of reproductive system	Time required	Contribution to complete egg
Ovary	7 to 9 days	yolk
Oviduct	24 to 25 hours	all non-yolk components
Funnel	15 minutes	site of fertilization
Magnum	3 hours	thick albumen
Isthmus	1¼ hours	inner and outer shell membranes
Uterus	19 to 20 hours	shell, shell pigment and water
(shell gland)		to form thin albumen
Vagina	1 to 10 minutes	expulsion of egg

the parts of the developing egg added in each section of the oviduct are shown in Table 12-5.

The thick *white* or albumen is added to the yolk during its 3-hour sojourn in the magnum. The thick gelatinous white secreted by the magnum contains practically all of the nitrogen in the total white of the fully formed egg. The remainder of the egg white, the thin white, is formed after the egg leaves the magnum. Water secreted by the uterus and isthmus passes through the shell membranes and mixes with the thick white secreted in the magnum. The *chalazae*, the two whitish, twisted, albuminous cords extending from opposite poles of the yolk, do not become visible until the egg is in the uterus, even though the materials from which they are formed are secreted in the magnum. The chalazae result from rotation of the albumen about the yolk.

Both the inner and outer *shell membranes* are secreted as sticky fibers by the glands of the isthmus in a little over an hour's time. The fibers after being secreted cross each other in all directions and become matted. At first the membranes cover their contents snugly, but as the egg leaves the isthmus the membranes are quite loose.

The shell which is mostly calcium carbonate is secreted during the egg's 19- to 20-hour stay in the uterus or shell gland. Shell secretion commences as soon as the egg enters this region, at a slow rate for the first 5 hours, but thereafter continues at a faster and more uniform rate until the egg is laid. The pigment that colors brown-shelled chicken eggs and forms the spots on turkey eggs is also secreted in the uterus.

As pointed out earlier, estrogen secreted by the developing ovary stimulates the development of the oviduct including the proliferation of the albumen-secreting glands, but estrogen alone will not bring about albumen secretion. A second hormone, either androgen or progesterone, acting in combination with estrogen is necessary for albumen secretion, and the presence of the yolk or some other object in the oviduct is necessary to bring about the discharge of the albumen into the oviduct. Shell membrane secretion is hormonally controlled in a similar fashion to albumen. The mobilization of calcium salts and secretion of shell by the uterus is controlled by estrogen assisted by *parathormone*, the secretion of the parathyroid gland, which increases the calcium level of the blood.

H. Egg Laying (Oviposition)

When the egg is completely formed, it is usually turned 180° with the large end to the rear and passed into the vagina. The egg is forced through the vagina by contractions of the vaginal and abdominal muscles. The act of laying the egg requires only a few minutes. The vagina is everted through the *vent* (anus) and normally the egg does not come into contact with contents of the cloaca. Injections of the hormone oxytocin

from the posterior pituitary causes premature expulsion of hard shelled eggs in just a few minutes; however, surgical removal of the posterior pituitary does not interfere with laying of the egg. It appears that the posterior lobe of the pituitary serves as a reservoir for this hormone which is secreted by the hypothalamus. Surgical removal of the ruptured follicle from which the yolk was ovulated delays laying of the egg containing that yolk for several days. The exact manner in which the ruptured follicle affects the posterior pituitary or any other egg expulsion mechanism has not been determined.

I. Broodiness

Broodiness is the expression of the maternal instinct in fowls in which they desire to sit on the nest and hatch and rear chicks. Indications of broodiness in chicken hens are continuous nest-sitting, ruffled feathers, clucking, and a cantankerous disposition. In turkeys broodiness is harder to detect as the hens usually have only the nest-sitting characteristic. Under natural conditions broodiness is a necessary part of the reproductive complex; however, in the commercial production of chickens and turkeys, it is considered undesirable because normally no eggs are laid during broody periods. Even when detected early and steps are taken to break-up broodiness, the average non-laying period is about 15 days for each broody period in both species.

Broodiness is under endocrine control and is an inherited characteristic. Increased secretions of the hormone prolactin by the anterior pituitary causes broodiness. It is necessary to inject more prolactin to induce broodiness in the relatively non-broody strains and breeds than in those in which broodiness is of common occurrence. Sufficiently large doses of prolactin will cause even males to brood or "mother" chicks. Whether prolactin induces broodiness directly, or indirectly by the suppression of estrogen secretion by the ovary, is in dispute. Broodiness can be terminated in chickens by injections or implantations of estrogens or androgens. Estrogens and androgens do not interrupt broodiness in turkeys, but progesterone when given in a readily absorbed form does (van Tienhoven, 1959). A long-used and practical way of interrupting broodiness is confining the hens for several days to well ventilated wire bottom coops to discourage nesting. Certain environmental factors including high temperatures, darkness, accumulation of eggs in the nest and presence of baby chicks contribute to the induction of broodiness.

J. Molting

Molting, which is the shedding of old feathers and growing of new ones, is related to reproduction in that fowls usually do not molt and lay eggs at the same time (see Chapter 17). As long as the ovary is active molting is retarded. The exact mechanisms controlling molt remain undetermined, however, a few facts about molting are established. One is that molting can be induced in laying hens by feeding or injection of thyroid materials. On the other hand, thyroidectomy or the feeding of the thyroid depressant, thiouracil, does not prevent molting but merely delays it. Large doses of progesterone result in an immediate

decline in egg laying and molt induction. Molting also results from withholding feed or water or both for a long enough time to stop egg production. Another management factor that will cause molting is abruptly reducing the daily light periods. This is not surprising when it is considered that domestic fowls usually molt in the fall months when the day lengths are decreasing.

III. SEXUAL BEHAVIOR

As compared with wild avian species the sexual behavior patterns of domesticated fowls is less complex. In chickens courtship actions of the male usually include *waltzing*, in which he drops one wing and shuffles with short steps in front of the hen; approaching the hen from the rear sometimes with the neck stretched and hackle extended; and *"tidbitting"* or pecking and scratching at some object on the floor and characteristic vocalization (Fig. 12–7). Some other male courting actions observed are circling the hen with high steps; *nesting* in corners in which he shifts about with nest-building movements of body and beak with accompanying vocalization; and wing flapping in

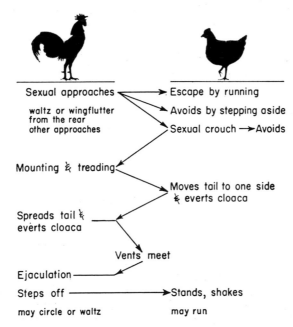

Fig. 12–7.—Diagram showing sexual behavior with copulatory locomotor patterns in chickens. (*Feom Guhl, 1962, in The Behavior of Domestic Animals. E. S. E. Hafez, edit., London. Courtesy Bailliere, Tindall & Cox, Ltd.*)

which he raises himself and flaps wings vigorously and audibly (Wood-Gush, 1954). There is considerable individual variation in the courtship activity with the most active males receiving the most crouches or invitations from their mates. Courtship activities decline with age and physical condition.

While breeding males must be sexually active to fertilize a high percentage of their flock mates, there are reasons to believe that sexual activity (libido) in chicken males beyond certain limits not only does not increase fertility but may decrease it. Wood-Gush has reported that highly active males produce less semen than those that are less active sexually. Also when a number of ejaculates are intercepted in relatively short time in mating trials with hens, successive ejaculates contain fewer sperms. Sexual activity in males is inherited; the sons of highly active males mate more frequently than sons of less sexually active sires. Social position in a flock and sex drive are not necessarily related, but the dominant male does most of the mating by preventing others from mating freely; therefore, if the dominant male is not sexually active a fertility problem is created (Guhl, 1953). With females there is a negative correlation between their social rank and frequency of mating, the dominant hens being courted and mated less often than their social inferiors.

A receptive hen reacts to the male by *crouching* or *squatting* with her wing fronts elevated and spread. The male mounts from the rear, placing his feet on the back of the female and grasps her by the comb, head or neck feathers with his beak. As the male applies pressure with his feet the female's tail is raised to one side and the vaginal region of the oviduct is everted. The male dips his tail with exposed reproductive apparatus making contact with the everted oviduct and ejaculates. To complete the mating the male steps forward and the female raises and shakes herself and simultaneously the everted oviduct with the deposit of semen returns to its normal position. Copulation in chickens requires only a few seconds. Most natural matings take place in the afternoon.

The sexual behavior of turkeys varies somewhat from chickens. The courting action of the male is strutting. The female appears to be the aggressive sex because she usually issues the invitation by crouching in the vicinity of the male(s). Turkey females become very receptive shortly before egg laying commences, and if unmated they even crouch when the attendant enters the pen. The female turkey crouches very much like the chicken hen and the tom usually mounts, orientates himself toward the female's head, lowers his wings for balance and stomps or *treads* the female with his feet. Contact and semen deposition are similar to those described for chickens. With heavy breeds of turkeys there is a tendency for the males to be clumsy and as a consequence some of the females run out from under the males before the mating is complete. More time is required for copulation in turkeys than in chickens.

Sexual activity is influenced by the sex hormones. Copulatory or treading actions can be induced in chicks or turkey poults less than a month old by testosterone injections. Early receptivity can be induced in female chickens by estrogen treatment. The male copulatory pattern, including treading, can be induced in both sexes and capons by androgens, but the female copulatory pattern cannot be induced in either males or capons by estrogens.

Neither courtship nor mating is necessary for optimum egg production in either chickens or turkeys; the males are required only to fertilize eggs that are produced for hatching.

IV. FERTILIZATION AND EARLY EMBRYONIC DEVELOPMENT

A. Fertilization

Fertilization takes place in the oviduct of fowls and probably is restricted to the funnel; however, for a long time it was thought the sperm penetrated the follicular membranes and fertilized the yolks while contained by the ovary. A yolk from a mated hen that is removed, ovulated *in vitro*, and substituted at time of ovulation for the yolk in an unmated hen is infertile when laid. Furthermore yolks from unmated hens are laid as fertile eggs when transplanted into fertilized hens (Olsen & Neher, 1948). Fertilization takes place shortly after the yolk is ovulated, usually within 10 minutes.

One sperm fertilizes the egg; however, more than one and often several may penetrate the vitelline membrane and become supernumerary sperms. Although only one sperm fertilizes one egg, some 90 to 100 million sperm must be inseminated for highest fertility in chickens and about half as many in turkeys.

B. Sperm Transport and Life Span in Oviduct

Since sperm deposition or insemination occurs at the posterior end of the oviduct and fertilization of eggs at the opposite or anterior end, sperm must travel the entire length of the oviduct. Sperm travel up the vagina, through the *uterovaginal junction* into the uterus by their own motility aided possibly by *rheotaxis*. The exact mechanism of sperm transport in the anterior oviduct of domestic fowls is obscure. In pigeons a pro-ovarian ciliary band (cilia beating toward the ovary as opposed to general ciliary motion directed posteriorly) has been observed. Muscular activity of the oviduct also may play a role.

Sperm travel the entire oviduct from the vagina to the funnel, within 1 hour after natural mating. When sperm are placed in the uterus they are transported to the funnel in as short a time as 15 minutes (Allen & Grigg, 1957). The utero-vaginal junction appears to be a barrier to sperm movement up the oviduct. Dead sperm inseminated intra-vaginally do not pass it and only a relatively small percentage of live sperm pass through it into the uterus. Sperm do not acquire additional capacity to fertilize eggs on their passage up or stay in the oviduct, thus there is no evidence of sperm capacitation as in mammals. Sperm deposited in the ovarian pocket or the anterior end of oviduct just prior to ovulation fertilize eggs.

Avian sperm retain their fertilizing capacity for considerable periods of time in the female oviduct. Chicken sperm are viable for as long as 32 days after insemination, and turkey sperm for as long as 70 days. Sperm are stored in folds or *crypts*, sometimes referred to as *"sperm nests,"* in the lining of the oviduct. As the yolk passes through the funnel the oviducal walls are stretched liberating the sperm to "attack" the germinal disc on the yolk.

C. Onset and Duration of Fertility in Natural Matings

Even though sperm get to the funnel in a very short time few fertile eggs are laid the day following mating or insemination. Considering that the egg is not laid until about 24 hours after ovulation and subsequent fertilization this is not surprising. Hens inseminated in the afternoon, which is the most active time of mating, rarely lay fertile eggs the following day since the eggs would have already passed the funnel at time of insemination. A high percentage of fertility in a breeding flock of chickens usually is not attained until 10 to 14 days after the males are introduced into the flock since some hens are not mated soon by the males. The time required for a satisfactory level of fertility to be reached depends to some extent upon the relative number of males in the flock—the fewer the males the longer is the time required (Fig. 12–8). As high as 90 per cent fertility can be obtained from pens of turkey breeders as early as 7 days after the males are put with previously unmated females. As a usual practice, however, male and female turkey breeders are mated before egg production commences.

Duration of fertility, or the length of time fertile eggs are laid following removal of the males, is as much as 32 days for individual chicken hens; however, on a flock basis a fair level of fertility usually lasts for about a week with some decline in fertility 3 to 5 days after removing the males. With turkeys the percentage fertility in a flock usually drops very little during the first 2 weeks after removal of the males and thereafter shows a gradual decline to zero during the next 6 to 8 weeks. The average length of time geese and ducks continue to lay fertile eggs after mating is 10 to 13 days

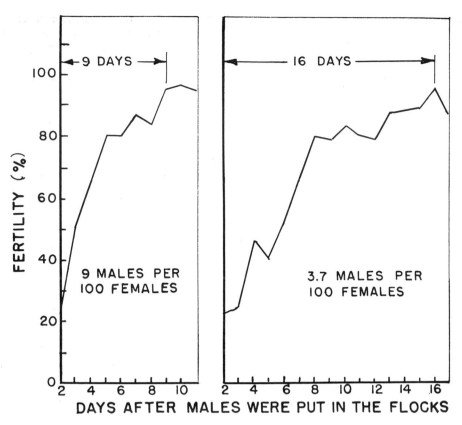

FIG. 12–8.—The relation of the relative number of males used in chicken breeder flocks (New Hampshires) to onset of fertility. Note that as the number of males increases less time is required for a high percentage of fertile eggs to be produced. (*Adapted from Parker & Bernier, 1950. Poult. Sci., 29, 379.*)

which is somewhat less than in chickens and much less than in turkeys.

D. Embryonic Development Before Laying of Egg

Commencing about 24 hours before ovulation important changes take place in the avian ovum in preparation for fertilization. The walls of the *germinal vesicle* begin to disintegrate and by the time of ovulation it is a thin sheet beneath the vitelline membrane (Olsen, 1942). Just before ovulation the first maturation division occurs, the first polar body is extruded, and the spindle for the second maturation division is formed. These changes are likely induced by LH since they can be induced prematurely by injection of pituitary preparations. Following ovulation and subsequent fertilization of

the egg the second maturation division occurs and the second polar body is extruded.

In both chickens and turkeys the first *cleavage* (*segmentation division*) of the fertilized egg usually takes place in the isthmus approximately 5 hours after ovulation. The second cleavage resulting in the 4-cell stage occurs 20 minutes later and by the time the egg has been in the uterus or shell gland for 4 hours it has reached the 256-cell stage. As cleavage continues a disc shaped layer of cells is formed. Most chicken and turkey eggs have proceeded to the *gastrula* stage before laying. The extent to which gastrulation has progressed prior to laying is related to the ability of the embryo to remain viable in storage prior to incubation and to its normal development during incubation. Eggs laid in the pre-gastrula or late gastrula stages do not hatch as well as eggs laid in the early gastrula stage.

E. Parthenogenesis

Parthenogenesis, the development of unfertilized ova, occurs rather frequently in turkeys and less frequently in chickens. In most cases the "embryos" begin to degenerate before the eggs are laid; however, development has continued in turkeys and poults have been hatched. The sex of parthenogenetic embryos and poults is always male and they have the diploid number of chromosomes. Experiments with turkeys by the U.S.D.A. at Beltsville, Maryland, where many of the observations on parthenogenesis have been made, show that through selective breeding lines of turkeys with a high incidence of parthenogenesis can be developed. Vaccination with embryo propagated *live fowl pox virus* or innoculation with *Rous sarcoma virus* increases the incidence of parthenogenesis of eggs laid by the treated females. Semen has been collected from a tom of parthenogenetic origin to inseminate successfully virgin females resulting in offspring of both sexes.

REFERENCES

ALLEN, T. E. & GRIGG, G. W. (1957). Sperm transport in the fowl. *Austr. J. Agr. Res.*, **8**, 788–799.

FRAPS, R. M. (1959). Photoperiodism in the Female Domestic Fowls. In: *Photoperiodism and Related Phenomena in Plants and Animals* by the American Society for the Advancement of Science. p. 767. Washington, D.C.

GRAY, J. C. (1937). The anatomy of the male genital ducts in the fowl. *J. Morph.*, **60**, 393–405.

GRIGG, G. W. & HODGE, A. J. (1949). Electron microscope studies of spermatozoa. I. The morphology of the spermatozoon of the common domestic fowl (*Gallus domesticus*). *Austr. J. Sci. Res., Ser. B*, **2**, 271–286.

GUHL, A. M. (1953). Social behavior of the domestic fowl. *Kans. Agric. Exp. Sta. Tech. Bull.* No. 73.

KOSIN, I. L. (1944). Some aspects of the biological action of x-rays on cock spermatozoa. *Physiol. Zool.*, **17**, 289–319.

KUMARAN, J. D. S. & TURNER, C. W. (1949). The normal development of the testes of the White Plymouth Rock. *Poult. Sci.*, **28**, 511–520.

LAKE, P. E., BUTLER, E. J., McCALLUM, J. W. & MacINTYRE, J. J. (1958). A chemical analysis of the seminal and blood plasmas of the cock. *Quart. J. Exp. Physiol.*, **43**, 309–313.

LORENZ, F. W. (1959). Reproduction in the Domestic Fowl: Physiology of the male. In: *Reproduction in Domestic Animals*. H. H. Cole & P. T. Cupps (edits.) Vol. 2, New York, Academic Press.

MUNRO, S. S. (1938). Functional changes in fow sperm during their passage through the excurrent ducts of the male. *J. Exp. Zool.*, **79**, 71–92.

NALBANDOV, A. V. (1953). Endocrine control of physiological function. *Poult. Sci.*, **32**, 88–103.

OLSEN, M. W. (1942). Maturation, fertilization and early cleavage in the hen's egg. *J. Morph.*, **70**, 513–533.

OLSEN, M. W. & NEHER, B. H. (1948). The site of fertilization in the domestic fowl. *J. Expt. Zool.*, **109**, 355–366.

PARKER, J. E. (1949). Fertility in Chickens and Turkeys. In: *Fertility and Hatchability of Chicken and Turkey Eggs*. L. W. Taylor (edit.) New York, John Wiley.

PARKER, J. E., McKENZIE, F. F. & KEMPSTER, H. L. (1942). Fertility in the male domestic fowl. *Mo. Agric. Exp. Sta. Res. Bull.* No. 347.

PARKES, A. S. & MARSHALL, A. J. (1960). The Reproductive Hormones in Birds. In: *Marshall's Physiology of Reproduction*. A. S. Parkes (edit.). Vol. 1: Part 2. London, Longmans.

ROMANOFF, A. L. (1960). *The Avian Embryo*. pp. 35–43. New York, Macmillan.

VAN TIENHOVEN, A. (1959). Reproduction in the Domestic Fowl: Physiology of the Female. In: *Reproduction in Domestic Animals*. H. H. Cole & P. T. Cupps (edits.) Vol. 2, New York, Academic Press.

WOOD-GUSH, D. G. M. (1954). The courtship of the Brown Leghorn cock. *British J. Anim. Behav.*, **2**, 95–102.

QUESTIONS

1. In what important respects does reproduction in fowls differ from mammals?
2. How does the copulatory apparatus of the cock differ from that of the mammal?
3. Explain why the comb growth of developing males exceeds that of females?
4. What evidence can you give to support the statement that avian sperm undergo a maturing or ripening process as they pass through the excurrent ducts of the male?
5. What evidence is there to support the view that avian LH is different from mammalian LH?
6. Name the 5 sections or regions of the avian oviduct and the contribution of each to the complete egg.
7. How would you go about demonstrating to a skeptic that the domestic hen's egg is fertilized in the funnel of the oviduct and not while the egg is contained in the ovary?
8. List 10 effects of estrogen or stilbestrol administration to fowls of both sexes.
9. When does ovulation occur with respect to oviposition? What causes ovulation? Does the oviduct influence ovulation?
10. What is broodiness and what causes it? Why is it undesirable to the commercial egg producer?

15

Part III

PATTERNS OF REPRODUCTION

Chapter 13

The Reproduction of Cattle

By L. C. Ulberg

The majority of cattle used for milk or beef production are of the genus *Bos* and include *B. Taurus* (European domestic cattle) and *B. Indicus* (Zebu or humped cattle) of the family *Bovidae*. This places them in the animal kingdom as belonging to a group known as *Artiodactyla*, or even-toed animals. They are polyestrous and ovulate spontaneously. The males tend to produce sperm throughout the year.

I. SEXUAL MATURITY

A. Development of the Reproductive Organs of the Male

The testes descends into the scrotum at the time of birth. Differentiation of testicular tissue begins at 3 to 4 months of age with the formation of the cells of Leydig. Spermatocytes can be observed in the tubules at 2 to 3 months of age. At 6 months of age mature sperm are formed which become free in the lumen of the seminiferous tubules one month later. An abundance of free sperm are not observed in the tubules until 8 to 10 months of age. Normally semen can be collected at this age providing the bull shows sufficient sex drive to serve the artificial vagina. If sex drive is lacking at this stage of development semen can often be obtained by the use of an electro-ejaculator. However, the youngest age at which a bull can produce semen varies considerably. Most reports indicate that this age is younger in dairy breeds than in slower maturing beef breeds. Puberty is also influenced by level of pre-puberal feed intake as well as other factors which have an effect upon rate of development of the animal. Reid (1959) states that the age for onset of semen production can be controlled by the level of energy intake. However, the total amount of energy intake to bring a bull to age of puberty remains fairly constant.

There is no physiological reason why a bull should not be used occasionally as soon as he reaches puberty. Unlike a young heifer, which has to carry the burden of pregnancy, limited semen production will cause no permanent physiological damage.

B. Development of the Reproductive Organs of the Female

Well formed follicles are found in ovaries of pre-puberal heifers, which become atretic and regress to be replaced by others, which in turn grow larger and regress. One or more of these follicles may ovulate before the heifer exhibits external signs of estrus.

(229)

As in the bull calf, the age of puberty (first estrus) varies for the heifer according to breed, level of feed intake, season of birth and many other factors and ranges from 6 to 18 months. Again, as in the male, those factors which tend to interfere with growth will delay puberty so that first estrus occurs when the animals reach a certain weight rather than a certain age (Table 13–1). A certain live weight must be attained (600 lb. for Holsteins) before first estrus occurs.

Table 13–1. Effect of Nutrition on Age and Size of Holstein Heifers at First Estrus

(*Data from J. T. Reid, 1962, personal communication*)

| | Plane of nutrition* | | |
	Low	Medium	High
Number of animals	33	34	34
Age of animals (months)	20	11	9
Body weight of animals (lb.)	636	582	612

*From birth to time of first calving

II. BREEDING SEASON

A non-pregnant cow, after puberty, in a temperate climate, on a normal feeding regime will exhibit estrus every 17 to 24 days throughout her life-time. The most common exception to this is during the first 30 to 90 days *post partum*. The length of this interval is influenced by many factors. For example, Holstein cows milked twice daily had an interval from calving to first heat of 46 days, but when cows were milked 3 or 5 times daily these values became 60 or 69 days. Cows which nursed calves required 72 days for first heat after calving (Clapp 1937; Casida & Wisnicky 1950). This may explain why this interval is generally longer in beef cows than in dairy cattle. Both beef and dairy cattle which produce calves in winter have a longer interval to post partum estrus than those which calve in the summer. However, failure to also express estrus (quiet ovulation) as well as inactive ovaries (true anestrus) occurs at any time in the non-pregnant cow. Brahman cattle, for example, suckling calves on poor pasture are inclined to develop a period of true anestrus

during certain seasons of the year. Bond *et al.* (1960) have produced anestrus experimentally in Milking Shorthorn heifers, by placing them in a constant ambient temperature of 90°F. This demonstrates the effect of environmental conditions on a physiological reaction by acting through the endocrine system.

III. ESTROUS CYCLE

Some of the major events in the estrous cycle specific for the cow include follicular growth, ovulation after end of estrus, unusual estrous behavior and metestrual bleeding.

Consider first follicular growth. The presence of large atretic follicles (over 20 mm.) are common 7 days after the end of estrus. These large follicles regress and have no known function or effect on reproduction. Further evidence that follicular growth is controlled by hormone stimulation can be seen in the pre-puberal heifer. Black *et al.* (1953) report cleavage, up to 8 cells, in ova recovered from inseminated, hormone-treated, 6-week-old dairy calves.

The cow is also peculiar, among farm animals, in that she has a short estrous period so that ovulation occurs several hours after cessation of estrus. However, when time of ovulation is measured from onset of estrus she is similar to other species of farm mammals.

Because a cow has a short estrus it may occur but escape detection. However, because of her unusual behavior during estrus this period can be detected without special effort on the part of the observer. Since cows tend toward homosexuality they will mount a female in estrus. Perhaps this one characteristic has done more to promote artificial insemination than any other one thing. Females approaching estrus will show increased activity and will attempt to mount other cows. Often times heifers will stand to be mounted by others of their group but will not permit mounting of a strange animal except very near the midpoint of the estrous period. These observations indicate that the beginning and end of estrus is not as clear cut as it might be.

From a practical standpoint behavioral

estrus is only important as a measure of time of ovulation. Recently cervical mucus has been used to determine the time of estrus. This mucus will crystallize into "fern" patterns when there is an actively developing follicle in the ovaries (Plate XXVIII). After estrus, metestrous bleeding, varying in amounts from microscopic to a profuse flow, occurs in most cows on the second day after onset of estrus (Chapter 5).

IV. FERTILITY

Ovulation Rate and Twinning. Normally the cow has one ovulation per estrous period, occurring about 60 per cent of the time on the right ovary. The per cent of all births which are twins is about 2 for dairy cattle and ranges downward to about 0.5 for certain beef breeds and are due mostly to multiple ovulations (fraternal twins). Monozygotic twins (identical twins) account for only about 5 per cent of the total number of twins born. Multiple ovulations can be produced experimentally by the administration of gonadotropins. It would therefore seem reasonable to speculate that spontaneously occurring multiple ovulations are the result of an increase in the level of gonadotropins available to the ovaries just prior to ovulation and consequently increase the rate of multiple births. An example of this can be seen in dairy cows treated for or

recovered from follicular cysts. They tend to have more multiple births, and certainly they have been subjected to an abnormal endocrine system. The beef cow along with a lower twinning rate rarely becomes a nymphomaniac suggesting that she has a more stable endocrine system than does a dairy cow.

Fertilization Rate. Most evidence indicates a high fertilization rate in cattle as in other species studied. Some observations on virgin heifers, inseminated with high quality semen, place this rate as high as 100 per cent, after animals with obvious abnormalities are removed. This rate will range downward to as low as 50 per cent in so-called "repeat-breeder" cows or even lower in cows bred to bulls producing poor semen. Under practical conditions the fertility rate is high if some attention is given to the use of semen of high quality and the removal of cows, from the herd, with obvious structural genital abnormalities.

Development of the Embryo and Fetus. The weight of the fetus starts a very rapid increase after the first 120 days of gestation (Table 13–2). However, the per cent increase in weight would be greatest at the end of the first month of gestation. The day-to-day change in size of the amnion is so great between 35 to 50 days of pregnancy

Table 13–2.—Measurements of Bovine Embryos and Fetuses by Age from Cows of Mixed Breeding

(Adapted from Winters et al. 1942. Minn. Tech. Bull. No. 151.)

Age (Days)	Weight (gm.)	Crown-rump Length (cm.)	Chest Circumference (cm.)	Tail Length (cm.)
25		0.313		
27		0.358		
30	0.28	1.113		
40	1.55	2.28		
50	4.94	3.85	3.7	0.75
60	13.78	6.60	5.4	1.95
		Forehead-Rump length		
90	160	16.4	11.5	4.00
120	820	27.1	20.1	7.60
150	2,746	36.8	31.4	10.30
185	6,685	54.0	39.4	17.20
215	16,102	70.0	53.3	24.00
245	26,988	82.0	63.5	28.00
260	31,298	87.0	70.0	34.00

that the date of breeding can be determined fairly accurately by palpating the size of the amnion *per rectum*. There is a possibility, however, of a breed difference in fetal growth during the 2nd month of pregnancy so that if a standard of measurement, which has been developed for dairy cattle, is used on beef cattle the age of the embryo may be overestimated.

The placental attachment becomes established in healthy animals by the beginning of the 2nd month of pregnancy. From this stage of development to term the total loss of potential young is less than 5 per cent. With fertilization rate high and the prenatal loss after 35 days post-mating low, the major portion of the loss has to occur after fertilization but before the establishment of the placental attachment.

The birth weights of calves will vary according to breed of cow. For example a 1200 lb. beef cow can be expected to produce a 70 lb. calf, while a dairy cow of the same weight is expected to produce a 100 lb. calf. Within breeds the birth weight is influenced more by the genotype of the calf than the genotype of the dam.

V. LOWERED FERTILITY

Low fertility, sometimes called temporary sterility, differs from sterility in that reproduction is possible in a given pair of animals when the proper combinations of factors occur. On the other hand, an animal is sterile when reproduction can no longer occur. It is the problem of low fertility rather than one of sterility that causes the greatest economic loss in cattle reproduction. There are three major criteria involved in maximum reproductive efficiency of a particular mating. First there must be viable sperm at the fertilization site at the proper time; second there must also be a viable ovum at this site at the same time; and third there must be a suitable uterine environment to support the potential offspring during the period of pregnancy. Any deviation from the optimum for these criteria can cause a lowering of the rate of fertility.

A. Low Fertility in the Male

There are two major factors which determine the total fertility, and consequently the number of offspring produced by a particular bull for a given situation. First he must be able to serve properly by having sufficient sex drive with no physical impairments to interfere with this service. Second he has to produce semen with highly fertile sperm.

The fertility of sperm varies considerably between bulls, but more important it varies between ejaculates for the same bull (see Chapter 3 & 8). It is not possible to completely control this variation at the present time because of insufficient understanding of the physiology of spermatogenesis and the storage of sperm within the reproductive duct system of the male. A sterile bull will be detected after a short period of use because all his mating will be unsuccessful, but a bull with a low fertility may go undetected for a long period of time. As the use of long term storage of sperm becomes more widespread, through artificial insemination, a fertility check can be made on individual ejaculates by mating a few cows with that ejaculate.

The bull is subject to the same type of anatomical aberrations of the reproductive system as that of males of the other species of farm livestock. Cryptorchidism occurs when the testes fail to pass through the inguinal canal or when the canal is not sufficiently closed an inguinal hernia occurs. These abnormalities are generally caused by gene action. Any constriction or block along the duct system, such as in the ductus differens or epididymis, due to infection or other damage which prevents passage of sperm also brings about sterility.

B. Low Fertility in the Female

The cow, like all mammals, has at least a double role in the reproductive process. First she has to produce viable ova and second, she has to supply a proper uterine environment for the sperm after deposition to the time of fertilization (capacitation) and for the embryo and fetus during the period of gestation.

PLATE XXVIII

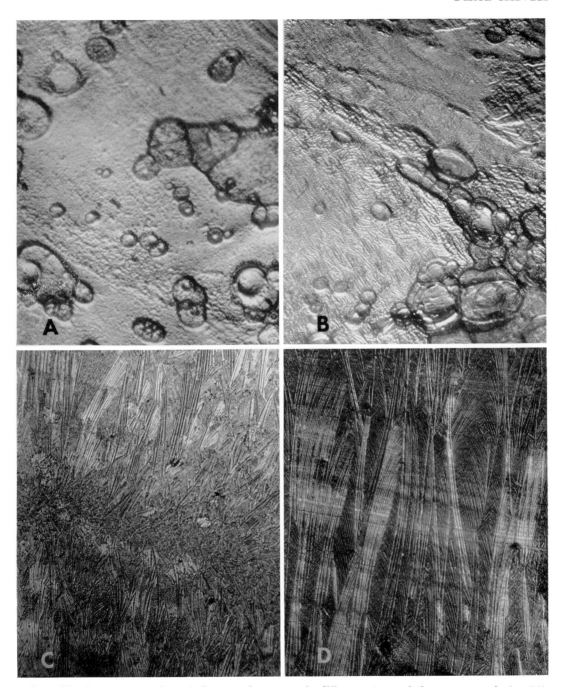

Crystallization patterns of cervical mucus from cows in different stages of the estrous cycle ($\times$ 32).

a. Luteal phase; no evidence of crystallization.

b. Eighty-four hours before onset of estrus; short crystals forming around bubbles.

c. Immediately prior to onset of estrus; a mixture of both short and long crystals.

d. During estrus; long crystals form "fern-like" pattern. This type of crystal starts to disappear before ovulation.

(From Alliston et al. 1958. J. Anim. Sci. 17, 322.)

1. ABNORMAL OVARIAN FUNCTION

The failure of an ovum to be released from the ovary accounts for lowered fertility and can be classified into two categories: those in which there is no ovarian or estrous activity (anestrus) and those in which excessive follicular growth occurs (cystic follicles). Both are caused by a malfunction of the endocrine system.

Anestrus. Inactive ovaries are found in cows under various forms of stress. For example, Zebu cows suckling calves during periods of high temperatures and on low levels of energy intake are especially subject to this condition. The physiological mechanism involved is not understood. Another common condition which results in estrus failure is where the corpus luteum remains functional in a non-pregnant animal. Usually this occurs because of uterine infection where the uterus is distended as in cases of pyometra. Somehow this prevents the regression of the corpus luteum which in turn prevents follicular growth and consequently failure of estrus to occur.

Cystic Follicles. Excessive follicular growth is caused by abnormal endocrine function in that the luteinizing hormone never reaches a level high enough to bring about ovulation. The injection of this hormone directly into the cyst, or the blood stream, will cause ovulation. This, in turn, causes the establishment of an active corpus luteum, and presumably the production of progesterone to terminate the condition. The same results can be obtained with extended administration of progesterone (daily injections of 50 mg. for 2 weeks).

Cystic follicles cause three types of animal reaction: continued estrous behavior (nymphomania); no estrus (anestrus); cyclic estrous periods which appear to approach normality. The behavior of the nymphomaniac is most dramatic and perhaps the most common in cows with cystic follicles. These cows are in estrus most of the time. Because they are under the influence of high levels of estrogen the vulva becomes hyperemic, the relaxation of the ligaments permits the pelvis to tilt forward causing the development of a high tail head. If the condition persists adhesions form around the ovaries and the cow becomes permanently sterile. The occurrence of cystic follicles with the complete absence of estrus is less frequent and much more difficult to detect from external appearance of the cow. The third type occurs in cows with periodic estrous behavior which approach normal in appearance. Apparently cysts go through cycles of development, one will grow, develop to a point and then regress. As the first one regresses a second one will develop and estrus will occur as the cyst reaches a certain stage of development. These "cystic cycles" can be produced experimentally by daily administration of low levels of progesterone. The continuation of the cystic condition and the variation in the external behavior is believed to be due to the degree of luteinization of the follicular wall which in turn alters the level of estrogen:progesterone ratio circulating in the system.

Quiet Ovulation. The term "quiet ovulation," sometimes called silent heat or still heat, implies ovulation without the usual behavioral estrus. In practice this condition may be more apparent than real, because it can often be explained in a herd on the basis of failure to detect a short or weak estrus. Much of the apparent problem of quiet ovulation can be removed from such a herd by detailed observation for estrus, especially with the aid of a "teaser" such as a steer or nymphomaniac cow. This makes it a problem of detecting estrus rather than one of aberrant physiological function. However, the stimulation of behavioral estrus, through some external force, in this case the presence and activities of the teaser, may be a factor. These external stimuli could cause changes in the endocrine system which in turn would cause changes in the degree of estrus expression.

Certainly, there are cows which occasionally will not stand for copulation but will ovulate. This can be seen in a young beef heifer or a cow that is on the bottom of the "peck order." The heifer may be frightened by a strange male or a very timid cow will be frightened by all other animals. In checking through the records of some herds having troubles with quiet ovulation, it will be noted that there is an absence of single cows in estrus. This may mean that when certain cows come into estrus alone, they are not detected. When they come into estrus with another cow, they mount each other and both are detected.

Because the estrous period is short in duration in the cow it can occur unobserved. Since estrus is a behavioral response, anything that influences the behavior of the cow can interfere with heat detection, such as factors that place the cow under stress. These factors can range from high air temperature to foot rot and must be considered as problems of management and not physiological, since the ovaries are functioning normally. They simply indicate the necessity for extremely close observation of the cow when she is under adverse environment conditions. Even a bull, in a system of pasture mating and lacking libido, can miss cows in heat under adverse conditions.

2. ANATOMICAL DEFECTS

Consider first the anatomical abnormalities which interfere with the availability of a viable ovum to a viable sperm. They are of two types, congenital and post-natal (acquired).

Congenital. The most widely discussed congenital abnormality, and one which is limited to cattle is the free martin (heifer born co-twin with a bull). About 93 per cent of such heifers are permanently sterile because of missing parts in the reproductive system. The degree of abnormality ranges from slight alterations to complete absence of a reproductive system. Sometimes the gonads will be partly ovarian tissue and partly testicular tissue (ovi-testes). The physiological explanation given for such abnormalities as the free martin was put forth by Lillie in 1917, and is still accepted as correct, states that the hormones produced by the bull calf get into the blood stream of the heifer calf, through a fusion of the blood vessels of the two calves, and interfere with the proper differentiation of the female reproductive organs. This explains why some heifers born co-twin with a bull are not sterile (there has been no fusion of the blood vessels of the two chorions), while others are sterile. It also permits the checking for admixture of blood at birth to determine the possibility of future sterility of the heifer.

Other congenital abnormalities, such as double os cervix, interfere with reproduction but do not always cause sterility.

Acquired. Among the more common acquired anatomical abnormalities are: tubal blocks, which usually involve the Fallopian tube and develop areas of trapped fluid called hydrosalpinx; adhesions of the infundibulum to the ovary or uterine horns which interfere with the pick up of the ovum; or some mechanical destruction of part of the duct system due to a previous pregnancy. Five per cent of any group of females of breeding age can be expected to have some anatomical abnormality which obstructs the meeting of the ovum and the sperm. Some of these abnormalities can be detected by rectal palpation, others can not.

3. IMPROPER UTERINE ENVIRONMENT

The second major cause where the cow contributes to lowered fertility is through her failure to supply proper uterine environment for the sperm, the ova or the embryos while they are in the reproductive duct system. Again, because it is difficult to determine which one of the three respond to the abnormal conditions, only speculations can be made on the proper physiological explanation. For example, very little information is available on the effect of the uterine environment on the sperm between the time of sperm deposition and the time of fertilization. It is known that sperm capacitation is important in some species, it could also exist in cattle. The ovum is also exposed to the environment of the reproductive duct system after ovulation but before fertilization. Therefore the presence of an unfertilized ovum 3 days post mating can be due to aberrant environment on an ovum, viable at ovulation, or a sperm, viable at time of deposition. However, unfertilized ova contribute very little to low fertility in a group of cows mated to high fertility bulls. Therefore if uterine environment is to be a factor, prior to fertilization, it must act as a "carry-over" affect to cause

Table 13-3.—Fertilization Rates and Estimated Embryonic Death Rates in Dairy Heifers Inseminated with Semen from Bulls of High or Low 60-90 Day Non Return Rate

(*Adapted from Kidder et al. 1954. J. Dairy Sci. 37, 691.*)

Non-return rate	Fertilization rate*	Estimated Preg. rate†	Estim. Fertilized Ova dying by 60-90 days
	(%)	(%)	(%)
High (NR 67-79%)	100	74	26
Low (NR 40-66%)	72	61	15

*Normal ova from test heifers 3 to 5 days post heat.

†Per cent non-return minus 5.5 (the amount NR over-estimates actual pregnancy rate) divided by percentage of cows having neither genital abnormalities nor defective ova (as estimated from a group of test heifers).

death of the embryo some time later in its development.

Prenatal Death. The major contribution to general low fertility in the cow is due to early embryonic death. It has been estimated by Kidder and associates (Table 13-3) that 25 per cent of fertilized ova from heifers mated to bulls with a high non-return rate (67 to 79%) were lost by 60 to 90 days post mating. In other work the loss of pregnancies after 40 days post mating, in non-infected cows is not over 3 to 5 per cent. Therefore most of the loss of fertilized ova occur very early in the gestation period. Again a physiological explanation is lacking for this high rate of pre-natal death. It is apparent that death occurs after the embryo reaches the uterus. Therefore a great amount of research effort has been directed toward the elucidation of a possible physiological explanation, based on endometrial function. It has, for the most part, been unsuccessful. This leaves the possibility of an aberrant physiological function acting prior to the arrival of the embryo into the uterus with death as only a delayed effect. It becomes imperative for a complete understanding of the problem that the abnormal physiological mechanisms responsible for prenatal death be determined before proper preventive treatment can be most effective.

Some loss of pregnancies occur throughout the gestation period in non-infected cows, however, it is less than 3 to 5 per cent after 40 days post mating. Even part of this percentage may be due to infectious diseases,

yet unknown. Because of this normally low rate of loss after the first 40 days of gestation any sudden increase in loss of pregnancies suggests an infectious disease and requires immediate attention (see Chapters 19 & 20).

Non-infectious Abortions. Spontaneous abortions include hereditary factors which cause abnormal formation of some vital organ or general lowered viability of the fetus. These are not understood at the present time. Nutritional deficiencies in the pregnant female have been used to experimentally produce abortions. But these deficiencies are usually much greater than that found in rations normally fed to cattle (Chapter 18).

Abortions can also be produced experimentally by alteration of the endocrine system. Removal of the corpus luteum prior to the first 150 days of gestation will terminate the pregnancy. When the corpus luteum is removed, daily injections of 75 to 100 mg. of progesterone will prevent abortion. However, the corpus luteum is not necessary for pregnancy maintenance during the last third of the gestation period. High levels of an injected estrogen, such as 2 to 3 daily injections of 50 mg. estradiol, will cause a high percentage of abortions during any period of gestation. Although these high levels of estrogen are above any physiological level, they may be responsible for an alteration of some other hormone in the endocrine system which is directly responsible for pregnancy maintenance at a physiological level.

4. Retained Placenta

It is a common occurrence, in the cow, for the fetal tissues to be retained within the uterus after parturition. This occurs when the villi of the fetal cotyledons fail to become detached from the maternal caruncles. Normally the shrinkage of the villi after parturition occurs due to the cessation of fetal blood flow to that area.

Cause of the retention of the fetal tissues is not completely understood at the present time. There is some indication that it is associated with infections such as *Brucella abortus or Vibrio fetus*. Apparently anything that causes swelling of the tissues involved is a potential cause. Two of the main after effects of retained placenta are pyometra and delayed involution of the uterus. It is not clear at this point if these are the direct result of the retained tissue or are caused by the same factors which cause the retention in the first place.

The removal of retained tissue should only be attempted by someone with experience and even then there are times when it should not be removed because of the danger in causing damage to the endometrium. This damage could be through further infection or permanent destruction of the caruncles which will interfere with future fertility.

5. Inheritance of Low Fertility

The reported heritability values for fer-tility in cattle are very low. This is not to imply that genes are not important in fertility, but rather the environmental factors mask the expression of most of the genetic factors. There are known recessive lethal genes in the cattle population. Some are responsible for the birth of abnormal calves such as the so-called "bull-dog" calf in certain dairy breeds or the mummification of the fetus during mid pregnancy in beef breeds. The incidence of these, however, is low except where inbreeding is high.

6. Role of Environment of Low Fertility

The effect of environment on fertility can be well demonstrated by the changes which occur in the reproductive pattern, within herds, for different months of the year. This pattern in six Holstein herds practicing year-around artificial insemination for a 10-year period in North Carolina, is shown in Figure 13–1. The rate of return to estrus after first service reached a high 56 per cent for first services during the month of August to a low of 38 per cent for first services during the month of January. This is based on a total of 6,415 first services of which less than 10 per cent were in any given month. Cows, which calve in May and are due to be inseminated in July and August, a season of low fertility, had the longest interval from calving to the onset of

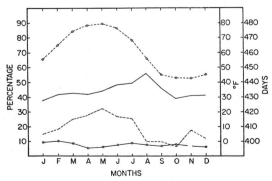

Fig. 13–1.—Monthly changes in the reproductive performance of six dairy herds, located in North Carolina (lat. 36°N). Cows were artificially inseminated at first estrus after 70 days *post-partum*. Note the association of the average high air temperatures during the second and third month *post-partum* (the date when cows should be rebred) with the length of the calving interval. Note also the greatest per cent of return to estrus after breeding occurs in August, which is generally the month of highest air temperatures for this area.

Legend:

―――― Per cent return from first service by 60 to 90 days post mating.

– – – – Length of subsequent calving interval (days), based on month of calving.

o – – o Average high air temperatures (°F.) 2nd and 3rd month subsequent to the month of calving (period of expected breeding).

o―――o Percentage of all calves born during each month.

(Adapted from Poston, H. A., 1961. Ph.D. Thesis, North Carolina State College, Raleigh, N.C.)

the next successful pregnancy. This longer interval is due to the failure of estrus to occur and return to estrus following service.

It is known that ambient temperatures influence fertility in some species (see Chapter 18). A close association is seen (Fig. 13–1) between calving interval (the number of days from the time a cow calves and her next calving date) and the average air temperature at the time she should be rebred for the next pregnancy. An entirely different reproductive pattern would be expected in areas with severe winter temperatures and more temperate summer temperatures.

VI. IMPROVEMENT OF FERTILITY

The physiology responsible for fluctuation in reproductive performance in both the bull and cow are not completely understood at the present time. It is known that conception rate differs between two ejaculates from the same bull collected a few minutes apart. Also the fertility of a given ejaculate can only be predicted within rather broad limits by visual observations of semen quality. The ability of the cow to produce a viable ovum and furnish proper uterine environment for embryonic development varies from period to period and is demonstrated by conception in a cow which has had several unsuccessful services to fertile bulls. Therefore, conception must be the result of the proper combinations of many complex factors in both the male and the female.

Increase in fertility is further hindered by the lack of precise measure of fertility in any given group of cattle at any given time. At best a measure can only be comparative and based on past performance. The measure of fertility for bulls, used in artificial insemination, is to compare the rate of non-return to estrus (60 to 90 days post mating) for first service when their semen is used in a number of herds inseminated by a number of technicians. The assumption is made that the non-return approximates the pregnancy rate and any error is equal for all bulls. Attempts to measure individual cow fertility is made by calculating the number of services per conception; length of the

service period; or the length of the calving interval. Fertility in beef cows is commonly measured by the per cent of cows in the breeding herd which produce a calf subsequent to a given period of breeding. These measures fail to account for the potential reproductive performance of the cow. They either fail to account for the cow which never exhibits estrus or never conceives; and they are all confounded with bull fertility. Further they all measure fertility for some period too far in the past to be most useful for the present. Since pregnancy can be easily determined in cows, by rectal palpation for amnionic resiliency, by 40 days post mating, an accurate estimate of level of fertility can be made to within 40 days of the present time. If it is found to be low, corrective measures can be taken before much time is lost. However, there still remains a need for a "fertility index" which will measure, as near as possible, the current reproductive status of the female herd.

Such an index must include the following criteria: (a) the proportion of the herd classified as non-pregnant and (b) the number of days, on the average, since last date of calving. Under certain systems of management, where seasonal breeding is used, all cows in a herd may be non-pregnant, however the average number of days since calving will be small. In herds where there is no seasonal breeding a lower proportion of the herd will be non-pregnant, but the average number of days since calving will increase for the non-pregnant cows when the herd has a problem with fertility.

A. Improvement of Male Fertility

Obviously the only important function of a bull is to furnish an adequate supply of viable sperm. The number of ova which can be fertilized by the sperm from one ejaculate of semen produced by a highly fertile bull is never used to a maximum. The degree of this sperm wastage will depend on the method of mating used. For example the least efficient method is "pasture mating," where the bull is placed with 30 to 40 cows where there are several services per estrous period. This is followed by "hand mating," where a bull is permitted to serve a cow naturally once during the heat period. Dilution of an ejaculate for use in artificial insemination as fresh or liquid semen stored for 2 to 3 days adds to the efficiency of sperm use. The bull is unique among farm animals in that his sperm can be stored for long periods of time without a loss of fertility. This fact has made it possible to increase greatly reproductive efficiency of the bull, or the individual ejaculate by inseminating cows and selecting, for future use, those bulls or ejaculates which have proven to be most fertile. This cannot be accomplished with any other system of breeding.

B. Improvement of Female Fertility

The highest fertility possible in a group of non-pregnant cows or heifers would be one successful pregnancy for each animal in the group over a 3 week period. To attain this degree of reproductive efficiency each animal in the group must be in estrus and have initiated a successful pregnancy during the period. In practice, failure of either one to occur is perhaps, equally responsible for less than maximum reproductive performances.

The greatest loss of potential calves in mated or inseminated cows is caused by early embryonic death occurring so soon after conception that little or no delay is observed in the time of the subsequent estrus. Unlike deaths which occur later in the gestation (see Chapter 19) many of these are not caused by a known infectious disease. They occur in all herds, under all kinds of conditions and herd management and until the responsible aberrant physiological mechanisms involved are better understood no specific recommendation for their prevention can be made.

Pregnancy Detection. Perhaps one of the most valuable techniques available for improvement of reproductive efficiency is that of determining early pregnancy through palpation for amnionic resiliency after 34 days post mating. At this stage of development the amnion moves freely within the chorion and is much more turgid than the chorion. It will usually be located in the uterine horn on the side of the corpus luteum, just anterior to the external bifurcation of the uterine horns. The cervix is located by using the same method as that for artificial insemination. The reproductive tract is pulled caudally so that the two horns of the uterus can be palpated between the thumb and two fingers (Casida 1960). The horn with the embryo will contain more fluid and consequently will be larger in diameter. As the period of pregnancy progresses, the horn with the embryo will become increasingly larger than the non-pregnant horn and the whole reproductive system will also be pulled further into the abdominal cavity. The period between 60 to 90 days post mating is most difficult for a positive determination of pregnancy, because the whole tract is often in the abdominal cavity and can not be easily manipulated. After 100 days post mating cotyledons become developed well enough to be felt by palpation. Other methods of pregnancy detection in cows are either impractical or lack reliability.

Management Practices for High Reproductive Efficiency. Improvement of fertility in many healthy herds, supplied with recommended levels of nutrition can be obtained through better management. Some of the more common practices used in successful herds with artificial insemination or natural service are as follows:

(a) All events in the reproductive cycle should be recorded for each animal in the herd. These include dates of estrus, breeding or calving and incidents of dystocia, abortion, retained placenta or any treatments. These records should be used continually to determine any changes in the reproductive pattern of the herd.

(b) The breeding cow should be checked for estrus, 30 minutes, twice daily at 12-hour intervals. Distractions, such as feeding, should be reduced to a minimum during the checking periods. Obviously there are situations where it is more economical to have some lowered fertility than it is to meet the necessary requirements for the higher reproductive efficiency. Estrous cows should be inseminated 12 hours after the first detection of estrus with high fertility semen.

(*c*) In systems of "pasture mating," the semen quality of bulls should be determined periodically before and during the mating season so that those producing poor quality semen can be replaced.

(*d*) The reproductive status of cows should be determined by rectal palpation under the following conditions: (*i*) 40 to 60 days after mating to check for pregnancy, (*ii*) When estrus has not occurred by 60 days post partum, to determine conditions of ovaries. The presence of a corpus luteum suggests failure to detect estrus. If uterine involution is not complete it would also be detected at this time. (*iii*) When there is any abnormal vaginal discharge or enlarged uterine horns suggesting uterine infection. (*iv*) When the estrous cycles are shorter than 17 days or longer than 24 days. Follicular cysts are usually responsible for short cycles while embryonic deaths are responsible for true long cycles. Problems of estrus detection should be suspected where cycles approach multiples of 20 days (*i.e.* those of 40 or 60 days in length).

REFERENCES

BLACK, W. G., ULBERG, L. C., CHRISTIAN, R. E. & CASIDA, L. E. (1953). Ovulation and fertilization in the hormone-stimulated calf. *J. Dairy Sci.*, **36**, 274–280.

BOND, J., McDOWELL, R. E., CURRY, W. A. & WARWICK, E. J. (1960). Reproductive performance of milking Shorthorn heifers as affected by constant high environmental temperature. *J. Anim. Sci.*, **19**, 1317. (Abst.).

CASIDA, L. E. (1960). Research techniques in physiology of reproduction research in the female. In: *Techniques and Procedures in Animal Production* Research. Monograph pp. 116–117. Am. Soc. Anim. Production.

CASIDA, L. E. & WISNICKY, W. (1950). Effects of diethylstilbestrol dipropionate upon postpartum changes in the cow. *J. Anim. Sci.*, **9**, 238–242.

CLAPP, H. A. (1937). A factor in breeding efficiency of dairy cattle. *Proc. Amer. Soc. Anim. Prod.* 30th Annual Meeting, 259–265.

KIDDER, H. E., BLACK, W. G., WILTBANK, J. N., ULBERG, L. C. & CASIDA, L. E. (1954). Fertilization rates and embryonic death rates in cows bred to bulls of different levels of fertility. *J. Dairy Sci.*, **37**, 691–697.

LILLIE, F. R. (1917). The freemartin: a study of the action of sex hormones in the fetal life of cattle. *J. Expt. Zool.*, **23**, 371–452.

REID, J. T. (1959). Effect of energy intake upon reproduction in farm animals. *J. Dairy Sci.*, **43** (*suppl.*), 103–122.

QUESTIONS

1. Discuss factors which influence the age of puberty in the bull and heifer.
2. (*a*) At what age are free sperm found in the lumen of the seminiferous tubules of bulls?
   (*b*) At what age can follicles be first observed in the ovaries of heifers?
3. In determining the stage of a pregnancy, *per rectum*, what is the length of the amnion at 40 days post mating; at 50 days post mating and at 60 days post mating.
4. What two main roles does the cow have in the reproductive process?
5. Explain Lillie's theory on the causes of a "free-martin."
6. How is reproductive efficiency measured in a group of cows?
7. List and discuss factors involved in the management of a herd for highest reproductive performance.
8. What are some theories used to explain the formation of follicular cysts? Suggest an explanation for differences in behavior in "cystic" cows.
9. Why do some males produce infertile sperm?
10. Discuss abortion (non-infectious) and retained placenta in cattle.

Chapter 14

The Reproduction of Sheep

By C. E. TERRILL

DOMESTIC sheep (*Ovis aries*) belong to the family *Bovidae*, of hollow horned ruminants. They are even-toed, hoofed mammals of the order *Artiodactyla*. Efforts to increase the reproductive rate in sheep are dependent on an understanding of the various aspects of reproduction and the factors which affect them. In this chapter reproduction in sheep is discussed in relation to sexual maturity and the breeding season; estrus, ovulation, pregnancy and parturition; and reproductive efficiency, infertility and ways in which fertility may be improved.

I. SEXUAL MATURITY

A. Male

Differentiation of sexual organs in sheep commences about the 35th day following conception and the scrotum is apparent in the 50 to 60 day fetus. The testes of the ram lamb are generally descended at birth. However, full development of the reproductive organs are not reached until puberty at an age of about 100 to 150 days or longer. Spermatogenesis may commence about 80 to 90 days and live sperm may be ejaculated with resulting fertility as early as 140 or 150 days. The penis remains infantile with preputial adhesions and can be protruded only slightly until just before puberty. The breakdown of the preputial adhesions to the mature form appears to be dependent on the testis hormone and may be used as an indication of onset of sexual maturity (Wiggins & Terrill, 1953).

Sexual maturity is related to both age and body weight and is influenced by hereditary and environmental factors, especially climate and nutrition. Sexual maturity of ram lambs seems to be more closely related to body weight than to age, occurring at body weights in the range of 40 to 60 per cent of mature weight. Sexual maturity varies with breed being earlier for fast growing breeds, (*e.g.* Hampshire & Suffolk) than in slower growing breeds (*e.g.* Merino). Crossbred lambs generally mature earlier than the average of their purebred parents. Sexual maturity may be delayed even beyond one year of age on a low plane of nutrition or under unfavorable climatic conditions.

From 10 to 50 per cent of rams at 6 to 7 months of age can be expected to be highly fertile and the proportion might be higher under favorable feed and climatic conditions. Sperm production of lambs is generally less than for mature rams and abnormal sperm, particularly immature types, may be more frequent. While ram lambs may be used successfully in breeding, they should be used for a limited mating season. Rams are more commonly mated first at 18 to 20 months of age and fertility at this age is similar to that in 3 to 5 year old rams.

B. Female

Age and weight at puberty in ewe lambs is similar to that for ram lambs, although the first estrus may be expected slightly later in life than first sperm production. In general, the first estrus would occur at 5 to 10 months of age with live weight of 40 to 60 per cent of mature weights. However, many ewe lambs do not have even one estrus until in their second year (Hafez, 1952). Season is an important factor in age of sexual maturity. Ewe lambs which do not show estrus during the first breeding season (fall of the year) will probably not do so until the same time of year after yearling age. With slower maturing breeds this may not occur until after 2 years of age for at least a part of the ewes. A low plane of nutrition may delay sexual development and maturity of ewe lambs and the age of onset of first estrus and development of the reproductive organs is earlier in faster growing, heavier lambs. The optimum plane of nutrition for maximum sexual development in various breeds has not been well defined. Ovulation without heat generally precedes the first estrus by the length of one estrous cycle.

Under favorable conditions with early maturing breeds such as the Hampshire, about 50 to 60 per cent of ewe lambs exposed will become pregnant. Under range conditions with Rambouillets this might be as low as 10 per cent. Ewes bred first as ewe lambs will generally produce more lambs during their lifetime than ewes bred first as yearlings, although their productive lives may average slightly shorter. Ewes are commonly bred first at the breeding season following one year of age.

II. BREEDING SEASON

A. Male

The male of domestic sheep does not show a restricted breeding season so common in the female, but seasonal variations in semen production and characteristics are evident. In the central and northern United States there is generally a decline in proportion of normal sperm in the spring and summer months with an increase in the fall and winter. Sperm concentration, total sperm and motility showed similar trends. These vary not only with temperature but also with day length as in Egypt highest semen qualities were observed in March and April (*spring equinox*) and in September and October (*fall equinox*) and low semen qualities were found during July with the longest days and December with the shortest days (Fig. 14–1). While there was a decline in both total sperm and motility in the summer there was no summer sterility.

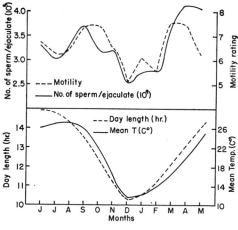

Fig. 14–1.—Seasonal variation in semen characteristics of the ram in relation to day length and ambient temperature in Egypt (latitude 30° N.). Note that the highest spermatogenic activity coincides with the spring and autumnal equinox. (*Data from Hafez et al., 1955. J. Agric. Sci., 45, 283.*)

The testes of rams are normally kept at temperatures about 5°C. below body temperature. Increased body and thus testicular temperatures results in reduced sperm production, lowered fertility and sterility. When air temperatures are continuously above about 30°C. it becomes increasingly difficult for some rams to maintain normal testicular temperature and thus summer sterility follows. Artificial cooling of the rams will correct or prevent summer sterility and shearing of rams before hot weather is helpful (Dutt, 1960).

B. Female

The ewe of wild or primitive sheep normally breeds during a restricted season of the year so that the young tend to be born at the most favorable time, the late spring. Breeding seasons of domestic sheep vary from only a few estrous periods per year to year round breeding in some breeds. There is also considerable variation among individuals and among years in the date of onset and the duration of the breeding seasons. Seasonal fluctuation in day length is an important factor affecting the length of the breeding season in different parts of the world (Fig. 14–2). The breeding season usually commences as the days become shorter. Furthermore, the breeding season tends to become shorter at latitudes close to the poles. In the tropics and sub-tropics the ewes may tend to show estrus throughout the year i.e., there is no restricted breeding season. The breeding season is also affected by ambient temperature (see Chapter 18). Year to year variations are not easily explained by climatic differences. The presence of the ram may hasten the onset of first estrus near the beginning of the breeding season.

Breed differences in the number of estrous

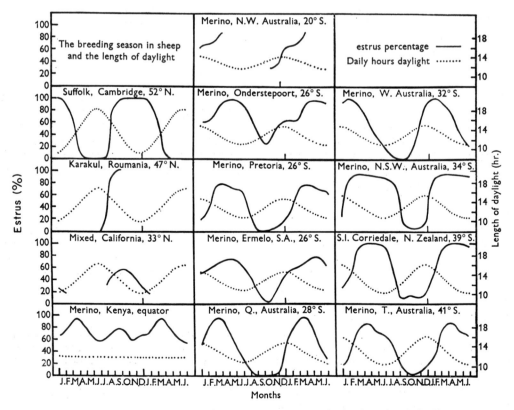

FIG. 14–2.—The relationship between the breeding season and the length of daylight at different latitudes. (Breed, locality and latitude are shown in that order in each graph.) (*From Hafez, 1952. J. Agric. Sci., 42, 189.*)

Table 14–1.—Breed Differences in Reproductive Phenomena of the Ewe

(Adapted from McKenzie & Terrill, 1937, Mo. Agric. Exp. Sta. Res. Bull. 264; Hafez, 1952, J. Agric. Sci. 42, 189; other sources.)

Breed	No. of estrous periods/year		Duration of estrus (hours)		Length of estrous cycle (days)	
	Range	Means[1]	Range	Means[1]	Range	Means[1]
Bikaneri	*	*	12–80	35	15–19	17
Blackface Mountain	5–10	7	6–37	23	13–23	17
Border Leicester	5–9	7	24–35	29	15–24	17
Corriedale			12–72	29–43	15–24	17
Dorset Horn	10–17	12	32–56	45	6–23	17
Hampshire	2–15	8–10	3–60	29–34	5–49	16–17
Iceland					13–23	16
Lincoln			12–96	41		
Masai	*	*	3–81	36		18
Merino	*	*	1–96	18–40	3–68	16–22
Merino (Palas)			20–90	28	10–30	18
Navajo						16
Norwegian			12–96	30		
Persian	*	*	3–57	30–48		18
Rambouillet			3–72	26–40	5–55	17
Romney Marsh	9–11	10	8–60	32–36	4–55	17
Shropshire			3–48	24–28	8–49	16
Southdown			3–54	23–27	9–26	16
Suffolk	9–12	10	9–46	23–39	7–23	17
Welsh Mountain	4–9	7	35–52	42	12–20	17

[1] Where more than one study is reported the range of means is given.
*Reported to breed all the year around

periods per year (Table 14–1) show that mountain breeds tend to have a shorter breeding season, while the Dorset Horn and Merino have the longest season of those breeds which have been studied.

III. ESTRUS AND OVULATION

Detection of Estrus. Sexual behavior of ewes is relatively inconspicuous and is not evident in the absence of the ram. The ewe in estrus may seek out the ram, but the only real evidence of estrus is the willingness of the ewe to stand and allow the ram to tease and mount. The difficulty of detecting estrous ewes with the attendant labor involved is a practical factor in limiting the extensive use of artificial insemination in this species. Vasectomized or aproned rams must be used to detect ewes in heat. The use of marking harness or marking material on the ram's brisket is subject to some error unless it is supplemented with direct observation. Some rams can complete service without leaving a mark and ewes are sometimes marked which are not in estrus.

Coincident with estrus is the occasional enlargement of the vulva, high epithelium of the vagina, and the liquefaction and flow of mucus from the cervix. These are often unnoticed externally.

Cornification and sloughing of the vaginal epithelium occurs following estrus. The vaginal smear is much less diagnostic of the stages of the estrual cycle than in many other species, although it is of considerable help to the trained observer. Arborization of the cervical mucus is of help in detecting estrogenic effects.

Duration of Estrus. The duration of estrus varies from a few hours up to 3 to 4 days or more with an average of 24 to 48 hours. Estrus is generally shortest for ewe lambs with yearlings being intermediate (McKenzie & Terrill, 1937). It is often shorter near the beginning and end of the breeding season. Breed differences in duration of estrus are not clear cut (Table 14–1), although wool breeds may tend to have longer estrous periods than mutton breeds.

Ovulation. Ovulation normally occurs near the end of estrus, although it may take place from several hours before to several hours after the end of estrus. The time of ovulation from the onset of estrus has been reported to be longer with twin than with single ovulation, although the duration of estrus was unaffected. Twin ovulations may be separated for more than 7 hours with a mean difference of almost 2 hours. The time of ovulation is independent of copulation, although it does tend to vary with other factors affecting the duration of estrus. Ovulations follow no regular pattern between both ovaries, although they occur more often in the right ovary. The factors affecting ovulation rate will be discussed later under Section V and VII.

Length of Estrous Cycle. The normal estrous cycle in the ewe ranges from 14 to 19 days with a mean of 17 days. Multiple cycles resulting from ovulation without estrus occur occasionally and are more common in some mountain breeds. Other causes of abnormal cycle lengths include failure of ovulation and luteinization, early regression of the corpus luteum and early prenatal death of the embryo. Abnormal cycle lengths are more common early and late in the breeding season. The length of the estrous cycle tends to be shortest at the peak of the breeding season and increases toward the end. It is also longer on a low as compared to a high plane of nutrition but breed differences are not clear cut (Table 14–1). Mutton breeds may have slightly shorter cycles than wool breeds.

The occurrence of estrus and ovulation during lactation is quite variable and often infrequent. Ewes may show post-partum estrus within a few days. Lactation anestrus generally varies from about 4 to 10 weeks with an average of about 5 weeks (Hafez, 1952), although many ewes may not return to estrus until the onset of the next breeding season. Non-suckling ewes return to estrus earlier and are more likely to conceive from mating at this first estrus.

Synchronization of Estrus. Progesterone, when injected over a period of 12 to 14 days or the feeding of orally-active forms of the hormone during the breeding season, will prevent estrus and ovulation. Dosages usually employed are 6 to 12 mg. progesterone injected daily or 10 to 20 mg. every other day. When such treatment is stopped estrus and ovulation will occur in 2 to 3 days and normal fertility is usually obtained. If ewes fail to conceive or are not bred at this estrus, they will return to estrus after a normal cycle and subsequent reduction in fertility is not apparent. Thus, apart from the tedium of repeated injections, treatment with progesterone offers a practical means of synchronizing estrus so that the lambing period can be reduced to 10 days or less for ewes conceiving at the estrus following progesterone treatment. Ewes lambing from normal breeding over the time equivalent to one estrous cycle would lamb over a period of 20 days or more.

IV. PREGNANCY AND PARTURITION

Sperm travel through the reproductive tract of the ewe at an average of 4 cm. per minute although considerable individual variation occurs. They reach the upper Fallopian tubes as early as 20 minutes after ejaculation (Schott & Phillips, 1941). Sperm survive longer (up to 3 days) in the cervix than in other parts of the tract where survival is up to 12 hours in the vagina and up to 30 hours in the uterus and Fallopian tubes.

A. Pregnancy

A simple reliable, test for pregnancy is not yet available for sheep. The viscosity and appearance of the cervical mucus as early as 45 to 60 days may have promise. Diagnosis by *x*-ray after the 55th day has been reported (Benzie, 1951) but is limited for practical use.

Sexual activity in the ewe occasionally occurs during pregnancy, particularly at the time of the normal breeding season. Ovulation generally does not occur but fertilization during pregnancy and superfetation have been reported. This has not occurred under carefully controlled experimental conditions and is certainly rare.

The mean length of pregnancy for various breeds varies from 144 to 155 days (Table 14–2), although individual normal pregnancies may vary from 138 to 159 days. Extremely short and long periods may be of questionable normality. The early maturing mutton breeds (*e.g.* Southdown, Dorset Horn, Hampshire & Shropshire) have short gestation periods averaging about 144 to 148 days. Slow maturing fine wool breeds (*e.g.* Merino or Rambouillet) have long periods varying in average length from 148 to 152 days. Long wool mutton breeds (*e.g.* Lincoln and Romney) and crossbred types (*e.g.* Corriedale, Columbia & Targhee) have intermediate average gestation periods in the range from 145 to 150 days. Individual gestation periods within a breed will vary up to 15 days with a standard deviation of approximately 2.2 days.

Table 14–2.—Breed Differences in Length of Pregnancy and Weight at Birth of Sheep

(*Adapted from Terrill & Hazel, 1947, Am. J. Vet. Res. 8, 66; Thomson & Aitken, 1959, Sheep: World Survey of Reproduction and Review of Feeding Experiments, Commonwealth Bur. An. Nutr. Tech. Comm. 20; & other sources.*)

| Breed | Breed means (days) in length of pregnancy | Mean birth weight (lbs.) by sex and type of birth | | | | | | |
		All individuals	All males	All females	Single males	Twin males	Single females	Twin females
Awassi					10	8	9	8
Biella					10	8	9	8
Bikaneri		6						
Blackface Mountain		6						
Cheviot	148	8						
Columbia	148	9						
Corriedale	150	9			10	9	9	8
Cotswold		10						
Dorset Horn	146	7						
Finnish		4						
Hampshire	145				11	10	10	9
Heidschnucke	148	5						
Karakul	151	8	11	9	11	10		
Kerry Hill			11	11	13	10	12	10
Landrace (Swedish)		6						
Leicester (English)		9			10		10	
Leine		9						
Lincoln	146							
Merino	150	9	9	8	9	8	7	7
Merino (Mutton)	149	10			11		10	
Navajo	149	8						
Ossimi	152	8			8	6	9	6
Oxford Down		11						
Precoce	149	9						
Rahmani	155	8			9	7	8	6
Rambouillet	151	9	11	10	11	9	10	8
Rhön	151							
Romanov			7	6				
Romnelet		9			10	8	9	8
Romney Marsh	148							
Sokolka					9	7	8	7
Shropshire	145	9			9	8	8	7
Southdown	144	7			8	7	8	7
Suffolk	147							
Targhee	149							
Tsigai	149				10	8	9	8
Welsh Mountain		8	8	7	9	8	8	7
Württemberg		10						

Hereditary factors play an important role in the duration of pregnancy as would be expected from the breed differences (Terrill & Hazel, 1947). A significant half-sib correlation for sires indicates that the sire influences the length of gestation of the ewes to which he is mated and this influence must be exerted through characteristics which the sire transmits to the lamb. An equal hereditary effect of the dam would be expected to be transmitted to the lamb and in addition other maternal factors must operate because of individual physiological characteristics of the dam. This is substantiated by a higher maternal than paternal half-sib correlation for gestation lengths. Further evidence is shown in breed crosses where the intermediate gestation length is closer to the dam's breed. Pregnancy is shorter for twin lambs than for singles and increases with age of dam. Effect of sex of lamb is not important. A low plane of nutrition tends to reduce gestation length particularly in late pregnancy and for twins.

B. Parturition

Near the end of pregnancy there is a relaxation of the pelvic ligaments, vagina and cervix. This is accompanied by increased irritability of the uterus and activity of the fetus (see Chapter 10). The first external signs of parturition are uneasiness, pawing, frequent turning or lying down and standing up. These occur up to a few hours before parturition and are often accompanied by an intense interest in lambs of other ewes. Older ewes will often "steal" lambs from younger ewes and this is most prevalent just prior to parturition. Mature ewes show signs of parturition for a shorter period before lambing than young ewes. Malpresentation of the lamb is the most common cause of difficulty, although young ewes may have difficulty even with normal presentation. The fore feet normally appear first just in front of the head. The most common forms of malpresentation are with one or both front legs turned back. A few are presented with the hind legs or breech first. The ewe licks the lamb dry following birth. The lamb will usually stand within 15 to 30 minutes and suckle within an hour or two.

Lambings are spread throughout the 24 hours but slightly more may come from midnight to morning. The placenta is generally expelled from 2 to 4 hours following birth. Involution of the uterus follows rapidly and is usually complete by one month.

C. Sex Ratio

Reports of the sex ratio from over 200 thousand births are extremely consistent in showing 49 to 50 per cent males (Rae, 1956). A slightly higher ratio of males in fetuses and a decreasing ratio with increasing number of young born at one time suggest higher prenatal mortality of males, although this is not evident with stillborn lambs. Data on the frequency of like-sexed twins do not give evidence of the occurrence of identical twins in sheep, but other evidence indicates they occur but with extremely low frequency. Several cases of the freemartin condition in sheep have been reported.

V. REPRODUCTIVE EFFICIENCY

Reproductive efficiency depends on the proportion of ewes mated which become pregnant and the lambing rate. Lambing rate (number of lambs born of ewes lambing) depends on the number of ovulations minus those ova which failed to become fertilized or embryos which died and were resorbed before birth. The proportion of lambs born of ewes lambing is markedly affected by age and by breed (Table 14–3).

A. Male

Sperm Production. The length of the spermatogenic cycle is approximately 49 days (see Chapter 3). Ortavant calculated the average daily production of sperm of Ile-de-France rams to be in the region of 5.5 billion, although this may vary with season or length of day. Sperm production may improve with age up to 3 or 4 years, but little difference has been found in fertility of rams of different ages. Adequate nutrition is essential to high sperm production and underfeeding can be detrimental, although overfatness following high levels of feeding may also be detrimental.

Table 14–3.—Breed Differences in Fertility of Sheep

(*Adapted from Thomson & Aitken, 1959, Sheep: World Survey of Reproduction and Review of Feeding Experiments, Commonwealth Bur. An. Nutr. Tech. Comm. 20; other sources.*)

Breed	Infertile matings	Lambs born of ewes lambing	Stillbirths
		Ranges in mean per cent of[1]	
Awassi	1	109	
Blackface Mountain	0–15		10
Border Leicester	4		
Cheviot	1–7	141–158	
Cheviot (North Country)	2–5		7–12
Clun Forest	1–5		5–13
Columbia	7–17	120–136	8–9
Corriedale	0–20	110–114	6
Cotswold		144–150	
Dorset Horn	4–7	127–158	
East Fresian		206	
Finnish		200–400	
German Black-headed Mutton	1–10	121–125	
German White-headed Mutton		150–230	
Hampshire	1–6	115–163	
Heidschnucke	4	103–106	
Iceland	3–8		
Karakul	4	100–125	
Landrace (Swedish)		123–195	
Leicester (English)		120–167	
Leine	5	125–150	
Lincoln	2–8	129–157	
Merino	7–32	103–161	4–9
Merino (German)	5–11	120–150	
Merino (Mutton)	8–12	106–162	
Merino (Palas)	9	127	
Navajo	11	141	2
Oxford Down	6–10	135–172	
Pramenka	1–19		
Precoce	13–14	120–150	2–4
Rahmani		124	
Rambouillet	4–15	110–161	6–9
Rhön	6–10	107	
Romanov	1	195–231	
Romnelet	7–15	139	
Romney Marsh	6–27	131–142	
Sokolka		124–180	
Shropshire	1–10	125–158	
Southdown	3–15	116–170	
Suffolk	4–5	152	
Targhee	16	129–138	7
Tsigai	4–5	114–151	2–5
Welsh Mountain	2–5		
Wensleydale	4	182	
White Swiss Mountain		150–170	
Wrzosowka		185	
Württemberg	2–18	107–156	

[1] The ranges of means reported from different studies are given.

Seasonal variations in sexual expression show a similar trend to that of sperm production, although a high intensity of sexual expression does not insure high sperm production or high fertility. Sperm production may be increased under conditions of mild hyperthyroidism and is generally improved from a low to a high plane of nutrition. Cooling of rams during hot weather has a marked beneficial effect on sperm production.

Frequency of ejaculation, motility of sperm, proportion of live sperm, and absence of abnormalities, particularly those of the sperm head, broken necks or tailless heads have generally shown highest predictive value for subsequent fertility of the ram. High quality ram semen should have at

at the rate of once every 1 to 5 hours when continuously with ewes in heat.

B. Female

Ovulation rate, through its important relationship to number of lambs weaned per ewe bred, may be the most important aspect of reproduction in sheep. Marked differences have been found in ovulation rate due to breed, age, year, season, and nutrition. Ovulation rate, often deduced from number of lambs born at one time, is most commonly one, often 2, occasionally 3, and rarely 4, but has been reported as high as 7. It increases to a maximum from 3 to 6 years of age and then may decline slightly with advancing

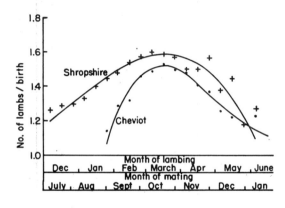

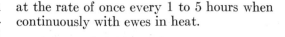

Fig. 14–3.—Seasonal variation in fertility in the Swedish Shropshire and Cheviot. (*Adapted from Johansson & Hansson. 1943 Annals Agric. College of Sweden 11, 145.*)

least 1 to 2 billion sperm per cc., with rapid swirling motility, a pH of 7.0 or more acid and with less than 25 per cent abnormal sperm or less than 5 per cent abnormal heads. Semen from electro-ejaculation will usually have lower sperm concentration and more alkaline reaction than normally ejaculated semen.

Copulation. Rams vary widely in the frequency with which they copulate. Rams under continuous observation with one or more ewes in heat mated an average of once every 3 hours, but varied from once in 10 hours to almost twice an hour (Hulet *et al.*, 1961). The frequency of copulation is higher when the ram is first introduced to a pen of ewes and also increases with an increase in the number of ewes in heat. Rams may copulate 2 or 3 times in a few minutes when first turned with a ewe but they tend to mate

age. Ovulation rate tends to be high near the middle of the breeding season and decreases toward its end (Fig. 14–3). Year differences are often confounded with nutrition and are not well understood. The tendencies for the ovulation rate to be higher as sheep are kept at latitudes closer to the poles and to be higher for sheep with faces free of wool covering, as has been shown in a number of breeds, may be related to seasonal or nutritional effects but are not well understood.

The restricted breeding season of many breeds of sheep has led to attempts to alter the breeding season so that lambs can be produced at any season of the year. This often has marked economic advantages. The fact that some breeds of tropical or subtropical origin, will breed at any time of the year, indicates that the breeding season could be extended by genetic means. The heritability of the length of breeding season is appreciable and selection experiments are now underway to eliminate anestrus of some breeds or strains through breeding. Rate of twinning and milk production are also heritable although to a low or moderate degree.

The use of artificial treatment to extend the breeding season offers hope of more rapid gains if practical methods can be developed. Shortening of the length of day and cooling have both been shown to be effective in permitting ewes to be bred out of season but the interactions between these treatments have not been established.

Injections of 10 to 12 mg. progesterone for 12 to 16 days, followed by gonad stimulating hormone (800 to 1000 i.u. of PMS) in 1 or 2 days may induce estrus and ovulation during the non-breeding season (Robinson, 1959). However, sheep often vary in their response to these treatments and high fertility is not usually obtained.

The successful artificial induction of estrus and ovulation is desirable not only to obtain fertility during anestrus, but also for correction of sterility and for breeding during lactation to increase the number of lamb crops per year. Estrogens alone in sufficient dosage will produce estrus in ewes but without ovulation or fertility. Ewes can be kept in heat (often atypical) continuously by repeated injections or implants of estrogens. Marked changes may occur in the reproductive tract including vaginal hyperplasia, prolapse of the vagina and uterus, and initiation of lactation and failure of conception may follow. Estrogenic substances in plants, particularly subterranean clover, produce such effects sometimes resulting in permanent sterility.

Gonad stimulating hormones, particularly pregnant mare serum (PMS) or human chorionic gonadotropin (HCG), will usually induce ovulation during anestrus but must be repeated after a 16 to 17 day interval in order to produce both estrus and ovulation. This along with the observation that quiet ovulation almost always precedes the first estrus of the breeding season indicate that progesterone must precede estrogen in order for estrus to occur with ovulation. Unfortunately the use of hormones to induce estrus and ovulation has often given inconsistent results and further refinement in hormone preparation and/or techniques is probably essential before widespread practical use can be made.

Acceleration of the ovulation rate provides a practical means of increasing the lamb crop, although it must be remembered that an increase in the number of fetuses and in number of lambs born increases the nutritional needs both during late pregnancy and lactation and also in the care required at lambing time.

The use of gonad stimulating hormones on about the 11th to the 13th day of the normal cycle to increase the ovulation rate (mild superovulation) is often effective if the proper dosage (500 to 750 i.u. PMS) is given but considerable labor is involved in checking for estrus and timing the hormone injections properly. Therefore, it may be questioned if the procedure is practical but under certain conditions it may be very useful. Lambing percentages may be increased by about 30 per cent by such treatment.

The stimulation of lactation in the non-lactating ewe, though possible, is generally of little practical use. Likewise the stimulation of lactation when it fails following parturition has generally not been useful. The increase of lactation rate by use of thyroxine or other like materials, though effective, has not proven to be of practical benefit. These methods are useful for experimental purposes and under intensive systems of production more practical uses may be developed.

Birth weight of the lamb varies not only with breed, sex and type of birth (Table 14–2), but also with length of pregnancy, nutrition and temperature (Thomson & Aitken, 1959). Birth weights from normal gestation lengths may range from a few pounds up to 15 to 18 pounds or more. Extremely low weights often result from premature births or from high temperatures during pregnancy. Survival is best from birth weights slightly above average.

VI. INFERTILITY

Permanent or lifetime sterility is quite

rare in sheep, although low fertility and temporary infertility are common. Various kinds of reproductive failure will be discussed here.

A. Male

Abnormalities of the reproductive organs in the ram include *intersexes* with predominantly male traits, *hypospadias* (abnormal opening of the urethral canal) and an *infantile* development of the male organs. Defects of the penis or sheath may result in inability of the ram to copulate.

The above abnormalities may have a genetic cause but this is usually obscure. Unilateral or bilateral cryptorchidism are often of genetic origin, depending on a single pair of recessive genes. This gene is sometimes linked with the polled gene particularly in fine wool strains. Only unilateral cryptorchids may be fertile. Lack of sex drive and level of semen production, although somewhat independent, seem to be heritable although to a moderate or low degree.

Nutritional deficiencies, particularly of calories, protein, phosphorus, and vitamin A, may lead to low levels of semen production and thus infertility in some cases.

Climatic factors, particularly sustained high temperatures, are the most common cause of temporary sterility of rams. Summer sterility of rams is well known over much of the United States. Sudden cold storms are reported to result in infertility of rams but this work is not well substantiated experimentally. Both high temperature and high humidity may have indirect effects on fertility through lowered feed intake and/or parasitism.

B. Female

Some abnormalities of the ewe reproductive organs include those due to intersexes, and to infantilism or failure of mature development. In the latter case, ewes are in permanent anestrus. *Atresia ani* with a common opening of the lower intestine and the vagina sometimes occurs. Closure of one or both Fallopian tubes may result in infertility. Prolapse of the vagina and/or

uterus, usually near the time of parturition is relatively common in ewes. While prompt attention will correct the defect, such ewes should not be retained for further breeding.

Death of the embryo or fetus at any time from conception to birth is a common cause of lowered fertility. This may result from a variety of causes, particularly high temperatures, nutritional extremes and genetic causes. The embryo is particularly vulnerable to high temperatures during the first few days (Dutt, 1960). High levels of nutrition or over-fatness may result in high embryo mortality during early gestation, although underfeeding may also increase prenatal mortality. Close inbreeding may result in increased prenatal and postnatal mortality. Estimates of the extent of prenatal death in sheep indicate that reductions of 15 to 30 per cent may occur. Prenatal death rates increase with higher ovulation rates.

Abortions or the premature birth of young do not always indicate the presence of infectious diseases, although diagnosis is often uncertain. About 1 per cent of ewes can be expected to abort normally. Common causes of prenatal death which occur late in pregnancy probably account for these. Prenatal deaths early in pregnancy are probably followed by resorption of the embryo or fetus and do not result in abortion.

Stillborn lambs result from death of the fetus at the time of parturition. Reports from various breeds indicate a range of about 2 to 13 per cent of lambs born are dead at birth (Table 14–3). Breed differences are relatively small.

Genetic factors may play a part in any expression of sterility or lowered fertility in the ewe. Inherited lethal traits may be expressed before or at the time of birth. Some examples of inherited lethals or semi-lethals include muscle contracture, earless, cleft palate, paralysis, rigid fetlocks, amputated, gray lethal, dwarfism, nervous incoordination, congenital photosensitivity, and blindness (Rae, 1956). Various abnormalities of the reproductive organs may be of genetic origin but proof is usually difficult.

Various deficiencies, particularly of vitamins A and E, selenium, iodine, copper, cobalt, phosphorus and protein may lead to infertility, although these may operate indirectly. Pregnancy toxemia, which occurs in late pregnancy in twin bearing ewes, involves a disturbance in carbohydrate metabolism of nutritional origin (Robinson, 1957) and often results in the death of both ewe and lambs (see Chapter 18).

Detrimental effects of high temperatures on ewe fertility are exerted mainly during pregnancy, although high temperature just prior to breeding may be detrimental. Early prenatal death often results from high temperatures at the time of or following fertilization. Pregnancies completed during or following hot weather often result in unusually small lambs with high mortality at or following birth.

Annual variations occur in fertility of sheep which are consistent over rather large geographical areas but which cannot be explained from recorded climatic factors. These indicate that unknown climatic factors may exist which affect such fertility traits as date of onset of the breeding season, ovulation rate and proportion of infertile matings.

VII. IMPROVEMENT OF FERTILITY

A. Male

A practical measure of ram fertility is the per cent of infertile matings. Breed averages range from zero to over 30 per cent (Table 14–3). Five to 10 per cent of infertile matings can be expected from highly fertile rams. Improvement of ram fertility involves proper animal management, semen tests and selective breeding.

Animal Management. Management at breeding time is important in preventing sterility or low fertility. Adequate nutrition preceding and during breeding is important. However, rams should not be allowed to become overfat before breeding as high fitting for shows is often associated with sterility. Shipment of rams is sometimes followed by temporary sterility and should not immediately precede the breeding period. Shearing before breeding and cooling of the rams during the daytime are helpful in avoiding summer sterility.

Semen Tests. Semen tests are effective in detecting and eliminating sterile rams or those which are unable to serve and may be useful in eliminating low fertile rams. Great care must be used in interpreting such tests especially when using electrical ejaculation and when the history of the ram or the conditions under which he will be bred are uncertain. There is always danger with indiscriminate use of semen tests that fertile rams will be eliminated. Experience under a given set of conditions is necessary before reasonably accurate predictions of fertility can be made from sperm normality and motility.

Selection. Improvement of ram fertility usually involves elimination of defective animals as soon as they are detected, although it is difficult to distinguish between temporary and permanent sterility. Rams which fail to sire offspring when mated to a pen of ewes for a month or more, those which do not produce live sperm, those with known injuries to the testes and those with palpatable abnormalities of the testis or epididymis along with poor semen should be culled from the breeding herd. Highly valuable sires should be given repeated semen tests before culling to make certain that the infertility is not temporary. Rams with poor semen in one year may recover by the following year.

Selection against sterility factors is difficult because these factors persist even though sterile animals leave no offspring. Selection of males from highly fertile dams is desirable. Likewise selection of males with a high potential for twinning will be more effective genetically than selecting females for this trait because of the much higher selection differential which may be obtained with rams as compared with ewes. However, any genetic gain will not be realized until the daughters produce lambs. Selection under adverse conditions (*e.g.* high altitude or high temperature) will reveal the sires which remain fertile in spite of these unfavorable environments. This is especially desirable in breeding replacement stock for areas with such environments. Thus, in selecting against infertility it is helpful to select under stresses which tend to reveal the less fertile animals which might appear to be highly fertile under optimum conditions.

B. Female

Nutrition. Adequate nutrition is especially important in the last month of pregnancy and during lactation. Following weaning it is desirable to provide essential nutrients but to limit the plane of nutrition to prevent overfatness. In fact ewes should be in moderate condition up to a few weeks prior to the start of the breeding season. Then a high plane of nutrition (*i.e.* flushing) for 2 or 3 weeks just before the rams are introduced will usually increase the ovulation rate of mature ewes. This increased rate of feeding should probably be terminated after the first 2 weeks of breeding if not at the time the rams are put with the ewes. Ewes should gain up to 15 to 30 lb. or more during pregnancy but much of this is made in the last month.

Animal Management. Breeding in large and in rough or timbered pastures may result in the ram failing to breed some ewes. Mature ewes will often seek out the ram but young ewes may not. Increasing the number of rams to 4 or 5 per 100 ewes, introducing additional new rams during breeding, and periodic bringing together of all the sheep in the pasture may help. Hand mating, involving detection of ewes in heat with a teaser ram, and allowing each ewe to be mated only once or twice can result in high fertility if carefully done, but may result in a reduced fertility rate because the ewes are not as apt to be mated at the optimum time. Likewise turning rams in with the ewes for only a part of each 24 hours such as only in the day time or only at night may result in a decreased rate of fertility.

Selection for Twinning. The changing lambing rate with age of ewe provides a clue for selection for twinning. Very few ewes have twins at the first lambing and therefore those that do, have a high potential for twinning. Such twins may not express this potential at their first lambing because of their double environmental disadvantage of being both a twin and from a 2 year-old

mother. Such lambs weigh from 15 to 20 lb. less at weaning than single lambs from mature ewes. Ewes born as twins have a higher rate of twinning at all other ages in spite of the environmental advantage which single lambs retain throughout life. The curves turn up slightly after the 5th year probably because of selection practiced among these ewes on their own lamb production so that the lower producing ewes were not present at the later ages. It seems reasonable that the potential for twinning was highest for ewes born as twins from 2- and 3-year-old ewes because these represented only 3 per cent and 16 per cent, respectively, of the ewes lambing. Ewes having twins as 4- and 5-year-old represented 41 per cent and 44 per cent, respectively, of ewes lambing and therefore have a lower selection advantage for twinning potential than 2- and 3-year-old ewes. Thus in selecting for twinning it is desirable to favor the ram twins from 2- and 3-year-old mothers, as well as the ewe twins. It also pays to retain the ewes which twin at the young ages (Table 14–4).

Selection on the ewe's lamb production in the first year is an effective way to eliminate potentially low lamb producers before they leave offspring in the flock. Comparisons of lamb production in the first year to later production from 3 to 6 years of age on Rambouillet ewes (Table 14–4) shows predictive value for the 2-year-old production. Ewes which were infertile from first year mating had the highest rate of infertile matings in later years though these differences were small. Ewes having the highest proportion of stillborn lambs the first year also had the highest proportion in subsequent years. Ewes having singles and weaning a lamb their first year had generally higher lifetime fertility than those which failed to wean the first year. Ewes having twins the first year generally showed higher lifetime fertility than all other groups.

Wool covering on the faces of ewes is directly related to lamb production. Ewes with open faces, free from wool below the eyes, produced 11 per cent more lambs than covered-face ewes (Terrill, 1949). Thus, sheep born as twins, from young mothers, large sheep, and those with open faces,

Table 14–4.—Reproduction of Rambouillet Ewes Three Through Six Years of Age as Related to Lamb Production in Their First Year

(*Terrill, unpublished*)

Lamb production in the first year	No. of ewe years	Reproductive rates of the ewes at 3 through 6 years of age			
		Infertile matings	Twinning rate	Stillbirths	Live lambs born of ewes bred
		%	%	%	%
Infertile	302	6	21	6	107
One stillborn lamb	247	4	25	9	109
One live lamb born but not weaned	268	2	29	5	120
One live lamb born and weaned	2073	5	32		118
One stillborn lamb but foster lamb weaned	56	4	43	3	134
Twin lambs born	107	3	58	3	149

should be favored in selection to improve fertility.

Selection for high fertility under adverse climatic conditions such as hot temperatures should lead to the development of strains of high fertility under these stresses. Unimproved strains or breeds such as the Navajo sheep are noted for their high lambing rates and good mothering ability. These qualities were probably improved by natural selection under adverse conditions.

Under intensive conditions the synchronization of estrus and the use of artificial insemination may be practical (see Chapter 8). Embryo transfer may have important genetic implications if the procedure becomes relatively easy and inexpensive, but in the immediate future it is most likely to facilitate genetic and physiological research (see Chapter 6).

REFERENCES

BENZIE, D. (1951). X-ray diagnosis of pregnancy in ewes. *Brit. Vet. J.*, **107**, 3–6.

DUTT, R. H. (1960). Temperature and light as factors in reproduction among farm animals. In the effect of germ cell damage on animal reproduction. *J. Dairy Sci.*, **43** Suppl., 123–141.

HAFEZ, E. S. E. (1952). Studies on the breeding season and reproduction of the ewe. *J. Agric. Sci.*, **42**, 189–265.

HULET, C. V., ERCANBRACK, S. K., PRICE, D. A., BLACKWELL, R. L. & WILSON, L. O. (1961). Mating behavior of the ram in the one-sire pen. *J. Anim. Sci.*, **20**, 972 (Abstract).

McKENZIE, F. F. & TERRILL, C. E. (1937). Estrus, ovulation and related phenomena in the ewe. *Mo. Agric. Exp. Sta. Res. Bull.* No. 264.

RAE, A. L. (1956). The genetics of the sheep. *Advances in Genetics*, **8**, 189–265. New York, Academic Press.

ROBINSON, T. J. (1957). Pregnancy. In: *Progress in the Physiology of Farm Animals*, J. Hammond (edit.) Vol. III, London, Butterworths Scientific Publications.

ROBINSON, T. J. (1959). The estrous cycle of the ewe and doe. In: *Reproduction in Domestic Animals*. H. H. Cole & P. T. Cupps (edit.) Vol. 1, New York, Academic Press.

SCHOTT, R. G. & PHILLIPS, R. W. (1941). Rate of sperm travel and time of ovulation in sheep. *Anat. Rec.*, **79**, 531–540.

TERRILL, C. E. & HAZEL, L. N. (1947). Length of gestation in range sheep. *Amer. J. Vet. Res.*, **8**, 66–72.

TERRILL, C. E. (1949). The relation of face covering to lamb and wool production in range Rambouillet ewes. *J. Anim. Sci.*, **8**, 353–361.

THOMSON, W. & AITKEN, F. C. (1959). Diet in relation to reproduction and the viability of the young. II. Sheep: World Survey of Reproduction and Review of Feeding Experiments. *Commonwealth Bur. of Anim. Nutr. Tech. Commun. No. 20.*

WIGGINS, E. L. & TERRILL, C. E. (1953). Variation in penis development in ram lambs. *J. Anim. Sci.*, **12**, 524–535.

QUESTIONS

1. Give the age of puberty in ram and ewe lambs and explain the factors affecting it.
2. What semen traits have useful predictive value for ram fertility?
3. What variations may be expected within breeds and between breeds of sheep in the duration of estrus, length of estrous cycle, and length of the breeding season?
4. List the factors affecting ovulation rate in sheep and describe the effect of each.
5. Describe sexual behavior in the ram and ewe and indicate how this may affect fertility.
6. How does fertility vary with age and breed?
7. List five ways in which the reproductive processes of sheep can be altered artificially and show how these can be used to improve fertility.
8. What is known about the heritability of various aspects of reproduction in sheep?
9. Describe the effects of high temperatures on various traits of reproduction in sheep.
10. What steps should be taken to reduce infertility and increase the reproductive rate through selective breeding?

Chapter 15

The Reproduction of Swine

By B. N. Day

Swine are litter-bearing mammals with a shorter generation interval than sheep, cattle or horses. These characteristics inherently provide this species of livestock with a high reproductive potential for the production of market animals.

I. SEXUAL MATURITY

Male. Primary spermatocytes first appear in the testis at about 3 months of age, secondary spermatocytes at 4 to 5 months, and sperm are present at 5 to 6 months of age. Weight at puberty is related to prepubertal feeding level but age at puberty and subsequent sperm production are not significantly influenced by moderate limited-feeding (Dutt & Barnhart, 1959). Similarly, season has little influence on age at puberty.

Young boars should be allowed to reach 8 to 9 months of age before they are used for breeding. Close observations on the physical condition, sex drive, and semen quality can be used to considerable advantage in determining how frequent an individual boar should be used for breeding.

Female. The ovaries of gilts show germ cell activity several weeks before the onset of puberty. Multi-layered Graafian follicles

appear in the ovaries of the gilt at about 7 weeks of age and follicles containing an antrum become evident at about 15 weeks of age (Casida, 1935). Puberty occurs as a result of further growth and development of the follicles and the subsequent production of ovarian hormones by mature follicles. The level and balance of hormones necessary to initiate this expression of sexual maturity in the gilt are not well established. Restricting the energy level to approximately two-thirds of a full-feed has been found to have either no influence on age at puberty or in gilts reaching puberty at younger ages and lighter weights. However, more severe restrictions in the energy intake delay puberty as does excessive fatness.

II. ESTRUS AND OVULATION

A. Estrus

Estrus persists for 2 to 3 days with a variation in length of 1 to 4 days not uncommon. A clear delineation of the beginning and end of estrus is difficult since the expression of estrus is a gradual phenomenon and also, an accurate determination is dependent on the normal behavior of not only the female but also the male at the time of mating. This variation causes some difficulties in determining the optimum time for breeding in order to obtain the most efficient reproductive performance.

Parity, breed, and endocrine abnormalities affect the duration of estrus. Gilts frequently fail to show estrus for more than 1 day, whereas sows usually show sexual receptivity for 2 days or longer and the average duration of estrus is 12 to 18 hours longer in sows than in gilts. Cystic ovaries is an example of an endocrine disorder that will disrupt the normal behavioral signs of estrus.

Post-partum Estrus. Post-partum estrus is exhibited 2 to 3 days after farrowing. The frequency of estrus at this time has not been fully determined but in one observation, only 3 sows out of a total of 88 failed to exhibit post-partum estrus (Burger, 1952). The occurrence of post-partum estrus has posed the question of the feasibility of breeding sows shortly after farrowing in order to increase reproductive performance; however, this is not a fertile estrus since there is a lack of follicular growth and ovulation does not occur.

Post-weaning Estrus. Sexual receptivity is not exhibited during lactation except during the terminal stages of milk production when estrus is manifested in some sows. However, weaning at any stage of lactation will initiate estrus. It is not clear whether a cessation of milk production, the removal of the nursing stimulus or other factors associated with weaning permit the resumption of the estrous cycle.

Post-weaning estrus usually occurs 3 to 8 days after weaning when the young are separated at 6 to 8 weeks after farrowing, but the interval to estrus following early weaning, 2 to 3 weeks after parturition, is longer and more variable. It is commonly reported that estrus is induced in lactating sows by removing the pigs from the sows for a few nights. This has been observed when litters were weaned at 6 to 8 weeks of age, but the separation of sows and litters from 6 p.m. to 6 a.m., starting between 5 and 31 days after parturition, did not induce estrus (Burger, 1952).

B. Ovulation

Ovulation occurs during estrus in the sow and the majority of the ova are released 24 to 36 hours after the onset of estrus. Double-matings using differences in body color as genetic-markers, and observations made following slaughter, have been used to determine the time of ovulation. Knowledge of the relationship of ovulation to estrus is important in determining the optimum time for breeding or inseminating sows, since viable sperm should be available for fertilization when the ova are released. Further consideration must be given to the time lapse from the beginning to the end of ovulation. The interval from the first to last ovulation, at a given estrus, varies from 1 hour in length to perhaps as long as 7 hours.

Ovulation Rate. Sows are polytocous animals and the rate of ovulation varies considerably with 10 to 20 ova being the usual range. Parity, age, nutritional level and breed influence the ovulation rate. Gilts have a lower ovulation rate than sows and the number of ova produced by gilts increases with each successive estrus. The average increase from the first to the second estrus following puberty is about two ova. The amount of feed energy consumed by the gilt during the estrous cycle prior to ovulation is closely related to the rate of ovulation. A high ovulation rate is promoted by full-feeding high-energy feeds, and increasing the energy intake by feeding glucose or lard also induces a "flushing" effect on gilts. The maximum improvement in ovulation rate through flushing is dependent on a high-energy intake during the latter half of the previous estrous cycle. The physiological basis for the relationship between plane of nutrition and ovulation rate is not clear but the level of nutrients available immediately prior to the time of ovulation is thought to be of primary importance. This is suggested by the low correlations of backfat thickness or body size with ovulation rate (Self *et al.*, 1955) and the fact that a maximum response can be obtained by increasing the energy intake during a relatively short feeding period. The mode of action of the plane of nutrition on ovulation rate may be a direct effect on the developing follicle or perhaps indirectly through an increased release of gonadotropins. A severe restriction in the energy intake does not influence the gonadotropin concentration but will cause a decrease in the weight of the anterior pituitary.

Although breed differences in ovulation rate have not been investigated extensively, the available evidence indicates that some breeds show a consistently higher ovulation rate than others when compared in controlled experiments. However, breed differences in ovulation rate vary considerably if comparisons are not made under similar environmental conditions. Further evidence of a genetic influence on ovulation rate is illustrated by the decreased rate of ova production in inbred animals (Table 15-1).

occurs into the central cavity of the ruptured follicle. The granulosa cells, and to some extent, theca interna cells are luteinized to form luteal tissue. Complete formation of the corpora lutea require about 6 to 8 days. Corpora lutea vary from flesh red to pink in color and corpora albicantia are light yellow in appearance. In the absence of pregnancy, the corpora lutea begin to regress on the 14th to 16th day of the estrous cycle (Fig. 15-1). The physiological factors regulating the maintenance of the corpus luteum during pregnancy are not known but recent findings showing that hysterectomy prevents the regression of the corpus luteum in nonpregnant gilts are of particular interest (Anderson et al., 1961).

Cyclic histological changes occur in the

Table 15-1.—Influence of Mating Systems on the Ovulation Rate of Poland China Gilts

(Adapted from Squiers et al., 1952, Mo. Agric. Expt. Sta. Res. Bull. 494.)

Line of Breeding	No. Gilts	Mean % of Inbreeding	Number of Corpora Lutea	
			Mean	Difference
II and VI	81	36.5	10.4	
(II X VI) Cross	20	9.0	11.7	1.3
II and V	91	35.7	10.6	
(II X V) Cross	24	0.0	12.6	2.0
V X VI	96	28.9	11.2	
(V X VI) Cross	13	0.0	11.2	0.0

C. Estrous Cycle

The cycle length (19 to 23 days) is relatively constant between sows and gilts and among various breeds. Sows are polyestrous since they exhibit estrous cycles throughout the year. Changes in temperature and intensity of light have little influence on the regularity of estrus in swine. Endocrine abnormalities and pathological changes in the reproductive tract frequently result in an increase in the length of the estrous cycle. Conception followed by complete embryonic mortality will also cause an extension in the cycle length.

Cyclical Changes. Following ovulation the follicular wall collapses and hemorrhage

reproductive tract throughout the estrous cycle. The epithelial lining of the vestibule and vagina is thickened at estrus but consist of low epithelial cells of few layers during di-estrus. Vaginal smears show a larger migration of leucocytes and sloughing of epithelial cells into the vaginal contents the first week after estrus with the fewest number present just before estrus. Although a few cornified cells are present throughout the estrous cycle, the pronounced cornification of vaginal epithelium that occurs at estrus in the rat and some other rodents does not occur in the sow. The external appearance of the vulva also shows cyclic variations with the most pronounced changes being a marked swelling of the labia and an increase in the amount of mucous

17

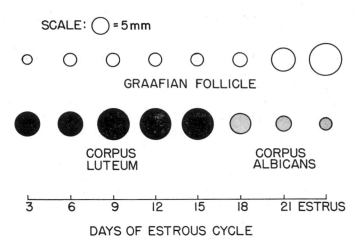

SCALE: ◯ = 5 mm

GRAAFIAN FOLLICLE

CORPUS
LUTEUM

CORPUS
ALBICANS

3   6   9   12   15   18   21 ESTRUS

DAYS OF ESTROUS CYCLE

FIG. 15–1.—Relative morphological changes in the ovary during the estrous cycle. Note the rapid increase in follicular size shortly before ovulation. Also, corpora albicantia regress in size rather rapidly but are still evident at the subsequent estrus.

secretion which accompanies the onset of estrus (McKenzie, 1926).

D. Modification of Reproductive Activity

Control of Estrus and Ovulation. Interest in the development of a method for controlling the breeding dates of swine has gained renewed interest during recent years due to the availability of new hormonal compounds, changes to more intensified management and breeding systems, and the use of this breeding technique in conjunction with artificial insemination.

A major problem confronted in attempts to control estrus and ovulation has been a marked decrease in the conception rate of the treated animals. Exogenous progesterone interrupts the normal estrous cycle and effectively synchronizes estrus but low conception rates and an increase in the incidence of cystic ovaries occur at the first estrus following termination of the treatment. Estrus can also be synchronized with synthetic progestins (*i.e.* 6-methyl-17 acetoxyprogesterone) which has the advantage of being orally effective. The influence of this treatment on conception rate at the first post-treatment estrus is not clearly established. Estrogen or gonadotropin injections also alter the estrous cycle but are only partially effective in the synchronization of estrus and ovulation.

Induced Estrus During Lactation. Induced estrus and ovulation in sows during lactation anestrus would provide a means of increasing yearly sow productivity. The injection of 750 to 1,000 i.u. of PMS provides a means of successfully inducing estrus and ovulation after the 6th week of lactation; however, the same treatments fail to induce estrus during earlier stages of lactation (Cole & Hughes, 1946). It is difficult to evaluate the reasons for the differential response when so little is known about the physiological basis of lactation anestrus in swine.

Superovulation. Superovulation and ova transfer have received little attention in swine. However, gilts and sows can be superovulated by the injection of gonadotropins during the follicular stage and, to a lesser extent, during the luteal phase of the estrous cycle.

III. PREGNANCY

Conception rate and fertilization rate are both employed to evaluate the reproductive performance of sows whereas these terms are more nearly synonymous when applied to monotocous animals such as cattle. In swine, conception rate is used to signify those animals in which some of the ova are fertilized whereas rate of fertilization is usually restricted to the proportion of available ova fertilized in sows that conceive. The percentage of sows bred that conceive varies considerably but in well-managed herds a conception rate of 85 to 90 per cent can be expected. Fertilization is essentially an all or none process, since all of the ova are frequently fertilized in those females that conceive.

Cessation of estrus is the only method available for making an early pregnancy diagnosis in swine since biological and chemical tests for pregnancy are not available and anatomical limitations restrict the use of rectal palpation. The cessation of estrus is usually a reliable predictor of pregnancy, but estrus is occasionally manifested in pregnant sows.

The gestation period (111 to 117 days) is relatively constant in length with few cases of major deviations from the average due to environmental fluctuations, age of the sow, or litter size. The range in the average gestation length of different breeds is approximately 3 days.

The approach of parturition in the sow is characterized by restlessness, mastication and rearrangement of bedding material into a nest, and an enlargement of the external genital organs and mammary gland. The presence of milk in the teats preceeds farrowing by 18 to 48 hours. The physiological mechanisms involved in the initiation of parturition are not known. Hormonal treatments involving the use of oxytocin and estrogens have not been too successful in the induction of parturition at a predetermined time.

IV. LITTER SIZE

The culmination of a successful breeding program is the production of large litters of healthy young at farrowing. In order to attain this goal, emphasis must be directed toward each phase of the reproductive cycle from the prepubertal growth period through the farrowing process.

Swine are very prolific in comparison with other farm mammals, but reproductive efficiency is not high when measured in terms of the potential litter size that is actually realized at farrowing. This loss in reproductive efficiency occurs at all stages of the reproductive cycle but losses at certain phases are considered to be the major controlling factors of litter size at farrowing. In arriving at an appraisal of the losses occurring in the reproductive efficiency of gilts and sows, sterility is found to occur in approximately 10 per cent of the breeding population. Fertilization failure does not appear to be a major factor, since only about 5 per cent of the ova are not fertilized in those animals that conceive. However, embryonic mortality is of considerable importance since, on the average, approximately 30 per cent of the ova are not represented by live embryos on the 25th day of gestation and an additional 15 per cent decrease in litter size occurs when based on the number of living young farrowed. In turn, due to these losses only about one-half of the ova produced by the average group of sows bred to fertile boars are represented by viable young at farrowing.

Litter size varies considerably among individual animals as well as between sub-

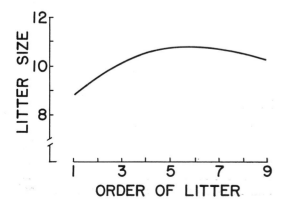

Fig. 15–2.—Litter size at farrowing increases with age and parity. Note that maximum litter size is reached between the 5th and 7th litter. (*Adapted Lush, J. L. & Molln, A. E. 1942. USDA Tech. Bull. 836.*)

sequent farrowing by the same sow. Specific environmental fluctuations that affect ovulation rate or prenatal death are the cause of much of this variation. However, other factors known to influence litter size are age, parity, and inherent reproductive ability. Young sows farrow more pigs per litter than gilts. Age and previous reproductive activity are both apparently involved in the increased litter size of sows but a separation of the physiological effects of each is difficult due to the concurrent advance of both following puberty. Litter size is larger in gilts farrowing for the first time late in life than for those bred at the usual age; but less than for sows of a comparable age that have farrowed previously. The peak of increased litter size with parity occurs at the 5th to 7th litter (Fig. 15–2). An increase in the embryonic death rate is considered to be the cause of the decline in litter size in older sows.

Heritability estimates for litter size average about 15 per cent which shows that a relatively small portion of the parent's superiority over the herd average for this trait is transmitted to the offspring. Similarly, size of the first litter is not a good measure of subsequent litter size which further demonstrates the important influence of environmental variations on reproductive performance. Although heritability estimates for litter size are low, a different type of genetic influence on litter size is clearly evident. Breed averages differ as much as 3 to 4 pigs per litter. Also, inbreeding causes a pronounced depression in reproductive performance and crossbreeding increases litter size. The manner by which inbreeding and crossbreeding alter litter size has not been determined, although it seems likely that changes in the secretion rates of gonadotropic and ovarian hormones are major factors.

V. LOWERED FERTILITY

Most causes of impaired fertility and sterility can be classified as being anatomical, physiological, psychological, or infectious in origin. Genetic and environmental factors and the interaction of the two contribute to all of these types of sterility.

A. Male

Cryptorchidism is an example of an anatomical cause of sterility. The defect may be bilateral or unilateral, although unilateral cryptorchidism is more common. Bilateral cryptochid boars are sterile, whereas in unilateral cryptorchidism normal sperm production occurs in the descended testicle. The defect is genetic in origin and appears to be due to a recessive, sex-limited gene. In turn, unilateral cryptorchid boars should not be used for breeding and, in addition, lines of breeding showing a high incidence of the condition should be avoided in the selection of breeding stock. Other anatomical defects that impair fertility are testicular hypoplasia, scrotal hernia and umbilical hernia.

Endocrine deficiencies result in sterility by causing impotency and faulty or inadequate sperm production. Little information is available on the frequency of these disorders due to the difficulties in establishing hormone secretion rates. A lack of sex drive is frequently observed in highly inbred boars (Hauser *et al.*, 1952), and it seems likely that an imbalance or deficiency of testosterone production may be the major cause. Pronounced variation occurs between boars in the capacity for sperm production which would seem to reflect variations in gonadotropin secretion rate; especially when consideration is given to the parallel factors involved in germ cell production in the sow.

Psychic factors contribute to reduced fertility or sterility in boars as they influence sex drive. The cause of psychic refusal to breed can be traced, in some cases, to previous injuries or improper handling that the boar associates with copulation. Other factors that are known to cause sterility include genital diseases, physical injuries to muscles, nerves, or the reproductive organs, and degeneration of the seminiferous tubules.

B. Female

1. ANATOMICAL ABNORMALITIES

Anatomical abnormalities of the genital organs are fairly common causes of sterility (Plate XXIX). Studies made at Wisconsin and Illinois on sterile or "repeat breeding"

**Table 15–2.—Anatomical Condition of the Reproductive Organs of 79
"Sterile" Gilts and Sows**

(*Adapted from Wilson et al., 1949, J. Anim. Sci. 8, 558.*)

Abnormalities	Gilts %	Sows %
No abnormalities	47.1	67.9
Gross abnormalities (total)	52.9	32.1
Hydrosalpinx & pyosalpinx	31.3	3.6
Cystic follicles with corpora lutea	7.8	7.1
Unilateral blind segment	7.8	3.6
Unilateral missing segment	2.0	3.6
Cystic follicles—no corpora lutea	0.0	7.1
Infantilism	2.0	0.0
Blind uterine body	2.0	0.0
Other conditions	0.0	7.1

females revealed that approximately 45 per cent of the gilts and about 15 per cent of the sows had gross abnormalities of the reproductive tract other than cystic ovaries (Table 15–2).

Hydrosalpinx (the accumulation of fluid in the Fallopian tubes) and *pyosalpinx* (a similar condition in which leucocytes and cellular debris are also present) are the most common causes of anatomical sterility. Although attempts to reproduce these conditions by innoculating the Fallopian tubes of normal animals with the contents of affected Fallopian tubes have been unsuccessful, it is not established whether these disorders are due to a congenital lesion or to other factors. Bilateral missing segments and occlusion of unpaired tubular parts of the reproductive tract are also causes of anatomical sterility.

2. Endocrine Disorders

Cystic Ovaries. Cystic follicles are anatomical aberrations that result from an endocrine disturbance and these disorders are a major cause of impaired fertility and sterility. A descriptive classification of cystic ovaries in swine varies from numerous small cysts on the ovary to one or more cysts that are many times larger (up to 4 or 5 cm.) than the normal Graafian follicle (Plate XXIX); the condition may be bilateral or unilateral; some follicles may ovulate and others become cystic on the same ovary or all follicles may be cystic.

Cystic follicles prevent conception, but they are also found in pregnant sows (Nalbandov, 1952). The etiology of cysts formation is not understood and corrective measures have not been developed.

Infantilism. The ovaries of these animals are undeveloped with the follicles failing to reach ovulatory size and in turn, the duct system remains immature due to the absence of estrogen stimulation. Limited evidence suggests that infantilism is due to hypofunction of the pituitary gland.

Other aberrations that are apparently due to a temporary deficiency or imbalance in hormone secretion rates are the lack of sexual receptivity in conjunction with ovulation (quiet ovulation) and an extended interval between weaning and estrus.

3. Embryonic Mortality

Embryonic mortality rate or prenatal death loss is frequently defined as the difference between the ovulation rate and litter size at a specified stage of the gestation period. The estimate is biased by including fertilization failure and by not including losses in animals that conceive but are not pregnant when the measurement is taken. Losses due to these variables are usually determined on separate groups of animals when detailed comparisons are made on reproductive efficiency.

The early studies of Hammond and Corner first brought attention to the large discrepancy between the number of corpora lutea and litter size at various stages of gestation. Following these studies, extensive investigations have been conducted to determine the possible causes of prenatal death loss.

Stage of Pregnancy. Early pregnancy is the most critical stage for survival of the conceptus. Approximately two-thirds of the total prenatal death loss occurs prior to the 25th day of gestation. Most of the embryonic death is thought to occur at the time of implantation (12 to 20 days after conception); however, specific environmental or genetic factors causing failure of implantation are not evident.

Age of Dam. Prenatal mortality apparently increases with age and parity, since the increased ovulation rate that occurs in sows is not accompanied by a comparable improvement in litter size. However, at a constant age, the percentage of prenatal death loss is positively associated with ovulation rate and, in turn, the magnitude of the direct effect of age on embryonic viability is confounded with a concurrent increase in ovulation rate.

Nutrition. The influence of the *general nutrition* of the sow on embryonic viability is not clearly understood, but a deficiency of specific nutrients does not appear to be the cause of the high prenatal death rates commonly observed. However, the *level of energy* intake is established to be related to embryonic survival. The physiological cause of high prenatal death losses occurring in sows maintained on a high-energy plane of nutrition is not known, but it is likely related to both the daily intake of energy during early pregnancy and to the body composition of the dam.

Intra-uterine Environment. There is little doubt that unfavorable intra-uterine environment will cause embryonic mortality, and it is also well established that progesterone and estrogen are largely responsible for the initiation of uterine conditions conducive to embryonic survival. However, little is known about the optimum secretion rates or balance between these hormones that will induce the most favorable uterine environment. The use of hormonal therapy to decrease prenatal death losses has not given consistent results. The injection of a combination of estrogen and progesterone at the time of implantation promotes some improvement in embryonic survival rate in intact and ovariectomized gilts. However, treatment during early pregnancy with progesterone or estrogen alone has failed to induce a beneficial response. Although sufficient evidence is not available for a conclusive evaluation, these results indicate that consideration of the proper combination of exogenous hormones may be of importance in developing effective hormonal treatments capable of decreasing the rate of embryonic mortality.

Heredity. Inbreeding increases the embryonic mortality rate and crossbreeding reduces prenatal death losses (Squiers *et al.*, 1952). This depression is likely due to the combined losses resulting from maladjustment in the uterine environment and, to a lesser extent, an increase in the number of genetically defective embryos.

Disease. Although bacteria are usually not found in dead embryos and pathological conditions in the endometrium are not commonly present, there is some evidence which suggests that embryonic mortality is reduced by feeding high levels of antibiotics. Cholera vaccination during the first month of pregnancy with either virulent virus or attenuated live virus causes fetal anomalies with an increase in prenatal mortality rate (Young *et al.*, 1955).

4. Abortion (Non-infectious)

Non-infectious abortion in sows is not common since, in general, it is associated with the immediate death of all young in the litter at one time. Prenatal death loss of part of the litter is usually resorbed or, during the latter stages of gestation, mummified and expelled at parturition. A severe vitamin A deficiency in the diet will result in some sows aborting their litters, but the influence of specific nutritional deficiencies is more generally demonstrated as mortality of some of the fetuses in the litter and still-

PLATE XXIX

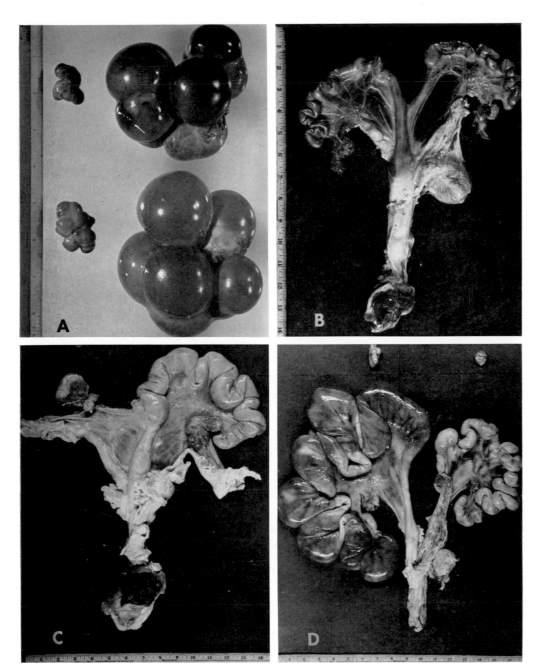

A. Ovaries containing large, cystic follicles (right) are compared to the appearance of normal ovaries (left) with corpora lutea.

B. A segment of the right uterine horn failed to develop in this reproductive tract.

C. All of the left uterine horn is missing. Note the presence of the left ovary.

D. An example of a double cervix. Note that only the left uterine horn is gravid. Right cervix has been incised to show internal structure.

(Photographs B, C & D from Lerner et al. 1957. Mo. Agric. Expt. Sta. Res. Bull. 629.)

births at farrowing. For example, the incidence of stillborn and weak pigs is increased in sows fed an iodine deficient diet, but abortion is not a characteristic of the deficiency. Abortions are also caused by other factors including systemic diseases, high ambient temperature, physical injuries, and chemicals or drugs with abortifacient actions such as large doses of estrogens. However, most abortions are caused by infectious diseases and for this reason, the disease status of the breeding stock should be carefully examined when abortions become a herd problem.

5. STILLBIRTHS

Young classified as stillborn frequently include mummified fetuses, pigs that died shortly before or at the time of farrowing and, in some cases, those that were born alive but died shortly after birth. The frequency of stillbirths averages about 6 per cent, but considerably higher rates have been observed in some herds. It appears that several factors are related to some extent to the occurrence of stillbirths. Of these, asphyxia of the offspring at the time of farrowing, nutrition and age of the dam, hereditary factors, and disease appear to be major contributing factors. The incidence of stillbirths is higher in sows with prolonged farrowings and there is some evidence which suggests that the rate of stillbirths is decreased in sows injected with oxytocin after the spontaneous onset of uterine contractions to assist in, or to hasten, the completion of the farrowing process.

VI. IMPROVEMENT OF FERTILITY

The answer to fertility improvement in many cases is simply to apply the existing knowledge available on swine reproduction, but in other cases improvement is dependent on research gaining further insight into the direct causes of reproductive failure so that more effective corrective measures can be developed. There is little doubt that considerable improvement can be, and will be, made in both areas as efficiency of production continues to become a more objective value to the swine producer.

Male. Perhaps a solution to the problem of determining the reproductive ability of the boar without making exhaustive breeding tests on females is of paramount importance to increased reproductive efficiency. This would not only provide a very useful tool to the producer but would also be of considerable assistance to research workers in measuring the effects of various treatments on sperm production and sex drive. Other areas that appear to offer possibilities for making significant improvements with increased knowledge are *in vitro* storage of sperm, sexual behavior, hormonal treatment of aspermia and impotency, and the relative importance of genetic and environmental factors on reduced fertility as a basis for determining the type of corrective measures that should be employed to eliminate a disorder from the population.

Female. Much research work is needed on methods of improving fertility in the sow. Embryonic mortality is clearly established to be of considerable magnitude, but the causes are not as well known. Various treatments of prenatal death loss have shown promise, but most have not shown consistent improvements. A better understanding of the factors affecting implantation may prove to be of considerable assistance. Many other variations observed in reproductive ability such as differences in ovulation rate, also need to be studied more extensively in order to provide the basic information needed in the development of corrective measures. The relative importance of environmental and genetic influences on specific components of the reproductive cycle, in addition to the final measurement

Table 15–3. Estimated Variation of Some Female Reproductive Phenomena

Phenomena	Range (includes about $\frac{2}{3}$ of all females)
Duration of estrus	2–3 days
Length of estrous cycle	19–23 days
Weaning to post-weaning estrus	3–8 days
Ovulation rate (herd average)	± 2.5 ova
Gestation length (breed average)	± 0.5 days
Litter size (herd average)	± 2.0 young

Table 15–4.—Summary of Reproductive Performance in Gilts and Sows

Phenomena	Average Estimate
First appearance of vesicular follicles in ovary	15 wks.
Ovulation rate: gilts	8–14 ova
sows	12–20 ova
Percentage of sterile females	10%
Fertilization rate	95%
Prenatal death rate*:	
at 25th day of pregnancy	30%
at term	45%
Percentage of stillbirths	6%
Litter size at farrowing:	
most prolific breeds	11 pigs
least prolific breeds	8 pigs
increase 1st to 6th litter	2 pigs
heritability estimate	15%

*Percentage of corpora lutea not represented by living young.

of litter size at farrowing, is another area of study that needs further clarification.

Perseverance in the form of applying recommendations on feeding levels and management practices not only at the time of breeding, but at all stages of reproduction is of utmost importance to the production of large litters at farrowing. The two major factors controlling litter size, ovulation rate and embryonic viability, can be reduced considerably by failing to make adjustments in the level of energy intake of the sow. Crossbreeding offers a means of increasing litter size significantly and improved efficiency can also be obtained by selecting replacement gilts from large litters, culling sows that produce two or more small litters, breeding on both the 1st and 2nd day of estrus, avoiding animals and lines of breeding with a high incidence of inherited defects and by following a good disease control program in the breeding herd. The average and the range of some of the female reproductive phenomena are summarized in Tables 15–3 & 15–4.

REFERENCES

ANDERSON, L. L., BUTCHER, R. L. & MELAMPY, R. M. (1961). Subtotal hysterectomy and ovarian function in gilts. *Endocrinology*, 69, 571–580.

BURGER, J. F. (1952). Sex physiology of pigs. *Onderst. J. Vet. Res. 2 (Suppl.)*, 1–218.

CASIDA, L. E. (1935). Prepubertal development of the pig ovary and its relation to stimulation with gonadotrophic hormones. *Anat. Rec.*, 61, 389–396.

COLE, H. H. & HUGHES, E. H. (1946). Induction of estrus in lactating sows with equine gonadotrophin. *J. Anim. Sci.*, 5, 25–29.

DUTT, R. H. & BARNHART, C. E. (1959). Effect of plane of nutrition upon reproductive performance of boars. *J. Anim. Sci.*, 18, 3–13.

HAUSER, E. R., DICKERSON, G. E. & MAYER, D. T. (1952). Reproductive development and performance of inbred and crossbred boars. *Mo. Agric. Expt. Sta. Res. Bull. No.* 503.

MCKENZIE, F. F. (1926). The normal estrous cycle in the sow. *Mo. Agric. Expt. Sta. Res. Bull. No.* 86.

NALBANDOV, A. V. (1952). Anatomic and endocrine causes of sterility in female swine. *Fertil. & Steril.*, 3, 100–114.

SELF, H. L., GRUMMER, R. H. & CASIDA, L. E. (1955). The effects of various sequences of full and limited feeding on the reproductive phenomena in Chester White and Poland China gilts. *J. Anim. Sci.*, 14, 573–592.

SQUIERS, C. D., DICKERSON, G. E. & MAYER, D. T. (1952). Influence of inbreeding, age and growth rate of sows on sexual maturity, rate of ovulation, fertilization and embryonic survival. *Mo. Agric. Expt. Sta. Res. Bull. No.* 494.

YOUNG, G. A., KITCHELL, R. I., LUEDKE, A. J. & SAUTTER, J. H. (1955). The effect of viral and other infections of the dam on fetal development in swine. I. Modified live hog cholera viruses—immunological, virological and gross pathological studies. *J. Amer. Vet. Med. Assoc.*, 126, 165–171.

QUESTIONS

1. What advantages do swine possess for use as experimental animals in studies on the reproductive physiology of farm mammals?
2. Discuss the anatomical changes that occur in the reproductive tract of the sow during the estrous cycle.

3. Why do sows fail to conceive when bred at post-partum estrus? List the interval from regression of the corpus luteum to estrus, parturition to post-partum estrus and weaning to post-weaning estrus.
4. Discuss the relative importance of factors that influence ovulation rate in swine.
5. Discuss in detail environmental factors that affect litter size in swine. What is the major cause of the marked differences found in litter size at farrowing among sows of the same herd.
6. Does the genotype of the sow exert a major influence on litter size? Explain.
7. List and define two anatomical abnormalities and two endocrine disorders that cause sterility.
8. Outline an experiment designed to study fertilization rate, embryonic mortality rate to the 25th day of pregnancy, and total prenatal death loss in gilts. Include number, age, and breeding of the animals and detailed experimental procedure.
9. What would your leading questions be in trying to determine the cause of a low herd average in litter size at farrowing?
10. Give five examples where a deficiency or imbalance of hormones may be a major cause of reduced reproductive efficiency in swine.

Chapter 16

The Reproduction of Horses

By Y. Nishikawa and E. S. E. Hafez

THE present varieties of the domestic horse (*Equus caballus*), draft, light and pony, are members of the family *Equidae*, which belongs to the order *Perissodactyla*. Many aspects of reproductive endocrinology and pregnancy in horses are of particular interest to the student of reproduction.

I. SEXUAL MATURITY

A. Male

In the early fetus, the testes of the horse are yellowish-white but at birth become dark brown or black. The testes descend in the scrotum at the age of 2 to 3 weeks; in a few cases the testes are already down in the scrotum at birth. Postnatal growth of the testes begins during the eleventh month, with the left testis usually developing earlier and growing more rapidly than the right. At this time, there is also a gradual outward development of the seminiferous tubules around the *rete testis*.

At the age of 1 year, the sperm is first produced in the testes. Stallions may attain sexual maturity in the age of 2 years and show intense sexual desire when approached by estrous mares. Although semen from pubertal stallions can be used for artificial

insemination, the general practice is *not* to use males for natural breeding until they are 3 to 4 years old. In practice the age at which stallions are first used for breeding is determined primarily by managerial factors; for example, the use of Thoroughbred stallions for breeding at the age of 5 years is probably much more dependent upon the fact that they are raced until that time, on the average, rather than upon stage of sexual maturity.

B. Female

A common observation among horsemen is that 15 to 18 months is the pubertal age in fillies. In areas where there is a definite breeding season, the age of sexual maturity is greatly influenced by the month of birth. In such areas sexual maturity is generally attained in spring or summer of the 3rd year after birth, *i.e.* at the age of 25 to 28 months.

The cyclical changes in the ovary, the duration of estrus, and time of ovulation are similar in pubertal and adult mares. However, behavior during diestrus tends to be more passive. When approached by the stallion at this time, the pubertal mare does not resent courtship as do adults. After 2 to 3 estrous cycles, the sexual behavior of the pubertal animal becomes similar to that of the adult.

II. BREEDING SEASON

Sexual activity in both sexes is influenced by the season of the year and is related to daylength. Activity is usually greatest during the spring and summer period, when the days are long. There is evidence that the length of the breeding season is shorter near the poles than in tropical and subtropical regions, where the breeding season may extend through the whole year (Hammond, 1960). Breed differences in the length of the breeding season have not been established but Thoroughbreds tend, probably as the result of artificial selection, to have an earlier breeding season than other horses. Race horses are usually aged from January 1 in the year that they are foaled, and it has been the practice to breed them as early in the year as possible so that, in racing as 2 year olds, they have maximum physical advantage.

A. Male

The breeding season of the stallions is not well marked and semen can be collected throughout the year. In some areas, how-ever, the behavioral responses of the stallion are more pronounced during the spring and summer. In these areas there are also seasonal variations in the quantity and quality of the ejaculate. The volume of semen is highest during the spring and summer. The concentration of sperm (Bielanski, 1960) and ergothioneine and citric acid concentration of semen (Mann et al., 1956) tend to increase during the fall and winter.

The ejaculate normally contains a large fraction of gelatinous material; in some cases the ejaculate is devoid of such material. In Japan (latitude of 37°N.) there are marked seasonal variations in volume of semen ejaculate and of gelatinous fraction (Fig. 16–1). The vesicular glands (commonly called seminal vesicles) are the source of gelatinous material. The absence of gelatinous material from the semen does not affect the motility and fertilizing capacity of the sperm.

In general, the seasonal variation in sexual behavior and semen characteristics may be related to seasonal fluctuation in daylength, and can be controlled to some degree artificially. In the Northern hemisphere, an additional 5 hours of artificial light daily after sunset during November enhances sex drive and improves the semen.

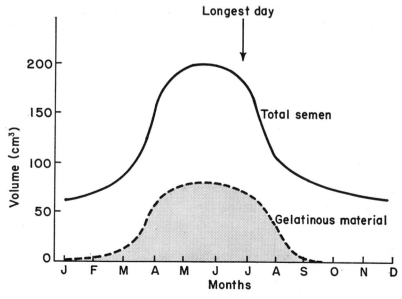

Fig. 16–1.—Seasonal variation in the volume of semen and gelatinous fraction in the stallion in Japan (37°N). Note the volume is greatest during the breeding season coinciding with the longest days of the year. During the non-breeding season the semen is devoid of gelatinous material.

B. Female

The literature pertaining to the nature of the breeding season in the mare is conflicting and inconsistent. This apparent inconsistency probably reflects real differences among the samples studied with regard to heredity and environment (reviewed by Berliner, 1959). Mares can be classified into 3 categories: (*a*) defined breeding season: the wild breeds of horses manifest several estrous cycles during a restricted breeding season coinciding with the longest days of the year; the foals are born during restricted period of the year, (*b*) transitory breeding season: some domestic breeds and some individual mares manifest estrous cycles throughout the year, but ovulation accompanies estrus only during the breeding season, the foals are born during a limited foaling season; (*c*) year-round breeding: some domestic breeds and some individual mares exhibit estrous cycles accompanied by ovulation throughout the year and foals are born throughout the year. Thus it is evident that although some mares, at certain latitudes, may show estrous cycles throughout the year, they do not necessarily conceive at all periods. For example, the conception rate of mares in South Africa is markedly influenced by the season of breeding (Fig. 16–2).

In localities where there is a breeding season, the two transitory periods preceding and following the breeding season, are characterized by extreme variability of ovarian activity and sexual behavior. At this time the ovarian follicles develop only to a limited degree and then undergo atresia. Also there is a high frequency of prolonged estrus or estrus of short duration as well as irregular estrous cycles.

Near the equator, there is little seasonal variation in the length of the estrous cycle. At latitudes of the British Isles the cycle length is very long during the spring and gradually shortens thereafter. At the same latitude, about 50 per cent of the mares are anestrus during the winter. When the mare is deeply in anestrus, the ovaries are hard and relatively small.

Data by Burkhardt (1947) and by Nishikawa (1959) suggest that the exposure of mares to additional hours of light during winter will induce estrus and advance the onset of the breeding season.

The ovaries of the anestrous mare cannot be activated, even by the injection of fairly large doses of serum gonadotropin, PMS, or chorionic gonadotropin, HCG, in contrast to the anestrous ewe, which responds to either hormone. Estrogen therapy may, however, be useful; daily injections of 5 to 10 mg. of stilbestrol for 10 to 20 days during the luteal phase of the cycle, given in the later part of the breeding season, will inhibit follicle development for 2 to 4 months after the last injection. After this period,

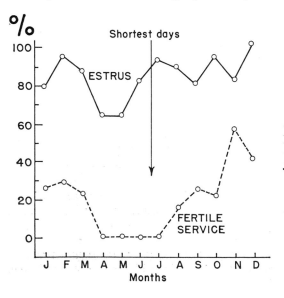

Fig. 16–2.—The breeding season of the mare in Onderstepoort, South Africa (25°S). Note the lowest frequency of estrus and of fertile services coincide with the shortest days of the year. (*Adapted from Quinlan, et al., 1950. Onderst. J. Vet. Res. 25, 105*).

ovarian functions resume and estrus occurs at regular intervals throughout the non-breeding season (Nishikawa, 1959). Such estrus is accompanied by ovulation, and normal pregnancy and parturition may result on breeding the mare.

III. ESTRUS AND OVULATION

A. Estrus

During estrus the vulva becomes large and swollen; the labial folds are loose and readily open on examination. The mucous membrane of the vulva is congested, scarlet or orange, wet, glossy and covered with a film of transparent mucus. The vaginal mucosa is highly vascular, and thin watery mucus may accumulate in the vagina. Such mucus spreads uniformly on a glass slide and leaves very little residue on drying. The cellular components of the vaginal smear have no value for detecting estrus in the mare. In estrus, the cervix dilates enough to admit 2 to 4 fingers; during diestrus 1 finger only can be inserted.

Intensity. The intensity of behavioral estrus varies both throughout the estrous period and among individual mares at comparable stages of the period. Responses have been graded in 8 phases ranging from *very receptive* to *very actively resistant* by Andrews & McKenzie (1941). The intensity increases slowly at the onset of estrus, reaches its maximum within 2 or 3 days, is maintained at this level for 2 or 3 days, and declines following ovulation. There is no correlation between intensity of estrus and degree of follicular development (Mahaffey, 1950).

Duration. The duration of estrus varies between individuals and also between estrous cycles of the same mare (Fig. 16–3). In most cases, it ranges from 2 to 11 days with an average of 6 days. The long duration of estrus in the mare may be due to the following factors: (*a*) the ovary is surrounded for the most part by a serous coat and some time is necessary for follicles to grow large enough to reach the ovulation fossa and rupture. The long duration of estrus reflects the length of the follicular phase in this species; (*b*) the ovary is less sensitive to exogenous FSH than other species (*e.g.* cattle, sheep) and it may take a long time for the follicle to reach maximum size immediately before ovulation; (*c*) the level of LH is low compared with FSH and this delays ovulation.

The duration of estrus is generally prolonged in old mares, in underfed mares and during the early parts of the breeding season.

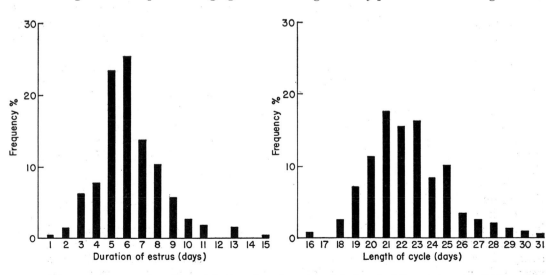

FIG. 16–3.—Frequency distribution of the duration of estrus and the length of the estrous cycle in the mare. (*Adapted from Nishikawa, 1959. Studies on Reproduction in Horses, Tokyo. Courtesy Japan Racing Association.*)

It is very rare for estrus to continue for more than 24 to 48 hours after ovulation occurs; except when there are twin ovulations with the separation of some days between them. This interval may vary from 1 to 10 days (Day, 1957). Breed differences in the duration of estrus in different localities may be magnified by differences in methods of testing for estrus and analyzing the data.

B. Ovulation

The ovary of the mature mare is kidney-shaped and larger than in the other farm mammals. Right and left ovaries do not necessarily ovulate alternately at successive estrous periods; the left tends to be more active than the right. The frequency of twin-ovulations may range from 3 to 30 per cent depending on the breed and season of year, being rare in pony breeds and during spring. The incidence of twin pregnancy varies from 1 to 5 per cent. Usually one member of the twins dies before birth and twin births occur only in very few cases.

Ovulation Fossa. As mentioned earlier, the ovary of the adult mare has a thick serous coat except at the ovulation fossa; this fossa is a marked depression 4 to 7 mm. deep. The rupture of the Graafian follicle and the formation of the corpus luteum occurs only at the ovulation fossa (Plate XXXI).

Time of Ovulation. Ovulation occurs 1 to 2 days before the end of estrus, irrespective of its duration; *i.e.* the time of ovulation is more closely related to the end than to the onset of estrus. The fertility of mating gradually rises to a peak about 2 days before the end of estrus and then falls sharply on the final day. From the changes taking place in the ovary it is possible to detect the time of ovulation with reasonable accuracy. One of the ovaries enlarges and the developing follicles occupy much of the ovarian stroma. After ovulation the volume of the ovary decreases markedly, and becomes very soft and flaccid. The developing corpus luteum cannot be detected by rectal examination after it is 48 hours old be-cause it develops within the ovarian stroma (Plate XXX).

C. Estrous Cycle

Length of Cycle. In general the length of the normal estrous cycle varies from 16 to 24 days, with an average of 22 days. The length of the cycle is prolonged under poor nutritional conditions and during the early spring.

The length of diestrus, the interval from the end of estrus, to the onset of the next, is 14 to 19 days in most cases. When ovulation does not occur the length of diestrus is usually 7 to 10 days.

Cyclical Changes. The cyclical changes that occur in the reproductive organs are summarized in Table 16-1. and Plate XXXI. A few days before the onset of estrus a developing follicle of about 2 cm. in diameter can often be detected by palpation of the ovary *per rectum.* As estrus progresses, the follicle markedly increases in size. Other follicles, an average of 22 per ovary, also grow during estrus. The maximum diameter of the corpus luteum never reaches the maximum size of the mature follicle.

The characteristic changes in the vulva and vagina during diestrus reach a maximum about 10 days after the end of estrus and disappear 1 to 2 days before the next estrus. During the entire luteal phase of the cycle the mucus is tenacious and adheres to a glass slide, giving a spotted pattern. The cellular components of the vaginal mucus are: leucocytes (chiefly neutrophils, rarely eosinophils), vaginal epithelial cells and ciliated epithelial cells. The occurrence of leucocytes and epithelial cells is not closely related to a particular stage of the cycle, but ciliated cells characterize the luteal phase (Plate XXXII).

D. Post-Partum Estrus (Foal Heat)

Post-partum estrus usually occurs 5 to 15 days after foaling. Some mares, however, may show estrus as late as 45 days after parturition; such estrus may have been preceded by a quiet ovulation. The interval between post-partum estrus and the fol-

PLATE XXX

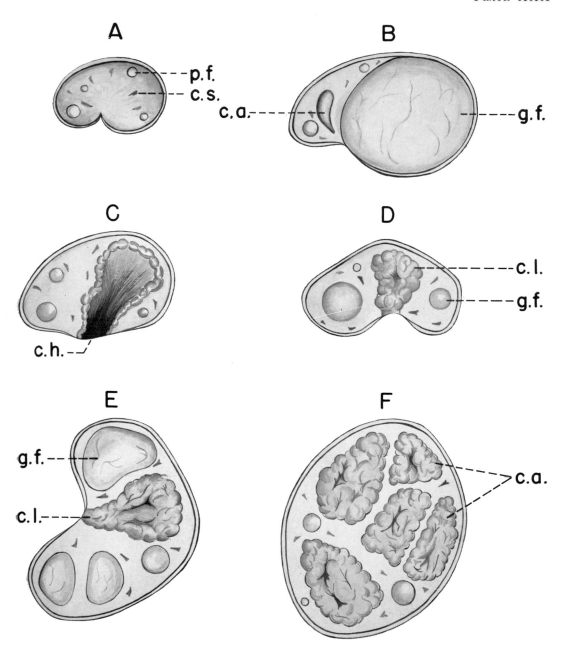

Microdrawing of cross section of ovaries (drawn to scale) of the mare at different stages of reproduction.

A. Non-breeding season: the ovary is small and contains primary follicles (p.f.) and scars (c.s.) from degenerating corpora lutea.

B. Breeding season: during estrus, the ovary contains a mature Graafian follicle (g.f.) and corpus albicans (c.a.) from previous ovulation.

C. Three days after ovulation: the corpus hemorrhagica (c.h.) develops from the walls of ruputred Graafian follicle.

D. Ten days after ovulation: fully developed corpus luteum (c.l.). Graafian follicles (g.f.) starts to develop for subsequent cycle.

E. Pregnancy—60 days: the corpus luteum of pregnancy (c.l.) is maintained and Graafian follicles (g.f.) develop as a result of circulating P.M.S.

F. Pregnancy—80 days: accessory corpora lutea (c.a.) develop from the unruptured follicles.

PLATE XXXI

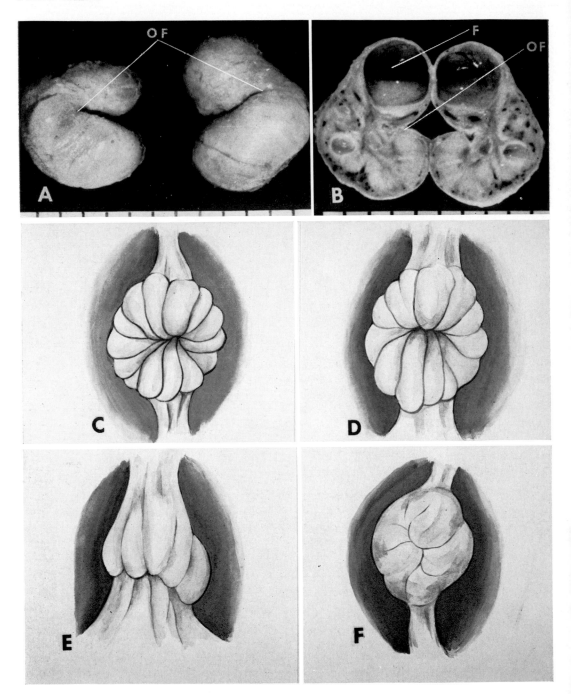

A,B. Ovaries of non-pregnant mare during the breeding season. *O.F.*, ovulation fossa; *F.*, Graafian follicle. *A.* Note the protruding follicle on the right ovary, *B.* Ovary cut into half.

C,D,E,F. Microdrawings of the *os cervix* in the mare as seen by clinical examination during estrous cycle and pregnancy. *C.* Diestrus, 10 days after ovulation: the cervix is hard and the folds are well defined; *D.* Onset of estrus (1st day): the cervix is somewhat swollen, the folds are shallow and less defined, and the orifice of the cervix is opened; *E.* End of estrus (6th day): the cervix is markedly swollen and relaxed and the upper folds hang down in a "membranous" appearance and covering the orifice; *F.* Pregnancy (4 to 6 months): the cervix is hard and bud-like in appearance and covered with pasty mucus and the orifice is tightly closed.

Table 16–1.—Cyclical Changes During the Estrous Cycle of the Mare

(*Adapted from Sato & Hoshi, 1934 &1936. J. Jap. Soc. Vet. Sci., 47, 411 & 49, 195 & Nishikawa, 1959. Studies on Reproduction of Horses, Tokyo, Japan Racing Assoc.*)

Characteristics	Stage	Estrus First half	Estrus Second half	Metestrus (1–2 days after end of estrus)†	Diestrus
Response to stallion		intense	most intense	no interest	aggressive
Ovary	Size	large	largest	small	small
	Follicle diameter (cm.)	2–3	3–6	none	none or 1
Vulva	Size	large	largest	small	smallest
	Appearance	swollen, rhythmic contractions	relaxed	relaxation less	contracted
Vagina	Color	scarlet	orange yellow	orange yellow less	pale
	Congestion	marked	most marked	congestion less	anemic
	Appearance	moist & glossy	wet & glossy	not glossy	dry & not glossy
Cervix	Size	large	largest	small	smallest
	Appearance	swollen	swollen & edematous	swelling disappears	contracted
	Orifice	opened	opened	closed	firmly closed
Vaginal & cervical mucus*	Volume	large	large	large	small
	Consistency	thin & watery	viscous & stringy	concentrated	adhesive
	Mucous clots	none	none	none or few	abundant
	Ciliated cells	none	none	none or few	abundant

* Mucus clots and ciliated cells are detected microscopically.
† Proestrus (1–2 days before estrus) resembles metestrus.

lowing estrus may be affected by the milk-production of the mare (Britton & Howell, 1945; see also discussion on lactation anestrus —Chapter 15).

Jennings (1950) presented some evidence that breeding at the post-partum estrus may cause an increased percentage of abortions, dystocias (difficult parturition), stillbirths and retained placentas. This may be due to the introduction of bacteria into the uterus before it is completely involuted and while it still lacks contractability. Frequently, the uterine epithelium is not completely restored for some time after foaling.

Loy has found that the so-called "30-day" heat or second heat after foaling occurs regularly among Thoroughbred mares in the University of California herd; the mares are successfully bred at that time. A high percentage of normal pregnancies will result when mares are bred at their third estrus after foaling. In practice, however, most race mares are bred at the post-partum estrus and a high conception rate is obtained only when the mare is completely back to normal condition.

IV. PREGNANCY DIAGNOSIS

The primary corpus luteum of pregnancy has a functional life of more than 40 days, after which time it degenerates. Between the 40th and 70th day of pregnancy, new *accessory corpora lutea* are formed as a result of the follicular development (some follicles may even rupture) initiated by the high level of circulating gonadotropin.

Ovarian activity then diminishes until about the 150th day, by which time all activity ceases. Progesterone, necessary to maintain pregnancy after cessation of ovarian function, is considered to be secreted from the placenta. This section is devoted to the diagnosis of pregnancy, other aspects of pregnancy in the mare being discussed in Chapter 10.

A. Clinical Methods

Clinical diagnosis is based on the examination of the vulva, vagina and cervix with the speculum and inspection lamp; and palpation of the ovaries and the uterus *per rectum*. Clinical diagnosis is usually done at 30 to 40 days after conception.

1. EXTERNAL GENITALIA

During pregnancy the vulva becomes small, contracted and difficult to open. The exposed mucous membrane of the vulva and vagina becomes pale and dry. Insertion of an unlubricated speculum into the vagina is difficult because of the adhesive mucus. The cervix becomes small and dry and the cervical orifice is closed; the neck of the cervix resembles a closed flower bud where it protrudes into the vagina (Plate XXXI). The cervical smear contains ciliated epithelial cells (Plate XXXII).

The cervical mucus becomes adhesive and pasty; it contains mucous globules as it does during diestrus. Such symptoms are not peculiar to pregnancy *per se* but reflect high levels of circulating progesterone. For this reason, clinical methods of pregnancy diagnosis based upon the above criteria are not absolutely reliable. However, during and after the third month of pregnancy, reliability of the diagnosis is much enhanced as the symptoms mentioned above are markedly intensified.

2. RECTAL PALPATION

Fourty to fifty days after conception pregnancy is successfully diagnosed by palpating the ovaries and the uterus *per rectum*.

Ovaries. Since the corpus luteum develops within the ovarian stroma and does not protrude as in other species, it cannot readily be palpated *per rectum*. From 1 to 3 months after conception, the ovary enlarges due to extensive follicular development. These follicles may ovulate and corpora lutea form; and/or they may become luteinized without ovulating. After the 3rd or 4th month of pregnancy the ovary returns to normal size.

Uterus. As early as the 21st day onwards of pregnancy the turgidity of the uterus together with the tacky appearance of the mucin on the cervix are a good indication of pregnancy and the fetal sac can be first felt about 30 to 45 days. In the earliest stages of pregnancy the fetal sac usually develops in the uterine horn but occasionally in the body where it is more difficult to palpate. About 60 days after conception, it is possible to feel the twin pregnancies. After this time the individual fetal sacs grow so that they merge into one and twins can no longer be diagnosed (Day, 1957). The distension of the uterus by the fetal sac is felt at 100 days, and then the fetus itself is first felt, rather in the way that one would touch a floating apple, bobbing against the hand.

During the 1st month, the conceptus grows to the size of a hen's egg and may be felt as a slight swelling in the uterus. During the 2nd month, the conceptus reaches the size of a grapefruit and it is possible to detect the difference in size between the pregnant and non-pregnant horn. By the 3rd month, the conceptus is the size of a human head and the uterus gradually sinks into the abdominal cavity; the broad ligaments are then suspended perpendicularly and can be detected by palpation.

Care must be taken to distinguish the signs of pregnancy from those of pyometra. In the latter case, the uterus may be large and swollen, but the contents are not restricted to one particular section and can move about; both horns are large and symmetrical. The uterine wall is thin and lacks contractility.

B. Hormonal Methods

There are two possible hormonal methods of pregnancy diagnosis (see Chapter 10), but they are only used in exceptional cases, since the manual diagnosis *per rectum* is simple and more practical.

Detection of Gonadotropins in the Blood. A high concentration of gonadotropin, PMS, appears in the blood at about 45 days, reaches a maximum at 70 days and eventually disappears on about the 120th day. The concentration may reach 150 to 300 i.u./ml. of blood serum. Blood is collected

PLATE XXXII

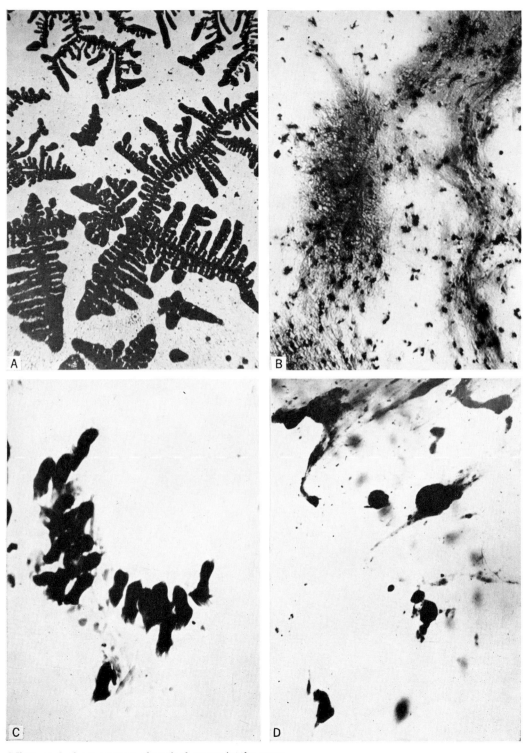

Microscopical appearance of vaginal smear in the mare
A. Fern-like crystals of dried mucus during estrus (× 32)
B. Ciliated epithelial cells and mucous clots at 22 days of pregnancy (× 75).
C. Ciliated epithelial cells at 22 days of pregnancy (× 400).
D. Mucous globules at 101 days of pregnancy (× 24).

from the mare and centrifuged to obtain the serum which is injected subcutaneously into immature female mice or rats. The mice are autopsied and the presence of hemorrhagic follicles or corpora lutea in the ovaries is an indication of pregnancy.

Detection of Estrogen in the Urine. A high amount of estrogen, which can be detected by biological or chemical methods, appears in the urine at the 4th month of pregnancy and reaches a maximum at the 7th to 9th month. In the chemical technique, pregnancy diagnosis is based on a fluorescent reaction between warm sulfuric acid (added in the test) and the phenolic fraction of the steroid hormone (present in the urine).

A. Male

Causes of lowered fertility in the stallion (Table 16–2) can often be determined by observation of the reproductive organs and the semen. Failure to ejaculate si a common cause of lowered fertility in stallions. A simple way to insure that ejaculation has taken place after intromission is to hold the hand under the base of the penis. In the absence of ejaculation a few weak urethral waves may be felt, but when ejaculation takes place it feels like the contents of a 10 cc. syringe going along the urethra. In a stallion of good fertility it is usual to feel about 5 of these waves; in the lower fertility

Table 16–2.—Some Causes of Lowered Fertility in the Stallion

Condition	Description
Defects in the penis	phallocampsis (curvature of penis when erect) or injuries
Ejaculatory disturbances	incomplete or inhibited ejaculation as a result of testes dysfunction or psychological inhibition
Small volume of ejaculate	atrophy in one or more of the accessory sexual glands or closure of the discharge ducts
Oligospermia	the total number of sperm per ejaculate is small; associated mainly with underdeveloped testes, but occasionally with testes of normal sizes
Azoospermia	no sperm in the ejaculate
Poor quality semen	low sperm motility or high percentage of dead and abnormal sperm, may be congenital

V. LOWERED FERTILITY AND INCREASING FERTILITY

Reproductive efficiency in horses is low as compared to that in other farm mammals. In general the conception rate ranges from 60 to 65 per cent and the foaling percentage is no more than about 50 per cent. In well-managed ranches, conception rate may reach 90 per cent and foaling percentage varies from 80 to 85 per cent.

The incidence of lowered reproductive efficiency varies with management and may often be due to improper detection of estrus in the mare and failure to breed at the right time, using the proper breeding techniques. In general, lowered fertility is more frequent where horses are used for heavy draft or housed in unsanitary stables.

stallion, it is sometimes only about $1\frac{1}{2}$ (Day, 1957).

B. Female

Some of the more common anatomical and physiological abnormalities are summarized in Table 16–3.

Abnormal Estrus. "Quiet ovulation," anovulatory estrus, "split estrus" and prolonged estrus are not uncommon in the mare. The characteristics of quiet ovulation are similar to those in other farm animals. Anovulatory estrus is due to the low LH output in the species, for in other farm animals, especially cattle and sheep, it is rarely encountered.

Split estrus commonly observed in healthy mares and during the early spring occurs at

18

Table 16–3.—Some Causes of Lowered Fertility in the Mare

Condition	Description
Ovarian hypoplasia	the ovaries of adult mares are small and lack follicle development; estrus does not occur
Ovarian hypo-function	small- or medium-sized follicles develop but degenerate before reaching maximum diameter; estrus is weak, irregular or absent; usually temporary
Follicular cyst or atresia	relatively large follicles develop in succession but degenerate before ovulation; a large follicle persists for a long time; estrus is intense and long; usually temporary
Luteal cyst	luteal tissue develops in the epithelial lining of a mature large follicle containing fluid possibly mixed with blood; estrus does not occur
Salpingitis and Hydrosalpinx	blocked Fallopian tube and accumulation of fluid; usually accompanies endometritis; fairly rare
Infantile uterus	the uterus is small, with a thin and relaxed wall lacking contractility; usually temporary but can be permanent
Metratrophis	atrophy of the uterus after long period of anestrus
Defects in the cervix	abnormal shape or position of the cervix; narrow cervical canal preventing the transport of sperm to the Fallopian tubes; torn cervix causes permanent sterility

all stages of maturation of the Graafian follicle. In such cases, behavioral estrus is interrupted by an interval of sexual non-receptivity. Fairly frequently the follicle which is present at the beginning of the first part of the split estrus will continue its growth normally throughout the period and will ovulate. The split estrus is strictly a behavioral phenomenon rather than related to endocrine physiology *per se*; *i.e.* it may be related to the mare's behavioral threshold, to estrogen, in the central nervous system. In other instances the first follicle may regress and a second follicle matures and ovulates during the second part of the split estrus

Prolonged estrus, lasting 10 to 40 days may also occur in early spring, and in mares used for heavy draft.

Abortion (Non-infectious). The average rate of abortion in mares is high (10%). This may possibly be due to peculiarities in the hormonal balance of the mare during pregnancy.

Some investigators report that abortion is most frequent at about the 5th month of pregnancy. Others report that maximum abortion occurs before 100 days of pregnancy and 10 months of gestation. The endocrinological basis of abortion is still uncertain. It is possible that abortion at about the 5th month of gestation is due to deficiency of progesterone which normally takes place when the placenta takes over the production of progesterone from the ovary. Abortion in the later stages of pregnancy may be due to low steroid production by the placenta.

During the 5th and 10th months of pregnancy, the mares are endocrinologically susceptible to abortion owing to hormonal deficiencies. It is a wise precaution to avoid sudden changes in the diet or the amount of physical exercise at these times. Nishikawa (1959) has reported that abortion may be prevented in mares which have experienced a previous failure by administering HCG. Day has recommended 300 mg. of progesterone implanted subcutaneously after 120 days of conception.

Stillbirth and Neonatal Mortality. Most (approximately 80%) of neonatal mortality occurs within 10 days after foaling. Neonatal mortality may be a result of weakness of the mother or the foal or bacterial infection through the umbilical cord of young. Proper management, clean stables for foaling and sanitary precautions at foaling are the common preventive methods of neonatal mortality. It appears doubtful that nutrition plays a very extensive role.

C. Recommendations for Breeding Techniques

Stallions. Stallions used for breeding should possess well developed testes fully descended in the scrotum. The semen should be evaluated before using for breeding. The sperm of the stallion are less viable than those of some other farm animals (see also Saunders, 1926; Laing, 1943) and some individuals produce relatively few sperm.

The detrimental effect of frequent ejaculations on the number of sperm per ejaculate is pronounced in the stallion. In natural breeding, where several mares may exhibit marily on the time and number of insemination (Table 16–4). In one experiment, for example, the conception rate was 55 per cent when the mares were inseminated once during estrus and 70 per cent when they were inseminated twice or more during one estrus. At the height of the breeding season, when a number of mares are receiving the attention of one stallion, the mare may receive one copulation; at such times it may be wise to inseminate the mare artificially 2 to 3 times in 2 days' interval during estrus to ensure conception.

On occasions, the mare may strain (as in micturition and defecation) after mating and evacuate most of the semen from the uterus.

Table 16–4.—Time of Insemination and Conception Rate

(Adapted from Sato & Hoshi, 1934. J. Jap. Soc. Vet. Sci., 47, 545).

	Day of insemination (ovulation = 0)							
	Days before ovulation					On Day of ovulation	Days after ovulation	
	−5	−4	−3	−2	−1	0	1	3
No. of mares inseminated	30	20	89	124	164	256	13	1
Conception rate (%)	10	40	52	65	60	60	54	0

estrus simultaneously, a stallion may copulate several times on one day; this causes a decline in fertility. The use of A.I. during such periods of mating will improve the conception percentage. The stallion ejaculates directly into the uterus and in most cases there is very little semen left in the vagina. Insemination to transfer semen from the vagina to the uterus is seldom necessary, but it is recommended with wriggling mares or if a stallion is apt to come off the mare with the penis still erect, as this pulls semen back into the vagina.

Mares. Careful testing for estrus with the stallion, routine examination of the vagina and rectal palpation of the reproductive organs may help to improve conception rate. Whenever possible, the time of ovulation should be predicted since the duration of estrus and the time of ovulation from the onset of estrus may differ markedly between individuals. Conception rate depends pri-

This may be prevented by having the mare walk for a while after mating. From the practical standpoint, several breeding techniques have been recommended (Ensminger, 1956; Day, 1957). The mare is susceptible to endometritis, especially after foaling since the cervix of the mare is not a strong barrier to the introduction of bacteria. Sanitary management is needed to keep free from endometritis. When it does occur, it should be treated as early as possible.

The mare is more prone to a deficiency in LH than other farm mammals; such deficiency may be alleviated by the use of exogenous LH. The intravenous injection of 1,500 to 3,000 i.u. of HCG will cause ovulation in animals suffering from anovulatory estrus, providing the ovarian follicle is at least 3 cm. in diameter.

Estrus and ovulation can be induced artificially during the non-breeding season by alteration in light or by repeated injections of estrogen as previously mentioned.

Since stallions produce semen throughout the year, there may be certain conditions in which out-of-season breeding of the mare becomes feasible and economically useful.

REFERENCES

ANDREWS, F. N. & McKENZIE, F. F. (1941). Estrus, ovulation and related phenomena in the mare. *Mo. Agric. Exp. Sta. Res. Bull.* No. 329.

BERLINER, V. R. (1959). The estrous cycle of the mare. In: *Reproduction in Domestic Animals.* H. H. Cole & P. T. Cupps (edits.) Vol. 1, pp. 267, New York, Academic Press.

BIELANSKI, W. (1960). *Reproduction in Horses.* I. *Stallion.* Inst. Zootech. Dzial Wydawnictwa Wlasne, No. 116, pp. 42.

BRITTON, J. W. & HOWELL, C. E. (1945). Observations on sterility. *Vet. Med.,* **40**, 264–268.

BURKHARDT, J. (1947). Transition from anoestrus in the mare and the effects of artificial lighting. *J. Agric. Sci.,* **37**, 64–68.

DAY, F. T. (1957). The veterinary clinicians approach to breeding problems in mares. *75th Ann. Congr. Brit. Vet. Assoc.* (Cambridge, England), pp. 8.

ENSMINGER, M. E. (1956). *Horses and Horsemanship.* 2nd ed. Danville, Ill., Interstate.

HAMMOND, J. (1960). *Farm Animals.* London, Arnold.

JENNINGS, W. E. (1950). Twelve years of horse breeding in the army. *J. Amer. Vet. Med. Assoc.,* **116**, 11–19.

LAING, J. A. (1943). Observations on the survival of stored spermatozoa in the genital tract of the mare. *J. agric. Sci.,* **33**, 64–66.

MAHAFFEY, L. W. (1950). Studies on fertility in the Thoroughbred mare. 1. Introduction. 2. Early post-partum oestrus ("foal heat"). *Aust. Vet. J.,* **26**, 267–273.

MANN, T., LEONE, E. & POLGE, C. (1956). The composition of the stallion's semen. *J. Endocrin.,* **13**, 279–290.

NISHIKAWA, Y. (1959). *Studies on Reproduction in Horses.* Tokyo, Japan Racing Association.

SAUNDERS, H. G. (1926). On the fertility of stallions. *J. agric. Sci.,* **16**, 466–491.

QUESTIONS

1. Describe one method to detect the following in the mare: estrus, ovulation, diestrus, early pregnancy (2nd month).
2. Describe some of the changes which occur in the reproductive tract of the mare throughout the estrous cycle.
3. Write short notes on: split estrus, ovulation fossa, PMS, oligospermia, luteal cysts, ovarian hypoplasia.
4. Discuss ten recommendations to keep a high fertility level in horses.
5. Discuss the nature of the breeding season in the mare.
6. Describe two methods to hasten the onset of the breeding season in the mare.
7. List five causes of lowered fertility in mares and stallions. Discuss the method of diagnosis.
8. Puberty in the stallion is a gradual phenomenon. What is the evidence for this?
9. Discuss the seasonal changes which occur in semen characteristics of the stallion.
10. When does the post-partum heat occur? When is the best time for breeding after foaling? Why?

Chapter 17

The Reproduction of Poultry

By I. L. KOSIN

AN avian egg, to be reproductively useful, must first be ovulated and fertilized, then surrounded by several layers of nutrient and protective matter, and finally oviposited. The product, an egg, has to be also hatchable, *i.e.* an embryo within it must be capable of normal development, while the extra-embryonic substratum must be suitable for sustaining the embryo through a complete incubation period. Furthermore, the environmental conditions outside an egg must be favorable for the embryo's growth. All this calls for a close integration of hereditary and environmental factors, a situation complicated in case of domestic poultry by artificial selection, in response to what are essentially commercial considerations. Among the latter, one can list need for high egg production, large egg size and rapid growth rate. In poultry, this has led to the evolvement of biological types which differ considerably, in their physiology and morphology, from their wild prototypes and contemporary counterparts.

I. EGG PRODUCTION

Of the domestic poultry, only the chicken and the duck can be regarded as truly annual reproducers. These two species have been subjected from the days of antiquity to selection for high egg production, and as a result the mature females of both species lay eggs and the males are sexually active irrespective of the season. By contrast, in the turkey, the goose, and the guinea fowl, egg laying and mating activity are normally confined to a rather clearly restricted breeding season. In the northern hemisphere, this extends through the months of March, April and May. Differences in the average egg production of species of domestic poultry during their first 18 months of life are shown in Table 17–1.

Within the last two decades, in response to commercial demand, improvement in egg laying of the turkey has been receiving increased attention. Although some progress has been made in the desired direction, the domesticated turkeys biologically still remain close to their wild-type relatives.

Advances in quantitative genetics and the increasingly more rapid application of new breeding methods to poultry husbandry has led in the last 20 years to rapid improvement in the egg laying capacity of today's chicken. There is no longer any talk of egg laying "ceilings," particularly with respect to population averages. The U. S. Department of Agriculture estimates show that within

(277)

Table 17–1.—Comparative Reproduction* in Domestic Poultry and the Pheasant

Species	Incubation period (days)	Age at Sexual maturity (months)	No. eggs/year	Egg weight (gms)	Fertility %	Hatchability of fertile eggs %
Chicken (*Gallus gallus*)	21	5–6	220	58	90	80
Turkey (*Meleagris gallopavo*)	28	7–8	75	85	70	65
Duck (*Anas platyrhyncos*)	27–28	6–7	120–180	60	95	70
Goose (*Anser anser*)						
Small type	30	9–10	60	135	70	80
Large type	33	10–12	50	215	65	75
Pheasant (*Phasianus colchicus*)	24–26	10–12	40	30	95	85
Guinea fowl (*Numida meleagris*)	27–28	10–12	40–70	40	90	95

*Averages and, where appropriate, ranges of performance by different breeds and varieties, at different locations, on different planes of nutrition and under different management practices.

the last 20 years the average number of eggs laid a year by a hen in the United States increased from 100 to 170. Not all of this success in raising the rate of egg lay in chickens can be attributed to breeding. Genetic gains would have been greatly impeded, unless there had been a concurrent improvement in environment.

A. Nutrition

Nutrition is undoubtedly the most important environmental factor governing the long-term egg production record of a bird. Sustained egg laying requires energy from feedstuffs considerably above the maintenance requirements of a laying bird. The basic maintenance energy requirement of a mature White Leghorn hen is close to 140 Calories per day. Besides that, at least 100 Calories of gross energy must be provided to a bird for each egg laid by it (Mitchell et al., 1930). Improvements in poultry rations have reflected an increasing appreciation of this basic relation between energy intake and energy output of a laying hen, as well as a better understanding of the hen's need for physiologically essential nutrients.

B. Daylength

All species of poultry respond to light, whether natural or artificial. The ratio of light-dark periods within a diurnal cycle and the rate of change of this ratio during bird's growth influences the onset and maintenance of subsequent egg production. *The distribution of light and dark phases within such a cycle determines the time of oviposition.* In general, the egg is laid during the light phase.

The actual duration of light within the 24-hour period is not a critical factor in determining the degree of light response by a maturing or a mature bird. What is important is the temporal distribution of light stimulation. Flashes of intense light every hour throughout the 24-hour period approach in effectiveness the more accepted regimen of 13 to 14 hours of continuous light. The wave length of light is of secondary importance, provided it is within the visible spectrum. However, shorter wave lengths (blues, indigos) are less effective in stimulating the production of FSH than are longer wave lengths (red, orange) (Benoit et al., 1950). Light intensity above one foot candle power is not a factor, except in special cases: *e.g.* where the total duration of light exposure is strictly delimited, as is the case in the flashing light regimen referred to above.

The turkey hen is more susceptible to light effects than the chicken: the turkey hen and the goose will not begin to lay eggs until they have been properly preconditioned by adequate exposure either to artificial or natural light. Chickens and ducks will initiate but not sustain egg laying in darkness, though usually after a delay of several weeks beyond the normal starting date. When poultry is growing in a season first of increasing and then of decreasing day-length (as is the case with spring-hatched birds), egg production is initiated at the time when hens normally become sexually mature: 5 to 6 months in the chicken, 7 to 8 months in the turkey. As has been already indicated, contrary to the chicken hen, the turkey hen, in order to come into egg lay, needs some additional light to supplement the waning natural light of the autumn months.

As with other domestic farm animals, in poultry the light acts on the hypothalamic-pituitary complex via the optic nerve. A bird which is somatically ready to respond to this stimulus does so by increasing the supply of circulating FSH. The hormone, in turn, initiates further ovarian activity, which eventually results in ovulation and oviposition (Lacassagne, 1956). Light *refractoriness* is a factor in photostimulation (light stimulation) of birds. It is a condition in which a bird, normally sensitive to such stimulation, temporarily becomes unresponsive. The phenomenon was first demonstrated in migratory birds. A refractory animal is incapable of releasing the levels of FSH necessary for stimulating ovarian activity. The situation can be corrected by placing the organism in either complete or near-darkness for several weeks. In poultry, refractoriness to light usually appears when birds are nearing what normally would be their chronological age for sexual maturity during a season of constantly increasing day length. In the northern latitudes, this would be true of birds hatched between November and January. The chicken is less prone to develop light refractoriness than is the turkey.

The role of light in egg production has led to the development of housing schemes which provide for a complete confinement of laying chickens. This gives the operator full control of light exposure, especially where off-season (late autumn—early winter) hatched birds are desired.

C. Ambient Temperature

Within rather wide limits, ambient temperature is not a major factor affecting the rate of egg laying in poultry (Hutchinson & Taylor, 1957). So long as the birds can maintain their body temperature within the normal range of 40.5 to 43°C., it is not at all easy to demonstrate the effect of environmental temperature on egg production. While the range of thermoneutrality (ideal ambient temperature) for laying hens extends between 15 and 25°C., the birds can adapt, mostly by physical means, for temperatures above or below these extremes. Between 25 and 30°C. the bird, in order to maintain its internal homeostasis, will reduce its physical activity and feed intake without any deleterious effect on egg laying. The lower range of temperature "tolerance" is wide, extending between 15° and −10°C. In this case, increased energy intake (as feed) and increased physical activity help to overcome the otherwise detrimental effects of low ambient temperature, provided such periods are short, *e.g.* 1 to 2 days. The difficulty arises when physical regulation of the body temperature proves to be inadequate and chemical regulation, via increased basal metabolic rate, is called upon for assistance. At this point, egg production declines.

D. Living Space and Social Pressure

The growing need to use the available valuable land more effectively has favored the development of cage system of operation at the expense of so-called floor system. In the latter, the birds are kept in the pen on the floor covered with some type of litter. Commercial cage operations usually involve the use of "community cages," of a type in which a dozen or more laying hens are placed together in a cage. Some strains of chickens adapt more easily to cage conditions than others, a fact which to a large extent, accounts for variation in the reported results comparing the two systems. When this factor of strain difference is taken into account, there is little doubt that egg production in cages is lower than when comparable birds are kept in floor pens (Table 17–2). These differences reflect still unsolved problems involving nutrition and, possibly, psychological adjustment of birds to close confinement.

Table 17–2.—Egg Production in Cages and in Floor Pens* at the California Chicken Random Sample Egg Test

Method of Housing	Year			
	1957	1958	1959	1960
Floor pens	260	271	275	278
Cages	242	258	240	254

*Floor space per hen and the number hens used were same in both methods of housing.

The above can be considered to be the more important aspects of gross environment affecting egg production. Some attention now will be given to another set of factors which more directly reflect the biological status of the avian organism.

E. Age and Molt

All species of domestic poultry lay most intensively during their first year of life, *i.e.*, before the birds have gone through their first *annual molt*. The general molt of body feathers normally occurs in the chicken some 16 months after hatching, after a hen has been in egg production for 10 to 11 months. If a hen is kept beyond that time, each year thereafter there is about a 20 per cent decrease in her egg production. The period of egg lay, which is finally terminated by the general molt, is known as *"the biological year."* Its length, which measures the egg laying *persistency* of a hen, is controlled by the interaction of genotype and environment. In other species of domestic poultry, molting is of less concern because the period of egg production is shorter than in the chicken. Turkeys, geese, and even ducks usually stop laying well ahead of the start of the annual general molt.

Length of the biological year cannot in itself assure an adequate egg record. The *intensity* at which eggs are laid within that period, *i.e.* rate of egg production, is another important variable. All birds lay eggs in *clutches* of varying lengths. The clutch here is defined as the number of eggs laid on consecutive days (see Chapter 12). Obviously, the larger the average clutch size, the more eggs will be credited to a hen in a given period. Clutch can be regarded as an expression of inherent intensity. Genetic variance of intensity and of persistency of egg laying in poultry is low, pointing to the importance of environment in determining their expression.

II. FERTILITY FOLLOWING NATURAL MATING

A. Species Differences

The term fertility denotes the proportion of eggs, laid by mated birds, which show unmistakable signs of embryonic development following incubation. On the average, chickens and ducks typically are more fertile, than turkeys and geese. No reliable information is available on guinea fowl; what data exist indicate that fertility in this species is similar to that of turkeys and geese. The apparent species differences in fertility (Table 17–1) reflect both the effect of current managerial practices applied to a particular species and of traits which in each instance have been emphasized in selection. *It is unlikely that the observed differences represent an immutable biological phenomenon.*

B. Behavioral Adjustments

Obviously, high levels of fertility can be achieved only when sexual activity of the male is synchronized with egg laying in the female; failure to accomplish this for any reason will depress fertility. In birds with relatively long annual cycles, *e.g.* chickens, both males and females have adequate time before and after the onset of sexual maturity in which both sexes can fully adjust to each other. Furthermore, the two species, chickens and ducks, which under domestication are highly fertile, are truly *polygamous*, showing little evidence of *preferential mating*. Except in cases of single-sire breeding groups, mutual or unilateral sexual rejection, even when it occurs, need not lead to infertility: a bird rejected by one mate usually will be accepted by another. Generally speaking, it is the hen that determines whether or not sexual advances of a particular male will lead to copulation. Wood-Gush & Osborne (1956) suggest that she does this on the basis of "behavioral and physical attributes of the male." The ability to recognize pen mates has been demonstrated for different species of poultry and, undoubtedly, provides the basis for preferential mating.

In the seasonal reproducers, *i.e.* the goose and the turkey, relative shortness of the annual mating season adversely affects the opportunity for sexual and social adjustment between the sexes. This is aggravated by the fact that the sexual activity of turkey males and ganders can be relatively easily depressed by such unfavorable environmental conditions as extremes of ambient temperature, inadequate light exposure, uncomfortable quarters (drafty or wet) and disturbances by extraneous noise. Geese tend to maintain stable mating units, *i.e.* one gander will mate only with 3 or 4 females. In turkeys there is no such limitation on mating activity, although preferential mating is more common than in chickens. Moreover, the prime emphasis on large body size in most breeding programs involving turkeys and geese has led to the evolvement of phenotypes which often have considerable mechanical difficulty in copulating.

C. Ambient Temperature

In general, both annual and seasonal reproducers show long-term fertility trends (*i.e.* trends extending over a breeding season or a biological year) which clearly can be attributed to environmental influence. Fertility tends to be highest when the birds are exposed to temperature and light regimens which also favor maximum egg production. Hens which are physiologically in optimal condition for intensive egg laying also are more receptive to male attention. Conversely, the males under such conditions will be most highly endowed with the capacity to fertilize their mates successfully. This trend is particularly clear in turkeys (Fig. 17-1). There is evidence that ambient temperature also exerts a direct physiological effect on the fertilizing capacity of the male bird, via the testes. Testes of the male turkeys which have passed through their first breeding season regress in size with the advent of cold winter months (Law & Kosin, 1958). No spermatogenesis could be detected in the seminiferous tubules of such testes. On the other hand, the testes of comparable birds, maintained in an environment of 10°C. remained functional.

Excessively cold weather, aside from its effects on the ratio of input and output of energy, can depress mating activity through shear physical distress of mates. Frost-bitten combs and wattles in chickens is probably the most prominent example of such a condition. In temperate zones, higher fertility coincides with periods of moderate temperature.

D. Light

Preconditioning with light can be a critical factor in goose and turkey flocks intended

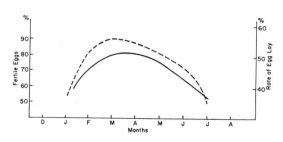

Fig. 17-1.—Seasonality of egg laying (– – –) and of fertility (———) in the domestic turkey.

(*Based on breeding pen records of a Broad Breasted Bronze flock at Pullman, Washington, U.S.A. The birds, hatched in April, were 8 months old when first subjected to 14 hrs. of artificial light/day. The males were lighted on December 8 and the females on December 15, the day the birds were mated. Daily egg records were kept from the following January. The rate of lay expresses the number of eggs actually laid, as percentage of the total, theoretically possible, number of eggs in a given period (e.g. month). Fertility was determined first by candling and then by breaking out all of the infertile eggs thus revealed, and examining their germ discs.*)

for the production of hatching eggs ahead of the normal breeding season. In this case, not only the "off-season" egg production has to be induced, but the males have to be brought into a state of sexual activity 3 to 4 weeks before the onset of egg lay. This can be done by subjecting males to an artificial light regimen of 14 hours per day 5 weeks ahead of the females. This will induce mating 10 to 14 days before the first egg is laid. The females are lighted at the time of mating. The intensity of artificial light need not be over 2 foot-candle power of light at bird's back. Brighter light not only is wasted, but it can lead to a type of refractoriness to light similar to that described earlier, in section I.

E. Nutrition

It is difficult to affect fertility in the domestic fowl by nutrition unless the intake of energy falls below maintenance requirements. Some evidence, however, indicates that extreme deficiency either of tocopherols or of carotenes will lower the fertilizing capacity in the male. This is accomplished through depression of spermatogenesis. The presence of adequate levels of vitamin E is necessary not only for effective use of androgens by the male organism, but also for the maintenance of adequate storage levels of FSH in the pituitary. Low level of vitamin E in the ration results in fewer basophilic cells in the anterior pituitary (Herrick, 1952). Aside from this, no one as yet has demonstrated unequivocally the effect of diet on fertility *per se*. Breeding males frequently lose weight during periods of intense mating but the factor involved here is not, however, that of quality of the diet but rather that of energy intake by the sexually active male.

F. Age of Breeding Birds

Age of breeding males and females is definitely related to fertility. With the possible exception of geese, where best fertility is commonly observed in 2- or 3-year-old birds, all other domestic fowl record their highest fertility in their first breeding year, *i.e.*, before they are 18 months old. Decline in fertility with age is

particularly strongly expressed in turkey males. In this species, the rate of testis recrudescence in birds approaching their second breeding season, following the short-daylight period of winter months, is slower than in males nearing their first breeding season. A similar though less extreme situation is observed in the chicken. Apparently the threshold response by the quiescent avian testis to FSH rises with age. This hormone is essential not only for somatic growth of the testis, but also for growth and subsequent meiotic division of primary spermatocytes.

G. Molt

As has already been pointed out, extensive molting depresses fertility. If molting is not general in the female, the effect on fertility is likely to be slight, being expressed largely in reduced receptivity to mating. Artificial insemination can overcome that condition. A hen in a general molt, which involves tail and flight feathers, usually will cease egg production. The mature male bird molts continuously a few feathers at a time and such molting does not affect his fertilizing capacity. However, if for some reason (such as excessive exposure to light, high ambient temperature, or gross nutritional deficiencies) molting becomes more extensive, then not only will his libido be depressed but semen volume and sperm concentration will be reduced as well. In extreme cases, such a bird will become temporarily sterile.

H. Body Size

In chickens and turkeys, the genetic variation in body weight is associated with body conformation, *i.e.* it is affected by the relationship between width and depth of body and keel length. This association is due to massive pectoral muscles. Birds richly endowed with such muscles are commercially desirable. They are, however, characterized by lower fertility levels when mated naturally. Artificial insemination as a rule will correct the situation, thus indicating that lower fertility of such birds is not an inherent trait, but is due to excessively large body size. Large difference in the body size between mates results in lower fertility, largely because of mechanical difficulties in completing copulation successfully.

I. Size of Breeding Unit

Fertility is also affected by the size of the breeding unit. Under wild conditions, geese and guinea fowls prefer monogamous mating, although under domestication a single sire will mate with several females. Chickens, turkeys and ducks mate in large aggregations without any tendency to pair off. In chickens, a single White Leghorn male will mate successfully with as many as 20 females. In heavy breed chickens, e.g. New Hampshires, and in turkeys, this ratio is reduced to 1:12. The corresponding ratio for ducks is 1:6. Ten to 14 days should be allowed for the establishment of fertility in a mass-mated flock. This interval is needed to permit the males to mate at least 2 to 3 times with all of the females that are in egg production at the time. Not all initial matings assure the fertilization of a series of ova ovulated subsequent to a single copulation. Repeated matings are necessary to reach the highest attainable level of fertility in a given breeding population.

Mating activity in a breeding pen is at its highest at a time when females have laid their daily quota of eggs. A hen with a hard shell egg in the uterus usually will not accept a male. Most eggs are laid in the morning and early afternoon hours. This accounts for the fact that under a normal distribution of daylight hours, when females begin to lay in the morning, most matings occur between 2 and 3 p.m., i.e. within 2 hours of the mode for the diurnal pattern of egg laying in chickens and turkey.

J. Competition Among Males

Excessive number of males in a mass-mated flock leads to fighting among them, all competing for the attention of their female pen mates. Under such conditions there is bound to be frequent interference with mating, resulting in incomplete copulations and, thus, in lower fertility. Introduction of a new male in an established breeding population invariably results in renewed turmoil among males in the immediate vicinity of the stranger. The latter usually suffers attacks from other males whose social rank in the flock hierarchy has been long established. This often leads either to the death of the "intruder" or to his *psychological castration*, a condition which describes a male which, though physiologically capable of mating, had his libido depressed by social competition to a point where he will not make sexual advances to a female. Such phenomenon is also observed in male birds which are of low social rank in a mass-mated pen.

K. Effect of Drugs

Certain chemical compounds, used both as prophylactic and therapeutic drugs in poultry pathology, are known to reduce fertility. For example, certain nitrothiazoles, valuable in the prophylaxis and treatment of enterohepatitis in turkeys, definitely depress fertility in the males and delay the onset of egg laying in females. Furazolidones, useful in the control of Salmonella and histamonas infections in turkeys and chickens, also depress testis function when fed at prophylactic levels.

III. HATCHABILITY

Incubation in avian species corresponds to gestation in mammals. Allowing for breed and individual variation, its duration is reasonably constant within a species (Table 17–1).

A. Ambient Temperature

Climatic environment of the breeding stock, particularly immediately before and during the mating season, may affect the hatchability of fertile eggs. For example, the hen's ability to mobilize calcium is affected by high ambient temperature, an effect which is reflected in the reduced level of blood calcium and, in the end, in poorer quality shell. The shell of an egg, aside from its purely mechanical function as a protective outer envelope, serves as the main source of calcium for the embryo.

Ambient temperature may also affect the blastoderm directly, both before and during incubation. The embryo is unfavorably affected by any ambient temperature which fails to support the level of cellular and organismal metabolism optimal for a particular embryonic stage. Extended exposure of eggs to low temperature during the interim pre-incubation period reduces hatchability, while freezing of the egg will destroy it as a reproductive unit. An egg will freeze at temperatures below −2°C.

On the other hand if, prior to incubation proper, the eggs are kept in a thermal environment that permits limited development, *i.e.* 20 to 35°C., the future hatching potential of the egg will be sharply lowered. This will be due to the initiation of growth which would proceed at a sub-optimal rate, with the concomitant expenditure of energy. The net result will be some measure of distorted embryogenesis.

Even under otherwise optimal conditions, the egg rather rapidly loses its capacity to hatch when the pre-incubation period is extended beyond 7 days. This is because there is continuous intra-cellular activity in the blastoderm during this time, even though on gross examination the egg appears to be quiescent. Continuous cellular metabolism, largely catabolic, unrelieved by any evidence of rejuvenation of the organism through normal cell proliferation, gradually leads to blastodermal senescence and moribundity (Kosin, unpublished). The biological objective of the pre-incubation storage is to reduce this process to a minimum without, however, adversely affecting the developmental potential of an aging blastoderm. This is best accomplished by storing hatching eggs at 12.5°C.

Once the eggs are set in an incubator, environment within the machine becomes the main controlling factor in hatchability. The avian embryo starts out as a completely *poikilothermic* organism (*i.e.* an organism in which body temperature fluctuates with the temperature of its environment). Only gradually, toward the end of its normal incubation period, though still imperfectly, it becomes *homoithermic* (*i.e.* able to maintain a relatively constant body temperature, regardless of environment). During incuba-

tion, external heat is needed for normal development. Respiratory exchange is the essential feature of morphogenesis, with some of the released energy being used for maintenance purposes, and the balance for further ontogeny. Reduced temperature depresses the latter activity first.

Disregarding species differences in the heat requirements during incubation, the acceptable incubation temperature for poultry ranges between 37.5 and 40°C. The actual optimal temperature varies not only with the species but also with the incubation conditions. In natural incubation, when eggs are under a setting hen, or in artificial incubation when still-air incubators are used, each egg shows a considerable temperature gradient within it: the highest temperature is on its dorsal side. This condition does not occur in modern, forced-draft, electric incubators, which heat the egg uniformly on all sides. These incubators perform best when the operating temperature range is narrow, no wider than ± 0.5°C.

B. Humidity

Water constitutes about 70 per cent of the total weight of an avian egg. In a hatching egg, it must be conserved for the future use of the embryo. Aside from being the solvent for physiologically vital solutes coming from the yolk, albumen and shell, and for the embryo's own metabolic wastes, water also serves in an important thermo-regulatory capacity. The low heat of conductivity of water (only 0.001 cal./cm./sec./°C) helps to guard the embryo against harmful, externally-imposed, fluctuations in its body temperature.

To reduce water loss to a minimum during pre-incubation storage, hatching eggs are kept in an environment of 12.5°C. and 80 to 85 per cent relative humidity. During incubation, the relative humidity is 60 to 65 per cent.

A chicken egg loses 8 to 10 grams of water during incubation, or about 25 per cent of its total water content. This loss is partly made up by the 2 gm. of water that the embryo, on the average, gains from the combustion of fat. All in all, however, humidity is important in the incubator because its level is the major factor determining the rate at which the hatching egg loses water. In the average chicken egg this loss is reasonably well balanced between the two halves of the 21-day incubation period. A large differential between air humidity and that found in the air cell of the egg will create a moisture imbalance in the micro-environment surrounding the embryo.

Aside from the already mentioned more general considerations concerning the role of water in the physiology of the avian embryo, the two following points should also be taken into account. One is that an excessive rate of evaporation during incubation will lead to the drying, in a relative sense, of the chorio-allantoic complex. This will interfere with the outward flow of CO_2, a by-product of embryo's metabolism, and with the intake of oxygen. The other consideration is that an excessive loss of water by the fluids which fill the chorio-allantoic and amniotic cavities (Fig. 17–3) will upset their normal electrolyte balance through increased osmotic pressure. Inadequate rate of evaporation is nearly as harmful because the gaseous exchange within the developing organism is pressed by the "water-logged" chorio-allantoic and the two shell membranes.

C. Velocity of Air in Incubator

Although the velocity of air movement in an ordinary incubator has no effect on hatchability, the rate of air exchange between the outside and the inside of a machine is definitely a factor. A rapidly developing embryo needs a constant supply of oxygen. Furthermore, the concentration of CO_2 in the air for best results should not exceed 0.5 per cent. Some CO_2, however, is necessary in the embryo's atmosphere to facilitate the dissociation of calcium from calcium carbonate of the shell. Toward the end of incubation, CO_2 is also needed for the maintenance of proper muscle tonus in the embryo, a prerequisite for its successful emergence from the shell.

D. Utilization of Energy

As the embryo develops, it uses the available energy sources in the egg, and at the same time eliminates larger amounts of heat (Table 17–3). When many eggs are involved in a setting, up to 60,000 in some modern incubators, the problem of coping with excessive heat becomes more acute, especially toward the end of the incubation period. At that time, for example, 10,000 fertile chicken eggs set in a single machine will be producing 35,000 Calories of energy per 24-hour period (Barott, 1937).

Table 17–3.—Energy Exchange* in Chicken Eggs

(*Adapted from Barott, 1937. USDA Tech. Bull. No. 553*)

Days of incubation	Heat Elimination, (Calories, Kg.)	O₂ Consumption, (liters)
5	2.0	0.6
8	7.6	1.9
11	18.5	4.5
14	47.3	12.4
17	82.0	21.6
20	120.0	33.2

*Per 100 eggs in 8 hours; 37° C., 60% R.H., 21% O_2, 0.5% CO_2.

Chickens and turkeys utilize about the same relative quantities of energy during their respective incubation periods. The ducks and geese are somewhat more efficient in this respect (Fig. 17–2). Thus, the hatched weight of a chicken is approximately 60 per cent of the original weight of the egg. This value is 75 per cent in the duck. The 25 to 40 per cent loss includes the discarded shell and embryonic membranes. Furthermore, in chickens, turkeys, geese and ducks, the loss in the weight of a hatching egg during incubation from day 1 through the day just preceding hatching constitutes between 11 and 14 per cent of its original weight. Any major deviation from these values, regardless of causes, usually leads to the death of the developing organism.

The total energy value of an average chicken egg is 95 to 100 calories, of which some 25 per cent is used in providing the embryo with the energy necessary for development. The rest of the original available energy becomes incorporated into the embryo.

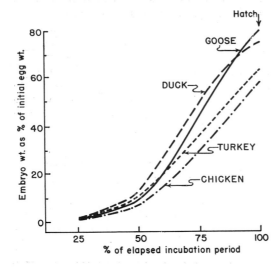

FIG. 17-2.—Growth of the avian embryo.

E. Nutrition

Although hatchability is a heritable trait, the genetic potential of an embryo to hatch can be easily depressed by a nutritionally inadequate diet of its parents, particularly that of the dam. The fertilized avian egg is a self-sufficient reproductive unit, in which all but the minute *parental pronuclei* (*i.e.* the nucleus from the ovum and the nucleus from the sperm) represent a highly concentrated source of food energy provided by the maternal organism. The avian embryo has to depend on the extra-embryonic egg components for sustenance during both the incubation and the initial post-incubation periods.

It is not surprising, therefore, that the avian embryo and its adult counterpart possess many proteins in common. This has been demonstrated by immunological procedures which have shown that a species has certain characteristic antigens, regardless of age of the donor organism. The avian embryo obtains some of these common proteins directly from its own micro-environment, *i.e.* yolk and albumen. Thus, blood serum-like proteins have been identified in unfertilized eggs (Schechtman, 1955). Other proteins are synthesized *de novo*, a process which is associated with a phase-like pattern in the appearance of many key enzymes. For example, Solomon has demonstrated the existence in the chicken embryo of such a pattern for glutamic dehydrogenase, an important liver enzyme.

To achieve this continuous series of syntheses, the avian embryo must be provided with appropriate amino acids by the egg in which it is developing. Some of these amino acids are physiologically essential in that they must be supplied in the ration to the hen before they will find their way to the hatching egg; they cannot be easily, if at all, synthesized by the maternal organism. To this group belong lysine, arginine and tryptophan. Several vitamins, particularly B$_{12}$ and D, and minerals such as calcium, manganese and iron are essential for hatchability.

F. Age of Female Parent

Age of the maternal organism affects hatchability. The biological efficiency of the maternal organism to make use of the available nutrients for reproduction drops down rapidly after the first year. Such maternal effect does not stem from the fact that older hens lay larger eggs, because such effect can be observed even when appropriate corrections are made for egg size. This is not to be interpreted to mean that egg size *per se* is not a factor in hatchability. In a population in which age is not a variable, larger eggs, as a group, will show lower hatchability than eggs weighing slightly below the mean egg weight characterizing a particular population. There is no evidence to show that the age of the sire is a factor in hatchability.

G. Characteristics of Eggs

Shape of the egg, provided it falls within a normal range of variability, does not affect hatchability. Only eggs of extreme length in relation to width, or *vice versa*, show a distinct tendency for lower hatchability. Such eggs are usually characterized by thin or otherwise imperfect shell.

In breeds of chickens with brown-shell eggs, eggs with excessively light colored shells do not hatch well. This may be related to shell defects (*e.g.* roughness or excessive porosity) which in such eggs is associated with low calcium content of the shell. In those turkey varieties which normally lay eggs with spotted shell, eggs lacking such spotting frequently have defective shells and, hence, are low in hatchability. Some evidence exists that for best hatchability, the optimum ratio of the weight of albumen to that of yolk is 2:1; a wider or narrower ratio leads to lower hatchability.

This has been attributed in such eggs to an imbalance between the available source of energy for the avian embryo. In birds, fats and carbohydrates provide about 91 and 4 per cent of the total energy, respectively, which is needed for normal embryonic development. Practically all the fat is in the yolk. On the other hand, the albumen has nearly three times as much water as the yolk. The early embryo draws first on its carbohydrates and then on fats for energy. Efficiency of the embryo's utilization of these components, as well as their total availability is a major factor that determines subsequent viability of the embryo. As development progresses, water plays an increasingly important role in protein metabolism, particularly as a passive carrier for nitrogenous wastes.

Although season is known to affect albumen "quality" (the proportion of thin albumen is increased by prolonged exposure of breeding females to temperatures above 35°C.), the ratio of thin and thick albumen does not affect hatchability. Neither is it affected by the presence, in the egg, of such inclusions as blood and meat spots.

H. Miscellaneous Traits

Hatchability in chickens and turkeys is indirectly associated with intensity of egg production: eggs laid in multiple-egg clutches, particularly in three-egg clutches, hatch better than eggs laid in single- or two-egg clutches. The position of an egg within a multiple-egg clutch has no bearing on its hatching potential.

Time of day the egg is laid frequently affects hatchability. Thus, in chickens the best over-all hatches are obtained from eggs laid between mid-morning and mid-afternoon. In turkeys, this can be said for eggs laid late in the afternoon or early evening. No definite explanation of this observation is yet available, although studies of chicken blastoderms by McNally & Byerly (1936) and of turkey blastoderms (Kosin, unpublished) may have a direct bearing on this point. The eggs laid during the above mentioned optimal periods were found to be characterized by a high rate of embryonic development. Evidence points to the fact that such eggs are in more advanced stages of gastrulation when oviposited.

An important and frequently overlooked factor in hatchability is the age of sperm within the oviduct. In the chicken, at least,

Table 17–4.—Effect of Aged Sperm on Hatchability in Chickens

(*Adapted from Nalbandov & Card, 1943. Poult. Sci. 22, 218; Kosin, 1947. Poult. Sci. 26, 548, & unpublished*)

Estimated minimum age of sperm in the hen's oviduct		
1–10 days	11–20 days	
% Fertile eggs hatched		Source
65	47	Nalbandov & Card
(660)*	(113)	
76	62	Kosin
(1017)	(705)	

*Figures in parentheses indicate number of fertile eggs.

embryos resulting from the fertilization of eggs by aged sperm (*i.e.* sperm which have been in the oviduct for 14 days or longer) possess lower viability. This leads to lower hatchability (Table 17–4). Because mating in poultry may occur, especially in mass-mated pens, at infrequent intervals, the relevance of the problem of aged sperm becomes self-evident. The effect of aging of gametes in mammals has been discussed in Chapter 6.

I. Normal Embryogenesis

The embryo begins its development within a well defined area of the yolk known as the *germ disc*. This area is clearly visible to the naked eye when the egg is broken out. Normally the germ disc is found on top side of the yolk, because the hemisphere that contains the disc has a slightly lower specific gravity than its counterpart. In a fertile, unincubated egg, the germ disc represents a greatly flattened *gastrula*. Upon some incubation, the definitive embryo arises within the central translucent region, *area pellucida*, while the extra embryonic portions of the original blastoderm spread rapidly over the yolk's surface. As a general rule, the embryo becomes oriented along the axis which is perpendicular to the long axis of the egg.

In common with other vertebrate embryos, the avian embryo shows its most rapid initial development in the head region. Thus, in the chicken, several subdivisions of the brain, arising from the *neural fold*, become clearly visible by the end of the first 24 hours of incubation. Posteriorly, a rapid differentiation of the neural fold proceeds, giving rise to the definitive spinal cord and its neural appendages. Concurrently, the endodermal and mesodermal layers rapidly differentiate, so that by the time the chicken embryo is 48 hours old, it has both the functional heart and the vestigial alimentary canal. A 48-hour chicken embryo already has established a closed-type of blood circulation between itself and its immediate micro-environment—the yolk.

In the absence of the placenta, the avian embryo has to depend upon extra-embryonic membranes with their intricate blood vascular network, to carry out the necessary metabolic functions associated with nutrition, respiration and excretion. Oxygen and food are obtained on the periphery of the blood vascular mesh and carried to the embryo. Waste products of metabolism move in the opposite direction. By the end of the third day, the chicken embryo starts to develop a full complement of extra-embryonic membranes, including the allantois, the chorion, and the amnion. The allantois, which at first serves as a storage organ for nitrogenous wastes, later joins with the chorion, to form a complex membrane, the chorio-allantois, the major part of which is closely apposed to the shell (Fig. 17–3). This membrane serves as the embryonic respiratory organ until the pulmonary type of respiration takes over about 24 hours before hatching.

The morphogenetic changes in an avian embryo proceed so rapidly, that the general outline of the definitive organism is fully recognizable at the end of the initial third of the incubation period. By that time also, the various essential internal anatomical systems become established, *e.g.* the urogenital, pulmonary, nervous, muscular and sensory systems. The sex of the chick embryo can be determined histologically as early as the 5th day of incubation. Embryos of the domestic poultry species are fully covered with down by the middle of the incubation period.

For several days after the start of incubation the embryo partly floats within the amniotic fluid. It is important for the embryo's future survival to remain at that time capable of relatively free movement within the cavity. Even later, after the embryo, together with its extra-embryonic membranes, has grown to fill all of the available space within the shell, it must retain considerable latitude in being able to shift periodically. This freedom must prevail to within the last 3 to 4 days of actual hatching, and is the reason why the egg up to then must be turned several times a day: to prevent the embryo from adhering to its chorio-allantoic membrane. The shell and its shell membranes protect the embryo from invasion by harmful micro-organisms, such as pseudomonas and molds. Additional

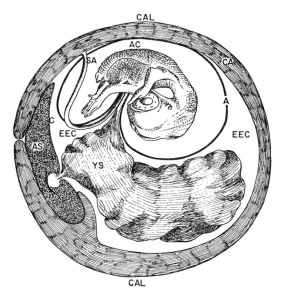

FIG. 17–3.—A semi-diagrammatic presentation of the *in-situ* relationship between the 10-day old chicken embryo and the extra-embryonic membranes. A, Amnion; *AC*, amniotic cavity; *AS*, albumen "sac;" *C*, chorion; *CA*, allantoic cavity; *CAL*, chorio-allantois; *EEC*, extra-embryonic vacity *SA*, allantoic stalk; *YS*, yolk sac. (*Adapted from Needham. 1942. Biochemistry and Morphogenesis, Courtesy Cambridge University Press.*)

protection is afforded by the mildly bacteriostatic action of the albumen.

J. Embryonic Mortality

Hatchability of fertile eggs reflects the level of embryonic mortality. While this mortality occurs through the entire incubation period, its incidence is not uniform. There are at least *two mortality peaks*: the first occurs early in incubation; the second, and the more pronounced of the two, is prominent just before the embryo breaks into the air cell, *i.e.* 2 to 3 days before hatching. In the chicken, the two peaks occur on the 2nd or 3rd day and on the 19th day. In turkeys, the peaks are shifted to the 4th or 5th day and the 25th day. Corresponding mortality peaks in embryos have been observed in other species of poultry.

These peaks become exaggerated when hatching eggs are exposed to suboptimal conditions, before and during incubation, or when breeding birds are fed deficient rations (*e.g.* deficient in vitamins D and E). Both peaks are associated with the gaseous exchange and the accumulation of lactic acid in the embryo's tissues and its immediate surroundings, resulting in a reduction of free available energy. The second peak precedes a critical stage in the embryo's life, *i.e.* when it shifts from the chorio-allantoic to the pulmonary type of respiration.

About halfway through the incubation period, the avian embryo assumes what is regarded to be a normal position: it comes to lie on its left side along the longitudinal axis of the egg, with the head, which is partly tucked under the right wing, facing the large end of the egg. Any other position is considered to be a malposition which either hinders or completely blocks the embryo's attempts to break out of the shell. It is recognized, however, that not all of the observed malpositions are necessarily a cause of embryo's death. Undoubtedly, in many instances they merely reflect the fact that the embryo died when it was in that particular position. On the other hand, a malposition in which the embryo lies with its head in the small end of the egg invariably leads to the death of the embryo.

K. Embryonic Terata

The appearance of various *terata* in avian embryos, either of hereditary or environmental origin, usually involves the most rapidly developing regions of the embryo, such as the head and the limbs. The sensitivity of these regions to teratogenic agents is the direct result of the speed with which morphogenetic changes occur in these

19

rapidly elaborating organs and tissue complexes. The involved areas are physiologically most active, *e.g.* they possess the highest oxidation-reduction gradients, a fact which has been experimentally demonstrated by histochemical tests. Each component of such highly dynamic and physiologically charged systems must be ready to play its part at the proper time. For example, the growth of long bones involves the interaction of ecto- and meso-dermal derivatives. The initiation of limb-forming capacity is predicated on the presence of a small ectodermal cap over the future limb area. The continuation of the process is controlled, however, by the mesoderm. Lagging pace in one will lead to suboptimal differentiation of the other. Furthermore, the proper synchronization of these processes and their future normal course depends on the concurrent development of adequate blood vascular system. "Creeper," a hereditary type of *phocomelia* in the domestic fowl is expressed by the shortening of all long bones, as well as distortion of the head. In the homozygous Creeper embryo, the eventual lethal condition is presaged, as early as the 3rd day of incubation, by a drastic reduction in extra-embryonic vascularization.

IV. ARTIFICIAL INSEMINATION

Although the principle of artificial insemination (A.I.) in poultry was first developed and applied in the chicken, its widest practical application has been in turkey breeding.

A. Limitations of A.I.

The factors which have limited the usefulness of A.I. in poultry breeding in general can be summarized as follows:

(*a*) Fertility has never been a serious problem in commercially important chicken breeds. With fertility from natural matings averaging over 85 per cent in hatching eggs from commercial supply flocks, little can be gained from artificial insemination.

(*b*) An active breeding rooster, particularly if he is of a small body-type such as White Leghorn, can mate naturally with at least as many hens, and thus be responsible for as many fertile eggs, as can be accomplished through A.I. With heavy-type breeds, the practice may have a small advantage, but the extra expense involved in using A.I. again mitigates against its general acceptance.

(*c*) The avian semen quickly loses its fertilizing capacity on storage. For best results, it must be used within 30 minutes of ejaculation.

(*d*) The commonly available diluents for avian semen add little to the ultimate usefulness of the available specimen. The diluted specimens must be used in larger volumes to achieve results comparable to those secured with undiluted semen. Furthermore, these diluents not only fail to extend the life span of the sperm but, in fact, shorten it.

B. Advantages of A.I.

Under a particular set of circumstances, A.I. can, however, be useful in poultry breeding. Among these, the more important are:

(*a*) Failure of the natural mating to maintain a desired level of fertility. This is especially applicable to turkey breeding flocks with fertility records lower than 70 per cent.

(*b*) Conditions which make natural mating impossible or impracticable: in single laying cage operations or in cases of large body size disparity between the potential mates. A.I. becomes a method of choice when an otherwise valuable male cannot mate either because of injury or old age.

(*c*) Need for a large number of small experimental matings. This would be true of research institutions and highly specialized commercial breeding organizations.

(*d*) When it is desired to exchange male germ plasm between countries. A.I. becomes the only available procedure in cases where males cannot be imported or exported.

C. Collection of Semen

The following description of A.I. is that of a procedure used in turkey breeding. With certain modifications, necessitated by anatomical and other peculiarities of the birds

PLATE XXXIII

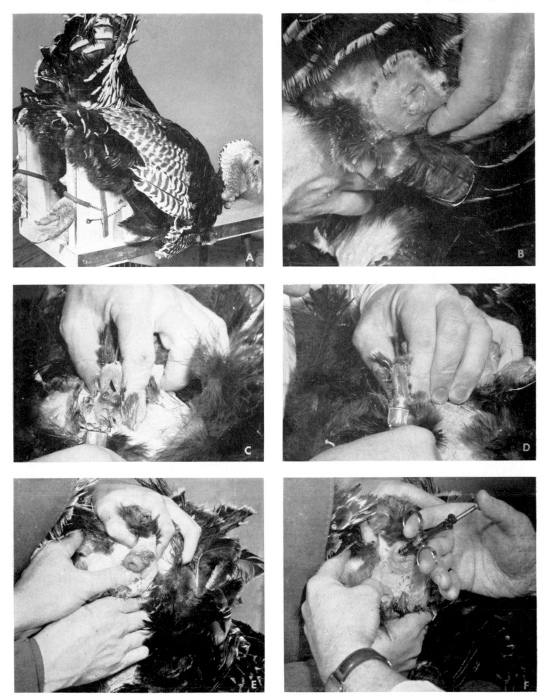

Steps in the artificial insemination of turkeys.

A. The male is secured on a special stand. As an alternative, the male may be held on a table or other suitable support.

B. The position of hands for stimulating the ejaculatory reflex in the male.

C. The male is ready to ejaculate: the vent becomes partly everted, revealing the turgid phallic and lymph folds. The massaging should stop.

D. The semen is being collected into a vial.

E. The left oviduct of a laying hen is everted with very little pressure from below the cloacal region.

F. After the syringe is inserted into the oviduct, the vagina and the cloaca should be allowed to become withdrawn to their normal position.

(From Johnson, 1953. Artificial Insemination of Turkeys. Publ. No. 897, Courtesy of Canada Dept. of Agric.)

PLATE XXXIV

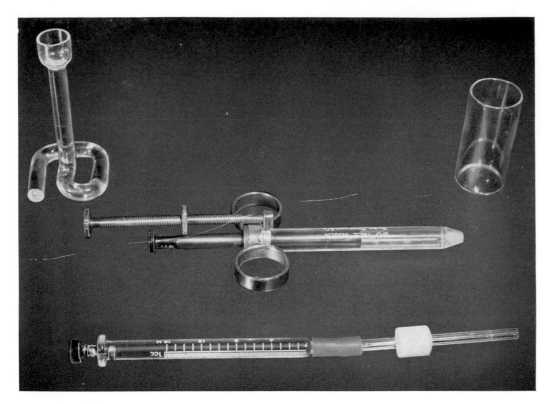

Equipment used in artificial insemination of chickens and turkeys. Either of the two types of beakers should prove to be satisfactory under conditions involving relatively small flocks. The two types of syringe have specific uses. The nut on the threaded rod and metal grips (the upper syringe) facilitate delivery of accurate dosage in mass mated flocks. The detached glass tube on the lower syringe is useful in pedigree breeding: each tube contains semen from an individual male.

(From Johnson, 1953. Artificial Insemination of Turkeys. Publ. No. 897, Courtesy of Canada Dept. of Agric.)

involved, the same procedure can be applied to other species of poultry.

In commercial turkey breeding operations, artificial insemination is done by specialized teams. These work on a definite schedule, inseminating all hens within a flock at 2 to 3 week intervals. The size of the team ranges from 2 to 14 operators according to the nature of the breeding program. Usually, an insemination team consists of two specialized units: one to work with the males, the other with the females. In this way there is a minimum of lag between collection of the semen and insemination.

Unless some special holding device is used to restrain the male before and during ejaculation, it takes two men to collect the semen specimens. This is particularly true in an insemination program involving turkeys. The male is held on some supporting surface by an operator, who restrains the bird by the legs, pinning its wings down, to prevent flapping (Plate XXXIII). The ejaculator then stimulates the male with his right hand (if he is right-handed) by rhythmically massaging the extreme caudal portion of the bird's body just under the pubic bones. The purpose is to induce an ejaculatory reflex. A small, suitable container for the semen—usually some form of a beaker or a graduate cylinder is held in the palm of the right hand, leaving the fingers essentially free to carry on the stimulation. Simultaneously, the left hand, bending the tail feathers cephalad, presses gently on the uropygial region. When the ejaculatory reflex occurs, the thumb and the index finger of both hands, working in unison, "milk" the male until the reflex disappears. In this operation, fingers of the left hand are also used to trap the semen in the lower end of the vasa deferentia. This is done to insure complete ejaculation. In large scale commercial operations, a specially designed suction apparatus is frequently used to collect the semen directly from the male's copulatory organ into a thermos bottle kept at 10 to 15°C., a temperature level which slows the metabolic activity of the sperm without damaging the cells. This apparatus also permits a more complete collection of the semen.

D. Storage and Dilution of Semen

Best results are obtained when the interval between ejaculation and insemination is less than 30 minutes and, certainly, not over one hour. The sperm remain immotile while in the male's excurrent ducts, but upon coming into contact with air they immediately become extremely agitated. The later activity involves both oxidative and glycolytic processes leading to rapid chemical exhaustion of the substratum in which the sperm exist. If diluents are to be used, they should be added just before insemination. The simplest and most practical diluent is a 1.025 per cent physiological saline solution buffered at pH 7.0 to 8.0. It gives best results when used 1:1 with the semen.

E. Insemination Techniques

The recommended dosages for insemination vary according to the species involved. In the main, this variability is due to an inverse relationship between the concentration of the sperm in the semen and the required dosage. The recommended dosages for insemination with whole (undiluted semen) are: the chicken—0.1 ml.; the turkey—0.025 ml.; the duck—0.3 ml.; the goose—0.05 ml. As yet, A.I. has not been used to any great extent in duck and goose breeding.

The process involved in inseminating a chicken or a turkey hen is relatively simple. The bird, resting on the left hand of an operator, is induced by him to evert its oviduct through a gentle pressure with the palms of both hands on the cloacal and visceral regions (Plate XXXIII). Only a laying bird will respond easily to this treatment. When the lower end of the vagina is thus exposed, a syringe containing the semen is quickly inserted to the depth of about 3 cm. and semen is deposited. Before the syringe is withdrawn, the pressure upon the abdomen is relaxed to permit the retraction of the oviduct. This is to avoid losing any semen through its being squeezed out by the retracting vagina. The procedure usually does not appear to bother the hen in any way. In fact, many laying hens will evert the vagina as soon as they are picked up, or when their lumbar region is touched gently.

Both collection of the semen and insemination require practice on the part of the operator. The female, and certainly the male, need some conditioning before they will cooperate with the ejaculator and the inseminator. Some birds may be unresponsive despite repeated attempts to induce a desired reflex. Once started, A.I. should be repeated at weekly intervals in the chicken, and every 2 to 3 weeks in the turkey. When hens which are laying at an intense rate are inseminated artificially with highly functional sperm, they will lay their first fertile egg 48 hours after the insemination.

F. Factors Affecting Success of A.I.

Success of A.I. in poultry can be affected by a number of factors, some of which are directly under the control of a breeder. The more important are:

Cleanliness of Collected Semen. The peculiar anatomy of the urogenital and digestive tracts in birds can easily lead to contamination of semen specimens with urates and feces. Handling of birds during A.I. frequently leads to some defecation. This is particularly true of males, a situation entirely absent in normal mating. The presence of feces in the semen specimen is detrimental to the survival of the sperm. It also aggravates the problem of microflora in the specimen by contributing organisms to the semen which are endemic to the colon: the coliform bacteria and staphylococci. These types of bacteria are also found in large numbers in all parts of the cloaca. The resulting bacterial load of an average semen specimen is bound to be particularly heavy when the semen is obtained through manual stimulation. Semen collected aseptically from the vasa deferentia is free from microbial contamination.

Cloacal Exudates. These exudates come, according to Lake, from the lymph folds of the *proctodaeum* and the numerous vascular areas near the terminal points of the vasa deferentia (see Chapter 12). Their presence cannot be entirely avoided in the course of

artificial stimulation of a male, but when the massaging and squeezing are unduly strong and prolonged, the resultant high level of exudate in the seminal fluid can be detrimental to the survival of the sperm.

Ambient Temperature at Semen Collection. Temperature above 20°C. is detrimental to the maintenance of fertilizing capacity of sperm. This is attributed to the resultant high metabolic rate of sperm *in vitro*, and to the growth of bacteria within the semen sample. Low ambient temperature at the time of semen collection and insemination does not unfavorably affect the results of A.I.

Antibiotics. Streptomycin, tetracycline and penicillin have been recommended as a means of controlling the endemic seminal microflora. While these additives may be effective in cases of extreme contamination, a more prudent plan is to keep the contamination to a minimum.

Presence of an Egg in Uterus. An intra-oviducal egg, especially one with a hard shell, can partially block the forward progress of the sperm. This is the reason for the usual recommendation to inseminate late in the afternoon.

Mixed Semen. Seminal fluid carries agglutinins of a type which characterize the blood. This may provide an explanation for the rather frequently observed occurrence of spermatozoal clumping when semen specimens from several males are pooled for insemination. Such clumping is a form of agglutination among the seminal antigens and the corresponding naturally occurring antibodies. When this condition assumes serious proportions, fertility can be expected to be depressed. In such cases it would be desirable to identify the conflicting specimens and to eliminate the offending donors, or to resort to single sire specimen insemination. The latter, however, is not a practical procedure under commercial conditions. A similar immunological incompatability may account for the infrequent occurrence of completely unsuccessful attempts to fertilize an otherwise fertile hen with the semen of a particular male, also of proven fertilizing capacity (Sampson & Warren, 1936; Munro & Kosin, 1945). This problem, of course, does not arise when pooled semen is used.

This brief review of several aspects of reproduction in poultry has largely ignored the basically important factor of management. Despite the existence of inherent homeostatic mechanisms in the avian organism, routine husbandry practices will largely determine the ultimate phenotypic performance of a given reproductive unit, be it a breeding bird, a mating flock, or a hatching egg.

REFERENCES

BAROTT, H. G. (1937). Effect of temperature, humidity, and other factors on hatch of hens' eggs and on energy metabolism of chick embryos. *USDA Tech. Bull.* No. 553.

BENOIT, J., WALTER, F. X., & ASSENMACHER, I. (1950). Nouvelles reserches relatives à l'action de lumières de différentes longueurs d'onde sur la gonadostimulation du canard mâle impubere. *C.R. Soc. Biol., France*, **144**, 1206–1211.

HERRICK, E. H. (1952). Endocrine glands and reproduction. In: *Biennial Report of Director, Kansas Agric. Expt. Sta., Manhattan.* pp. 57–58.

HUTCHINSON, J. C. D. & TAYLOR, W. W. (1957). Season variation in the egg production of fowls: effect of temperature and change of day length. *J. Agric. Sci.*, **49**, 419–434.

LACASSAGNE, L. (1956). Controle endocrinien et nerveux de l'ovulation chez la poule. Facteurs internes. *Annal. de Zootech.*, **4**, 335–362.

LAW, G. R. J. & KOSIN, I. L. (1958). Seasonal reproductive ability of male domestic turkeys as observed under two ambient temperatures. *Poult. Sci.*, **37**, 1034–1047.

McNALLY, E. H. & BYERLY, T. C. (1936). Variation in the development of embryos of hen's eggs. *Poult. Sci.*, **15**, 280–283.

MITCHELL, H. H., CARD, L. E. & HAMILTON, T. S. (1930). The minimum nutritive requirements of Single Comb White Leghorns. *Proc. 4th World's Poult. Congr.*, pp. 323–328.

MUNRO, S. S. & KOSIN, I. L. (1945). Proof of the existence of pre-oviposital embryonic deaths in chickens and their bearing on the relation between "fertility" and hatchability. *Canad. J. Res.*, D, **23**, 129–138.

SAMPSON, F. R. & WARREN, D. C. (1936). Sterility in the fowl. *Poult. Sci.*, **15**, 413–414.

SCHECHTMAN, A. M., 1955. Ontogeny of the blood and related antigens and their significance for the theory of differentiation. In: *Biological Specificity and Growth*, E. G. Butler, (edit.) Princeton, N.J., Princeton U. Press.

WOOD-GUSH, D. G. M. & OSBORNE, R. (1956). A study of differences in the sex drive of cockerels. *Brit. J. Anim. Behav.*, **4**, 102–110.

QUESTIONS

1. What have been some of the more important effects of domestication of the fowl?
2. Would poultry, kept outdoors in an equatorial region, show reproductive seasonality of a type usually observed in poultry flocks kept in more temperate zones of the globe?
3. Are there any real biological bases for the "biological year" concept in poultry reproduction?
4. Why are fertility and hatchability frequently considered to be a single biological complex?
5. Would you expect environment to be more of a factor in determining the hen's phenotype for hatchability than for fertility? Explain.
6. Is it reasonable to regard the fertility trait in male birds as a counterpart of the egg laying capacity in hens?
7. Some consider an oviposited fertile avian egg to be an "independent reproductive unit." Do you agree?
8. Is it just a coincidence that in the fowl, best egg layers are also usually characterized by high fertility and by high hatchability of their eggs?
9. In a broad outline, what are the minimum conditions needed for the preservation of maximum functional capacity of avian semen?
10. What is the likely future role of A.I. in poultry reproduction?

PART IV

STRESS AND DISEASES

Chapter 18

Effects of Stress on Reproduction

By N. T. M. Yeates and J. T. Parer

In extremes of climate, at very high altitudes, or when nutrition is inadequate, animals become stressed and reproduction may be impaired. In this chapter we will examine such reproductive losses, recognizing that of the climatic influences, excessively high temperature is by far the most serious.

I. HEAT STRESS

A. Effects on the Male

The seasonal changes which occur in the semen quality of many animals are primarily under the control of the variations in day length. Irrespective of such normal photoperiodically controlled cycles, however, high environmental temperature predisposes to a lowering of fertility in males. Thus, rams, bulls and boars sometimes display lowered fertility in hot weather and this has been referred to as "summer sterility" in the case of rams. Less is known regarding such effects in the stallion.

Cryptorchid males have long been known to produce little or no sperm, and this condition can be produced experimentally by transferring the testes from the scrotum to the abdominal cavity (see Chapters 2 & 3). Increased testicular temperature due either to artificial heating of the scrotum or to wrapping the scrotum in an impervious material to interfere with heat loss, also results in a decline in fertility.

Similarly, high air temperatures leading to increased body temperatures and subsequently increased scrotal temperatures, are associated with poor semen quality in rams and bulls, while febrile conditions associated with infection or with blow fly strike may cause degeneration of sperm in rams (Gunn et al., 1942). Rams and bulls which are poorly adapted to heat are known to be of low fertility in hot regions. Also, males acclimatizing to a hot environment (*i.e.* newly imported from a cooler to a hotter environment) may be temporarily infertile. Experiments in climate control laboratories which allow accurate separation of the environmental components, such as day length, air temperature and nutrition, leave no doubt that high ambient temperatures are responsible for sperm degeneration. Southdown rams in Kentucky kept in an air temperature of 32°C. during winter months were of inferior fertility compared with unheated control animals, while those kept at 8°C. air temperature during summer months proved to be of higher fertility than animals which were not cooled. Similarly,

Casady and associates have shown that dairy bulls subjected to an air temperature of 30°C. for 5 weeks suffered impaired spermatogenesis.

In rams the most severe damage to semen quality has generally been noted about 5 weeks after the commencement of heat treatment, indicating that the earlier stages in spermatogenesis are the most severely affected. Six to eight weeks after the removal of heat treatment, semen quality usually returns to normal (Dutt, 1960). It is not yet known why high temperature causes seminal degeneration. Bogart & Mayer (1946) improved fertility of rams in summer by administering thyroxine. From this the suggestion arose that the temperature effect might operate through the thyroid gland which is known to secrete less thyroxine during hot weather. However, results of subsequent experiments have been inconclusive, and it is more likely that an optimum balance of hormones, including thyroxine, is important.

The testes of rams suffering from seminal degeneration are soft and flabby, as contrasted to the firm testes of healthy, fertile rams. The seminiferous tubules of the healthy testis appear rounded and full, with numerous sperm in the lumen, while the germinal epithelium reflects active proliferation. In rams suffering from seminal degeneration, the germinal epithelium appears flat and inactive, while the lumen is relatively large and empty. The semen from such heat-affected animals is typified by low sperm count with a high proportion of abnormal sperm. The main abnormalities consist of cells which are tailless and those which are broken at the junction between head and neck. Other abnormalities include deformed heads and tails, pear-shaped heads, diminutive heads, double heads, double tails, kinked tails, thickened necks and tails, and truncated tails (see Chapter 12).

Two muscles, the external cremaster and the tunica dartos, aid thermoregulation of the scrotum. Normally the temperature of the testes is 4 to 5.5°C. lower than that of the body. In the ram, when air temperatures rise above 21°C. these muscles relax and a greater area of scrotum is exposed, thus aiding heat loss. Also, the sweating system of the scrotum is well developed. Droplets of sweat can be seen on the inside of impervious materials wrapped round the scrotum. Rams in a hot room at 41°C. air temperature and 31 mm. Hg vapor pressure produced 1.5 gm./hr. of sweat per scrotum, compared with 0.6 gm./hr. per scrotum at 27°C. and 19 mm. Hg.

Despite the fact that libido can be impaired by high temperature, rams in the field during summer may seek out estrous ewes in the heat of the day. Such physical activity particularly if it includes copulation will increase body temperature and may precipitate seminal degeneration. A high or very low plane of nutrition may also increase susceptibility to heat stress, with a consequent deleterious effect on spermatogenesis.

B. Effects on the Female

Heat stress of the female is known to result in lowered reproductive efficiency in some species of farm animals. In simple field observations the specific effects of temperature on female reproduction are not always apparent, because of concurrent changes in other environmental factors such as day length and nutrition, and because the male may also be affected.

In tropical Australia, where spring matings of sheep are common, the correlation coefficient between mean monthly maximum temperatures and lambing percentages (lambs surviving to ewes mated) is −0.65. Many ewes, judged to have conceived by nonreturn to estrus over a period of two cycles, subsequently fail to lamb, thus suggesting death of the embryo. Such losses, through embryonic mortality, have been estimated at 25 to 33 per cent for sheep in hot areas of Australia (Moule, 1960) and similar losses probably occur elsewhere.

Studies in a climate laboratory have shown that pregnancy frequently fails in ewes exposed to high temperatures (Yeates, 1953; 1958). The degree of reproductive failure depends on the length of time and severity of the ewes' exposure to heat. Thus, with increasing length of exposure fewer lambs are born, while those which do survive to term show reduction in average birthweight (Table 18-1).

Table 18-1—Decrease in Number and Size of Lambs Born to Romney Marsh Ewes Exposed Daily for 7 Hours to 41° C. Dry Bulb, 31° C. Wet Bulb During Pregnancy

(*Yeates, 1953. J. Agric. Sci., 43, 199.*)

	Months of exposure to 41° C. during pregnancy			
	0	last 1½	last 3	5
Number of ewes	8	6	6	6
Ewes failing to lamb	0	1	3	5
Lambs born	8	6	4	1
Average weight of lambs (lb.)	9.3	8.0	6.7	6.8

The early stages of pregnancy in sheep are particularly sensitive to high temperature. Exposure of ewes to an air temperature of 32°C. commencing 6 days before mating reduced fertilization from 93 per cent in unheated controls to 52 per cent in heated animals (Dutt, 1960). Moreover, by commencing heating of ewes one day after mating (when fertilization would be completed), lambings were reduced from 100 per cent in unheated control ewes to 20 per cent in the heated animals. On the other hand, when heating of the ewes was commenced 8 days after mating, embryo survival and lamb birth weight were affected little, if at all, after the ewes were exposed to 32°C. air temperature for 16 days.

The chief ovum abnormalities noted among experimentally heated ewes have been shrunken cytoplasm, enlarged cytoplasmic globules or vacuoles, ruptured vitelline membrane, broken zona pellucida or fragmenting ova (see Chapter 6). Under natural conditions a higher proportion of abnormal sheep ova has been reported early in the breeding season both in New Zealand and U.S.A. when the weather is often still hot, but it is unknown whether or not high temperature is the cause.

Ability of the uterus to maintain the fetus may be affected by thermal stress. Embryos from donor rabbits heated for 6 days after conception developed normally when transplanted into unheated recipients; but, when embryos from unheated donors were transplanted into heated pseudopregnant females, most of the young were resorbed (Shah, 1956). Similarly in sheep heated from 5 days prior to estrus, embryos transferred from donor ewes kept at 21°C. air temperature to ewes at 32°C. showed a decreased survival rate compared with controls. A reduction in survival rate was also obtained in embryos transferred from donors kept at 32°C. to recipients at 21°C., thus indicating a delayed deleterious effect of heat on the ova, which appeared normal at the time of transfer (Alliston & Ulberg, 1961).

High ambient temperatures do not affect the length of the estrous cycle or the duration of pregnancy in sheep (Yeates, 1953; Dutt, 1960). However, opinion differs regarding the effect of high temperature on the seasonal onset of the breeding season, Dutt finding a delay in dark-faced cross northwestern ewes at Kentucky U.S.A., while Yeates found no such effect in Romney Marsh ewes at Brisbane, Australia.

Little evidence of female reproductive inefficiency due to heat stress in other farm mammals has been gathered, though Ragsdale and associates reported that two Holstein cows, 4½ and 6 months pregnant, aborted 2 days after a 27-hour exposure to 38°C. No abortion or fetal resorption was noted in 85-day-pregnant sows when they were subjected to heat stress for a few days (Heitman *et al.*, 1951). Dale and associates have shown that calves kept at 27°C. air temperature reached puberty later than those kept at 10°C. Lactation in dairy cows is affected indirectly by high temperatures. Thus, unacclimatized cows, exposed suddenly to high temperature, suffer reduced milk production but this appears to be a consequence of reduced feed intake. In the case of acclimatized cows, the effect of high temperature is to lessen persistency of lactation. This appears to be due to a lowering of metabolic rate as a result of depression of thyroid secretion rate.

C. Effects on the Offspring

As mentioned briefly in the previous section, exposure of ewes to heat stress during pregnancy results in the birth of underweight lambs, the degree of reduction in weight being proportional to the length of the exposure period. That this dwarfing of lambs is indeed a specific effect of temperature and not a concomitant effect of reduced feed intake in the ewe has been demonstrated by similarity of body weights of the two groups of ewes in psychrometric room studies (Yeates, 1958). Analysis of some of the bones, organs and endocrine glands of the small lambs shows the dwarfing effect to be quite distinct from the reduction in weight produced by undernutrition. The heat induced dwarfs are well proportioned miniatures, as distinct from the long-legged thin lambs from underfed ewes.

Breed differences in the degree of heat-induced fetal dwarfing are evident. Thus, in the Merino, a breed known to be more heat tolerant than the Romney Marsh, 5 months' exposure (7 hours daily) of the ewe to 44°C. is required to produce roughly equal fetal dwarfing to that produced in the Romney Marsh by only 3 months' exposure to 41°C. The mechanism of this fetal dwarfing is unknown.

Underweight lambs are a serious problem in tropical and subtropical areas. Moule has reported a correlation coefficient of −0.76 between the number of months during pregnancy with mean monthly maximum temperatures of over 35°C. and the mean birth weight of lambs in areas of Northern Australia, adjacent to the Tropic of Capricorn. Cattle are probably affected in a similar way, as Bonsma (1949) has reported that "miniature" calves are often born to unadapted cows of European breeds in sub-tropical South Africa following a summer pregnancy.

Prostration of newborn lambs due to heat stress is of particular importance in many sheep-raising areas. Lambs are not well adapted to withstand high temperatures early in life and this is true also of calves. Merino lambs between 2 and 7 days of age were unable to survive longer than about 2 hours at a temperature of 38°C. dry bulb and 31°C. wet bulb. Other observations on Merinos showed that when lambs were briskly exercised at an air temperature of 32°C., their rectal temperatures rose to 42°C., and due to this overheating the animals experienced difficulty in following their mothers under field conditions. Lambs succumbed after 3 hours' exposure to the direct rays of the sun at 40°C. air temperature, while their mothers were well able to tolerate these conditions. The short wool of lambs renders them more susceptible as it offers little insulation from the solar radiation.

II. COLD STRESS

There is no evidence that cold ambient temperatures *per se* have a harmful effect on production of ova or sperm in farm mammals. However, in some laboratory animals the local application of severe cooling (below freezing point) to the testes or scrotum has resulted in decapitation of the sperm or damage to spermatogonia. Heat loss from the scrotum is minimized in cold ambient conditions by contraction of the tunica dartos and cremaster muscles, which draw the testes and scrotum nearer to the body.

The most serious effects of cold stress on reproduction are indirect ones. Mating and parturition may be interfered with, while the nutritional requirements of reproduction may be inadequate owing to the extra requirements for maintenance of body temperature. If the effect of limited feed supply is aggravated in this way by cold, fetal development or lactation may be severely affected.

Cold prostration is particularly likely in the case of the newborn animal exposed to outside environment. This is because the thermoregulatory system is usually poorly developed, and owing to its small size the newly born animal has a relatively large surface area per unit weight from which to lose heat. Wetness due either to rain or to the amniotic fluid is a further hazard especially if accompanied by wind. Thus, in cold weather the newborn animal must seek warmth and be nursed in order to preserve its heat balance. In cold weather the rectal temperature of lambs fell 2 to 3°C. (Alexander & McCance, 1958) and that of piglets 2 to 5° C. (Pomeroy, 1953) in the first hour after birth, but in both cases the drop would be less severe if the animals suck. The temperature of underweight animals falls faster than that of normal individuals in both species. Furthermore, animals with lower temperatures become less inclined to suckle, so become rapidly weaker and may eventually die. These effects would also apply to calves and foals.

III. STRESS AT HIGH ALTITUDES

High altitude has adverse effects on testicular function and fertility. It is said that in early times horses, pigs and fowls did not reproduce at Jauja, 11,500 ft. above sea level in the Peruvian Andes and because of this the capital of Peru was changed from this city to Lima (at sea level) in the 16th century (Bishop & Walton, 1960). Male animals sometimes suffer testicular degeneration when taken to higher altitudes (*i.e.* over 14,000 ft.), or when exposed to corresponding low air pressures. The effect is apparently due to hypoxemia, resulting from the rarefied air at high altitudes. Males seem to be more affected than females. Rams imported from sea level to high altitude showed degenerate testes, disturbance of semen pH levels and impaired libido. However, it appears to be a temporary condition, as many animals, particularly sheep in Peru, are found to produce quite well if acclimatized to high altitudes of up to 16,000 ft.

In the Rocky Mountains, U.S.A., cattle have been observed up to 10,000 ft. with young calves, and a horse ranch was located at 8,500 to 9,000 feet., so it appears that these altitudes are not harmful to reproduction in these species (Moore & Price, 1948).

IV. NUTRITIONAL STRESS

A. Effects on the Male

Undernutrition in male farm animals may seriously affect reproductive performance by causing retardation of sexual maturity in growing stock and lowered semen quality in mature individuals.

A well-fed Merino ram will be sexually mature at 5 months of age, as indicated by loss of adhesions between penis and prepuce. However, such adhesions persist in the underfed animal. The development of sperm cells is another indication of puberty which is closely related to body weight, hence the appearance of free sperm in the reproductive tract is retarded in underfed males. A test on identical twin bull calves showed that a low plane of nutrition caused a delay of 4 months in the appearance of fructose and citric acid in the seminal fluid, and of one month in the appearance of the first sperm (Mann & Rowson, 1956). The semen of bulls being raised at 70 per cent of the recommended nutritional allowance was shown to be less dense and to have lower sperm motility than that of adequately fed animals.

In the adult animal spermatogenesis may not always be affected by undernutrition. Bulls fed a ration which resulted in a continued loss of body weight exhibited normal sperm morphology and sperm count, but the secretory function of the seminal vesicles was considerably reduced. Fructose and citric acid levels in the semen fell after 2 months on the deficient diet. Rams and boars have been noted to suffer seminal degeneration some months after being on a low plane of nutrition. Protein deficiency can affect fertility and sexual expression and in bulls the density and viability of the sperm has been shown to be in direct proportion to the amount of protein in the ration.

Vitamin A deficiency causes severe upsets to male fertility. In bulls, it delays sexual maturity and leads to testicular degeneration, giving lowered sperm production and quality. However, libido may be unimpaired. Males may be more susceptible to vitamin A deficiency than females. In vitamin A deficient rams, seminal degeneration is present whether the animals have lost body weight or not. Because of extensive liver reserves of vitamin A, many months (at least 6 for sheep) generally pass on low carotene diets before results of deficiency are noted. Recovery in sheep usually occurs about 2 months after the deficiency is remedied in the diet. However, it is more difficult to remedy the seminal degeneration with vitamin A supplementation in animals on a low plane of nutrition than in those on a high plane, apparently because of the added effect of poor nutrition *per se*. When seminal degeneration is first apparent as a result of this dietary deficiency, abnormal sperm together with cells or detritus from the germinal epithelium are noted in the semen. In contrast, the semen picture in degeneration due to heat stress is one in which abnormalities of the sperm are almost the only early changes noted, in particular free sperm heads.

Pituitary cysts have been recorded in vitamin A deficient bulls and rams, and administration of gonadotropins to rams showing seminal degeneration from this cause has had a palliative effect. Undernutrition probably affects the reproductive processes in the male either through decreased production of pituitary gonadotropins, or a lowered response of the testicular cells to these hormones.

B. Effects on the Female

Puberty in underfed female farm animals may be delayed. Also, the adult may be slow to come into estrus and show weak estrus and irregular cycle length (see Chapter 5). In the adult sheep undernutrition may cause "quiet ovulation" especially near the onset of the breeding season. Some ewes will ovulate and conceive when almost at the point of death from starvation; indeed, complete cessation of ovarian activity due to underfeeding has not been reported. However, in conditions of undernutrition, ovarian activity is reduced, as evidenced by reduction of follicle numbers and size, or ovulation rate. Conversely, a high plane of nutrition promotes increased ovulation, hence the practice of "flushing" sheep to gain higher conception rates (Allen & Lamming, 1961). Though ovarian activity is primarily controlled by pituitary gonadotropins, it is also certainly associated with available nutrients. The precise mechanism of this interaction between undernutrition and the reproductive hormones is unknown, but it is generally accepted as a pseudo-hypophysectomy effect.

Protein deficiency has been shown to have similar effects to gross energy underfeeding in cattle and swine and the same probably applies to other species. Heifers raised on protein deficient diets show no symptoms of estrus, and the ovaries and uterus are retarded in development (infantile). The impairment of reproductive performance due to underfeeding or protein deficiency is reversible, so that resumption of adequate feeding usually restores normal function.

Vitamin A deficiency may cause severe disturbances in fetal development and lowered viability of offspring. However, this deficiency has little effect on the activity of the ovaries, the functioning of the accessory sex organs or the estrous cycle. Thus, even when ewes are suffering from night blindness as a result of vitamin A deficiency, they may have normal conception rates, but may give birth to dead lambs or lambs of low viability. Sows deficient in vitamin A may produce litters having low viability, while severe fetal resorption and fetal abnormalities are not uncommon. Cows in similar circumstances may abort or produce weak or dead calves. Keratinization of the vaginal epithelium may occur, predisposing to infection. Deficiency of vitamin E and some of the B group vitamins has caused fetal deaths and lowered viability of offspring in swine.

Mineral deficiencies affecting reproductive performance in farm animals are those of copper, cobalt, selenium and phosphorus. Copper and cobalt deficiencies result in reduced viability of the offspring, the latter deficiency being normally restricted to ruminants. Selenium deficiency is thought to be responsible for lowered fertility of ewes in New Zealand. Phosphorus deficiency causes ovarian dysfunction and delays puberty, and in mature cows complete cessation of estrus may result.

C. Effects on the Offspring

Nutrition of the dam and offspring is intimately related, hence undernutrition in the dam may involve severe effects in the developing offspring. In sheep, moderate undernutrition during the first 3 months of pregnancy does not seriously affect fetal growth (Wallace, 1948). However, in the last 2 months, when 75 per cent of fetal growth occurs, undernutrition can seriously depress growth of the developing young. Even though the dam may be emaciated, growth of the fetus continues for the fetus competes very efficiently for nutrients in the blood stream of the dam (see Chapter 10). However, inadequate nutrition in late pregnancy may shorten the gestation period of ewes by several days, thus resulting in a lamb which is less well developed physiologically and has lower energy reserves in the form of body and tissue fat and stored carbohydrate. In cold weather the lamb must increase its metabolic rate to preserve body temperature, but its body reserves are such that it can only survive a few hours unless it gets additional energy from sucking its mother. Undernutrition in the dam may result in poor mothering instinct (Thomson & Thomson, 1948–49), delay in the onset of lactation, reduced persistence of lactation and altered composition of the milk, all of which lower survival rates. In cattle lowered milk production and altered milk composition are also well recognized effects of undernutrition.

Protein deficiency of the pregnant female has similar effects to energy underfeeding. In sheep, stillbirths, high lamb mortality, lowered milk production and lack of maternal instinct have been noted. In pregnant cattle and sows protein deficiency has similar effects. However, if the protein deficiency is moderate, the requirements of pregnancy can be met by mobilization of protein reserves in the mother, so effects on the offspring may not be severe.

Undernutrition in the last few weeks of pregnancy, particularly if associated with some form of environmental stress, may precipitate pregnancy toxemia in sheep which have been well fed beforehand. This is a metabolic disorder, typified by raised blood ketone levels; it is the result of the demands of the fetus (or fetuses, as it more often occurs in twinning) becoming greater than the ewe can supply during the final weeks of pregnancy.

REFERENCES

ALEXANDER, G. & McCANCE, I. (1958). Temperature regulation in the newborn lamb. I. Changes in rectal temperature within the first six hours of life. *Aust. J. Agric. Res.*, **9**, 339–347.

ALLEN, D. M. & LAMMING, G. E. (1961). Nutrition and reproduction in the ewe. *J. Agric. Sci.*, **56**, 69–79.

ALLISTON, C. W. & ULBERG, L. C. (1961). Early pregnancy loss in sheep at ambient temperatures of 70° and 90°F. as determined by embryo transfer. *J. Anim. Sci.*, **20**, 608–613.

BISHOP, M. W. H. & WALTON, A. (1960). Spermatogenesis and the structure of mammalian spermatozoa. In: *Marshall's Physiology of Reproduction*. A. S. Parkes, edit. 3rd Ed. Vol. I, Pt. 2. London, Longmans.

BOGART, R. & MAYER, D. T. (1946). Environmental temperature and thyroid gland involvement in lowered fertility in rams. *Mo. Agric. Expt. Sta. Res. Bull.* No. 402.

BONSMA, J. C. (1949). Breeding cattle for increased adaptability to tropical and subtropical environments. *J. Agric. Sci.*, **39**, 204–221.

DUTT, R. H. (1960). Temperature and light as factors in reproduction among farm animals. *J. Dairy Sci.*, **43**, (Suppl.) 123–144.

GUNN, R. M. C., SANDERS, R. N. & GRANGER, W. (1942) Studies in fertility in sheep. 2. Seminal changes affecting fertility in rams. *Bull. Coun. Sci. Industr. Res. Aust. No.* 148.

HEITMAN, H., JR., HUGHES, E. H. & KELLY, C. F. (1951). Effects of elevated ambient temperature on pregnant sows. *J. Anim. Sci.*, **10**, 907–915.

MANN, T. & ROWSON, L. E. A. (1956). Effects of different planes of nutrition on the composition of bull semen. *Proc. 3rd. Intern. Congr. Anim. Reprod.* Cambridge, England, Section 1, p. 21.

MOORE, C. R. & PRICE, D. (1948). A study at high altitude of reproduction, growth, sexual maturity and organ weights. *J. Expt. Zool.*, **108**, 171–216.

MOULE, G. R. (1960). The major causes of low lamb marking percentages in Australia. *Aust. Vet. J.*, **36**, 154–159.

POMEROY, R. W. (1953). Studies on piglet mortality. I. Effect of low temperature and low plane of nutrition on the rectal temperature of the young pig. *J. Agric. Sci.*, **43**, 182–191.

SHAH, M. K. (1956). Reciprocal egg transplantations to study the embryo-uterine relationship in heat induced failure of pregnancy in rabbits. *Nature* (Lond.), **177**, 1134–1135.

THOMSON, A. M. & THOMSON, W. (1948–49). Lambing in relation to the diet of the pregnant ewe. *Brit. J. Nutrit.*, **2**, 290–305.

WALLACE, L. R. (1948). The growth of lambs before and after birth in relation to the level of nutrition. Pts. II & III. *J. Agric. Sci.*, **38**, 243–302, 367–401.

YEATES, N. T. M. (1953). The effect of high air temperature on reproduction in the ewe. *J. Agric. Sci.*, **43**, 199–203.

———— (1958). Foetal dwarfism in sheep—an effect of high atmospheric temperature during gestation. *J. Agric. Sci.*, **51**, 84–89.

QUESTIONS

1. Discuss temperature control of the ram's testis and describe the likely effects of heat stress on semen quality.
2. In what way may high temperature adversely affect pregnancy in the ewe? Name other species in which heat stress is known to disturb normal fetal development.

3. How would you determine the exact stages in early pregnancy when heat stress affects fertility?
4. Discuss (*a*) heat prostration, and (*b*) cold prostration in newly-born farm animals.
5. Discuss the effect of pre-pubertal undernutrition on the development and function of the reproductive system of (*a*) young bulls, (*b*) heifers.

6. Imagine yourself to be confronted by a problem of poor fertility and low birth weight of offspring among either sheep or cattle in a hot, semi-arid environment. What are the various symptoms that might enable you to determine whether the problem is one of (*a*) high temperature, or (*b*) malnutrition?

Chapter 19

Bacterial and Mycotic Infections

By A. H. Frank and P. A. O'Berry

I. BACTERIAL INFECTIONS

Bacterial infection of the reproductive organs is the most important diagnosed cause of impaired fertility in farm animals. All males are carriers and disseminators of bacteria, which are potential causes of infertility. They may become infected from contact with infected animals or contaminated surroundings. Pathogenic bacteria may inhabit the prepuce or sexual organs without causing clinical signs. However, bacterial infection of the various genital organs may localize and produce induration resulting in infertility. Organisms from the prepuce or infected sexual organs may contaminate the semen.

All females carry bacteria in the vagina. Both pathogenic and nonpathogenic organisms may be present without causing clinical signs. These organisms are spread to males at service and to other females through the use of unsanitary techniques in genital examination and artificial insemination. The cervical canal separates the vagina from the uterus and serves as a barrier to uterine infection. It is relaxed during estrus and is protected from bacterial invasion by an outflow of thin mucus. Although uterine resistance to infection is highest during the estrous phase, it is still possible for organisms which are introduced into the vagina to enter the uterus and establish an infection.

The cervical canal is constricted during the progestational and gestational phases and is blocked by thick, tenacious mucus which serves to retard the entrance of organisms. During these phases, however, the uterus is quite susceptible to bacterial infection since it provides an environment for the nourishment of the embryo. This uterine environment is also favorable for bacteria that may enter the uterus by way of the cervix, blood or lymph.

Bacteria that survive and multiply in the uterus cause endometritis and impaired fertility. Endometritis may be inapparent or may be present with clinical signs of vaginitis, vulvitis, vaginal discharge, chills, fever, restlessness, and loss of appetite. It is usually associated with some phase of reproduction such as copulation, pregnancy, abortion, retention of placenta or dead fetus, or parturition.

Females may return to estrus 7 to 12 days after parturition, but at this time the reproductive tract has not completely involuted and may contain many bacteria. More females conceive and carry to term when bred at the second or third estrus than when

20

Table 19-1.—Description of Reproductive Diseases of Bacterial and Mycotic Origin

Disease	Species	Etiology	Clinical Signs	Diagnosis	Control
Brucellosis	Cattle	*Brucella abortus* (and other species)	abortion, impaired fertility, orchitis, epididymitis	blood test, cultural isolation, clinical signs	vaccination, test & slaughter, proper sanitation
	Sheep	*Brucella melitensis* (and other species)	abortion, mastitis, orchitis, epididymitis	blood test, cultural isolation, clinical signs	test & slaughter, proper sanitation
	Swine	*Brucella suis* (and other species)	impaired fertility, abortion, orchitis, epididymitis	blood test, cultural isolation, clinical signs	test & slaughter, proper sanitation
Vibriosis	Cattle	*Vibrio fetus*	temporary infertility, abortion	cultural isolation, vaginal mucus test	artificial insemination (treated semen), treatment of bulls, proper sanitation
	Sheep	*Vibrio fetus*	abortion	cultural isolation	vaccination, proper sanitation
Leptospirosis	Cattle and Sheep	*Leptospira pomona* (other serotypes)	abortion	blood test, cultural isolation	vaccination
	Swine	*Leptospira pomona* (other serotypes)	abortion, neonatal mortality	blood test, cultural isolation	vaccination, treatment

Disease	Animal	Causative organism	Symptoms	Diagnosis	Control
Listeriosis	Sheep	*Listeria monocytogenes*	encephalitis, abortion	cultural isolation, clinical signs, histopathology	vaccination, proper sanitation
Epididymitis	Sheep	Unclassified	epididymitis, orchitis, abortion, neonatal mortality	cultural isolation, blood test, clinical signs	test & slaughter, proper sanitation
Streptococcal Abortion	Horses	*Streptococcus genitalium* (and other species)	abortion, cervicitis, pyometra	cultural isolation, clinical signs	proper sanitation, surgical intervention
Equine Infectious Abortion	Horses	*Salmonella abortivoequina*	abortion	blood test, cultural isolation	vaccination, proper sanitation
Pullorum Disease	Poultry	*Salmonella pullorum*	death of chicks (first week)	blood test, cultural isolation	test & slaughter, proper santation
Fowl Typhoid	Poultry	*Salmonella gallinarum*	death of young birds	blood test, cultural isolation	test & slaughter, cultural isolation, selective breeding, proper sanitation
Mycotic Abortion	Cattle	*Aspergillus fumigatus* (and other species)	abortion	cultural isolation, histopathology	proper sanitation, (prevent contact with moldy hay)

bred at the first post-partum estrus. The reproductive diseases of bacterial and mycotic origin are described briefly in table 19–1.

A. Bacterial Infections of Cattle

The most common clinical sign of impaired fertility in cattle in repeat breeding, which is caused by either failure to conceive or early embryonic death. Both of these may be the result of bacterial infection of the uterus. Economic loss from these infections is reflected in a decreased calf crop and reduced milk production.

1. Brucellosis

Bovine brucellosis, one of the most important reproductive diseases of cattle, is an acute to chronic infectious disease characterized primarily by abortion. It is caused most commonly by *Brucella abortus*, but *Br. suis* and *Br. melitensis* have also been incriminated. Bernard Bang first isolated *Br. abortus* in 1897 from aborted bovine fetuses and proved it to be the etiological agent of bovine brucellosis (formerly known as Bang's disease). Brucellosis is worldwide in occurrence but is more prevalent in intensive cattle-raising countries. Annual losses in the U.S.A. have been estimated at 87 million dollars. (U.S.D.A., 1954).

Morphology and Growth. *Brucella abortus* is a small, Gramnegative, nonmotile, nonspore-forming coccobacillus. It grows fairly well on most ordinary laboratory mediums but requires an increased CO_2 tension for primary isolation.

Transmission. Transmission occurs most commonly by ingestion of viable *Br. abortus* in feed or water contaminated by infected genital discharges. However, organisms may enter the body of the host through the skin, the conjunctiva or the respiratory mucous membranes. Infected tissues and body fluids such as vaginal discharges, aborted material, milk, blood, feces, and semen serve as sources of infection. Calves ingesting milk from *Br. abortus* infected udders may shed these organisms in their feces.

Diagnosis. Diagnosis depends on clinical as well as cultural examination together with certain biological tests. Clinically, brucellosis is suspected in a herd when abortion occurs. Culturally, *Br. abortus* may be isolated from the placenta, aborted fetus, uterine discharges, milk, feces, blood, semen, and abscesses. Highly contaminated materials may be injected into guinea pigs to isolate *Br. abortus*. Several biological tests are used to detect brucellosis. Among these are those using serum, (the Standard Seroagglutination Tube and Plate Tests, Complement-Fixation Test, Heat Inactivation Test) as individual animal tests and those using milk (Milk-Whey Agglutination Test, Ring Test) as herd tests. Each test has its particular place in the diagnosis of bovine brucellosis.

Control. Control and eradication of this disease is being accomplished in the U.S.A. by a program of test and slaughter, calfhood vaccination, and enforcement of strict measures of sanitation. It has been established that vaccination of 4 to 8 month old heifers with *Strain 19 vaccine* produces a satisfactory level of lasting immunity in most animals. When infection is detected, sanitary measures should include isolation of the animal until slaughter. Aborted material should be carefully destroyed along with feed and bedding contaminated with vaginal discharges or feces. The surroundings and equipment should be carefully disinfected to avoid infecting other animals.

2. Vibriosis

Bovine genital vibriosis is an infectious venereal disease caused by *Vibrio fetus*. It is characterized as a temporary infertility and revealed by an increase in the number of services required per pregnancy. A delayed estrus often follows the first service to an infected bull. Abortion, which can occur any time during pregnancy, rarely affects more than 3 to 5 per cent of the infected animals. This disease was first reported by McFadyean & Stockman in 1913, but the greater importance of brucellosis in cattle effectively obscured vibriosis for the next 40 years. Attention was again focused on vibriosis in 1951 when it was shown to be the most prevalent cause of infertility in cattle. It has been reported from all continents.

Annual losses in the U.S.A. have been estimated at 137 million dollars (U.S.D.A., 1954).

Morphology and Growth. *Vibrio fetus* is a motile, Gram-negative organism. It is comma-shaped, S-shaped or composed of many undulations depending upon the age of the culture. It can be grown on solid or liquid medium in an atmosphere of 5 per cent O_2, 10 per cent CO_2, and 80 per cent N_2. It produces catalase, does not produce hydrogen sulfide and does not ferment sugars.

Transmission and Diagnosis. Transmission of *V. fetus* is venereal. It also can be spread by unsanitary instruments used in genital examination, and artificial insemination. Venereal transmission permits rapid dissemination of this infection within a herd once the bull has become infected. Diagnosis is made by cultural isolation and identification of *V. fetus* from semen, smegma, vaginal mucus, fetal fluid, or placenta. The vaginal mucus agglutination test is an aid in diagnosing this infection on a herd basis. A herd history of abortion and repeat breeding especially in females bred for the first pregnancy adds presumptive evidence to the presence of bovine genital vibriosis. This disease is asymptomatic in bulls. A reliable test for infection in a bull consists of breeding two virgin heifers and culturing the vaginal mucus 10 to 30 days later.

Control. Vibriosis has been controlled by artificial insemination (A.I.) using liquid semen extended at least 1:25, placed during the cooling phase in contact with 500 units of penicillin and 500 micrograms of streptomycin per ml. of extended semen, and held at 5°C. for no less than 6 hours before use (Hughes, 1956). Frozen semen presents a special problem since some organisms may survive the usual antibiotic treatment and freezing. However, in frozen semen, the usual antibiotic treatment has been found to be highly effective against *V. fetus* when supplemented by 1000 units of polymyxin B sulfate per ml. (Elliott *et al.*, 1961).

Other control programs may be followed if A.I. cannot be used exclusively. Attention must be directed toward the prevention of spread and the elimination of infection. Treatment of individual females is not practical. In females, the disease is self-limiting. In most cases, the infection disappears within 6 months except for a few individuals in which the infection persists until after the second calf is born. Infection in males has been said to be permanent, but evidence now indicates that many bulls recover spontaneously after a prolonged period of infection. Antibiotic treatment of the prepuce and penis has proven to be practical and reliable therapy for *V. fetus* infection in bulls.

Intestinal Vibrio. Florent (1960) has indicated that a second type of *V. fetus* is found in cattle. Morphologically, this type is similar to the venereal type described previously. Biochemically, some differences may be detected. It produces catalase and hydrogen sulfide. It will grow in the presence of glycine, whereas the other will not. After oral exposure it can be isolated from bovine feces for an indefinite period. It appears that this type remains in the reproductive tract for only a short time and may produce sporadic abortion. Further investigations are needed to clarify the relative importance of this intestinal type of *V. fetus*.

3. LEPTOSPIROSIS

Leptospirosis in cattle is an inapparent to acute febrile disease. It is caused by a variety of serotypes; *Leptospira pomona* being most common in the U.S.A. and Australia, *L. grippotyphosa* most common in Europe, and *L. australis* and *L. hebdomadis* most common in Asia. This disease was first described in 1935 by Soviet scientists and is known to be worldwide in occurrence. Economic losses attributed to bovine leptospirosis range from insignificant to high; with an estimated high of 112 million dollars lost in the U.S.A. (U.S.D.A., 1954).

Morphology and Growth. *Leptospira pomona* is a slender, spiral-shaped, motile spirochete of variable length with one end bent into the shape of a hook. Leptospires may be grown on solid or fluid medium containing serum, but their multiplication is characteristically slow. They require oxygen and do not ferment sugars.

Transmission. Since leptospires localize in the kidneys of infected animals, they are shed in urine and are transmitted by contact with urine contaminated materials. Leptospires invade the body through the nasal, oral, pharyngeal, and conjunctival mucous membranes or the abraded surface of the skin. In water, these organisms are able to survive for an indefinite period, but under other conditions they usually live only a short time outside the body (Alston & Broom, 1958). Contact exposure, therefore, must occur soon after the urine has been voided. Venereal transmission has been reported, but its frequency has not been established. The role of the feral animal in transmission is not known. It appears, however, that all warm blooded animals are susceptible to leptospiral infection and may serve to transmit the disease to other animals.

Diagnosis. Diagnosis of bovine leptospirosis is made on the basis of clinical signs, post mortem findings, serological tests, and demonstration of the organism in blood, tissues, or urine. Infected cattle may show signs of fever, decreased milk production, and hemoglobinuria (hemoglobin in the urine). Icterus, anemia, and a pinkish discoloration of the milk are less frequent signs. A high rate of abortion has been attributed to this infection, but controlled experiments have been successful in producing very few abortions. The agglutination-lysis test is the method of choice to demonstrate leptospiral antibodies in serum. At necropsy, grayish-white foci in the kidneys furnish presumptive evidence of leptospirosis. The demonstration of leptospires in kidney tissue of exposed cattle or laboratory animals is often possible. Isolation and identification of leptospires from, urine, blood or tissues serves to confirm the diagnosis.

Control. Control of bovine leptospirosis depends on the use of prophylactic and therapeutic measures. Prophylactic measures include production of immunity and prevention of exposure to leptospires. Vac- cines produce effective immunity for a short period. To prevent exposure to leptospires, new additions to the herd should be tested, isolated, and retested 30 days later before being introduced into the herd. Since swine are an important reservoir of infection, cattle should be separated from them. Therapy presently consists of parenteral use of broad spectrum of antibiotics and blood transfusions when the severe form of the disease is encountered.

B. Bacterial Infections of Sheep

Economic loss due to impaired fertility is of great concern to the sheep growing industry. Research indicates that in sheep, bacterial infections of the reproductive organs are primarily manifest by infertility and abortion.

1. VIBRIOSIS

Ovine vibriosis is an infectious disease of ewes produced by *Vibrio fetus* and characterized by abortion in late pregnancy. This disease was first described in 1913 in England and has been reported subsequently from every major sheep producing area in the world. Annual losses of 8 million dollars have been reported in the U.S.A. (U.S.D.A., 1954). Abortion has been observed in 70 per cent of the ewes in severely affected flocks (Marsh, 1958).

Morphology and Growth. Morphologically and culturally, the sheep strains of *V. fetus* are similar to those of cattle. Biochemically, they are similar to the intestinal type found in cattle.

Transmission and Signs. Infection occurs as a result of ingestion of *V. fetus* in vaginal discharges, aborted material, contaminated water and feed. Present evidence indicates that ewes recover from genital infection rapidly, except for a few which become carriers. The ram has not been found to transmit infection to females by copulation.

Clinical signs usually consist of abortion during the last trimester of pregnancy. Infected lambs born at term may be weak and unable to survive. Lamb production of the flock is usually satisfactory in the season following an outbreak of vibrionic abortion.

Diagnosis and Control. Diagnosis of this disease is made by isolation and identification of *V. fetus.* It has been isolated from placenta, vaginal discharge of the ewe, or stomach content, liver, and brain of an aborted fetus. Control of vibriosis may be accomplished by proper sanitary practices and vaccination. Aborting ewes should be isolated from the flock. The aborted fetuses and placentas should be burned promptly. Fresh running water should be provided for pregnant ewes. Sanitary wintering and lambing areas should be provided. A vaccine has been developed, but its effectiveness has yet to be fully evaluated . In experimental trials, the number of abortions was reduced when it was used before lambing and early in an outbreak.

2. Leptospirosis

Leptospirosis of sheep is an infectious disease of variable severity caused most commonly by *L. pomona.* Leptospirosis in sheep was first reported from New Zealand and Russia in 1952, and subsequently from Australia, Israel, Turkey, America, and other countries. Economic loss caused by this disease in sheep is not known. The morphology, growth, transmission, diagnosis and control are similar to leptospirosis of cattle.

3. Listeriosis

Listeriosis of sheep is an acute, highly fatal disease caused by *Listeria monocytogenes,* characterized by central nervous system disturbances and abortion. This disease was first described in 1931 in New Zealand and called "circling disease" because of the characteristic movement of affected animals. It occurs wherever sheep are raised, affecting from 1 to 10 per cent of the ewes in a flock. Losses usually are not severe except in very large feeder flocks.

Morphology and Growth. Listeria monocytogenes is a motile, Gram-positive, non-sporeforming-short rod. It is hemolytic, produces catalase and grows readily on ordinary mediums. Growth is enhanced by the presence of sterile serum or defibrinated blood.

Transmission and Diagnosis. There is evidence to indicate that infection occurs by ingestion or inhalation of *L. monocytogenes,* but the exact mode of transmission has not been definitely established. This microorganism is widely distributed in nature as a saprophyte of soil and a nonpathogen of small rodents. Transmission may be linked to the feeding of silage. The organism has been isolated from oat silage which had been fed to animals previous to outbreaks of listeriosis (Gray, 1960).

Diagnosis of listeriosis is dependent upon the presence of clinical signs, and the demonstration of characteristic histopathologic changes in the brain (Plate XXXV). Signs of encephalitis (inflammation of the brain) are varied but usually include moving in a circle, drooping one ear, and paralysis of the lower lip. Abortion is infrequent but may occur late in pregnancy. The diagnosis may be confirmed by isolating and identifying the organism from suspected animals. More infected animals will be found culturally positive if suspected material is stored at 4°C. and subcultured at weekly intervals for 4 to 6 weeks.

Control. Since there is evidence that *L. monocytogenes* is widely distributed in nature, control of this insidious disease is difficult. Isolation of affected animals and prompt disposal of dead animals is advisable. The use of an effective bacterin in flocks with a history of recurrent listeriosis may be of value in preventing losses.

4. Brucellosis

Brucellosis of sheep is an infectious disease usually caused by *Br. melitensis* and sometimes caused by *Br. abortus.* The disease is characterized by abortion, stillbirth, and mastitis in females and orchitis (inflammation of testis) and epididymitis in males. In many countries of the Mediterranean, Middle East, and the Soviet Union, brucellosis of sheep is an important cause of economic loss.

Morphology and Growth. Brucella melitensis is a small, Gram-negative, coccobacillus morphologically identical to other *Brucella.* Culturally, it does not require increased CO_2 tension for primary isolation as does *Br. abortus.*

Transmission and Diagnosis. Transmission is thought to occur by penetration of the skin or the mucous membrane of the conjunctiva, respiratory system, and alimentary tract. Diagnosis is made by cultural isolation and identification of the organism, by detection of serological evidence of infection, and by the observation of signs of this disease. The organisms may be cultured from aborted fetuses, vaginal discharges, necropsy specimens or other materials. The most common serological test used is the serum agglutination test, but there are many others (FAO/WHO, 1958).

Control. Brucellosis is controlled by test and slaughter of infected sheep. Infection is detected by serological tests to determine the presence of *Brucella* agglutinating antibodies. Attempts are being made to develop a vaccine to protect sheep against brucellosis, but it has not yet been put to the test of extensive field trials.

5. Epididymitis

Epididymitis in rams, caused by an unclassified bacterial organism, is described as a specific suppurative epididymo-orchitis (inflammation of epididymis and testis). In New Zealand, Buddle (1956) described the disease as widespread, causing impaired fertility in rams, abortion in ewes, and neonatal mortality in lambs. Economic loss attributable to this disease in ewes has not been determined, but loss in rams is significant because a high percentage of rams become permanently sterile.

Morphology and Growth. The causative organism is a small, Gram-negative, bacillus or coccobacillus, resembling *Brucella* in shape and size. On primary culture it requires 10 per cent CO_2 and a suitable Brucella medium enriched with 10 per cent bovine serum.

Transmission and Diagnosis. The organism is passed from infected rams to non-infected rams during the breeding season through service to ewes, and by direct contact when rams are run together. Ewes do not become infected by contact with infected ewes, but a small percentage become infected through service to infected rams. Infection may persist 3 years or longer in rams, but is significantly less persistent in ewes. Diagnosis in rams is made by palpation of lesions in the epididymis and testis, cultural isolation of the organism from semen, and microscopical examination of semen smears. Clapp (1961) reports the production of a satisfactory antigen for the complement fixation test.

Control. Infected rams and ewes should be removed from breeding stock. Infected rams have been successfully treated with antibiotics, but treatment is expensive and should be limited to valuable individuals.

C. Bacterial Infections of Swine

Losses in swine due to impaired fertility would force breeders to keep 15 per cent extra females to obtain the desired number of pigs. Bacterial infections of the reproductive tract is a contributing cause of impaired fertility. Losses caused by bacterial infection of the uterus may be manifest by anestrus, repeat breeding, fetal resorption, small litters of pigs, and abortion at any stage of pregnancy.

The anatomy and physiology of the cervix makes the uterus of the sow accessible to bacterial invasion. The boar ejaculates a large volume of dilute semen directly into the cervix. The relaxed cervix allows the semen to gravitate into the uterus and carry contaminating infectious agents with it. Any resulting uterine infection seldom prevents conception; it does, however, cause embryonic death. In swine as well as in other multiparous species, death of all or part of the embryos or fetuses may occur at any time during gestation. Frequently, the dead conceptus is resorbed; but it is not unusual to have dead, weak, and normal pigs born in the same litter.

PLATE XXXV

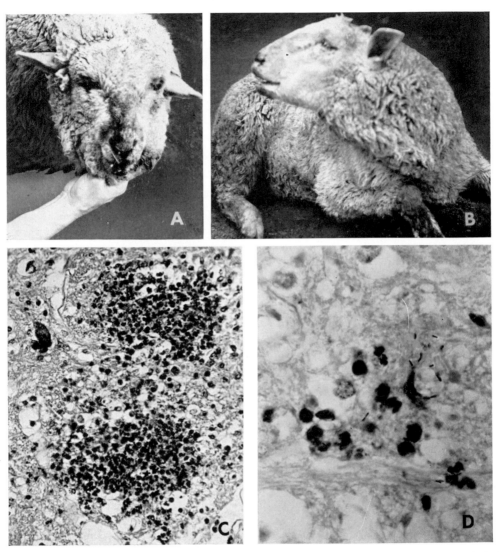

Listeriosis. (A) Drooped ear. (B) Encephalitic signs. (C) Brain lesion. (D) Organisms in brain lesion
(*From Marsh. 1958. In Newsome's Sheep Diseases, Baltimore, Courtesy The Williams & Wilkins Co.*)

PLATE XXXVI

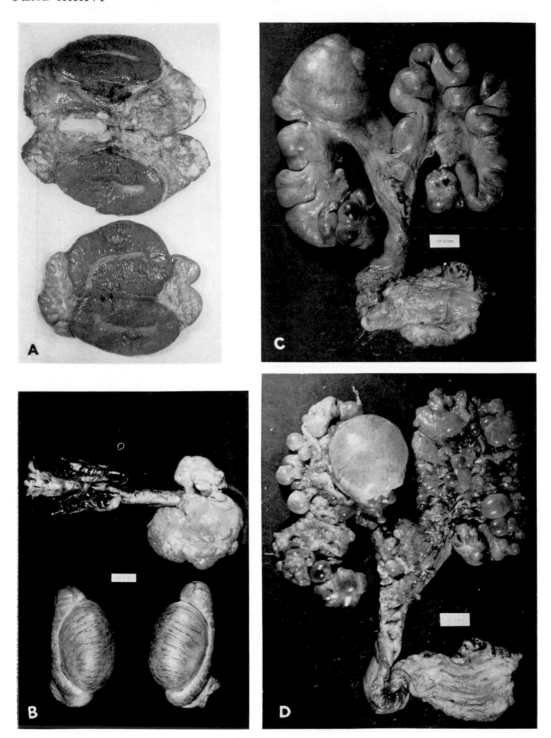

Swine brucellosis. (*A*) Testis of a boar showing multiple abscesses of the epididymis (*top*) and a normal testis (*bottom*). (*B*) Infection of vesicular gland (seminal vesicle) in a boar. Only one lobe is infected. The prostate and testes are normal. (*C*) Cystic uterus associated with *Br. suis* infection in a sow. (*D*) The uterus shown in (*C*) opened to show the cystic condition of the uterine mucosa.

(*From Manthei. 1958. In Diseases of Swine, Ames, Iowa, Courtesy of Iowa State University Press.*)

1. BRUCELLOSIS

Brucellosis of swine is an acute to chronic infectious disease caused principally by *Brucella suis*, however, both *Br. melitensis* and *Br. abortus* occasionally infect swine. This disease is characterized by abortion and infertility in the female, and by inflammation of infected sex organs and infertility in the male. *Brucella suis* was first isolated by Traum in 1914 from an aborted swine fetus and is today worldwide in occurence. It is widespread in the United States as indicated by a 1957 survey reporting about 5 per cent infection. Economic losses are serious, reaching as high as 10 million dollars annually (U.S.D.A., 1954).

Morphology and Growth. *Brucella suis* is a small, Gram-negative, nonspore-forming rod that is so short that it is frequently mistaken for a spherical bacterium. It grows readily in an ordinary atmosphere and fairly well in ordinary mediums.

Transmission and Signs. Infection is spread by ingestion and by contact, especially venereal contact. The organism may pass through mucous membranes and abraded or intact skin. Clinically, *Br. suis* infection causes abortion, birth of stillborn or weak pigs, and infertility in sows; posterior paralysis and lameness through bone infection in both sows and boars; and unilateral or bilateral orchitis with a loss of sex drive in boars (Plate XXXVI).

Diagnosis and Control. The serum agglutination test can be used to detect infected herds. Diagnosis in individual animals depends on cultural isolation and identification of the infecting organism (as described under cattle).

Proper sanitation is highly important in the prevention of swine brucellosis (Manthei, 1958). The scrubbing and disinfecting of pens, feed areas, transportation equipment; the wearing and proper disinfecting of rubber footwear, and the burning of aborted fetuses, membranes and contaminated litter, will do much to prevent the spread of porcine brucellosis. As a prophylactic measure, aborting sows must be isolated until the cause of abortion has been determined.

Brucella infected sows should be culled from the herd. Replacement animals should be purchased from a Brucella-free herd. Since this is a venereal disease in swine, community boars should never be used for breeding. The entire herd should be blood tested periodically with one ultimate goal: a brucellosis-free herd. Suggested plans of control for infected herds are available to the individual swine producer (Hay *et al.*, 1954).

2. LEPTOSPIROSIS

Leptospirosis in swine is an infectious disease caused most commonly by the serotype *Leptospira pomona*. This organism was first isolated from swine in Australia in 1939, but it is only in the past decade that worldwide attention has been focused on it. It occurs in all swine producing areas of the world, with incidence estimated as high as 20 per cent in some countries (Ferguson, 1958). Economically, this disease is most important as a cause of abortion and neonatal mortality.

Morphology and Growth. (as described under cattle).

Transmission and Signs. Leptospiruria (leptospires in urine) occurs frequently in swine, at which time the organism is found in greater numbers and for a longer time than in other farm animals. These conditions add importance to the role of swine in the transmission of leptospirosis to other animals and man through contamination of water, feed and surroundings.

In many infected swine, the disease is inapparent. However, when signs are present, the most common is abortion in pregnant sows infected during the second month of gestation. Some sows show only a high mortality of suckling pigs, fever, or anemia.

Diagnosis and Control. Diagnosis of leptospiral infection is made by serological tests, clinical signs (if present), as well as isolation and identification of leptospires from blood or urine. The most satisfactory serological test is the agglutination lysis test which may be used on entire herds or individual animals. Infected swine frequently shed large numbers of leptospires in the urine. These organisms may be demonstrated by microscopic examination of voided urine. Cultural isolation and identification of leptospires is accomplished by direct culture methods and inoculation of laboratory animals.

Control of procine leptospirosis is related to the identification of infected animals, broad spectrum of antibiotic therapy to eliminate the carrier state, and vaccines to increase the resistance of swine likely to be exposed.

D. Bacterial Infections of Horses

The prevention and control of bacterial infection in the reproductive systems of stallions and mares have increased the foal crop from an average of 50 per cent to a possible average of 90 per cent. As in the case of the sow, the anatomy and physiology of the cervix renders the equine uterus accessible to bacterial invasion. During estrus the cervix relaxes and may open sufficiently during copulation to allow the stallion to ejaculate directly into the uterus. Proper managing, feeding, and exercising to reduce excessive stress factors which lower resistance to infection are also important; but the application of sanitary techniques and health checks are the major factors responsible for the increase.

Sanitary techniques in horse breeding include thorough cleansing of the penis, vulva, buttocks, and wrapping the mare's tail in sterile bandage just prior to service. When infection is suspected, vaginal and cervical specimens from mares and semen samples from stallions should be obtained for culture and identification of pathogenic bacteria. Infected animals should not be bred.

Some mares become infected by the entrance of feces and foreign matter into the vagina between the lips of a flaccid vulva. In such cases, the dorsal portion of the vulva is surgically incised and sutured closed. The operated vulva is then opened surgically for breeding and foaling.

1. STREPTOCOCCAL ABORTION

Equine streptococcal abortion is the result of an infection of the female reproductive tract caused mainly by *Streptococcus genitalium*. Of all bacteria causing reproductive

infections in horses, this one is considered to be the most important. It is a problem of horse breeders everywhere and may cause 17 per cent of equine abortions and 25 per cent of foal deaths (Dimock *et al.*, 1947).

Morphology and Growth. *Streptococcus genitalium* is a small, round, Gram-positive organism. It grows readily on blood agar or in fluid mediums. This organism ferments sorbitol but not trehalose, which are biochemical characteristics assisting to identify it.

Transmission and Diagnosis. Streptococcal infection of the reproductive tract may become established as a result of mating, foaling, unsanitary genital examination, or fecal contamination of the vagina.

A presumptive diagnosis is made on the basis of signs of abortion, cervicitis, metritis (inflammation of the uterus), and pyometra (accumulation of pus in the uterus). The diagnosis is confirmed by the isolation and identification of pathogenic streptococci from the genital tract, aborted fetus, or fetal membranes.

Control. Streptococcal abortion may be prevented by using strict hygienic precautions at the time of mating, foaling, and examining the genital tract. It is further controlled by surgical intervention to prevent fecal contamination of the reproductive tract due to faulty conformation. No reliable vaccine for streptococcal abortion is available.

2. EQUINE INFECTIOUS ABORTION

Equine infectious abortion is an acute reproductive infection of mares caused by *Salmonella abortivoequina*. This organism was first isolated by Kilborne in 1893 in the U.S.A. and has been reported from other countries. Infection is generally limited to horses, and economic losses are relatively small in comparison to streptococcal abortion.

Morphology and Growth. *Salmonella abortivoequina* is a small, Gram-negative, motile rod occurring singly or in pairs. It is microaerophilic (requires small amounts of atmospheric oxygen) and grows abundantly on common laboratory mediums (Merchant & Packer, 1956).

Transmission and Diagnosis. Transmission occurs mainly by ingestion of this organism in contaminated feed, forage, or water. Venereal transmission may also occur, but it is thought to be infrequent.

Diagnosis is made by demonstration of this organism in placenta, fetus, or uterine exudate. The detection of specific agglutinins in the serum of infected animals is also a means of diagnosis.

Control. Equine infectious abortion is controlled by annual blood testing and eliminating reactors, isolating aborting mares, disinfecting contaminated surroundings, and promptly disposing of aborted fetuses and placental membranes. It may be prevented by vaccinating mares during the 4th or 5th month of pregnancy with a specific bacterin.

E. Bacterial Infections of Poultry

Poultry generally are not considered to be troubled by reproductive diseases comparable to those of farm mammals. However, several bacterial diseases are transmitted by way of infected eggs. Both male and female poultry are disseminators of bacteria through their reproductive system. Ejaculates from the male contain bacteria that may be deposited in the cloaca during copulation.

1. PULLORUM DISEASE

Pullorum is an infectious disease principally of chickens and turkeys caused by *Salmonella pullorum*. This organism, first described by Rettger in 1900, is worldwide in occurrence. Death losses may approach 90 per cent of an infected brood.

Morphology and Growth. Salmonella pullorum is a Gram-negative rod that is nonmotile and nonspore-forming. It grows well on a variety of mediums, and is a facultative anaerobe. The work done to characterize this organism by its biochemical activity has been summarized (Van Roekel, 1959).

Transmission and Diagnosis. Infected eggs serve as the principle means of transmission of this disease. These eggs are produced by hens which may show no signs of infection but have *S. pullorum* localized in their ovaries. If an infected egg hatches, the chick spreads the infection to others in the brooder through infected droppings. Transmission also occurs between adult fowl by contact with infected droppings or broken infected eggs. Diagnosis is based upon serological findings and bacteriological examination of blood and other body tissues.

Control. Control of pullorum disease is dependent upon breaking the cycle of transmission through the use of noninfected eggs from pullorum-free hens. Mature birds should be blood tested regularly and reactors eliminated from the flock. Furthermore, chicks should be purchased from pullorum-free hatcheries or flocks. No satisfactory vaccine has been developed.

2. FOWL TYPHOID

Fowl typhoid is an acute to chronic septicemic disease caused by *Salmonella gallinarum* affecting primarily pullets and mature chickens. It causes ovarian abnormalities and death of young birds. This disease was first reported by Klein in 1889, and is worldwide in occurrence. Losses range from an occasional bird in breeding flocks to 75 per cent or more of affected young fowl.

Morphology and Growth. Salmonella gallinarum is a relatively short, plump rod which has a tendency to stain more intensely at the ends. It is Gram-negative, nonsporeforming, aerobic, nonmotile, and grows more luxuriantly than does *S. pullorum*.

Transmission and Diagnosis. Transmission occurs by contact with contaminated material. Infected birds may shed organisms in eggs, droppings, and discharges from nostrils and mouth. Flies, rodents, and wild birds also have been incriminated as mechanical spreaders.

Pathological lesions such as rupture of the oviduct and flaccid, hemorrhagic or misshapen ova are indications of Salmonella infection. The blood agglutination test, using antigen made from *S. gallinarum* or

S. pullorum, can be used to detect diseased birds. A specific diagnosis can be made only by isolating *S. gallinarum* from birds or eggs.

Control. This disease is controlled by prevention and eradication. Prevention includes vaccination, the use of strict measures of sanitation, and the enhancement of natural resistance through selective breeding. Eradication measures include routine blood testing and elimination of carrier birds.

II. MYCOTIC INFECTIONS

A. Mycotic Infections of Cattle

1. Mycotic Abortion

Bovine mycotic abortion is considered to be a specific reproductive disease produced by fungus infection of the reproductive system. At least 18 different species of fungi have been incriminated as causative agents with the most common genera being Aspergillus and Absidia (Ainsworth & Austwick, 1959). The most common fungus associated with mycotic abortion is *Aspergillus fumigatus* which has been reported from 64 per cent of the cases of mycotic infection of fetal material examined (Austwick & Venn, 1961). Mycotic abortion has been known to occur in cattle since 1920, but only in the past few years has it been considered significant. It has been diagnosed in North America, Europe, and Australia. Most of these cases have been in the British Isles, where about 6 per cent infection rate has been observed by examination of the stomach contents of aborted fetuses.

Morphology and Growth. In fetal stomach contents and the placenta, *Aspergillus fumigatus* appears as narrow, branching filaments. This fungus and most others grow well on malt agar to which has been added penicillin and streptomycin to inhibit bacterial growth. The spores (reproductive units) are bluish-green in color.

Transmission and Diagnosis. The disease is sporadic and does not spread from one animal to another. Rather, it seems to be spread by inhalation of spores from moldy hay or straw. Invasion of the placenta is believed to be carried by the blood from the lungs.

Diagnosis may be made by cultural isolation or microscopic identification of fungi in thickened and necrotic placental cotyledons, in the intercaruncular areas, and in the fetal stomach contents. Occasionally skin lesions are present on the fetus (Plate XXXVII).

Control. Control of bovine mycotic abortion is difficult since its etiologic agents are common in occurrence. Care should be taken to prevent contact of pregnant animals with moldy hay. Fungicidal treatment of hay to reduce subsequent mold growth has been suggested.

III. PUBLIC HEALTH IMPORTANCE

Brucellosis. Human brucellosis is a serious and widespread disease resulting from contact with infected animals or their products. Infection with *Br. abortus* or *Br. suis* is known as undulant fever and that of *Br. melitensis* is known as Malta fever. These diseases are seen most frequently among livestock producers, veterinarians and abattoir workers. Symptoms are remittent undulating fever, cervical pain, headache, sweating, constipation, weakness, and anemia. Prompt cleansing of skin and disinfecting of clothing is imperative following contact with material contaminated with Brucella.

Leptospirosis. Leptospirosis in humans is a disease of major importance in some areas of the world. Human infection with *L. pomona* is called swineherd's disease, while *L. icterohemorrhagiae* (carried mostly by rodents) produces Weil's disease. Those most commonly affected are workers in abattoirs, rice fields, coal mines, and sewers as well as animal handlers and veterinarians. Infection occurs from contact with animal tissues and urine contaminated water or soil. Human symptoms are variable and although they are frequently severe, the mortality rate is low. Fever, headache, conjunctivitis, muscular pains, and enceph-

PLATE XXXVII

Lesions on skin of bovine fetus aborted because of *Aspergillus sp.* infection.

(From Hagan & Bruner. 1957. In the Infectious Diseases of Domestic Animals, Ithaca, N.Y., Courtesy Comstock Publishing Associates.)

alitic symptoms have been reported most commonly.

Vibriosis. Several cases of human vibriosis have been reported in Europe and the U.S.A. Fever, chills, and headache have been the most common symptoms. The method of transmission is unknown.

Listeriosis. Human listeriosis is increasing in incidence as indicated by a report of 700 bacteriologically proven cases between 1956 and 1960 (Seeliger, 1961). The mortality due to meningitis (inflammation of membranes that envelope brain and spinal cord) as a result of listeriosis in man approaches 70 per cent, and either physical or mental defects are common sequelae in recovered cases. Symptoms of encephalitis, fever, and conjuctivitis have been reported. The mode of infection is unknown.

Salmonellosis. Human infections with *S. pullorum*, *S. gallinarum* and *S. abortivoequina* are rather infrequent. However, they should be considered as potential infections in man. One rather large outbreak involving *S. pullorum* is reported to have caused gastro-enteritis in more than 400 men.

IV. SPORADIC INFECTIONS

In addition to the organisms described as specific causes for impaired fertility and abortion there are other bacteria that occasionally infect the reproductive system causing sporadic cases of infertility and abortion. Bacterial organisms isolated from aborted fetuses include various species of Streptococcus, Staphylococcus, Pasteurella, Salmonella, Alkaligenes, Diplococcus, Hemophilus, Flavobacterium, Clostridium, Escherichia, and Corynebacterium. Diseases of a more generalized nature occasionally result in abortion and their specific agents have been isolated from aborted fetuses. These organisms include the following: from cattle *L. monocytogenes*, *Mycobacterium bovis* and *M. avium*; from sheep, *S. abortus ovis*; from swine, *Erysipelothrix rhusiopathiae*; and from horses, *Shigella equirulis*, *Malleomyces mallei* and *Klebsiella genitalium*. Abortion

may occur without the female showing signs of infection, or it may be associated with fever, toxemia, or bacteremia.

REFERENCES

AINSWORTH, G. C. & AUSTWICK, P. K. C. (1959). *Fungal Diseases of Animals.* Commonwealth Agricultural Bureau, Farnham Royal, Bucks, England, 53–56.

ALSTON, J. M. & BROOM, J. C. (1958). *Leptospirosis in Man and Animals.* Edinburgh, E. & S. Livingstone Ltd.

AUSTWICK, P. K. C. & VENN, J. A. J. (1961). Mycotic Abortion in England and Wales 1954–1960. *Proc. IV Intern. Congr. Anim. Reprod.,* The Hague, Holland (in press).

BUDDLE, M. B. (1956). Ovine Brucellosis in New Zealand. *Proc. III. Intern. Congr. Anim. Reprod.,* Cambridge, England Sec. III, 37–38.

CLAPP, K. H. (1961). A Comparison of Various Antigens Used in the Complement Fixation Test for Ovine Brucellosis. *Aust. Vet. J.,* **37,** 188–190.

DIMOCK, W. W., EDWARDS, P. R. & BRUNER, D. W. (1947). Infections Observed in Equine Fetuses and Foals. *Cornell Vet.,* **37,** 89–99.

ELLIOTT, F. I., MURPHY, D. M. & BARTLETT, D. E. (1961). The Use of Polymyxin B. Sulfate with Dihydrostreptomycin and Penicillin for the Control of *Vibrio fetus* in a Frozen Semen Process. *Proc. IV. Intern. Congr. Anim. Reprod.,* The Hague, Holland (in press).

FAO/WHO (1958). *Third Report of Expert Committee on Brucellosis.* Geneva, Switzerland, 1–51.

FERGUSON, L. C. (1958). *Diseases of Swine.* 253–266. Ames, Iowa, Iowa State University Press.

FLORENT, A. (1960). Recent Progress in the Field of Vibriosis. *FAO Agric. Studies* No. 51, Rome, Italy, 5–17.

GRAY, M. L. (1960). Isolation of *Listeria monocytogenes* from Oat Silage. *Science,* **132,** 1767–1768.

HAY, J. R., GARRETT, H. V., HOERLIN, A. B., MANTHEI, C. A., ROSNER, L. A. & SHANNON, E. R. (1954). Report of Swine Brucellosis Committee. *Proc. 58th Annual Meeting of U.S. Livestock San. Assoc.,* Omaha, Nebraska, 204–206.

HUGHES, D. E. (1956). Notes on Vibriosis with Special Reference to the Isolation of *Vibrio fetus* from Semen and Preputial Fluids. *FAO Agric. Studies* No. 31, Rome, Italy, 41.

MANTHEI, C. A. (1958). *Diseases of Swine,* 267–289. Ames, Iowa, Iowa State University Press.

MARSH, H. (1958). *Newsome's Sheep Diseases.* 48–51. Baltimore, The Williams & Wilkins Co.

MERCHANT, I. A. & PACKER, R. A. (1956). *Veterinary Bacteriology and Virology.* Ames, Iowa, Iowa State University Press, 354–356

SEELIGER, H. (1961). Serological Problems in Listeriosis. *Walter Reed Army Res. Inst. Seminar,* Washington, D.C.

U.S. Department of Agriculture (1954). *Losses in Agriculture.* Washington 25, D.C., 129–135.

VAN ROEKEL, H. (1959). *Diseases of Poultry.* 165–166. Ames, Iowa, Iowa State University Press.

QUESTIONS

1. Discuss the anatomical and physiological barriers to uterine infection in cattle, sheep, swine, horses, and poultry.
2. Explain how calves may be disseminators of brucellosis in cattle.
3. Describe in detail how control and eradication of bovine brucellosis may be accomplished.
4. In what respects does bovine vibriosis differ from ovine vibriosis?
5. List the sanitary measures to be taken to prevent the spread of swine brucellosis.
6. Why are swine particularly important in the transmission of leptospirosis to animals and man?
7. How does streptococcal infection of the reproductive tract of mares become established?
8. What bacterial diseases of poultry are considered as reproductive diseases and why are they so considered?
9. How are fungal spores thought to enter the body and reach the placenta?
10. Define: (*a*) metritis; (*b*) endometritis; (*c*) micro-aerophilic; (*d*) histopathology, (*e*) leptospiruria (*f*) hemoglobinuria; (*g*) encephalitis; (*h*) induration; (*i*) pyometra; (*j*) orchitis.

Chapter 20

Viral, Rickettsial and Protozoan Infections

By W. J. Gibbons

Most infections are caused by organisms that pass from individual to individual of the same species. Sometimes infections are acquired from another species. Infections may be acquired directly or indirectly. The more common sources of infection are; contact with a diseased individual, indirect contact with infected material (*fomites*), contact with disease carriers, infections that are from food, water, or are air-borne, contact with blood-sucking arthropods (*vectors*) and infection from organisms normally present in the body. When organisms causing disease are classified, they fall into one of five groups; bacteria, bacteria-like pathogens of uncertain classification, (including the rickettsiae), pathogenic fungi, protozoa and the viruses. In this chapter, consideration is given to diseases of the reproductive organs caused by viruses, rickettsiae and pathogenic protozoa (summarized in Table 20–1).

I. VIRAL INFECTIONS

The exact nature of viruses is not completely known. The ability of viruses to invade living cells, their multiplication within the body, their dissemination from the body as highly infective, readily trans-missable agents makes it difficult to believe that viruses are not living micro-organisms. As a result of the intense program of research on viruses, it is now realized that viruses do not appear to be possessed of life in the usual sense. Viruses are thought of as chemical agents, similar to nucleic acids, resembling genes which are either abnormal or "wild." By gaining access to the chromosomes these agents so influence the parent cells as to cause abnormal metabolic processes which often lead to their damage and death. In the course of such abnormal processes, replication of virus-nucleic acid occurs, and this escapes to invade other cells. A clearer concept of the nature of viruses will probably emerge within a few years.

A. Viral Diseases of Cattle

1. Epizootic Bovine Abortion

A form of bovine abortion for which no etiological agent could be incriminated has long been widespread in California, and known to exist also in Germany. The frequent occurrence of bovine abortion of unknown etiology makes it probable that such abortion exists in different areas of the United States and in other countries. A

Table 20-1.—Reproductive Diseases of Viral and Protozoan Origin

Disease	Species	Etiology	Diagnosis		Control
			Clinical	Other	
Epizootic abortion	cattle	virus	abortion in late pregnancy, liver lesions in fetus	isolation of virus	none
Granular vaginitis	cattle	virus	nodular vaginitis, balanitis	—	none
Infectious pustular vulvo-vaginitis	cattle	virus	pustular vaginitis, balanitis	isolation of virus, serum neutralization test	isolation, cessation of breeding
Epizootic infertility (Epivaginitis)	cattle	virus	vaginitis, epididymitis, sterility	—	slaughter of infected, physical examination of herd additions
Infectious vaginitis	cattle	virus	catarrhal vaginitis	isolation of virus	isolation of infected, cessation of breeding
Virus diarrhea	cattle	virus	primary enteritis, secondary abortion	isolation of virus, serum neutralization tests	isolation, vaccination
Rift valley fever	cattle, sheep	virus	abortion, necrosis of liver	serum neutralization tests, isolation of virus	control of insect vector, vaccination
Ovine viral abortion	sheep	virus, P-LGV group	abortion, degeneration of fetus	staining elementary bodies in placenta, virus isolation, complement-fixation test	vaccination
Necrotic venereal disease	sheep	virus (*Scleus ulceris*)	ulceration of lips, legs, vulva & sheath	lamb inoculation	inspection of sale rams or purchased rams before breeding
Nairobi sheep disease	sheep	virus	nasal discharge, diarrhea, abortion	presence of ticks, inoculation of susceptible sheep	dipping for tick control, no vaccination

Disease	Animal	Etiology	Signs	Diagnosis	Control
Hog cholera	swine	virulent or modified live virus vaccination (*Tortor suis*)	stillborn pigs, edematous dead pigs	history of pregnant sow vaccination	vaccination at proper time for pregnant sows
African swine fever	swine	virus	disease resembling hog cholera, abortion in pregnant sows	exposure to warthogs or other infected swine	quarantine & slaughter of infected herds
Equine rhinopneumonitis	horses	virus (*Tortor equae*)	abortion in late pregnancy, respiratory disease in young	focal necrosis of liver & edema of lungs in fetus, inclusion bodies, guinea pig inoculation	vaccination by intranasal instillation of live virus
Equine viral arteritis	horses	virus	respiratory infection, cellulitis, abortion	none	isolation of infected
Coital vesicular exanthema	horses	virus	pustules on vulva, vagina, sheath, penis	none	isolation, cessation of breeding
Newcastle disease	poultry	virus (*Tortor furens*)	encephalitis, soft or imperfectly shelled eggs	isolation of virus, histopathology of central nervous system	vaccination with inactivated or live virus
Avian encephalo-myelitis	poultry	virus (*Legio gallinae*)	epidemic tremors, egg-borne infection	isolation of virus	vaccination with live virus
Trichomoniasis	cattle	protozoa (*Trichomonas fetus*)	infertility, pyometra & abortion in cows	examination for trichomonads	breeding rest, A. I.
Dourine	horses	protozoa (*Trypanosoma equiperdum*)	lesions of vulva, vagina, sheath, penis, prepuce, later-infection of nervous system, paralysis	complement-fixation test	destruction of infected
Toxoplasmosis	sheep	protozoa (*Toxoplasma gondii*)	encephalitis, abortion in pregnant ewes	histopathology, complement-fixation test	isolation, destruction of infected

virus has now been incriminated in this type of abortion. The virus can be isolated from aborted fetuses by yolk-sac inoculation of embryonated eggs; and it appears to be a member of the psittacosis-LGV group. The disease can be reproduced experimentally.

Symptoms and Diagnosis. In susceptible cattle the disease is characterized by sudden onset of abortion, this usually occurring in the 6th to 8th month of pregnancy. The disease affects cattle of all ages but after its initial appearance in a herd, older animals are apparently immune and abortions are confined to pregnant first-calf heifers. The incidence is seasonal, occurring from July through October; transmission by vectors is an obvious possibility.

Gross lesions in the aborted fetus are indicative of epizootic abortion (Howard *et al.*, 1956). Edema is present under the skin, and in the abdominal and pericardial cavities. The liver is nodular and swollen, friable, yellowish in color and shows red lines on the primary lobules. The spleen may be enlarged and petechial hemorrhages may occur in various parts of the fetus. The gross and microscopic pathology of the liver is diagnostic. Differential diagnosis depends upon the elimination of brucellosis, vibriosis, leptospirosis and trichomoniasis. A conclusive diagnosis is made by isolation of the viral agent.

Control. Apart from normal measures of hygiene, control of the disease is not yet possible. As the infection seems to be acquired in the foothills, possibly by vector transmission, the raising of breeding cattle in such areas and the avoidance of foothill ranges-pastures for non-native cattle might help in control. The fact that an attack apparently confers immunity and that the viral agent can be cultivated offers hope of possible vaccination in the future.

2. Granular Vaginitis

(Granular Venereal Disease; Nodular Vaginitis.)

Granular vaginitis of cattle is a common, widespread infection of the vulva and vagina of uncertain cause and characterized by varying degrees of inflammation and round-

cell nodule formation in the mucosa. The relation of granular vaginitis to infertility of cattle and its economic importance are very controversial subjects. Before the discovery of brucellosis and vibriosis, the disease was considered by some investigators as an important cause of abortion and infertility. This view has since been dropped. The existence of well-marked lesions in any herd and their presence in pregnant cows apparently makes this disease seem relatively unimportant. However, individual cattle or herds of cattle do exist in which marked lesions are accompanied by non-breeding; treatment of such cases usually results in conception. In herds with severe lesions, a 10 per cent fall in conception rate has been observed (Troutman, 1954). Although many types of bacteria have been isolated from the vagina of affected cows, it is usually held that the probable cause is a virus; one has been isolated but has proved difficult to culture for any length of time.

Symptoms. The lesions vary from a few hardly noticeable nodules and reddening of the mucosa to numerous nodules, more severe inflammation and a purulent exudate which can be seen when the lips of the vulva are parted. In severe cases, inflammation of the anterior vagina and external os of the cervix occurs. In the more marked cases, breeding induces straining, painful urination and bleeding of the granules. Aggravated lesions occur principally in heifers. Similar lesions are found on the penis and sheath of infected bulls. When the lesions are numerous and severe, the bull may either refuse to copulate or be slow in doing so.

Treatment. The treatment is symptomatic to overcome secondary infections and to relieve the symptoms in more severe cases, when they are accompanied by infertility.

3. Infectious Pustular Vulvo-Vaginitis

(Vesicular Venereal Disease; Coital Vesicular Exanthema; Blachenausachlag.)

Infectious pustular vulvo-vaginitis (IPV) is an acute, readily transmissable viral infection of the vulva and vagina characterized by papule formation, pustules and ulceration of the mucosa. The disease also affects the mucosa of the external genitalia of bulls. It commonly occurs in European countries and sporadic outbreaks are reported from the United States and Canada. The virus is cytopathogenic, producing intranuclear inclusion bodies in affected tissues or when cultured in bovine embryonic kidney cells. The virus of IPV has been found to be identical with the virus of infectious bovine rhino-tracheitis—IBR, a disease affecting the mucosa of the upper respiratory tract of cattle.

Transmission. The virus is present in discharges from the vagina and prepuce where lesions are present and the disease is rapidly spread by breeding, grooming, tail switching, washing the perineum or by washing the prepuce. The disease may be transmitted by artificial insemination, infected semen often carrying the disease even though treated with antibiotics.

Symptoms. The disease appears suddenly and spreads very rapidly with initial symptoms of frequent urination, tail switching, stomping with feet, and straining after urination. Examination of the vulva and vagina reveals numerous small white pustules in the mucosa. Within 24 to 36 hours the pustular lesions coalesce to form a yellowish membrane on the surface of the mucosa. The lesions start to heal in a few days and spontaneous recovery occurs in two weeks. Similar lesions occur on the penis and sheath of infected bulls (Kendrick *et al.*, 1958).

Control. All breeding should be suspended for 30 days. Grooming of the rear parts should be suspended. Although the disease abates spontaneously, symptomatic treatment is advisable because of the danger of secondary bacterial infections causing chronic vaginitis. Should IPV become a herd problem, vaccination with IBR tissue-culture vaccine would induce immunity.

4. Epizootic Infertility of Cattle

(Infectious Bovine Cervico-Vaginitis and Epididymitis; Epivag.)

Epizootic infertility is a chronic infection of the genitalia of cows and bulls, transmitted by copulation, and characterized by progressive lesions in the vagina, uterus, epididymis and testis. The causative agent is thought to be a virus, since the disease can be produced by bacteria-free exudates and semen. Information as to the type of virus is lacking, for it has been impossible to adapt the viral agent to mice or embryonated eggs. Infected unapparent carriers of the disease, such as African native Zebu stock, are the source and reservoir of infection. An infected cow may remain a permanent carrier and spreader unless treatment is carried out (Rep. U.S. Livest. San. Assoc. 1954*a*).

Symptoms. In cows, lesions are apparent 2 to 4 days after infection and consist of a variable number of diffuse, reddish purple, inflammatory patches or streaks on the anterior part of the vaginal mucosa and in the cervix. At 7 to 10 days there is a thick, tenacious, yellow, muco-purulent, odorless vaginal discharge. In severe cases, the inflammation spreads from the vagina to the uterus, producing a catarrhal metritis which may progress to the Fallopian tube. Approximately 25 per cent of untreated cases develop a chronic salpingitis with peri-ovarian adhesions and cysts.

In bulls, clinical symptoms only become apparent weeks or even months after exposure. One of the first physical signs of the disease is a slight palpable enlargement of the spermatic cord and tail of the epididymis which usually develops 4 to 10 weeks after exposure. As the disease progresses, the swelling extends to the body and head of the epididymis and eventually involves the testis. Atrophy and fibrosis of the testes results in complete sterility. In early cases, the concentration and motility of sperm are reduced, and in advanced cases the inflammation progresses so as to block the passage of seminal plasma and inhibit spermatogenesis.

Diagnosis. Diagnosis is based on suggestive herd history, impaired breeding performances, physical examination of female and male genital tracts, and histopathology when slaughter specimens are available. Specific serological tests have not been developed and differentiation from other viral vaginitis may be difficult. The diagnosis of epivag is most difficult in the early stages of the disease. When cases of vaginitis with copious discharge of opaque, odorless exudate are found in a number of cows and positive cases of epididymitis are present in the bulls, a positive diagnosis is justified.

Control. Antiseptic douches and antibiotic infusions may effect a cure in some cases but treatment must be instituted very early in the disease. Treatment of cows with advanced lesions or the treatment of bulls after the appearance of symptoms is useless. The physical examination of all cattle entering the herd and semen checks on bulls should help to prevent the introduction of infection into a susceptible herd. Breeding stock or semen should never be imported from countries known to have epizootic infertility.

5. Infectious Vaginitis

(Vagino-Cervicitis; Viral Vaginitis.)
Viral vaginitis has been reported from several areas of the world. The causative viral agent has been isolated from the vaginal secretions of naturally infected animals and the typical vaginitis has been produced experimentally by vaginal infusion of isolated virus (Kendrick *et al.*, 1956).

Symptoms. The disease causes lowered fertility but infected animals can usually conceive within 2 or 3 months of its onset. The vaginitis occurs as an enzootic during the breeding season and examination reveals hyperemia and edema of the vagina and cervix. The vagina contains a yellow, mucoid exudate which is periodically expelled. Rectal examination reveals no recognizable changes in the uterus, Fallopian tubes or ovaries. The course of the disease is 3 to 90 days. Bulls are not affected.

Control. Treatment does not alter the course of the disease but control may be aided by isolation of known infected animals, cessation of natural breeding, and breeding by A.I.

6. Virus Diarrhea

(Mucosal Disease; Virus Abortion.)

Virus diarrhea has been reported from several areas of the world and has been recognized as an economically important cause of abortion.

Symptoms. Virus diarrhea is characterized by fever, loss of appetite, salivation, ulcers in the mouth, sudden drop in milk flow and a watery diarrhea. In clinical cases affecting pregnant cows, abortions occur in 10 to 90 days. It is possible that many abortions of unknown cause are due to this viral disease.

Control. A vaccine has been produced experimentally against this disease.

7. Rift Valley Fever

(Enzootic Hepatitis)
Rift Valley Fever (RVF) is an acute, infectious virus disease of cattle, sheep, and other animals which is insect-borne (*e.g.* mosquitoes). Man is highly susceptible but the disease is not usually lethal.

Symptoms. The incubation period is very short, usually 24 to 72 hours following exposure. In adult cattle and ewes there is transient fever, sometimes profuse salivation, severe abdominal pain, and a high abortion rate in pregnant animals. The mortality in cattle does not exceed 10 per cent but in sheep may reach 20 per cent. Young lambs and calves are reluctant to move and often show signs of abdominal pain. The disease runs a rapid course and death frequently occurs within 24 hours. The mortality may be 95 per cent (Rep. U.S. Livest. San. Assoc. 1954*c*).

Diagnosis. RVF should be suspected if the disease is accompanied by extensive necrotic changes of the liver and if an influenza-like disease occurs in those persons who have associated with the infected animals. The diagnosis can be confirmed by serum neutralization tests using mice or by inoculating Swiss white mice intraperitoneally.

Control. Transmission by insect vectors can be controlled to some extent by the application of insecticides to animals, corrals and stables. Epizootics can be controlled by mass inoculation. Modified live virus vaccines have been developed. Vaccination should be carried out on cattle and sheep over 6 weeks of age, and preferably on non-pregnant cattle and sheep, although many pregnant cattle and sheep have been vaccinated without undesirable effects. Animals less than 6 weeks of age and pregnant adults should be treated with immune serum.

B. Viral Diseases of Sheep

1. VIRAL ABORTION IN EWES

(Ovine Viral Abortion; Enzootic Abortion in Ewes.)

This contagious disease is characterized by expulsion of fetuses, and retained placenta with necrosis of the afterbirth and cotyledons. The virus is of the psittacosis-lymphogranuloma group and by chicken embryo inoculation techniques, it may be isolated from the stomach contents, lung, liver, spleen and kidney tissues of aborted fetuses. There is no evidence to show that the disease can be transmitted by the ram. Ewe lambs and unbred ewes exposed to aborted fetal and maternal tissues at lambing time, may become infected and carry the infection with no outward manifestation until the next pregnancy, at which time they may abort.

Symptoms. Clinical evidence of the disease is manifested by abortions from mid-gestation through late pregnancy (Tunnicliff, 1960). Abortion follows a febrile period of 3 to 4 days and is accompanied by retained placenta and metritis which occasionally results in the death of the ewe. The expelled dead fetus is in varying stages of degeneration and mummification with a blackish, tightly drawn skin, corneal opacity and sometimes ascites. Ewes that have aborted lamb normally in the following year with no evidence of infection.

Diagnosis. A positive diagnosis can be made by any one of three methods—the complement-fixation test on blood serum; the isolation of virus from fresh fetal tissues, vaginal exudate or placenta; and the staining of elementary virus bodies in tissues examined microscopically. The disease must be

chiefly differentiated from vibriosis, in which the clinical manifestations are practically identical and the pathologic changes in both fetus and fetal membranes are grossly similar. In cases of virus abortion, inoculation of chicken embryos, guinea pigs or mice is the most accurate diagnostic method. Bacteriologic cultures should be used to determine the absence of *Vibrio fetus* or other bacterial etiological agents.

Control. Ewes have been successfully immunized by the use of formalin-inactivated vaccines and with chicken-embryo-yolk sac vaccines. First-lambing ewes or previously unexposed ewes in infected flocks should be vaccinated before breeding. Complete control may not be possible in flocks previously exposed to the infective agent.

2. NECROTIC VENEREAL DISEASE

(Ulcerative Dermatosis; Balanoposthitis; Lip and Leg Ulceration.)

Ulcerative dermatosis is an infectious disease characterized by necrotic ulceration of the skin and external genital organs. The disease is caused by a filterable virus which enters through a break in the skin.

Symptoms. General symptoms are absent and local lesions are found on the skin of the upper lip, the skin of the legs distal to the carpus or tarsus, around the preputial opening or involving the vulva. The lesion is an ulcer of varying size and depth covered by a scab or crust under which is a creamy, odorless pus. The ulcerative process and accompanying edema may completely or partially surround the preputial orifice, and extension to the glans penis may ruin the ram for breeding. The lesions of the prepuce, glans penis, and vulva occur as a result of transmission by breeding (Tunnicliff, 1949).

Diagnosis. The diagnosis is not difficult when examination reveals the specific lesion. The disease must be distinguished from contagious ecthyma. Ecthyma is rare in adult sheep, while ulcerative dermatosis affects sheep of all ages. The lesion in contagious ecthyma is proliferative, not ulcerative and the ecthyma-immune lamb is susceptible to ulcerative dermatosis. This disease has been confused with the non-transmissable condition known in Australia as sheath-rot or pizzle rot but has no relation to this disease.

Control. No specific treatment or immunizing agent has been found. Rams offered for sale or those to be placed with ewes at the beginning of the breeding season should be examined for posthitis and those showing lesions eliminated.

3. Nairobi Sheep Disease

The disease is a tick-borne gastro-enteritis caused by a filterable virus. The disease is not transmitted by direct contact but by infected ticks during any stage of their development (Rep. U.S.Livest. San. Assoc. 1954*b*).

Symptoms. The symptoms comprise a mucopurulent nasal discharge, rapid and painful respirations, and bright to dark green watery diarrhea. In the later stages the animal goes off feed and is unable to rise. In ewes the vulva becomes swollen and congested and at this stage pregnant ewes abort.

Control. No satisfactory vaccine has yet been developed nor has any medicinal treatment proved of value. Dipping sheep at weekly intervals, in areas where vector ticks are present, will serve to control the spread of the disease.

C. Viral Diseases of Swine

In general, viruses show various degrees of host specificity and tissue specificity. Many viruses such as the hog cholera virus are strictly host specific. Definite tissue affinities are also exhibited by most viruses. Up to the present, there has been no virus which specifically attacks the reproductive organs of swine. However, many virus particles of all species have the ability to pass the placental filter and attack the embryonic membranes or the embryo itself resulting in pathological changes which lead to death of the fetus and abortion. This is true of some viruses which cause disease in swine. The property of invading the reproductive organs may even be possessed by so-called modified "live" virus vaccines. So-called "killed" virus vaccines do not possess this property. This phenomena is of considerable importance in immunization against hog cholera.

1. Hog Cholera Vaccination and Reproduction

The use of virulent virus or attenuated virus on pregnant sows presents a problem. The use of active or "live" virus at breeding time or in the first month of pregnancy may result in ascites, subcutaneous edema, and a variety of other abnormalities in the fetus prior to parturition (Scutter *et al.*, 1953). Some authorities are of the opinion that vaccination with "live" viruses 3 to 4 weeks before parturition may result in the birth of stillborn pigs. To insure maximum safety, the use of anti-hog cholera serum with attenuated virus vaccines should be advocated for sows during the last 2 months of pregnancy. Active or "live" virus vaccination should never be used at breeding time or during the first month of pregnancy.

2. Secondary Infections

The invasion of the uterus and death of the fetus causing abortion occurs as a clinical symptom during the course of some generalized virus infections of swine. In *foot and mouth disease,* pregnant sows frequently abort. Losses from *vesicular exanthema* include condemnations, loss of young pigs, abortions, shrinkage and quarantine restrictions. The chief reason for the eradication of vesicular exanthema is that it is clinically indistinguishable from foot and month.

African Swine Fever is an acute, febrile, highly contagious viral disease of swine. It is characterized by a short course, a very high mortality, and gross lesions that closely resemble those of hog cholera. Clinically, African Swine Fever is similar in lesions and symptoms to American hog cholera, but it is immunologically distinct from it. During the course of the disease, pregnant sows usually abort.

Pseudorabies (Aujeszky's disease) causes a mild but highly contagious disease in adult swine but when pregnant sows are infected between 3 and 5 weeks from the end of term, a large percentage of stillborn pigs will result.

D. Viral Diseases of Horses

1. Virus Abortion

(Equine Rhinopneumonitis)

Over a long period of years virus abortion of mares has been described in various areas of the world, but only in recent years has it become known that the virus of equine abortion was identical with the virus of an influenza-like respiratory disease of horses (Doll & Kintner, 1954). Abortion in mares has been produced experimentally with the viral agent isolated from the respiratory disease and from enzootic abortion. The virus has been adapted to hamsters and to cultivation in embryonated chicken eggs.

Symptoms. Virus abortion in mares occurs with or without previous respiratory symptoms and the expulsion of the fetus is usually between the 8th and 10th month of pregnancy. Mares infected late in pregnancy may give birth to a live, weak, foal that generally dies within 36 hours. The respiratory disease is most frequent in yearlings and is characterized by rhinitis which appears in the fall. While recovery takes place in 8 to 10 days, these animals may be a source of infection for pregnant mares.

Diagnosis. Diagnostic lesions of the fetus consist of multiple necrotic foci in the liver and edema of the lungs with excessive pleural fluid. The diagnosis may be confirmed by characteristic intranuclear inclusion bodies in the liver cells and in the epithelial lining of the air passages. When virus material is injected into the fetuses of pregnant guinea pigs on the 35th day of gestation, the fetuses will be aborted 7 to 9 days later.

Control. Viral abortion is highly contagious and immediate isolation of infected animals is indicated. Following an abortion the stalls of the aborting animals should be thoroughly disinfected. This is especially important when other pregnant mares are kept in the same stable. Equines infected with respiratory disease should be isolated from pregnant mares. Virus abortions rarely occur in the same mare in successive seasons but may repeat several years after the first incidence. The immunity produced is therefore not lifetime but transient. In the control of the disease, immunization with a hamster-adapted live virus vaccine is recommended for all horses on farms where rhinopneumonitis and abortion have been enzootic. The vaccine is administered by instilling 3 ml. in one nostril in July and again in October. An infection-immunization program should be initiated with caution on isolated farms with no history of the disease.

2. Equine Viral Arteritis

(Equine Influenza)

Equine influenza is a septicemic disease characterized by high fever, respiratory infection, conjunctivitis, edema of various parts of the body, and frequently cellulitis of the extremities. The virus causing the disease is entirely different from that of viral abortion and because of its action on the cells of small blood vessels is termed viral arteritis. The disease is accompanied in some outbreaks by abortion in pregnant mares (Doll *et al.*, 1957).

Symptoms. Abortions occur during the febrile and early severe symptomatic stage of the disease in affected pregnant mares. The expulsion of the fetus is due to the invasion of the uterus by the virus.

Control. No control has been devised except for symptomatic treatment and immediate isolation of affected animals.

3. Coital Vesicular Exanthema

(Genital Horse Pox)

This genital disease primarily affects cattle, but the same or a similar disease appears in horses and occasionally in other species. The lesions and course are similar in both the bovine and equine species. Since the disease is chiefly spread by coitus, natural infection does not spread from one species to another. It has been reported that the disease is experimentally interchangable between horses and cattle.

Symptoms. The initial lesion is the appearance of many small papules on the surface of the genital epithelium. In a short time the lesions are confluent pustules and ulcers covered by a yellowish-white membrane and accompanied by a purulent exudate. The lesions are most prevalent on the epithelium of the penis, sheath, vulva, clitoris and vagina. Healing occurs spontaneously in about 2 weeks. Very little immunity is produced and infection may occur at a later date.

Control. There is little necessity for treatment since the disease runs a rapid course and recovery is spontaneous. When vaginitis is very severe, mild antiseptic douches are indicated. All breeding should be suspended during the course of the disease.

E. Viral Diseases of Poultry

In some viral diseases of poultry the causative agent invades the ovary and may cause abnormal egg production or infect the embryo and so lead to possible transmission through egg passage. The principal virus diseases affecting egg production are infectious bronchitis, Newcastle disease and avian encephalomyelitis.

1. INFECTIOUS BRONCHITIS

Infectious bronchitis is an acute, highly contagious, respiratory disease of chickens. The causative agent is a filterable virus, for which the name *Tarpeia pulli* has been proposed. The virus is not transmitted through the egg but the infection is a problem especially in adult laying flocks. In infected flocks, production declines and misshapen, rough and soft-shelled eggs may be laid. The laying of poor quality eggs may continue in some flocks even after recovery of full production. The eggs of recovered hens carry antibodies which are later absorbed by the hatched chick; these do not serve to completely protect the chick against natural infection. Live virus vaccines are widely used for the control of infectious bronchitis and are considered effective (Hofstad, 1952).

2. NEWCASTLE DISEASE

Newcastle disease is a highly contagious malady which chiefly attacks chickens and turkeys causing a high mortality. Various other poultry and birds, as well as certain mammals, including man, are susceptible to the disease. The virus is present in about one-third of the eggs laid during the pre-clinical and early acute stages of the disease, and may prevent development or kill the embryo of fertile eggs. A high percentage of hens lay soft or imperfectly shelled eggs during and up to 45 days after an outbreak. The presence of ND virus in eggs may permit, through breakage, the contamination of crates, incubators and other objects as well as the surrounding atmosphere. Control is by sanitary management and some form of vaccination. Both inactivated and active modified virus vaccines have been used. Inactivated vaccine is recommended on laying flocks and when devitalizing factors are present. For prevention in healthy birds an active virus vaccine is generally employed (Brandly, 1952).

3. AVIAN ENCEPHALOMYELITIS

The disease is an acute infection of chickens 6 to 8 weeks old and is characterized by ataxia and tremor especially of the head and neck (epidemic tremor). Adult laying birds acquire the infection without symptoms of visible disease and it persists in the visceral tissues (especially gonadal) and is eliminated via the genital or intestinal tracts. The virus is egg-borne and enters the yolk-sac in embryos in natural infection and then progresses to the brain and viscera. Hatchability of eggs is not influenced by an outbreak of encephalomyelitis. The control of the disease depends on vaccination of young birds with an active live virus vaccine of brain emulsion administered in the wing-web (Schaaf, 1960). When there is danger of exposure of laying hens to vaccinated young birds, a chemically inactivated virus vaccine should be used.

II. RICKETTSIAL INFECTIONS

The *rickettsiae* comprise a group of small rod-shaped, coccoid and often pleomorphic micro-organisms that are commonly found in the tissues of arthropods. The *rizkettsiae* appear to be intermediate between bacteria and viruses. They are usually non-filterable and can be cultivated outside the host only in living tissues, embryonated chicken eggs or rarely in media containing body fluids. The rickettsiae cause a number of diseases in man and domestic animals. Cattle are the host of an inapparent rickettsial infection, Q-fever of man, and an important source of human infection.

1. Anaplasmosis

Anaplasmosis is an infectious, noncontagious disease of cattle characterized by anemia and icterus and associated with the presence of certain bodies, termed *Anaplasma*, within the red blood cells (Fig. 20–1). Anaplasmosis has been classified as a protozoan disease, but recent research would indicate that the causative agent resembles the group of organisms classified as rickettsiae (Ristic, 1960).

The severity of clinical attacks of anaplasmosis is indicated by acute, mild or chronic types. The acute type with severe anemia and icterus is seen in mature cattle and is more serious in cattle in advanced pregnancy frequently resulting in abortion. A very significant factor concerning abortion or parturition of anaplasmosis-infected cattle is that the presence of red blood corpuscles in the uterine discharges or uterine hemorrhage contain anaplasma bodies and by attracting insects may serve as a source of transmissable infection. Aborted fetuses, fetal membranes and uterine exudates should be burned or disinfected. Cows that abort in the acute phase of the disease or those about to calve should be isolated and all precautions observed to prevent insect or other transmission.

2. Q-Fever

The causative agent of Q-fever is *Coxiella burneti* which has been isolated from man, animals, and ticks. The major impact of this disease is felt by the rural human population; the health and productivity of domestic animals are seldom affected. Cattle, sheep and goats become naturally infected and although not visibly sick, they discharge the rickettsiae in the placenta, feces, and milk. The infection is dust-borne and the dust-laden air of dairy cattle barns and of sheep and goat corrals and pens becomes highly infective and endangers the health of man when these animals are carriers of the infection. Early treatment with antibiotics is effective in man but the possibility of ending the carrier state in domestic animals has not been investigated (Meyer, 1955).

III. PROTOZOAN INFECTIONS

Protozoa are generally regarded as the first, and lowest phylum of the animal kingdom. All animals consisting of single cells and capable of carrying on all life processes independently are included. The soil, surface waters, vegetation and the intestinal tracts of man and animals are teeming with saprophytic protozoa. Only a small proportion are parasitic in habit and a very small proportion are disease producing. A number of very important diseases of man and animals are caused by pathogenic protozoa. The disease producing forms fall into four classes: *Sarcodina*, *Mastigophora*, *Sporozoa*, and *Ciliata*. The Mastigophora are sometimes called the *Flagellata* due to the fact that this class includes all the species that possess flagella during the greater part of their life span. Some members of this group live in the intestinal and genital tracts and others live in the blood. Two protozoa of the class, *Flagellata*, which affect the reproductive organs of domestic animals are *Trichomonas fetus* and *Trypanosoma equiperdum*.

1. Trichomoniasis in Cattle

Trichomoniasis is a worldwide venereal disease of cattle characterized by early abortions, pyometra and sterility and caused by the protozoan *Trichomonas fetus* (Fig. 20–1). The parasite was recognized late in the last century but its importance has only been demonstrated during the last 30 years. The organism is normally a pear-shaped or spindle-shaped structure resembling an undulating membrane and having 3 anterior flagella and a posterior flagellum. In fresh preparations the parasite has a characteristic degree of motility, rotating counterclockwise as it progresses jerkily, forward along an irregular path. The cow is infected at the time of coitus from an infected bull

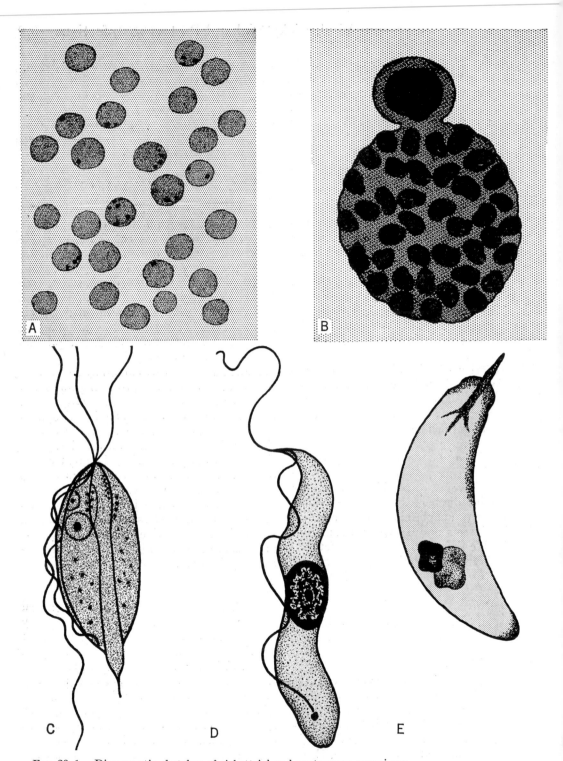

Fig. 20–1.—Diagramatic sketches of rickettsial and protoazoan organisms.

A. *Anaplasma* bodies (dark dots) in red blood cells of cow with anaplasmosis (× 1,400 approximately).

B. *Toxoplasma gondii*, showing intracellular proliferative forms in cytoplasm, to form cyst, and nucleus at end of cell (× 2,850 approx.).

C. *Trichomonas fetus*, side view; note 3 anterior flagella and 1 posterior flagellum (× 3,350 approx.).

D. *Trypanasoma*; note center nucleus and single flagellum (× 1,350 approx.).

E. *Toxoplasma*, in resting stage, with a single nucleus (× 4,650 approx.).

(330)

or *vice versa*. The infection is generally introduced into clean herds by purchase of an infected bull; occasionally it may result from the introduction of an infected cow or in some cases from the use of A.I.

Symptoms. After an infected bull or infected non-pregnant cow is introduced into the herd, symptoms of trichomoniasis may not become evident for some time. The first symptoms of slight vaginitis and an increase in the frequency of repeat breedings may be overlooked. The owner does not become aware of the problem until numerous repeat breedings, abortions and pyometra are evident. After the infection is established a slight or more severe vaginitis is usually present and the infection invades the uterus from the vagina frequently resulting in infertility. If conception occurs, the animal may abort within 2 to 4 months. In other cases the fetus dies, and is not expelled, but becomes macerated and lies in a thin nearly odorless fluid. The recently infected bull may develop a mild inflammation of the mucosa of the sheath and penis but this subsides quickly and the genital organs appear normal although the infection is chronic and permanent.

Diagnosis. In the diagnosis of trichomoniasis the breeding history of the herd is suggestive. Characteristic signs following the introduction of the infection in the herd are an increase in the number of services per conception, failure of conception after many services, return to estrus after considerable periods of apparent conception, early abortions and pyometra. Diagnosis in the cow may be accomplished by detecting trichomonads in the vaginal discharge, fetal membranes, the mouth cavity of the fetus, the stomach contents of the fetus, the fetal fluids or the exudate in the uterus. Following abortion the organisms disappear from the uterine exudate within 48 hours. In infected non-pregnant cows, the organism disappears from the vagina but may remain in the uterus, and produces endometritis lasting one to several months. During this time the organism appears periodically in the vagina.

Diangosis in the bull is made by finding the trichomonads in the sheath or glans penis. This is accomplished by introducing a 24-inch sterile plastic preputial pipette with attached rubber bulb into the sheath and by suction and gentle scraping of the glans penis from one to several ml. of smegma and fluid may be obtained (Bartlett, 1949). Part of the material from the pipette should be placed in a small amount of physiological saline for immediate microscopic examination and the remainder placed in 5 to 10 ml. of Rakoff's media for laboratory culture and examination. In known infected bulls, a positive diagnosis is not always possible. A bull is not considered negative for trichomoniasis until 6 negative samples have been found at weekly intervals. When possible, a recommended method is to breed the bull to 2 or 3 virgin heifers and subsequently examine the vaginas for evidence of infection.

Treatment. Individual treatment of cows is useless except insofar as it is necessary to treat cases of pyometra and abortion. Immunity will usually develop in infected cows after sexual rest of at least 90 days. The infection in bulls is chronic and no immunity develops. Many treatments have been advocated but the most effective is the massaging into the sheath and penis of "Bovoflavin ointment" which is composed of trypaflavine, (a protozoacidal agent) and an ointment base. As high as 80 per cent recoveries have been reported from this method of treatment, but unless infected bulls are extremely valuable they should be slaughtered.

Control. When trichomoniasis has been diagnosed as a herd infection, plans for control are usually favorable if the owner cooperates fully on a carefully planned program. Infection usually dies out in non-pregnant cows. The herd should be divided into non-infected animals on the basis of no exposure to an infected bull, and into those infected or possibly infected. The non-infected group should be bred to a clean bull or preferably by A.I. The infected or exposed group should be given 90 days breeding rest and then bred by non-infected bulls or bred by A.I. Pregnant cows possibly infected should be checked periodically until they are pregnant for 6 months. Recently calved cows exposed to infection at the previous breeding time should have 90 days sexual rest before breeding.

In the prevention of trichomoniasis, breeding stock should be purchased only from herds where the reproductive efficiency is high and all purchased bulls should be examined by preputial sampling. Repeated examination of vaginal secretion should be made on the first 3 or 4 females bred by introduced bulls. Non-virgin, non-pregnant cows purchased should be bred by A.I. or given sexual rest of 90 days before breeding and purchased pregnant cows should not be bred by natural service until 90 days after calving.

2. DOURINE

(Horse Syphilis)

Dourine is a contagious, venereal trypanosomiasis of horses transmitted by coitus and characterized by inflammation of the external genitalia, skin lesions, and disturbance of the nervous system. The disease is enzootic in Africa, Asia, southeastern Europe and South America. It has been eradicated from Canada and is considered to be eradicated from the U.S.A. The causative agent is the protozoan, *Trypanosoma equiperdum* (Fig. 20–1), which is found in the discharges from the urethra of the stallion and the vagina of the mare. The organism is incapable of surviving outside the host and disappears quickly in cadavers. Members of the family, Equidae, are the only animals affected. After exposure, the trypanosomes penetrate through the intact mucosa, multiply and produce lesions.

Symptoms. Specific symptoms usually appear within 8 to 14 days after exposure but occasionally local manifestations are delayed for weeks. The course is usually chronic and may be as long as several years with the affected animal alternately improving and relapsing. In Europe a more acute form of the disease has been reported with death occurring within a few weeks of the onset.

The first symptom in the stallion is an edematous swelling of the sheath, scrotum, prepuce and penis. After some weeks, depigmented, raised plaques, said to be pathognomonic of the disease, appear on the skin of the external genitalia. In the mare the first symptom is swelling of the labia of the vulva and shortly a discharge is evident at the vulva. Vaginal examination reveals a swollen and congested mucosa. In a few weeks, depigmentation of the vulva and clitoris occurs. After a variable time, edema of the nerves and spinal cord leads to a gradually developing paralysis of the rear limbs and penis. Abortions have been reported in pregnant mares. When the paralysis is well-marked, emaciation is present and humane destruction should follow in a short time.

Diagnosis and Control. When typical lesions are present, diagnosis can be made on clinical examination, but the existence of inapparent cases makes blood examinations, using the complement-fixation test, necessary for a complete diagnosis. The disease can be controlled by blood testing and destruction of infected animals. The absence of residual hosts assures success in eradication.

3. TOXOPLASMOSIS

Toxoplasmosis is a contagious disease of all species, including man, and manifested by genital infection especially in ewes and by encephalitis, pneumonia and neonatal mortality in all species. The infection is caused by *Toxoplasma gondii*, an intracellar parasite which multiplies after invasion and eventually fills and destroys the cell (Fig. 20–1). The clinical symptoms vary between species and between age groups. In cattle the disease runs an acute course with fever, dyspnea and nervous symptoms. Stillborn or weak calves which die soon after birth have been observed. In sheep, fever, dyspnea, general tremor, incoordination, abortion and stillbirths, are the common signs (Beverly & Watson, 1961).

Diagnosis and Control. Toxoplasmosis is diagnosed by the complement-fixation test. The accuracy of this test is affected by the fact that infected animals develop antibody titers only late in the disease. In abortions a positive diagnosis can be made by isolation of the organism from aborted fetuses. Due to lack of knowledge about the manner of spread of toxoplasmosis, effective control measures have not been developed. Because of the risk of transmission to humans, known infected animals should be slaughtered.

Infections of the genitalia of domestic animals are many and varied (see Chapter 19 & Table 20–1). There is considerable knowledge needed concerning these infections, especially those of viral origin. The relation of viruses to infertility, types of vaginitis, cervicitis and endometritis has not been fully explored.

REFERENCES

BARTLETT, D. E. (1949). Procedures for diagnosing bovine venereal trichomoniasis and handling infected herds. *J. Amer. Vet. Med. Assoc.*, **114**, 293–305.

BRANDLY, C. A. (1952). In: *Diseases of Poultry*, Biester, H. E. & Schwarte, L. H. (Edit.) Chap. 21, The Iowa State College Press, Ames, Iowa.

BEVERLY, J. K. A. & WATSON, W. A. (1961). Ovine abortion and toxoplasmosis. *Vet. Rec.*, **76**, 6–10.

DOLL, E. R. & KINTNER, J. H. (1954). A comparative study of equine abortion and equine influenza viruses. *Cornell Vet.*, **44**, 355–367.

DOLL, E. R., BRYANS, J. T., McCOLLUM, W. H. & CROWE, M. E. W. (1957). Isolation of a filterable agent causing arteritis of horses and abortion by mares. *Cornell Vet.*, **47**, 3–41.

HOFSTAD, M. S. (1952). In: *Diseases of Poultry*, Biester, H. E. & Schwarte, L. H., (Edit.) Chap. 19, The Iowa State College Press, Ames, Iowa.

HOWARD, J. A., MOULTON, J. E. & FRAZIER, L. M. (1956). Epizootic bovine abortion characterized by fetal hepatopathy. *J. Amer. Vet. Med. Assoc.*, **128**, 441–449.

KENDRICK, J. W., GILLESPIE, J. H., & McENTEE, K. (1958). Infectious pustular vulvo-vaginitis of cattle. *Cornell Vet.*, **48**, 458–495.

KENDRICK, J. W., McKERCHER, D. G. & SAITO, J. (1956). Preliminary report on studies on a catarrhal vaginitis of cattle. *J. Amer. Vet. Med. Assoc.*, **128**, 357–361.

MEYER, K. F. (1955). Q-Fever. In the *Zoonoses in Their Relation to Public Health*. Univ. of Calif. Press. Berkeley.

RISTIC, M. (1960). Structural characterization of *Anaplasma marginale. J. Amer. Vet. Med. Assoc.*, **136**, 417–425.

Report of the U.S. Livestock Sanitary Assoc. (1954*a*) *Foreign Animal Diseases*. Infectious or epizootic infertility of cattle, p. 64–68.

————— (1954*b*). *Foreign Animal Diseases*. Nairobi sheep disease, p. 118–120.

————— (1954*c*). *Foreign Animal Diseases*. Rift Valley fever, p. 149–158.

SCHAAF, K. (1960). Field control of avian encephalomyelitis. Proc. 64th An. Meet. U.S. Livestock Sanitary Assoc., 213–220.

SCUTTER, J. H., YOUNG, G. A., LUEDKE, A. D. & KITCHELL, R. L. (1953). The experimental production of malformations and other abnormalities in fetal pigs by means of attenuated hog cholera virus. Proc. 90th Amer. Vet. Med. Assoc., 146–150.

TROUTMAN, E. C. (1954). Granular vaginitis as a cause of infertility in dairy cattle. *J. Amer. Vet. Med. Assoc.*, **124**, 184–185.

TUNNICLIFF, E. A. (1949). Ulcerative dermatosis of sheep. *Amer. J. Vet. Res.*, **10**, 240–249.

————— (1960). Ovine virus abortion. *J. Amer. Vet. Med. Assoc.*, **136**, 132–134.

QUESTIONS

1. Name five methods by which pathogenic infections are acquired by animals.
2. Describe in detail the control of Rift Valley Fever.
3. Describe the methods which are used in the diagnosis of viral abortion in sheep.
4. Name two viral diseases affecting reproduction that are insect-borne. List the vector in each of these diseases.
5. At what period during gestation of the sow is "live" virus vaccination apt to be dangerous? What may result after such vaccination.
6. Discuss in detail the control of viral abortion in mares.
7. Name the four classes of protozoa that include the pathogenic protozoa.
8. List three ways by which trichomoniasis may be transmitted to a clean herd of cattle.
9. Discuss in detail the control of trichomoniasis in a herd of dairy cattle.
10. Name two pathogenic protozoa that are harbored by animals and cause disease in the human population.

APPENDIX

Glossary*†

A

abortive, *adj.* That which is imperfectly performed or developed; fails to reach fruition.

abscess (**L.** *abscessus, ab* away + *cedere* to go). A localized collection of pus in a cavity formed by the disintegration of tissue.

acidophil (**L.** *acidum* acid + **Gr.** *philein* to love). Cells with cytoplasmic granules which stain readily with acid dyes. One of 3 groups of cells in anterior pituitary.

acrosome (**Gr.** *acro* extremity + **Gr.** *soma* body). A cap-like structure that surrounds the anterior part of the head of a sperm, also called *galea capitis*.

acute, *adj.* (**L.** *acutus* sharp). Characterized by a short and relatively severe course.

adhesion (**L.** *adhaesio*, from *adhaerere* to stick to). Union of surfaces that are normally separate by growth of scar tissue.

adrenergic, *adj.* Nerve fibers which give rise to an adrenalin-like substance at their terminals.

adreno-cortico-tropin (ACTH). Hormone produced mainly by the anterior pituitary which conditions the structural and functional states of the adrenal cortex.

aerobic, *adj.* (**Gr.** *aero* air + *bios* life + *ic*). That which grows only in the presence of molecular oxygen.

agglutination. The aggregation, collection into clumps, of cells distributed in a fluid.

albumin (**L.** *albus* white). Protein found in milk; also surrounding the yolk of the avian egg.

allantochorion (**Gr.** *allantos* sausage + *chorion*). A compound membrane of the fetal placenta formed by fusion of the allantois and chorion. When the chorion becomes vascularized by the allantois, then this compound layer is designated allantochorion.

allantois (*allanto* + **Gr.** *edios* form) pl. *allantoide*. A tubular diverticulum arising from the hind-gut of the embryo; it fills the extra-embryonic coelom and later fuses to the chorion.

alveolus (**L.** *alveus* hollow) pl. *alveoli*. A special or oval sac lined with glandular cells and with a conspicuous free lumen. e.g. mammary; an air sac in the lungs.

amino acid. Acid containing the amino group, NH_2; the chief component of proteins. Before protein can be absorbed by animals it must be broken down during digestion into amino acids.

amnion (**Gr.** dim. *amnos* lamb). A thin membrane which forms a closed sac around the embryo. It contains the amniotic fluid, in which the embryo is immersed.

---

* Compiled by I. Gordon, E. S. E. Hafez and P. A. O'Berry

† *L.* Latin; *Gr.* Greek; *pl.* plural; *adj.* adjective; *dim.* diminutive form.

22

(337)

ampulla (**L.** *ampora, amphora* vesicle or jar) pl. *ampullae*. *Male*—of the vas deferens: a fusiform thickening of the vas deferens before it enters the urethra: glandular portion of the vas deferens. *Female*—of the Fallopian tube: dilated section of the oviduct which lies between the infundibulum and the isthmus.

anabolism (**Gr.** *anobolē* a throwing up). Process by which simple substances are converted by living cells into more complex compounds.

anaerobe (*an* negative + **Gr.** *aero* air + *bios* life). A micro-organism that usually only lives and grows in the absence of molecular oxygen.

anastomosis (**Gr.** *anastomosis* opening). A communication between two hollow parts, organs or vessels, that are normally separate.

anatomy (*ana* + **Gr.** *temnein* to cut). The study of the structure of the body and the relation of its parts. A branch of morphology dealing with the structure of living material, based on dissection.

androgen (**Gr.** *andros* man + *gennan* to produce). A steroid hormone secreted by the testis, adrenal and probably the ovary, having masculinizing properties.

anemia (*an* neg + **Gr.** *haima* blood). A deficiency in quantity or quality of blood.

anestrus (*an* neg + **L.** *öestrus* gadfly; **Gr.** *öestros* any vehement desire). Non-breeding season. A period of sexual inactivity between two breeding seasons.

anlage (**Gr.** *an* on + *leigen* to lie), pl. *anlagen*. First massing of cells in an embryo; the start of a developing tissue or organ.

anomaly (**Gr.** *anomalia*). Marked deviation; abnormal state.

antagonism (**Gr.** *antagonisma* struggle). Opposition or contrary action as between hormones or muscles.

anterior, *adj.* (**L.** *ante* before). At or towards the head of the body; opposed to posterior.

antibiotic (**Gr.** *anti* against + *bios* life). A chemical substance produced by micro-organisms having the capacity to inhibit growth of or kill other micro-organisms.

antibody (**Gr.** *anti* against + *body* material). A constituent of body fluids which reacts with its homologous antigen.

antigen (**Gr.** *anti* against + *gennan* to produce). A substance which, on entry into the animal body, stimulates production of antibodies.

antihormone (**L.** *anti* against + *hormone*). A substance which inhibits or counteracts the action of a hormone.

antiseptic (**Gr.** *anti* against + *sepsis* putrefaction). A substance that inhibits the growth and development of micro-organisms without necessarily destroying them.

antrum, (**Gr.** *antron* cave), pl. *antra*. A cavity formed by separation of follicular cells, within which lies the oögonium. It is lined by the membrana granulosa, and contains the liquor folliculi.

aplasia (*a* negative + **Gr.** *plassein* to form). Incomplete or defective development of a tissue or organ.

aspermia (*a* negative + **Gr.** *sperma* seed). Failure of formation or emission of semen carrying sperm.

ataxia (**Gr.** *ataxia* lack of order). Failure of muscular coordination.

atresia (**Gr.** *atretos* not perforated). Degenerative changes undergone by unruptured follicles in the ovaries.

atrophy (**L.**, **Gr.** *atrophia*). Diminution in size of a cell, tissue or organ of the body.

augmentation (**L.** *augere* to increase). State of being increased or enlarged.

autolysis (*auto* self + **Gr.** *lysis* dissolution). Spontaneous breakdown of cells by the action of their own enzymes; autodigestion.

axon (**Gr.** *axon* axle). Central core forming the essential conducting part of a nerve fiber.

B

bacillus (**L.** *bacillus* a rod), pl. *bacilli*. Any rod-shaped bacterium.

bacteriemia (**Gr.** *bakterion* bacteria + *haemia* blood). The presence of bacteria in the blood.

bacterin. A bacterial vaccine.

balanitis (**Gr.** *balano* the glans penis + *-itis*). Inflammation of the glans penis.

Bartholin's glands. A pair of female glands homologous to the bulbo-urethral glands of the male; located on each side of the urethral orifice; they secrete a lubricating mucus into the vestibule.

basophil (**L.** *basis* base + **Gr.** *philein* to love). A group of cells containing granules which stain readily with basic dyes.

behavior. The reaction of a living animal, usually a series of coordinated activities concerned with an adjustment, *e.g.* ingestive, sexual, maternal, social or agonistic behavior.

bioassay (**Gr.** *bios* life + *assay*). Qualitative or quantitative determination of a substance using living biological material, *e.g.* rats, mice.

bioclimatology. The science concerned with the effect of physical environment upon living organisms.

biogenesis (*bio* life + **Gr.** *genesis* origin). The origin of life, or of living organisms; history of the development and evolution of organisms.

blastocoele (**Gr.** *blasto* germ + *koilos* hollow). Fluid-filled cavity formed by the orientation of cells in the young embryo, the blastocyst.

blastocyst (**Gr.** *blasto* germ + *kystis* bladder). Blastodermic vesicle; name given to early embryo after formation of a blastocoele; outer cover comprising a layer of cells known as the primitive trophoblast.

blastoderm (**Gr.** *blasto* germ + *derma* skin). A membrane formed by the repeated segmentation of the blastomeres in the ova of most vertebrates.

broodiness. Desire of bird to sit in nest on eggs for purpose of hatching; maternal behavior for hatching and rearing young.

C

calory or calorie (small) (**L.** *calor* heat). Unit of heat; the amount of heat required to raise 1 gm. of water 1°C.

capacitation of sperm. Physiological preparation (maturation) of sperm within the reproductive tract of the female which facilitates fertilization of the ovum.

caruncle (**L.** *caruncula*, dim. of *caro*, flesh). Maternal cotyledons; specialized non-glandular areas of the uterine mucosa in ruminants which project into the lumen; sites for attachment of the fetal placenta.

castration (**L.** *castratio*). Removal of the testes or gonads.

catabolism (**Gr.** *katabolē* a throwing down). Process by which complex compounds are converted by living cells into simpler substances.

catalase (**Gr.** *katalysis* dissolution). An enzyme found in practically all cells except certain anaerobic bacteria, which specifically catalyzes the decomposition of hydrogen peroxide.

catarrhal, *adj.* (**Gr.** *katarrhein* to flow down). Of the nature of or pertaining to inflammation of a mucous membrane; especially inflammation of the air passages of the head and throat.

cellulitis (**L.** dim. of *cella* cell + *-itis*). Inflammation of cellular tissue; especially purulent inflammation of the loose subcutaneous tissue.

cervicitis. Inflammation of the cervix.

chemotaxis (*chemo* + **Gr.** *taxis* arrangement). Phenomenon shown by certain living cells turning toward or away from certain other cells or substances which exert some chemical influence.

cholinergic, *adj.* Nerve fibers which give rise to an acetylcholine-like substance at their terminals.

chromatin (**Gr.** *chroma* color). That part of the cell's nuclear substance which forms the most conspicuous part of the nuclear network; it includes the chromosomes, and stains deeply with certain types of dyes.

chromosomes (*chroma* + **Gr.** *soma* body). Small bodies, usually rod-shaped, discernible in the nucleus of the cell at time of cell-division. They contain the genes, or hereditary factors, and their number is constant for each species.

chronic, *adj.* (**L.** *chronicus,* from **Gr.** *chronos* time). Long duration; opposed to acute.

cilium (**L.**), pl. *cilia.* Minute, hairlike process attached to the free surface of certain cells.

cleft palate. A longitudinal opening in the roof of the mouth.

clinical, *adj.* (**Gr.** *klinikos* pertaining to a bed). That based on direct observation and treatment, as opposed to theoretical or experimental considerations.

clutch, in reference to birds. One or more eggs, followed by a day of rest, which is succeeded by another egg or series of eggs.

coccobacillus (**Gr.** *kokkos* berry, **L.** *bacillus* a rod). An oval bacterial cell.

colostrum. The fluid usually only secreted by the mammary gland shortly before and a day or two after parturition.

conceptus (**L.** *conceptus*). The whole product of conception throughout gestation; includes the embryo (or fetus) and placental fluids and membranes.

congenital, *adj.* (**L.** *congenitus* born together). Existing at, or dating from, birth; that which is acquired during pre-natal life.

conjunctiva (**L.** *conjunctiva*). The delicate membrane that lines the eyelids and covers the front of the eyeball.

conjunctivitis (**L.** *conjunctiva* + *itis*). Inflammation of the conjunctiva.

connective tissue. (**L.** *con* together + *nectere* to bind). Tissue binding organs together.

contagious, *adj.* (**L.** *contagiosus*). Capable of transmission one to another.

cornification (**L.** *cornu* horn + *facere* to make). Transformation of cells of the Malpighian layer (germinal layer) into cells of the corneum (horny layer).

cryptorchidism (*kryptos* hidden + **Gr.** *orchis* testis). Failure of the mammalian testes to descend into the scrotum.

cyst (**Gr.** *kystis* sac, bladder). A vesicle or sac containing a fluid or semisolid substance.

cytochemistry (*cyto* + *chemistry*). The science concerned with the biochemical structure and metabolic activity within the cell.

cytology. The science relating to cells, their origin, structure and functions.

cytolysis (*cyto* + **Gr.** *lysis* dissolution). Dissolution or destruction of cells.

D

deciduoma (**L.** *decidua* + *oma*). **pl.** deciduomata. A nodule of tissue formed as an injury reaction in the endometrium of primates and rodents.

defibrination (**L.** *de* from + *fibra* fiber). Removal of blood from the whitish, insoluble protein which is necessary in clot formation.

degradation. The reduction of a chemical compound to one less complex, as by splitting off one or more groups.

depletion (**L.** *deplere* to empty). Process of emptying; removal of fluid or metabolite.

dermatosis (**Gr.** *derma* skin + *osis*). Any skin disease.

deutoplasm (**Gr.** *deuteros* second + **Gr.** *plasma* something formed). Reserve food material, such as yolk, in the cytoplasm of an ovum.

diagnosis (**Gr.** *dia* through + *gnosis* knowledge). Distinguishing one condition or disease from another.

diencephalon (**Gr.** *dia* through + *enkephalos* brain). Posterior part of the forebrain in vertebrates; comprising the thalamus and related structures.

differentiation (**L.** *differe* to carry apart). The acquisition of individual characters by the cells and tissues of an embryo.

dilate. To distend; widen beyond normal limits.

diploid, *adj.* (**Gr.** *diploos* twofold). With two sets of chromosomes. Somatic cells are ordinarily diploid in chromosome constitution in contrast to the haploid gametic cells.

distal, *adj.* (**L.** *distans* distant). Remote, as opposed to close or proximal.

domestication (**L.** *domesticus* home). Process imposed by man whereby animals come to live and breed in a tame condition.

dorsal, *adj.* (**L.** *dorsum* back). Pertaining to, or situated near, the back of an animal, opposite to ventral.

duct (**L.** *ductus,* from *ducere* to draw or lead). A tube or canal that carries fluid or secretions from a gland.

dysfunction (**Gr.** *dys* difficult + *function*). Partial disturbance, impairment or abnormality in the function of an organ or system.

dyspnea (**Gr.** *dys* difficult + *pnoia* breathing). Difficult or labored breathing.

E

edema (**Gr.** *oidēma* swelling). The presence of abnormally large amounts of fluid in the intercellular tissue spaces of the body.

electrophoresis. The movement of colloidal particles under the influence of an electric field or force.

embryo (**Gr.** *embryon*). A young organism in the early stages of development; includes stages from a 2-cell ovum until morphogenesis is completed.

embryology (**Gr.** *embryo* + *logy*). The science dealing with the development of the embryo; the features and phenomena exhibited in the formation and development of an embryo.

encephalitis (**Gr.** *encephalo* head + *-itis*). Inflammation of brain tissues.

endocrinology (*endo* within + **Gr.** *krinein* to separate + *-logy*). The study of the actions and interactions of the secretions of the endocrine glands.

endogenous, *adj.* (*endo* within + **Gr.** *gennan* to produce). That which develops or originates within the body.

endometritis (**Gr.** *endo* within + *mētra* uterus + *-itis*). Inflammation of the uterine mucous membrane.

endometrium (**Gr.** *endo* within + *mētra* uterus). Inner layer of the wall of the uterus consisting of the epithelial lining of the lumen, the glandular layer and connective tissue.

enzootic, *adj.* (**Gr.** *en* in + *zōon* animal). Occurring endemically among animals.

enzyme (**Gr.** *en* in + *zymē* leaven). An organic compound capable of accelerating some biochemical change in its substrate for which it is usually specific.

epidemic, *adj.* (**Gr.** *epidēmios* prevalent). Attacking many people or animals in one region simultaneously.

epididymitis (**Gr.** *epi* on + *didymos* testis + *-itis*). Inflammation of the epididymis.

epiphysis. A segment of bone separated from a long bone in early life by cartilage, but later becoming an integral part of the larger bone.

epithelium (**Gr.** *epi* on + *thēlē* nipple), pl. *epithelia.* The tissue covering the external and internal surfaces of the body, including the linings of vessels and cavities.

epizootic, *adj.* (**Gr.** *epi* on + *zōon* animal). Pertaining to a disease of animals which is rapidly spreading and widely diffused.

estrus (**L.** *oestrus* gadfly). Period during which sexual receptivity of the female to courtship and copulation is evident; commonly called "heat;" estrous (estrual) period.

etiology (**Gr.** *aitia* cause + *-logy*). The study or theory of the causation of a disease.

excretion. The act, process or function of excreting; that which is excreted.

exogenous, *adj.* (*exo* outside + **Gr.** *gennan* to produce). That which is introduced into the body from outside.

experience. Sum total of events through which the animal has lived and participated.

exudate (**L.** *exsudatio,* from *ex* out + *sudare* to sweat). An adventitious material deposited in or on a tissue by a vital process or arising from a disease.

F

facultative anaerobe. A micro-organism with the ability to live under either anaerobic or aerobic conditions.

febrile *adj.* (**L.** *febrilis*). Pertaining to fever, feverish.

feral, *adj.* (**L.** *feralis*). That which is in a wild, untamed state.

fetus (**L.** *fetus* offspring), pl. *fetuses*. The young of an animal in the uterus, from time of complete tissue differentiation until birth.

fever. Abnormally high body temperature.

fibrosis (**L.** *fibra* fiber). The formation of fibrous tissue.

fluid. A non-solid substance (liquid or gas) in the body; capable of flowing.

flushing. Passing fluid through the lumen of an organ (*e.g.* Fallopian tube or uterus) to recover luminal contents.

fomite. Any substance other than food that may harbor and transmit infectious agents.

G

gamete (**Gr.** *gametē* wife). A germ cell of either sex, *e.g.* a sperm or an ovum (egg).

ganglion (**Gr.** *ganglia* knot), pl. *ganglia*. Any collection or mass of nerve cells that acts as a center of nervous influence.

gastro-enteritis (**Gr.** *gastēr* stomach + *enteron* intestine + *-itis*). Inflammation of the stomach and intestines.

gastrula (**Gr.** *gastēr* stomach). The early stage of the embryo which follows the blastula, when the organism consists of 2 layers, ectoderm and mesentoderm.

gene (**Gr.** *gennan* to produce). The ultimate unit of inheritance, which is carried by the chromosomes and transmitted in the germ cells.

genetics. The science dealing with the resemblances and differences which are exhibited by organisms related by descent.

germ disc (**L.** *germen* germ + *discus* disc). The flattish area in a cleaved ovum in which the first formation of an embryo is evident.

gland (**L.** *glans* acorn). Any organ that produces a specific substance or secretion to be used in, or eliminated, from the body.

glycoprotein (**Gr.** *glykys* sweet). Protein conjugated with a carbohydrate group.

gonad (**L.** *gonas*, from **Gr.** *gonē* seed). A primary sex gland, an ovary or testis.

H

haploid, *adj.* (**Gr.** *haploos* single). Single, referring to cells with a single set of chromosomes, as in the mature gametes.

hemoglobinuria (**Gr.** *haemia* blood + *globin* + **Gr.** *ouron* urine + *-ia*). The presence of hemoglobin in the urine.

hemolytic, *adj.* (**Gr.** *haemia* blood + *lysis* dissolution). Pertaining to or marked by release of hemoglobin from red blood cells.

hemorrhage (**Gr.** *haemia* blood + *rhēgnynai* to burst forth). The escape of blood from the vessels.

heredity (**L.** *hereditas* heirship). Genetic transmission of the physical and mental characteristics of parents to their offspring.

hermaphrodite (**Gr.** *hermaphorditos*). An individual possessing both male and female reproductive organs. True hermaphrodites are capable of producing both ova and sperm.

heterogametic (**Gr.** *heteros* other + *gametē* wife). Producing unlike gametes with respect to the sex chromosome.

heterozygous, *adj.* (**Gr.** *hetero* different + *zygotē*). Having genes for both members of at least one pair of allelomorphic Mendelian factors; opposed to homozygous.

histochemistry (**Gr.** *histos* tissue + chemistry).   The study of the chemical substances in the body tissues on a cytological scale, *e.g.* detection of glycogen or enzymes using color-chemical reactions.

histology (**Gr.** *histos*, tissue + *-logy*).   The study of the minute structure, composition and function of the tissues, called also microscopical anatomy.

histopathology (**Gr.** *histos* tissue + *pathos* disease + *-logy*).   The study of structural and functional changes in tissues caused by disease.

homeostasis (**Gr.** *homoisos* like + *stasis* standing).   A tendency to uniformity or stability in the normal body.

homozygous, *adj.* (**Gr.** *homo* same + *zygotē*).   Having genes for only one member of at least one pair of allelomorphic Mendelian factors.

hyperemia (**Gr.** *hyper* above + *haima* blood).   Excess of blood in any part of the body; congestion of blood.

hyperplasia (**Gr.** *hyper* above + **Gr.** *plasis* formation).   An increase in the number of cells in a tissue.

hyperthermia (**Gr.** *hyper* above + *thermē* heat).   An abnormally elevated body temperature.

hypertrophy (**Gr.** *hyper* above + *trophē* nutrition).   Excessive increase in size of an organ or tissue, as from unusual stimulation.

hypophysectomy (*hypophysis* + **Gr.** *ektomē* excision).   Removal of the hypophysis (pituitary) by surgery.

hypoplasia (*hypo* under + **Gr.** *plasis* formation). Arrested, incomplete, or defective development; organ remains below normal size.

hypotrophy (*hypo* under + **Gr.** *trophē* nutrition).   Degeneration or loss of vitality of an organ.

icterus (**Gr.** *ikteros*).   Jaundice; yellow pigmentation of skin and mucous membranes.

immunization (**L.** *immunis* safe).   The process of conferring immunity upon an animal.

immunity.   Security against any particular disease or poison; specifically the power which an animal may acquire to resist and/or overcome an infection to which it may be susceptible.

immunology.   The science of immunity; the study of the phenomena of resisting the ill effects of microorganisms or their products in the body.

induration (**L.** *induratio*).   An abnormally hard area.

infection.   Invasion of the body by disease producing micro-organisms.

infectious, *adj.*   That which is capable of being transmitted by infection.

inflammation (**L.** *inflammatio* to set on fire).   The tissue reaction to injury characterized by pain, heat, discoloration and swelling.

innervation (**L.** *in* into + *nervus* nerve).   The distribution of nerve supply to an organ.

inoculation.   Introduction of micro-organisms, infective material, serum or other substances into tissue or culture medium; introduction of a disease agent into a healthy individual to produce a mild form of the disease and confer subsequent immunity.

intersex.   An individual showing morphological and anatomical characteristics that lie between the typical male and female condition; especially relevant to the genitalia.

interstitial cells (**L.** *inter* between + *sistere* to set).   Cells found in the interspaces between tissues.

invagination (**L.** *in* within + *vagina* sheath).   Infolding of one part within another as in gastrulation, where one region infolds to form a double layer.

in vitro (**L.** *vitrum* glass).   That which takes place outside the living body.

in vivo (**L.** *vivus* alive).   That which takes place within the living body.

involution (*in* into + *volvere* to roll).   The return of a tissue to its normal size.

iso-electric point (**Gr.** *isos* equal + *electric*).   Point at which electric potential is the same.

isotope (**Gr.** *isos* equal + *topos* place). An element identical in chemical character to another occupying the same place in the periodic table, but differing from it in other characteristics, as in radioactivity or mass of its atoms.

K

keratinization (**Gr.** *keras* horn). The development of or conversion into keratin; the process of becoming horny.

17-ketosteroids. Compounds derived from the metabolism of certain adrenal and certain gonadal hormones.

L

laparotomy (*laparo* flank + **Gr.** *temnein* to cut). Surgical incision through the flank of the animal.

latency. That which is either hidden or not apparent.

leptospiruria (*Leptospire* + **Gr.** *ouron* urine + *ia*). Leptospires in urine.

lesion (**L.** *laesio*; *laedere* to hurt). Any pathological discontinuity of tissue or loss of function of a part.

libido. Sexual desire; drive originated from the sexual impulses.

ligament (**L.** *ligamentum*, *ligare* to bind). Rough, fibrous band of tissue serving to connect bones or to support an organ.

lipo-protein (**Gr.** *lipos* fat). A protein conjugated with a lipid.

locus, pl. *loci*. A defined anatomical position, used in reference to neural centers or linear arrangement of genes on chromosome.

lumen (**L.** *light*), pl. *lumina*. The cavity or channel within a duct or tubular or alveolar organ such as in the uterus, oviducts or mammary gland.

luteal phase. Stage of the estrous cycle when the corpus luteum is active and progesterone influence predominates.

M

mastitis (**Gr.** *mastos* breast + *-itis*). Inflammation of the mammary gland.

maternal, *adj.* (**L.** *maternus*; *mater* mother). Pertaining to the mother.

mean. The average value for all individuals considered in a given series or population.

mechanism (**Gr.** *mechane* machine). The manner of combination of organs or substances which serve a common function.

meiosis (**Gr.** *meiosis* diminution). The two divisions which precede the formation of gametes in which the members of each chromosome pair separate, and the chromosome number in the resulting daughter cells is reduced to half the somatic number; as distinguished from ordinary cell division (mitosis).

meningitis (**Gr.** *meninx* membrane + *-itis*). Inflammation of the membranes that envelop the brain and spinal cord.

menstrual cycle (**L.** *mensis* month). Reproductive cycle occurring in humans and some other species of primates in the absence of pregnancy.

mesonephros (*meso* middle + **Gr.** *nephros* kidney). Excretory organ of the embryo; the middle of the three pair of embryonic renal organs of vertebrates.

metabolite (**Gr.** *metaballein* to turn). Any substance produced by metabolism or by a metabolic process.

metamorphosis (**Gr.** *meta* after + *morphosis* a shaping). Change of shape or structure; a transition from one developmental stage to another.

metritis (**Gr.** *metra* uterus + *-itis*). Inflammation of the uterus.

micro-aerophilic *adj.* (**Gr.** *mikros* small + *aero* air + *philein* to love). Requiring small amounts of atmospheric oxygen for growth.

mitosis. Cell division involving the duplication of chromosomes, and the division of the chromosomes by a process of longitudinal splitting. Thus, each of the resultant

pubic symphysis (Gr. *sym* together + *phyein* to grow). The articulation between the pubic bones.

pustule. A small elevation of the cuticle filled with pus.

pyometra (Gr. *pyon* pus + *mētra* uterus). An accumulation of pus within the uterus.

R

reflex. Action performed involuntarily in consequence of a nervous impulse transmitted from a receptor or sense organ to a nerve center.

refractoriness. Unresponsive condition; does not readily change as a result of treatment.

rhinitis (Gr. *rhinion* nostril + *-itis*). Inflammation of the mucous membrane of the nose.

Rickettsia (Howard Taylor *Ricketts*). A genus of the family *Rickettsiaceae* and order *Rickettsiales*, made up of minute rod-shaped or coccobacillary micro-organisms, which are gram negative and stain lightly with aniline dyes.

S

sagittal, *adj.* Anteroposterior plane or section parallel to the long axis of the body.

saprophyte (Gr. *sapros* rotten + *phyton* plant). Growing on decomposing organic matter.

satiety (L. *satietas* enough). Full satisfaction of desire; may refer to sexual arousal, appetite, etc.

secondary infection. Infection by a micro-organism following an infection already established by other organisms.

secretion. The process of elaborating a specific product as a result of the activity of a gland or tissue. Any substance produced by secretion to perform a function.

segregation. The separation of allelic genes during spermatogenesis and oögenesis and the random recombination of the two kinds of gametes at fertilization; the result is that different genetic types appear in the F_1 as compared to the parental type.

septicemic, *adj.* (L. *septicus* due to putrefaction + Gr. *haima* blood + *-ic*). Pertaining to the presence of pathogenic bacteria and their associated toxins in the blood.

septum, pl. *septa.* A dividing wall or membrane; a partition.

serotype (L. *serum* "whey" + L. *typus* mark). The type of micro-organism as determined by the kind and combination of constituent antigens associated with the cell.

serum (L. "*whey*") pl. *sera.* The clear portion of any body fluid separated from its more solid constituents.

sex chromosomes. Chromosomes concerned especially with the determination of sex.

sex-linked, *adj.* Applied to factors located on the sex chromosomes or to the characters conditioned by them.

sinusoid (L. *sinus* cavity + Gr. *eidos* form). Resembling a sinus; a type of terminal blood channel consisting of a large irregular anastomosing vessel.

somatic, *adj.* Referring to body tissues; having two sets of chromosomes.

species. A group of animals or plants which have several characteristics in common that differentiate them from others; a subgroup of a genus but usually including several subspecies or varieties.

sperm, spermatozoon (Gr. *sperma* seed). A mature male germ cell.

spermatocytogenesis. The first stage in the development of sperm in which spermatogonia develop into spermatocytes and later into spermatids.

spermatogenesis (Gr. *sperm* a seed + *genesis* production). The process of formation of sperm which includes both spermatocytogenesis and spermiogenesis.

spermiogenesis. Stage in the formation of sperm during which the spermatids transform into sperm.

sphincter (Gr. *sphinktēr* binder). A ring-like muscle which contracts to close a natural opening.

sporadic, *adj.* (**L.** *sporadicus* scattered). Occurring only occasionally.

squamous, *adj.* (**L.** *squamosus* scaly). Plate-like; resembling scales.

stance. Position or posture adopted when the animal is stationary.

statistical significance. Expression of confidence that a measured difference (or correlation, or other statistic) does not differ from zero by chance alone. Statistical significance does not measure or depend solely on the magnitude of a difference, but is a joint function of (*a*) the magnitude; (*b*) the variation in results of repeated trials; and (*c*) the amount of evidence.

steroids. A group name for compounds that resemble cholesterol chemically and contain also a hydrogenated cyclopentophenanthrene-ring system; sex hormones are members of this group.

stimulus pressure. Physical events impinging on the receptors of an animal, capable of exciting those receptors and thus modifying behavior.

strain. A group of animals within a breed and differing in one or more characters from the other members of the breed, *e.g.* Milking Shorthorns or Polled Herefords.

stratified, *adj.* (**L.** *stratum* layer). That which is arranged or disposed in layers.

stroma (**Gr.** *stroma* covering). The tissue that makes up framework, ground substance or matrix of an organ.

subcutaneous, *adj.* (**L.** *sub* under + *cutis* skin). That which is situated or occurs under the skin.

substrate (**L.** *sub* under + *stratum* layer). A substance or medium upon which organisms or cells may live and be nourished.

suckling (**L.** *succus* juice). The act of obtaining milk, from the mammary gland, by the young.

superfetation (**L.** *super* above + *fetus*). Simultaneous development of two sets of fetuses, of different ages, in the uterus.

suppurative, *adj.* (**L.** *sub* under + *puris* pus). That which produces pus.

syndrome (**Gr.** *syndromē* concurrence). A symptom complex; a group of signs and symptoms that occur together, and characterize a disease; a disturbance or abnormality.

synergism (**Gr.** *syn* together + *ergon* work). The joint action of two or more hormones or structures so that their combined effect is greater than the sum of their individual effects.

syngamy (**Gr.** *syn* together + *gamos* marriage). The union of the gametes in fertilization.

synthesis. The production of a chemical compound by union of its elements.

T

tendon. The fibrous cord of connective tissue in which the muscle fibers end and by which the muscle is attached to a bone or other structure.

teratology (**Gr.** *teratos* monster + *-logy*). The science concerned with abnormal development and congenital malformations.

tetany (**Gr.** *teinein* to stretch). State of muscle when undergoing sustained contraction.

therapeutic, *adj.* Curative.

thermoregulation (**Gr.** *therme* heat + *regulation*). The regulation of temperature by the body.

threshold. The level or point at which a physiological effect becomes evident as a result of stimulation.

tonicity (**Gr.** *tonikos* tonic). The state of tension or partial contraction of muscle fibers while at rest; normal condition of tone.

toxemia (**Gr.** *toxikon* poison + *haemia* blood). A general intoxication of the body due to the absorption of bacterial products (toxins); toxins in the blood.

transient fever. An elevated body temperature lasting only a short time.

tremor (**L.** from *tremere* to shake). An involuntary trembling or quivering.

tumescence (**L.** *tumere* to swell up). A state of being swollen or tumid.

U

ulceration. Development of a condition whereby substance is lost on a cutaneous or mucous surface, causing gradual disintegration and necrosis of the tissues.

unilateral, *adj.* (*uni-* + **L.** *latus* side). That which affects but one side.

urethra. The membranous canal which carries urine from the bladder to the exterior; in the male it also conveys semen at the time of ejaculation.

V

vaccination (**L.** *vacca* cow). The administration of vaccine for the purpose of inducing immunity.

vaccine. A suspension of attenuated or killed micro-organisms, administered hypodermically for the prevention or treatment of infectious diseases.

vaginitis (**L.** *vagina* + *-itis*). Inflammation of the vagina.

vasectomy (**L.** *vas* vessel + **Gr.** *ektomē* excision). Surgical removal of all or part of the vas deferens.

vasoconstriction (**L.** *vas* vessel + *constriction*). The narrowing of the caliber of vessels; especially constriction of arterioles, leading to decreased blood flow in an organ.

vector (**L.** from *vehere, vectus* to carry). A carrier, especially the organism (usually an arthropod) which transfers an infective agent from one host to another.

venereal, *adj.* Due to or propagated by copulation.

vesicle. A small bladder or sac containing fluid.

villus (**L.**), pl. *villi.* A small vascular protrusion on a mucous surface.

virus (**L.**) A submicroscopic or nearly submicroscopic entity capable of introduction into specific living cells and of reproducing inside such cells only.

vitellus (**L.** *vitellus* yolk). Yolk of an ovum, or egg.

viviparity (*vivus* alive + **L.** *parere* to bring forth). Act of producing living young (as opposed to eggs) from within the body, as occurs in most mammals.

vocalization. Expression of voice, usually characteristic of the species.

vulvitis (**L.** *vulva* + *-itis*). Inflammation of the vulva.

Z

zygote (**Gr.** *zygōtos* yoked together). The cell produced by the union of sperm and ovum at fertilization.

REFERENCES

Dorland's Illustrated Medical Dictionary (1957), 23rd ed., Philadelphia, W. B. Saunders & Co.

Funk & Wagnalls New Practical Standard Dictionary, (1954), Vols. 1, 2, New York, Funk & Wagnalls Co.

Stedman's Medical Dictionary (1957), 19th revised edition, Baltimore, The Williams & Wilkins Co.

Webster's New Collegiate Dictionary (1954), Springfield, Mass., G. & C. Merriam & Co., Publishers.

Webster's New International Dictionary (1948), 2nd ed., Springfield, Mass., G. & C. Merriam & Co., Publishers.

General References

The following is a list of references recommended for specialized students going in research studies in reproductive physiology.

I. TEXTBOOKS AND REFERENCE BOOKS

ASDELL, S. A. (1946). **Patterns of Mammalian Reproduction.** Ithaca, N.Y., Comstock.

AUSTIN, C. R. (1961). **The Mammalian Egg, a study of a specialized cell.** Oxford, Blackwell Sci, Publication.

BEATTY, R. A. (1957). **Parthenogenesis and Polyploidy in Mammalian Development.** Cambridge, University Press.

COLE, H. H. & CUPPS, P. T. (1959) (edits.). **Reproduction in Domestic Animals.** Vols. I & II, New York, Academic Press.

ELLENBERGER, W. & BAUM, H. (1943). **Handbuch der vergleichenden Anatomie der Haustiere.** O. Zietzschmann, E. Ackerknecht, H. Grau (edit.) 18th Ed., Berlin, Springer.

FERGUSON, L. C. (1958). **Diseases of Swine.** Ames, Iowa, Iowa State University Press.

FOLLEY, S. J. (1956). **The Physiology and Biochemistry of Lactation.** Springfield, Ill., Charles C Thomas.

HAFEZ, E. S. E. (1962) (edit.). **The Behaviour of Domestic Animals.** London, Bailliere, Tindall & Cox.

HAMMOND, J. (1927). **Reproduction of the Cow.** Cambridge, University Press.

—————— (1954) (edit.). **Progress in the Physiology of Farm Animals.** Vols. II & III, London, Butterworths.

—————— (1960). **Farm Animals. Their breeding, growth and inheritance.** London, Edward Arnold.

KON, S. K. & COWIE, A. T. (1961) (edit.). **Milk: the Mammary Gland and Its Secretion.** Vols. I & II, New York, Academic Press.

KROLLING, O. & GRAU, H. (1960). **Lehrbuch der Histologie und vergleichenden mikroskopischen Anatomie der Haustiere.** 10th Ed., Berlin, Parey.

LLOYD, C. W. (1959) (edit.). **Recent Progress in the Endocrinology of Reproduction.** New York, Academic Press.

MANN, T. (1954). **The Biochemistry of Sperm.** London, Methuen.

MANTHEI, C. A. (1958). **Diseases of Swine.** Ames, Iowa, Iowa State University Press.

MARSHALL, A. J. (1960) (edit.). **Biology and Comparative Physiology of Birds.** New York, Academic Press.

MARSHALL'S **Physiology of Reproduction** (1958–60). A. S. Parkes (edit.) Vols. I & II, London, Longmans.

NALBANDOV, A. (1958). **Reproductive Physiology; comparative reproductive physiology of domestic animals, laboratory animals and man.** San Francisco, Calif., W. H. Freeman.

NISHIKAWA, Y. (1959). **Studies on Reproduction in Horses. Singularity and artificial control of reproductive phenomena.** Tokyo, Japan Racing Association.

PATTEN, B. M. (1948). **Embryology of the Pig.** 3rd Ed., Philadelphia, Pa., The Blackstone Co.

—————— (1958). **Foundations of Embryology.** New York, McGraw-Hill.

PERRY, E. J. (1960) (edit.). **The Artificial Insemination of Farm Animals.** New Brunswick, N.J., Rutgers University Press.

ROBERTS, S. J. (1956). **Veterinary Obstetrics and Genital Diseases.** Ithaca, N.Y., S. J. Roberts.

ROMANOFF, A. L. (1960). **The Avian Embryo.** New York, Macmillan.

ROMANOFF, A. L. & ROMANOFF, A. J. (1949). **The Avian Egg.** New York, John Wiley.

SALISBURY, G. W. & VANDEMARK, N. L. (1961). **Physiology of Reproduction and Artificial Insemination of Cattle.** San Francisco, Calif., W. H. Freeman.

SISSON, S. (1953). **Anatomy of Domestic Animals.** Revised by D. Grossman, 4th Ed., Philadelphia, Saunders.

SMITH, V. R. (1959). **Physiology of Lactation.** Ames, Iowa, Iowa State University Press.

STURKIE, P. D. (1954). **Avian Physiology.** Ithaca, N.Y., Comstock Publishing Associates.

TAYLOR, L. W. (1949). **Fertility and Hatchability of Chicken and Turkey Eggs.** New York, John Wiley.

TRAUTMANN, A. & FIEBIGER, J. (1952). **Fundamentals of the Histology of Domestic Animals.** Ithaca, N.Y., Comstock.

TURNER, C. W. (1952). The Mammary Gland. I. **The Anatomy of the Udder of Cattle and Domestic Animals.** Columbia, Mo., Lucas Brothers.

VAN ROEKEL, H. (1959). **Diseases of Poultry.** Ames, Iowa, Iowa State University Press.

VELARDO, J. T. (1958) (edit). **The Endocrinology of Reproduction.** New York, N.Y., Oxford University Press.

VILLEE, C. A. (1961) (edit.). **Control of Ovulation.** Oxford, England, Pergamon.

WILLIAMS, W. L. (1943). **Diseases of the Genital Organs of Domestic Animals.** 3rd Ed., Ithaca, N.Y., Miss Louella Williams.

YOUNG, W. C. (1961) (edit.). **Allen's Sex and Internal Secretions.** 4th Ed., Baltimore, Williams & Wilkins.

II. PROCEEDINGS OF CONGRESSES AND SYMOPSIA

The International Congress of Animal Reproduction
1st held in 1948 in Milan, Italy
2nd held in 1952 in Copenhagen, Denmark
3rd held in 1956 in Cambridge, England
4th held in 1961 in The Hague, Holland
The Biennial Symposium on Animal Reproduction, held in U.S.A.
1st held in 1953 in Ames, Iowa and Published in Iowa State College Journal of Animal Science
2nd held in 1955 in East Lansing, Michigan and published in Michigan State University Centennial Symposium
3rd held in 1957 at Fort Collins, Colorado and published by the Pergamon Press, New York.
4th held in 1959 in Urbana, Illinois. "The effect of germ cell damage on animal reproduction." Published in J. Dairy Sci., Vol. 43. Suppl.
5th held in 1961 in Knoxville, Tennessee.
Colloque de La Societe Nationale pour l'etude de la Sterilite et de la Fecondite. "Les Fonctions de Nidation Uterine et leurs Troubles." Masson et Cie, Libraire de l' Academie de Medecine, 120 Blv., Saint Germaine, Paris 6^e
Ciba Foundation Symposium—**Mammalian Germ Cells.** 1953. Boston, Mass., Little, Brown & Co.
Symposium on Mammalian Genetics and Reproduction (1960). J. Cell Comp. Physiol., Vol. **56** Suppl. 1, pp. 193, held in Oak Ridge, Tennessee.
Memoirs of the Society for Endocrinology, England, Cambridge, University Press.

No. 4 Comparative Endocrinology of Vertebrates, Part I, 1955.
No. 5 Comparative Endocrinology of Vertebrates, Part II, 1956.
No. 6 Implantation of Ova, 1959.
No. 7 Sex Differentiation and Development, 1960.
Transactions of the Annual Conference on "Gestation" starting in 1954, Sponsored by the Josiah Macy, Jr. Foundation, New York.

III. SCIENTIFIC PERIODICALS AND ABSTRACTS

Acta Agricultura Scandinavica. Hovslagargatan, 2^{III}, Stockholm C., Sweden

Acta Endocrinologica, Periodica, Skelmosevej 10, Copenhagen, Valby, Denmark

American Journal of Veterinary Research, American Veterinary Medical Association, 600 S. Michigan Avenue, Chicago, Illinois

Animal Breeding Abstracts, Commonwealth Bureau of Animal Breeding and Genetics, Edinburgh, Scotland

Animal Behaviour, Bailliere, Tindall & Cox, London, W. C. 2, England

British Poultry Science, Oliver and Boyd, Ltd., London, England

Endocrinology, Charles C Thomas, Springfield, Illinois

Fertility and Sterility, Paul P. Hoeber, Inc., New York, N.Y.

International Journal of Fertility, Ben Franklin Press, Pittsfield, Massachusetts

Journal of Embryology and Experimental Morphology, Oxford University Press, London, E. C. 4, England

Journal of Endocrinology, Cambridge University Press, Bentley House, 200 Euston Road, London, N. W. 1, England

Journal of the American Veterinary Medical Association, American Veterinary Medical Association, 600 S. Michigan Avenue, Chicago, Illinois

Journal of Agricultural Science, Cambridge University Press, Cambridge, England.

Journal of Animal Science, Boyd Printing Co., 49 Sheridan Avenue, Albany 10, N.Y.

Journal of Dairy Science, The Garrard Press, 510–522 North Hickory St., Champaign, Illinois

Journal of Reproduction and Fertility, Blackwell Scientific Publ., Oxford, England

Poultry Science, The Poultry Science Association. Texas A & M College System, College Station, Texas.

The Cornell Veterinarian, Cornell Veterinarian, Inc., Veterinary College, Ithaca, N.Y.

The Veterinary Record, 7 Mansfield St., London, W. 1, England

Zuchthygiene, Fortpflanzungsstorungen und Besamung der Haustiere, Verlag M. & H. Schaper, Hannover, Germany

Subject Index

Page numbers in **bold type** indicate references to illustrations